PHYSICAL
GEOLOGY

PHYSICAL
GEOLOGY
Second Edition

Charles C. Plummer   David McGeary
California State University, Sacramento

wcb   Wm. C. Brown Company Publishers, Dubuque, Iowa

wcb
group

Wm. C. Brown   *Chairman of the Board*
Mark C. Falb   *Executive Vice-President*

wcb

Wm. C. Brown Company Publishers, College Division

Lawrence E. Cremer   *President*
David Wm. Smith   *Vice-President, Marketing*
E. F. Jogerst   *Vice-President, Cost Analyst*
David A. Corona   *Assistant Vice-President,*
                      Production Development and Design
James L. Romig   *Executive Editor*
Marcia H. Stout   *Marketing Manager*
William A. Moss   *Production Editorial Manager*
Marilyn A. Phelps   *Manager of Design*
Mary M. Heller   *Visual Research Manager*

Cover photo © Pat O'Hara
Bryce Canyon National Park, view from Bryce Point, Utah

Copyright 1979, 1982 by Wm. C. Brown Company Publishers

Library of Congress Catalog Card Number: 81-67518

ISBN 0-697-05038-6

Fourth Printing, 1983

Printed in the United States of America

2-05038-03

Contents

exam 1

exam 2

exam 2

exam 2

exam 2

Boxes

Preface

Physical Geology is written for a college-level introductory physical geology course. It is intended for both
geology majors and nonmajor students who have had
no previous college science courses. Its language is
straightforward and clear. New terms are defined the
first time they are used, and unnecessary jargon has
been avoided. We have not slighted any topics that
are necessary for geology majors. Minerals, rocks,
surface processes, and internal processes are fully
covered. Two separate chapters are devoted to economic geology and to the geology of the solar system.
This second edition of *Physical Geology* should provide
a solid, stimulating foundation in geology for majors.

The organization of the book is traditional and
matches the organization of most lab manuals. Rocks
are covered first; then surface processes; and finally,
internal processes are covered in the last chapters.
As in the first edition, each chapter is written to be as
self-contained as possible. Because of this, the chapter sequence is flexible and can be rearranged if de-
sired.

There are many significant changes in figures and
text material in the second edition of *Physical Geology*.
Many of the line drawings used in the first edition have
been revised and enlarged; others have been replaced;
and new photographs have been added.

Chapter 1 has been rewritten completely to show
how earth processes are driven by solar energy and
gravity and to expand our introduction to plate tectonic
theory. Chapter 3, on volcanoes, has been revised to
include the Mount St. Helens eruption and an expanded
section on the plate tectonic origin of volcanic rocks,
such as oceanic basalts. The relation of metamorphic
rocks to plate tectonics is emphasized in chapter 7.
Chapter 10, on streams, has been modified to emphasize stream processes and the current uncertainty regarding landscape development. And a section on the
origin of glacial ages has been added to chapter 12.

Chapter 16, on earthquakes, has been rewritten
to include more discussion of quake first motion and

the relation of earthquakes to plate boundaries. The discussion of the earth's interior in chapter 17 has been reorganized to include more material on gravity anomalies and magnetic anomalies. Chapter 18, on mountains, has been shortened and the emphasis shifted from geosynclinal theory to plate tectonic theory. Chapter 19 now includes an interpretation as well as a description of sea-floor features. Chapter 20, on plate tectonics, has been rewritten to summarize material from the rest of the book, to emphasize plate boundaries, and to include backarc spreading. The discussion of geologic resources in chapter 21 now concentrates on geologic origin and occurrence of energy resources and metals. Chapter 22, on astrogeology, includes new information from recent space probes.

We have taken great care to avoid letting plate tectonics dominate this book to the exclusion of other topics. We introduce plate tectonics in the first chapter in such a way that students gain general knowledge of plate size and behavior. We then incorporate the ideas of moving plates into subsequent chapters on volcanoes, igneous rocks, metamorphic rocks, earthquakes, and mountains. In later chapters we discuss in detail the origin and evolution of plate tectonic theory. This organization allows students to develop a progressive understanding of plate tectonics and its ramifications as more data are presented. In this way readers can not only gain an appreciation for the interrelationships of data, hypotheses, and theory but they can also appreciate how plate tectonic theory has itself become a foundation upon which new hypotheses are based. Students discover that geology is a lively science, not just a body of "facts."

We feel that an important objective of any introductory science course, whether for science majors or for nonmajors, is to explain how the scientific method works and to give several examples of it. We carefully distinguish between facts and hypotheses throughout the text. Where appropriate, we give several examples of alternate hypotheses for a given set of data. We also show how data remain valid when a hypothesis is disproved and how theories evolve and change as new data are accumulated.

Each chapter includes several important features to help students absorb the material presented. The opening purpose in each chapter gives an overview of the material in the chapter and relates it to the rest of the text. Each new term appears in boldface type and

is defined the first time it is used. These new terms are listed in Terms to Remember at the end of the chapter, and they also appear with their definitions in the Glossary at the end of the book. A summary and a series of review questions to test recall and thought questions to challenge students to think and relate newly acquired information to earlier chapters are also included at the end of each chapter. Supplementary readings, which suggest further insight into subjects discussed and which close each chapter, were selected for their interest and readability.

Boxes within the text are another special feature of *Physical Geology.* Two categories of material are dealt with in the boxes: (1) topics of special human or environmental concern, such as the dangers of living in river cities or the amount of fresh water stored in glacial ice; and (2) topics slightly more difficult than the rest of the text, such as the electrostatic charge on clay minerals. The boxed material, while informative and interesting, should be considered supplemental to the text.

Metric measures and the Celsius temperature scale are used throughout the text. The English and Fahrenheit equivalents are shown in parentheses only where appropriate. In rare instances, English units appear—e.g., topsoil removal seems more understandable in tons-per-acre than in kilograms-per-hectare.

Physical Geology is accompanied by an instructor's manual, student study guide and a laboratory manual. The Instructor's Manual, written by the authors of the text, gives specific learning objectives for the twenty-two chapters in the text as well as numerous suggestions for possible demonstrations, discussions, lab experiments, and exam questions. The manual also suggests course outlines and a lab schedule and provides lists of suppliers of films, slides, rocks, and minerals and information for the course as a whole.

The Student Study Guide provides a solid foundation for a beginning geology student. Written by Esther Tuttle, a science editor, and Sherwood D. Tuttle, professor of geology at the University of Iowa, the guide stresses the fundamentals of geology, the vocabulary of the science, and the elements involved in successful learning in the field of geology.

The Laboratory Manual, by James Zumberge and Robert Rutford, has been especially designed to be used with *Physical Geology.* The new manual, written for the second edition, presents a good selection of experiments for use in the laboratory.

Acknowledgments

Susan Clark Slaymaker, of the Geology Department of California State University, Sacramento, wrote chapter 22, "Astrogeology," in *Physical Geology.* We are grateful for her assistance.

For all their help in photographic research and preparation, we thank the staff of the U.S. Geological Survey Photographic Library in Denver, the California Division of Mines and Geology at Sacramento, and the many other individuals who provided photographs.

The successful completion of *Physical Geology* is largely due to the efforts of our reviewers, who gave us invaluable advice and guidance throughout the writing and revision of the manuscript. We extend our special thanks and appreciation to those who reviewed all or part of the manuscript, including R. Scott Babcock, Department of Geology, Western Washington State University; Ronald C. Flemal, Department of Geology, Northern Illinois University; Howard Level, Earth Science Department, Ventura College; Gary D. Rosenberg, Department of Geology, Indiana University—Purdue University at Indianapolis; Richard Smosna, Department of Geology and Geography, University of West Virginia; Sherwood D. Tuttle, Department of Geology, University of Iowa; and W. R. Van Schmus, Department of Geology, University of Kansas.

We are deeply grateful for the unfailing support of our wives, Mary Ellyn McGeary and Kathleen Church Plummer, and for their continued assistance with this edition as with the first.

At Wm. C. Brown Company Publishers we have been assisted in the editorial process by Robert Stern. We thank him for the guidance necessary to produce *Physical Geology.*

We have tried to write a book that will be useful to both students and instructors. Comments of instructors and students on the first edition of *Physical Geology* were very helpful to us and we will be very grateful for any comments by users of this book so that we can improve future editions.

Charles C. Plummer
David McGeary

PHYSICAL
GEOLOGY

1

Introduction to Physical Geology

Purpose

Geology uses the scientific method to explain natural aspects of the earth—for example, how mountains form or valleys develop, or why oil resources are concentrated in some rocks and not in others. We briefly explain how and why the earth's surface, and its interior, are constantly changing. We relate this constant change to the major geological topics of the modern theory of plate tectonics, the rock cycle, and geologic time. These concepts form a framework for the rest of the book. An understanding of them will aid you in your study of the chapters that follow.

The Earth: A Giant Machine

In March 1980, after over a century of inactivity, Mount St. Helens in the state of Washington came to life. For six weeks the eruptions were relatively minor. A series of steam explosions puffed out fragments of old rock. Then on May 18, 1980 the once beautifully symmetrical, snow-capped cone blew apart with a force equal to about 10 million tons of dynamite exploding—500 times the energy released by the first atomic bomb.

As the north flank of the peak disintegrated, a huge avalanche composed of volcanic ash and searingly hot gases roared downward. This was followed by a tremendous lateral blast of steam and ash from the flank of the volcano, destroying about 600 square kilometers of forest. Great volumes of volcanic debris billowed into the atmosphere to be carried eastward by the prevailing winds. During the next few days large parts of Montana, Idaho, and eastern Washington were blanketed by volcanic ash fallout. Volcanic dust in the very high atmosphere was carried completely around the world.

Heat from the eruption melted the snow and glacial ice on Mount St. Helens. Mudflows (slurries of volcanic debris and water) sped down stream channels. A particularly large mudflow topped the banks of the Toutle River, destroying bridges and paralyzing traffic on major highways. Debris carried by the Toutle River was dumped into the Columbia River, blocking ship traffic between Portland, Oregon, and the Pacific Ocean.

Figure 1.1 Mount St. Helens before May 18, 1980. A minor eruption is taking place.
Photo by U.S. Geological Survey.

Figure 1.2 Mount St. Helens June 4, 1980. View of what once was the northern flank of the volcano.
Photo by U.S. Geological Survey.

Figure 1.3 Mount St. Helens May 18, 1980.
Photo by U.S. Geological Survey.

Figure 1.4 Toutle River valley clogged with mud and ash June 4, 1980. Mount St. Helens is in background.
Photo by U.S. Geological Survey.

The awesome energy released in this spectacle was a product of the earth's machinery. The machinery is driven by forces both within and on the earth. Mount St. Helens is only a small part of the constant, ordinarily slow, changing of the earth. Ocean basins open and close. Mountain ranges rise and are worn down to plains. Studying how the earth's machinery works can be as exciting as watching a great theatrical performance. Understanding the changes that take place in and on the earth, and the reasons for those changes, is the challenging objective of **geology,** the scientific study of the earth.

The earth can be visualized as a giant machine driven by two engines, one internal and the other external. Both are **heat engines,** devices that convert heat energy into mechanical energy. A simple heat engine is shown in figure 1.5. An automobile is powered by a heat engine. When gasoline is ignited in the cylinders, the resulting hot gases expand, driving pistons to the far end of cylinders. In this way, the heat energy of the expanding gas has been converted to the mechanical energy of the moving pistons, then transferred to the wheels, where the energy is put to work moving the car.

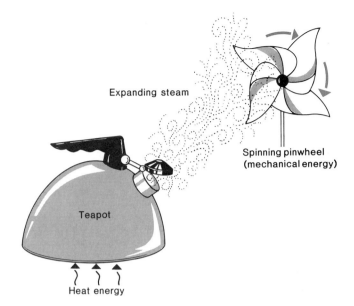

Figure 1.5 A pinwheel held over steam is an example of a heat engine.

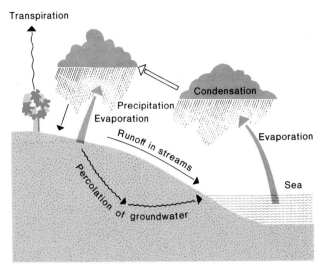

Figure 1.6 The hydrologic cycle. Water vapor evaporates from the sea and land, condenses to form clouds, and falls as precipitation. Water falling on land runs off over the surface as streams or percolates into the ground to become ground water. It returns to the atmosphere again by evaporation and transpiration.

The internal heat engine of the earth is powered by heat flowing from the hot interior of the earth toward the cooler exterior. The eruptions of Mount St. Helens are products of this heat engine.

The earth's external heat engine is essentially solar powered. Heat from the sun provides the energy for motion of the oceans and atmosphere, producing clouds, rain, and snowfall as well as daily and seasonal weather changes. Water, especially in the oceans, is evaporated by solar heating. The water vapor becomes part of the air. When the air cools, it loses its ability to hold and transport the water vapor, and clouds form. If the droplets become sufficiently large, they are attracted to the earth's surface by gravity and fall as rain or snow. The movement of water and water vapor from the sea to the atmosphere to the land and back to the sea and atmosphere is known as the **hydrologic cycle** (see figure 1.6).

Over long periods of time, moisture at the earth's surface helps rock disintegrate. Water washing down hillsides and flowing in streams loosens and carries away the rock particles. In this way mountains originally raised by the earth's internal forces are worn away by processes driven by the external heat engine.

Gravity is the force, always present, that causes streams to flow and that pulls material downward. We can think of **gravity** as mutual attraction between bodies. The greater the masses of the bodies, the greater the force. Because the mass of the earth is so vastly greater than any object on its surface, material is strongly attracted toward the earth's center.

The Mount St. Helens eruptions show how the two heat engines interact. The internal heat engine produced the eruptions that built the volcano over thousands of years and, in 1980, blasted a large part of it away. The ash was propelled into the atmosphere, where the wind, driven by the external heat engine, transported it hundreds of kilometers. As the velocity of the air decreased, gravity caused the ash and dust to settle to the earth's surface. The mudflows were mostly the work of the external heat engine. Water stored on the volcano as glacial ice had accumulated gradually from snowfalls on the peak. Heat from the volcano melted the ice, and the water and ash mixture flowed downhill.

Geologists are fascinated by volcanic eruptions, but also by more subtle, yet nonetheless interesting, geologic events. Like all scientists, geologists are curious, and they want to understand how the earth works. However, geology is pursued not only because of curiosity. There are many practical applications of geology. For example, hundreds or perhaps thousands of lives were saved because of what geologists had learned from years of studying Mount St. Helens and her sister volcanoes. When the 1980 eruptions began, U.S. Geological Survey scientists advised state and federal officials what to expect. Because of this advice, the most potentially dangerous areas were closed to public access—despite the outcry from many residents who thought that only mild eruptions would continue, or even die out. When the big eruption came, most of the sixty-three people who were killed had ignored the warnings and had gone into closed areas.

Mount St. Helens presents but one example of how we benefit from geology. Before we return to the topic of how the earth works, it is worth pointing out some other reasons why you, as an inhabitant of this planet, might benefit from a knowledge of geology.

Understanding Our Surroundings

Knowledge of geology will give you a greater appreciation of scenery. If, for instance, you were traveling through the Canadian Rockies, you might see the scene in figure 1.7 and wonder how these mountains were formed.

Some of the things you might want explained are: (1) Why are there layers in the rock exposed in the cliffs? (2) Why are the peaks so jagged? (3) Why are there glaciers? (4) Why does this mountain belt extend northward and southward for thousands of kilometers? (5) Why are there mountain ranges here and not in the central part of the continent? After completing a course in physical geology, you should be able to answer these questions and also understand how many other kinds of landscapes were formed.

Supplying Things We Need

The earth's heat engines, at work for billions of years, have concentrated in different parts of the earth the materials that people want and need for survival, comfort, and pleasure. By learning how the earth works and how and why different kinds of substances are distributed, we can intelligently search for metals, sources of energy, gems, and sand and gravel for construction purposes.

The economic systems of western civilization are dependent on abundant and cheap energy sources. Nearly all *our* engines—powered mainly by gasoline, coal, or nuclear power—depend on concentrations of energy derived from the earth and *its* engines. The United States economy in particular is geared to petroleum as a cheap source of energy. Americans have used up in a few decades much of the country's known petroleum reserves, which took nature hundreds of millions of years to store in the earth. Americans are now heavily dependent on imported oil. To find more of this diminishing resource will require more money and increasingly more sophisticated knowledge of geology. Although many people are not aware of it, we face similar problems with diminishing sources of other materials, notably metals such as iron, aluminum, copper, and tin, each of which has been concentrated in a particular environment by the action of the earth's engines.

Figure 1.7 A view of the Canadian Rockies from a highway in Alberta, Canada.

Protecting the Environment

Our demands for more energy and metals have, in the past, led us to extract them with little regard for effects on the environment, on the balance of nature within the earth, and, therefore, on us, earth's residents. Strip mining of coal, for example, can release acids into water supplies. Knowledge of geology is necessary if we are to lessen or prevent damage to the environment—just as it is necessary to find the resources in the first place.

A further threat to the environment arises from the fact that these are nonrenewable resources. Petroleum and metal deposits cannot grow back after being harvested. As demands for these resources increase, so does the pressure to disregard the environmental damage associated with extraction of the remaining deposits.

Some problems involved with petroleum extraction illustrate this. Oil companies employ geologists to discover new oil fields, while the public and government depend on geologists to assess the potential damage that removal of the oil from the ground may cause. Decisions must be made as to whether environmental risks in extracting oil are worth taking. An educated public and, especially, elected officials should have as thorough knowledge as possible of the geologic factors involved in each situation.

Avoiding Geologic Hazards

Geology may have a direct application in ensuring people's safety and well-being. For example, if you were building a house in an earthquake-prone area, you would have to know how to minimize danger to yourself and your home. You would want to build the house on a type of ground not likely to be shaken apart by an earthquake. You would want the house designed and built to absorb the kind of vibrations given off by earthquakes. Many

Box 1.1
The Alaska Pipeline—Threat to the Environment or Bulwark of the American Economy?

In the late 1970s the United States was importing almost half its petroleum, at a loss of billions of dollars per year to the national economy. This drain on the country's economy and the increasing cost of energy are major causes of inflation, reduced industrial productivity, unemployment, and erosion of standards of living.

Over a decade earlier, oil was discovered by geologists beneath the shores of the Arctic Ocean on Alaska's North Slope. Thanks to the Alaska pipeline, completed in 1977, Alaska now supplies about 16 percent of the nation's domestic oil.

Despite its important role in the American economy, some people consider the Alaska pipeline to be too great a threat to the environment to have been built. Oil spilled from a ruptured pipe would have a devastating effect on the fragile Arctic plant and animal life. Crude oil would stay on the surface of permanently frozen ground rather than be washed away by running water as in a temperate climate.

Among those who recommended against the construction of the pipeline along its present route were the geologists of the U.S. Geological Survey who conducted the official environmental impact investigation of the route before the pipeline was built. Their unfavorable report was overruled. The Congress and the President of the United States, because of their desire to maintain energy sources, exempted the pipeline from laws that require acceptance of a favorable environmental impact statement before a major project can begin. The 1.52 million barrels of oil a day that flow from the Arctic oil fields mean that over $10 billion a year remain in the American economy rather than being lost through the purchase of foreign oil.

The 1,250-kilometer-long pipeline crosses regions of ice-saturated, frozen ground and major earthquake-prone mountain ranges that geologists regard as serious hazards to the structure.

Figure 1.8 Road made on Alaska's North Slope. Ponds developed after thawing of the ground.
Photo by O. J. Ferrians, Jr., U.S. Geological Survey.

Figure 1.9 The Alaska pipeline.
Photo by Steve McCutcheon, Alaska Pictorial Service.

Box 1.1 *Continued*

Building anything on frozen ground creates problems. For example, the road in figure 1.8 was built during the exploration of Alaska's north slope oil fields. In building the road the protective vegetation was scraped off. During the summer thaw the road became a quagmire. As thawing continued, the ponds shown in the photo grew so big that the road will never be passable.

Building the pipeline over such terrain also presented enormous engineering problems. If the pipeline were placed on the ground, the hot oil flowing through it could melt the frozen ground. On a slope, mud could easily slide and rupture the pipeline. The pipeline was built after careful (and costly) engineering planned to minimize the hazards of frozen ground. Much of the pipeline is elevated above the ground. Radiators conduct heat out of the structure. In some places refrigeration equipment in the ground protects against melting.

Past records indicate that a strong earthquake can be expected every few years in the earthquake belts crossed by the pipeline. An earthquake would surely rupture a pipeline—at least, one made of conventional pipe as in the original design. However, the Alaska pipeline has been built so that in several places sections are specially jointed to allow the pipe to shift as much as six meters without rupturing.

The original estimate of the cost of building the pipeline was $900 million, but the final cost was $7.7 billion, making it the costliest privately financed construction project in history. The redesigning and construction to minimize the potential for an environmental disaster were among the many reasons for the increased cost. There have been some minor breaks in the pipeline. For instance, in January 1981, 5,000 barrels of oil were lost when a valve ruptured. However, the pipeline company maintains that there is virtually no chance of a major oil spill from the pipe. Some environmentalists are not so optimistic. It remains to be seen whether the best technology money can buy can prevent a disaster.

U.S. Geological Survey geologists have warned of another geologic threat to the North Slope oil. Although the Columbia glacier does not come close to the pipeline, nevertheless the glacier is posing a threat to the steady supply of oil from Alaska. The glacier ends in waters adjoining the channel through which tankers must pass to transport the oil from pipeline to refineries. Periodically icebergs break off the end of the glacier and float off to sea. Geologists have forecast that between six and eight times as many icebergs as normally enter the channel may break off between 1982 and 1985. If the concentration of icebergs in the shipping lanes becomes too great, the Coast Guard will stop ship traffic until the danger subsides. If this forces the pipeline to shut down for an extended period of time, serious problems could result. For instance, in winter the hot oil would solidify to a waxy solid and plug the pipeline until summer.

---

lives are lost to earthquakes each year throughout the world. An earthquake in 1976 in China is estimated to have killed nearly 600,000 people. Most of the deaths are caused by loose debris falling off buildings or by structures collapsing.

Similarly, landslides cause needless losses of property and lives. Houses on hillsides that are prone to landsliding may be monuments to the ignorance or indifference of their owners and builders. Sometimes the houses destroyed by slides are simply passengers on a naturally occurring phenomenon. But all too often construction techniques have triggered a slide by upsetting a delicately balanced slope, as indicated in figure 1.10.

An Overview of Physical Geology

Physical Geology is the large division of geology concerned with earth materials, changes in the surface and the interior of the earth, and the dynamic forces that cause those changes. We will look at how the earth's heat engines work and then show how some of the major topics of physical geology are related to the *surficial* (on the earth's surface) and *internal* processes powered by the heat engines.

Internal Processes: How the Earth's Internal Heat Engine Works

The earth's internal heat engine works because hot material deep within the earth moves slowly upward toward the cool surface. **Convection**—the upward movement of

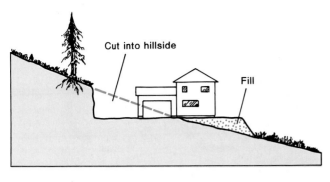

Cut into hillside

Fill

Fill slides due to overloading

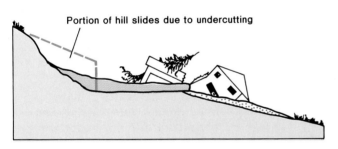

Portion of hill slides due to undercutting

Figure 1.10 Two ways a house built on a hillside may cause a landslide.

low-density material and downward movement of high-density material—probably accounts for most of the motion in the earth's interior. You can see the effects of convection in a pot of water heating on a stove. As the water at the bottom heats, it rises (figure 1.11). This is because most substances, when heated, become less dense (a particular volume of the material will weigh less). As the hot water rises, colder and denser water sinks along the sides of the pot, creating a circular pattern known as a **convection current.** We can see convection currents moving in liquids. Surprisingly, convection can also take place in solids, if the solid is capable of very slow flow (think of the movement as being comparable to that of toothpaste). If a solid behaves in this manner, we say that it behaves **plastically,** meaning it is capable of being molded.

Cold water

Hot water

Figure 1.11 Convection currents in a pan of water.

The Earth's Interior

Geologists believe that convection currents occur in the interior of the earth in the zone known as the **mantle,** the largest of the earth's three concentric zones (see figure 1.12). The other two zones are the **crust** and the **core.** The mantle is solid (except in a few spots) and probably composed of rock not very different from some kinds of rock observed at the earth's surface.

On top of the convecting mantle lies the crust of the earth. It is analogous to the skin on an apple. The thickness of the crust is insignificant compared to the whole earth. We have direct access only to the crust, and not much of the crust at that. We are like very tiny insects crawling on an apple, without the ability to penetrate its skin. We are concerned more with the crust than with the inaccessible mantle and core. The crust varies in thickness. Two major types of crust are *oceanic crust* and *continental crust.* The crust under the oceans is much thinner. It is made of rock that is somewhat denser than the rock that underlies the continents.

The lower parts of the crust and the entire mantle are inaccessible to our direct observation. No mine or oil well has penetrated the crust, so our concept of the earth's interior is based on indirect evidence (chapter 17). Of course, no one has actually observed convection in the mantle, and the extent of convection currents in the mantle is still being debated. Does convection originate at the base of the mantle, or is it restricted to the upper part of the mantle?

Whether or not convection involves the entire mantle is not so important as the point that the earth's crust seems to be moving, probably as a result of mantle convection. The effect of the internal processes on the crust is of great significance to geology. The **tectonic forces,**

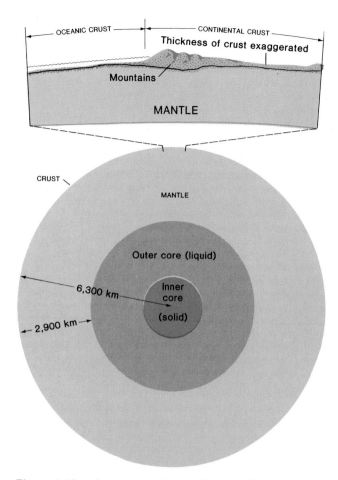

Figure 1.12   Cross section through the earth. Expanded section shows relationships between the two types of crust and the mantle. The crust ranges from five to fifty kilometers thick.

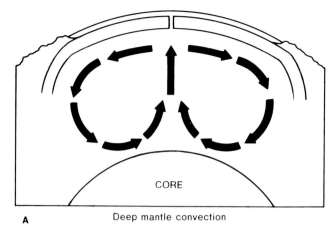

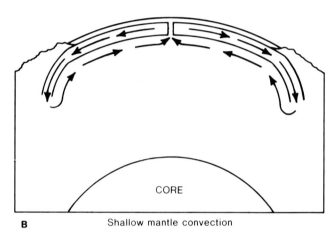

Figure 1.13   (A) Deep and (B) shallow mantle convection.

which are forces generated from within the earth, cause deformation of rock as well as vertical and horizontal movement of portions of the earth's crust. Mountain ranges attest to tectonic forces being strong enough to outdo gravitational forces. (Mount Everest, the world's highest peak, is made of rock that formed beneath an ancient sea.) Mountain ranges are built over extended periods of time as portions of the earth's crust are compressed and raised. Earthquakes, which are caused by movement of rocks underground, let us know that tectonic forces are acting.

Most tectonic forces are mechanical forces acting on the relatively rigid outer shell of the earth. Some of the energy from these forces is put to work deforming rock, bending and breaking it, and raising mountain ranges. The mechanical energy may be stored (an earthquake is a sudden release of stored mechanical energy) or converted to heat energy (rock may melt, resulting in volcanic eruptions). This elegant way the machinery of the earth works is called **plate tectonics.**

The theory of plate tectonics   From time to time a theory emerges within a science that revolutionizes the thinking of the scientists in that field. The plate tectonic theory, currently accepted by most geologists, is a unifying theory that accounts for many seemingly unrelated geological phenomena. The theory is perhaps as important to geology as the theory of relativity is to physics, atomic theory to chemistry, or the theory of evolution to biology.

Plate tectonics was seriously proposed as a hypothesis in the early 1960s, although the idea was based on earlier work. We present a brief overview here. In chapter 20 we give a more thorough discussion to show how material covered in intervening chapters leads up to the composite theory of plate tectonics. As we proceed, we will note how the theory explains particular phenomena, notably in connection with earthquakes, mountains, the sea floor, and the origin of different types of rocks.

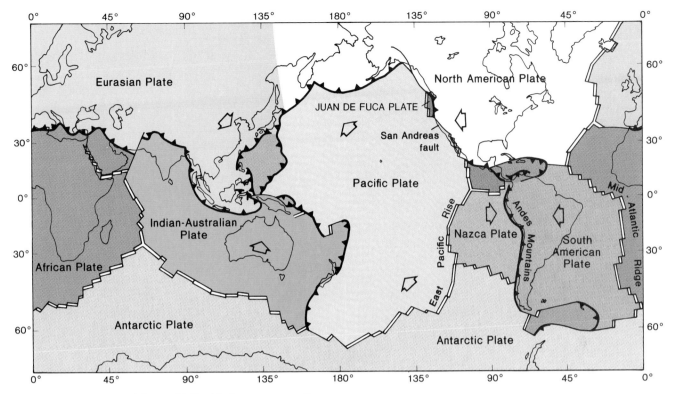

Figure 1.14 Plates of the world. Double lines are spreading centers. Lines with barbs are converging boundaries. Single lines are transform boundaries.
After W. Hamilton, U.S. Geological Survey.

According to the theory, the outer part of the earth is broken into *plates*. Each plate is made up of the rigid upper part of the earth—the crust and the uppermost mantle, which collectively are called the **lithosphere** (*lith* means rock in Greek). The lithosphere is in motion on the **asthenosphere,** a portion of the upper mantle that behaves plastically. The plates, which are much like segments of cracked shell on a boiled egg, are in motion relative to one another, sliding on the underlying asthenosphere. Much of what we observe in the rock record can be explained as the result of what takes place along plate boundaries, where two plates are pulling away from each other, sliding past each other, or moving toward each other.

According to plate tectonics, **spreading centers,** or **diverging boundaries,** exist where plates are moving apart (figure 1.16). Most spreading centers coincide with the crests of submarine mountain ranges, called **mid-oceanic ridges.**

A ridge is higher than deep ocean floor partly because the upward flow of hot mantle material pushes the lithosphere upward and partly because the rocks, being hotter there, are less dense. Tensional cracks develop along the ridge crest. These cracks tap localized **magma** (molten rock) chambers in the underlying hot mantle, and the magma squeezes into fissures (cracks through the lithosphere). Some magma erupts along the ridge crest and

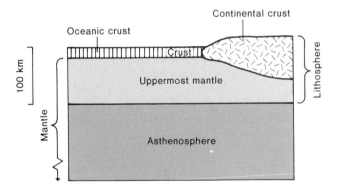

Figure 1.15 Cross section through a portion of the upper part of the earth showing the relationships of crust, mantle, lithosphere, and asthenosphere.

the rest solidifies in the fissure. Continued pulling apart of the ridge crest develops new cracks, and the process of filling and cracking continues indefinitely. Thus, new oceanic crust is continuously created at a spreading center. Not all of the mantle material melts; a solid residue remains under the newly created crust. New crust and residual mantle are the lithosphere that moves away from the ridge crest, traveling like the top of a conveyor belt. The rate of motion is generally one to ten centimeters per year—slow by human terms, but quite fast by geologic standards.

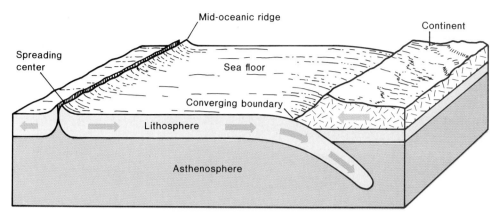

Figure 1.16 Plate motion away from a spreading center toward a converging boundary.

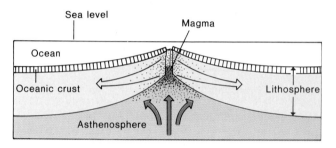

Figure 1.17 A spreading center at a mid-oceanic ridge. Hot asthenosphere wells upward beneath the ridge crest. Magma forms and squirts into fissures. Solid material that doesn't melt remains as mantle in lower part of lithosphere. As lithosphere moves away from spreading center it cools, becomes denser, and sinks to a lower level.

As the lithosphere moves away from the spreading center, the material slowly cools. As it cools it contracts and becomes denser (figure 1.17). The contraction of the lithosphere and its slow sinking because of the increased density explain why the floors beneath oceans deepen away from ridge crests.

The top of a plate may be composed exclusively of oceanic crust or may include a continent or part of a continent. For example, if you live on the North American plate, you are riding westward relative to Europe because the plate's spreading center is along the mid-oceanic ridge in the North Atlantic Ocean. The western half of the North Atlantic sea floor and North America are moving together in a westerly direction relative to the mid-Atlantic ridge plate boundary.

A second type of boundary, a **transform boundary**, occurs where two plates slide past one another. The San Andreas fault in California is regarded as this type of boundary, and the earthquakes along the fault are a byproduct of the plate motion.

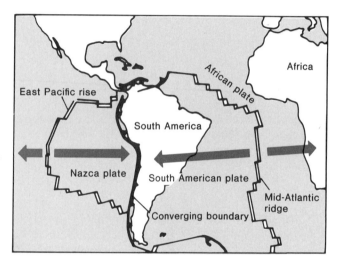

Figure 1.18 Converging boundary between the South American plate and the Nazca plate along the west coast of South America. Arrows show directions of plate movement.

The third type, one resulting in a wide range of geologic activities, is a **converging boundary,** where plates move toward each other (figure 1.18). If one plate is capped by oceanic crust and the other by continental crust, the less dense, more buoyant continental plate will override the denser oceanic plate. The oceanic plate sinks along what is known as a **subduction zone,** a zone where an oceanic plate descends into the mantle beneath an overriding plate. The entire oceanic plate becomes progressively hotter as it descends deeper in the earth. Where the two plates grind past one another, even greater temperature increases occur, due to the friction between the two plates (mechanical energy becomes converted to heat energy).

Many things happen in and adjacent to subduction zones (figure 1.19). Magma is generated as material with a low melting temperature is "boiled off." Volcanoes, such as Mount St. Helens, may be attributed to the action of

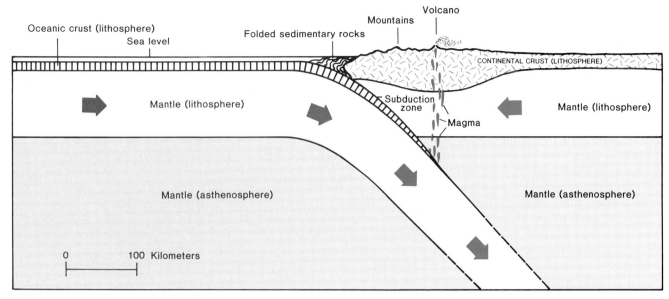

Figure 1.19 A converging boundary.

a small subsidiary heat engine produced by melting along the subduction zone. Magma is less dense than the overlying solid rock. Therefore, the magma created along the subduction zone works its way upward and either erupts on the earth's surface to solidify as *extrusive* **igneous rock** or it may solidify within the crust to become *intrusive* igneous rock. Rock that is near the subduction zone but does not melt may, due to the high pressure and high temperature, be transformed in the solid state to a new rock—a **metamorphic rock.**

Features of major mountain belts also show the effects of plate convergence. The compressional forces cause intense folding of layered rock along a boundary between two converging plates. In the process, rock that may have been below sea level is pushed upward to become a mountain range.

Surficial Processes: The Earth's External Heat Engine and the Hydrologic Cycle

The earth's external heat engine, driven by solar power and gravity, is best exemplified by the hydrologic cycle, described earlier (see figure 1.6). When rain or snow falls on the land surface, more than half the water is returned, rather rapidly, to the atmosphere by evaporation or by transpiration from plants. The remainder flows over the land surface as *runoff* in streams, or it trickles or percolates down into the ground to become **ground water.**

The hydrologic cycle is powered by heat energy derived from the sun, which causes water to evaporate, rise, and become part of the atmosphere. The air moves and cools, losing its ability to carry the water. Therefore, water precipitates as rain or snow. The rain or snow falls due to the gravitational attraction of the earth. Water flows downward, again by force of gravity, toward an ocean.

There is much more to the earth's external heat engine than is suggested by the hydrologic cycle. Our weather patterns are to a large extent a product of this heat engine. Hot air rises, where it is heated near the equator, for instance, and sinks in cold regions nearer the poles. Similarly, ocean waves and currents are largely caused by wind, generated in turn by solar heating. Glaciers, caused by continual snowfall at high elevations, where it is cold, are pulled downhill by gravity.

For physical geology it is important to focus on the interaction of surface waters and the atmosphere, on one hand, and the lithosphere, on the other. Streams running toward oceans are able to remove and transport some of the land over which they run. Landslides powered by gravity move material originally at high elevations to lower levels. Waves crashing along a shoreline cut back the coast. Glaciers moving downward under the influence of gravity grind away at underlying rock. In each case, rock originally raised to high elevations by the earth's internal processes is worn down by surficial processes.

The Rock Cycle and Equilibrium

Rocks formed at high temperature and high pressure deep within the earth and pushed upward by tectonic forces are unstable in their new environment. Air and water tend to cause the once deep-seated rocks to break down and form new materials. The new materials, stable under conditions existing at the earth's surface, are said to be in **equilibrium,** adjusted to the physical and chemical conditions of their environment, so that they do not change

Box 1.2
Plate Tectonics and the Scientific Method

We have described plate tectonics in a way that implies little doubt about the existence of the process. The theory of plate tectonics has only recently been accepted by a majority of geologists (this does not mean it is "true"). Plate tectonic theory, like all knowledge gained by science, has evolved through the processes of the **scientific method.** We will illustrate the scientific method by showing how plate tectonics has evolved from a vague idea into a plausible theory.

The basis for the scientific method is the belief that the universe is orderly and that by *objectively* analyzing phenomena, we can gain knowledge of its workings. The technique is best illustrated as a series of steps, although a scientist does not ordinarily go through a formal checklist in using the scientific method.

1. A question is raised or a problem is presented, usually after the gathering of facts, which scientists call *data.*
2. Tentative explanations or solutions, called **hypotheses,** are proposed after the available data on the subject have been analyzed.
3. Predictions are made to show what would occur in a given situation if a hypothesis were correct.
4. Predictions are tested. Incorrect hypotheses are discarded.
5. A hypothesis that passes the testing becomes a **theory,** which is regarded as having an excellent chance of being true. In science, however, nothing is ever accepted as being proved absolutely. All theories remain open to scrutiny, further testing, and refinement.

Like any human endeavor, the scientific method is not infallible. Objectivity is needed throughout. It is not difficult for someone to become attached to the hypothesis he or she has created and so tend subconsciously to find only supporting evidence. As in a court of law, every effort is made to have disinterested observers

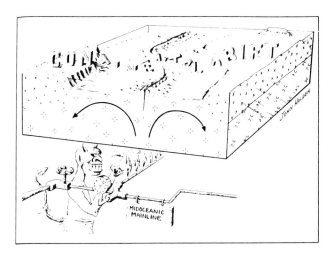

Figure 1.20 Continental drift, sea-floor spreading, and the internal heat engine according to John Holden. By permission of J. C. Holden and *Sea Frontiers.*

examine the logic of both procedures and results. Courts sometimes make wrong decisions; science, similarly, is not immune to error.

How the concept of plate tectonics evolved into a theory is outlined below.

Step 1: A question asked or problem raised
Actually, a number of questions were being asked about seemingly unrelated geological phenomena. What caused the submarine ridge that extends through most of the oceans of the world? Why are rocks in mountain belts intensely deformed? What sets off earthquakes? What causes rock to melt underground and erupt as volcanoes?

Step 2: Hypotheses proposed Most of the questions being asked were treated as separate problems, although some appeared interrelated. Hypotheses were proposed for each of the problems or for sets of problems. One hypothesis, **continental drift,** proposed by several workers, was best explained by Alfred Wegener, a German scientist, in a book published in the early 1900s.

Wegener postulated that the continents all were once a single supercontinent. The

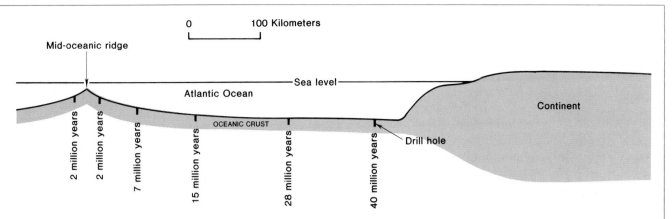

Figure 1.21 Ages of rocks from holes drilled into the oceanic crust. (Vertical scale of diagram is exaggerated.)

hypothesis explained why the coastlines of Africa and South America look like separated parts of a jigsaw puzzle. Some 200 million years ago this supercontinent broke up, and the various continents slowly drifted into their present positions. The hypothesis suggested that the rock within mountain belts becomes deformed as the leading edge of a continental crust moves against and over the stationary oceanic crust. Earthquakes were presumed to be due to continuing movement of the continents.

It was not until the 1960s, after new data on the nature of the sea floor were discovered, that the idea of continental drift was incorporated into the concept of plate tectonics. What was added in the plate tectonic hypothesis was the idea that oceanic crust, as well as continental crust, was shifting.

Step 3: Prediction An obvious prediction, if plate tectonics is correct, would be that since Europe and North America are moving away from one another, the distance between Europe and North America will be greater ten years from now than at present. To test this prediction, satellites are being used to try to make such measurements, but we do not yet have the results. Another prediction for the hypothesis was that the rocks of the oceanic crust would be progressively older with increasing distance from the spreading center, the crest of the mid-oceanic ridge.

Step 4: Predictions are tested Experiments were conducted in which holes were drilled in the deep sea floor from a specially designed

ship. Rocks and sediment were collected from these holes, and the ages of these materials were determined. As the hypothesis predicted, the youngest sea floor (generally less than a million years old) is near the mid-oceanic ridges, whereas the oldest sea floor (up to about 200 million years old) is farthest from the ridges (figure 1.21).

This test was only one of a series performed. Various other tests, described in some detail later in this book, tended to confirm the hypothesis of plate tectonics. Some tests, as well as detailed study of known data, did not work out exactly as predicted, so modifications in the original concept were made. The basic premise, however, generally is regarded as valid.

Step 5: The hypothesis becomes a theory Most geologists in the world consider the results of the testing to have been sufficiently positive to imply that the concept is probably true. It can now be called the plate tectonic theory. This, of course, does not mean that it is "proved." It would be unscientific not to leave open the possibility that other explanations might account for the observed phenomena. Furthermore, to accept the theory as dogma would require ignoring aspects of geology that cannot easily be reconciled with plate tectonics, and such aspects do exist. We should never become so arrogant as to think nature behaves as we want it to.

Like other new theories, the plate tectonic theory raises questions that call for more scientific investigation.

or alter with time. For example, most of the minerals in igneous rock that formed at a high temperature tend to break down chemically to clay minerals. Clay minerals are in equilibrium, are stable, at the earth's surface. The processes of disintegration and decomposition of unstable material at the earth's surface are called **weathering.**

The movement of air and water driven by solar energy and gravity results in erosion of the weathered material. **Erosion** is the loosening and removing of material. Erosion requires a transporting agent such as running water. Eventually the weathered material is deposited as loose **sediment** when the transporting agent loses its carrying power. For example, when a river slows down as it meets the sea, the sand it carries is deposited near the mouth as part of a layer of sediment.

In time a layer of sediment deposited on the sea floor becomes buried by another layer. This process may continue until great thicknesses of sedimentary layers accumulate. The pressure from overlying layers compresses the sediment, helping to consolidate the loose material. If cementation of the loose particles takes place, the sediment becomes **lithified** (cemented or otherwise consolidated) into a **sedimentary rock.**

The rock cycle   If the earth's internal engine had died, the external engine plus gravity would long ago have leveled the continents, and the resulting sediment would have been deposited on the sea floor. Everything would be at rest. Nothing would be changing. Which is to say, everything would be in equilibrium. But this is not the case. The internal and external forces continue to interact, forcing substances out of equilibrium. Therefore, the earth has a highly varied and ever-changing surface. A useful aid to visualizing the relationship is the **rock cycle** shown in figure 1.22. The three major rock types—igneous, metamorphic, and sedimentary—are shown. You can see how each may form at the expense of another if it is forced out of equilibrium with its physical or climatic environment by either internal or surficial forces.

Magma is molten rock. *Igneous rocks* are formed when magma solidifies. If the magma is brought to the surface by a volcanic eruption, it may solidify into an *extrusive* igneous rock. Magma may also solidify very slowly beneath the surface. The resulting *intrusive* igneous rock may be exposed later after uplift and erosion remove the overlying rock (as shown in figure 1.23). The igneous rock, being out of equilibrium, may then undergo weathering, and the debris produced is transported and ultimately deposited (usually on a sea floor) as *sediment*. If the unconsolidated sediment becomes *lithified* (cemented or otherwise consolidated into a rock), it becomes a *sedimentary rock*. As the rock is buried by additional

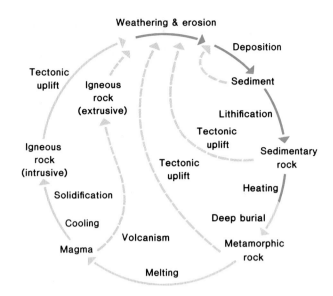

Figure 1.22   The rock cycle. Light arrows indicate internally driven processes. Dark arrows indicate surficial processes.

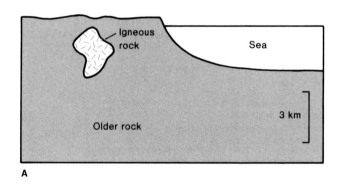

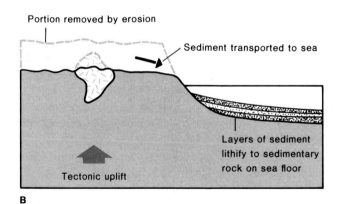

Figure 1.23   Uplift, erosion, and deposition. (*A*) Magma has solidified underground to become igneous rock. (*B*) Land is uplifted. Upper portion is weathered and eroded. Sediment is transported to the sea to become sedimentary rock.

layers of sediment and sedimentary rock, heat and pressure increase. Tectonic forces may also contribute to increasing temperature and pressure. If the temperature and pressure become high enough, usually at depths greater than several kilometers below the surface, the original sedimentary rock is no longer in equilibrium and recrystallizes. The new rock that forms is called a *metamorphic rock*. If the temperature gets very high, the rock melts and becomes magma again, completing the cycle.

The cycle can be repeated, as implied by the arrows in figure 1.22. There is no reason to expect all rocks to proceed through each step in the cycle, however. For instance, sedimentary rocks might be uplifted and exposed to weathering and erosion before being buried deeply enough to become metamorphosed.

In this book we describe the earth's materials in chapters 1–7. We subsequently consider the factor of time (chapter 8) and the processes that act on earth materials. We discuss in detail the work of the various agents of erosion and deposition, such as landsliding and related downslope movements, water, glaciers, wind, and ocean waves (chapters 9–14). We discover how these agents are able to sculpture landscapes and deposit sediment in distinctive styles. The jagged peaks in figure 1.7, for example, indicate erosion by glaciers.

Chapters 15–20 deal with the earth's interior, tectonic forces generated within the earth, and the effect these forces have on rocks of the crust.

Geologic Time

We have mentioned the great amount of time required for geological processes to occur. As humans, we think in units of time that we can relate to personal experience— seconds, hours, years, a human lifetime. It stretches our imagination to contemplate ancient history that involves one or two thousand years.

To be sure, some geological processes occur quickly, such as a great landslide or the eruption of Mount St. Helens. These events occur when energy is stored (just as energy may be stored in a car battery), sometimes for centuries, before being released suddenly. However, most geological processes are slow but relentless, reflecting the pace at which the heat engines work. It is unlikely that a hill will show visible changes in its shape or height during your lifetime (unless a natural catastrophe or human activities intervene). However, in a geologic time frame, the hill probably is eroding away quite rapidly. "Rapidly" to a geologist may mean that within a few million years the hill will be reduced nearly to a plain. Similarly, in the geologically "recent" past of several million years ago, a sea may have existed where the hill

is now. Some processes are regarded by geologists as proceeding at a "fast" rate if they are begun and completed within a million years.

The rate of plate motion is relatively fast. If new magma erupts and solidifies along a mid-oceanic ridge, we can easily calculate how long it will take for that igneous rock to move 1,000 kilometers away from the spreading center. At the rate of one centimeter per year, it will take 100 million years for the presently forming part of the crust to travel the 1,000 kilometers.

Uniformitarianism

Two hundred years ago you would have been declared a heretic in Christian countries if you believed the earth existed before 4004 B.C. Some astute observations and reasoning by an eighteenth-century Scotsman, James Hutton, profoundly changed people's thinking. He noted (as had others before his time) that layers of rock several thousand meters thick possessed textural and compositional features like those of loose sediment at the bottom of lakes or along shorelines. The rocks must, therefore, have formed by consolidation of similar sediments, he reasoned. Fossil sea shells in the rocks seemed to support this conclusion. But how could layers several thousand meters thick have accumulated? The standard answer at the time was that all the sediment had been deposited during the great Biblical flood of Noah's time.

Hutton's revolutionary hypothesis was that the layered rock could be explained by the same processes he observed taking place around him. He could see sediment settling slowly through water to collect in layers. The rock must have formed after a slow process of settling, too. The implication was that very large periods of time were needed for huge amounts of sediment to settle to the sea floor and later consolidate into rock. Hutton's hypothesis, which has become known as the **principle of uniformitarianism,** says that geological processes that are operating now are the same processes that have operated in the geologic past. This has been paraphrased in the following concise statement: "The present is the key to the past." Applying the principle, we can determine the past history of the earth by observing processes that are taking place in the present.

The principle of uniformitarianism should not be interpreted as excluding sudden or catastrophic events. For instance, a violent volcanic explosion may alter the earth's weather patterns for years. Similarly, one hurricane on the Gulf Coast of North America moves more sediment in a few hours than hundreds or even thousands of years of day-to-day processes. Nor can we apply the principle too rigidly. Processes that are slow today may have been more rapid in the past. For instance, it is extremely rare for a meteorite large enough to form a crater to hit the earth today. Yet, based on our studies of the moon, it is very likely that around 3.8–4.0 billion years ago the earth was bombarded by meteorites. Since the moon at that time was bombarded by meteorites, the earth certainly could not have escaped similar bombardment. The earth's meteorite craters were erased long ago by weathering and erosion, but those on the moon are preserved for eternity because the moon lacks an atmosphere and therefore an external heat engine.

What the principle of uniformitarianism *does* tell us is that we cannot violate the physical and chemical laws of the universe—we cannot invoke magic or supernatural powers to account for the earth's features and processes.

Although we will discuss geologic time in detail in chapter 8, table 1.1 shows some reference points to keep in mind. The earth now is estimated to be about 4.5 billion years old (4,500 million years). Fossils in rocks indicate that complex forms of animal life have existed in abundance on the earth for about the past 600 million years. Reptiles—most notably, dinosaurs—became abundant about 235 million years ago. Dinosaurs became extinct about 70 million years ago, and humans have been here only about the last 3 million years (the Flintstones notwithstanding).

Not only are the immense spans of geologic time difficult to comprehend, but very slow processes are impossible to duplicate. A geologist who wants to study a certain process cannot repeat in a few hours a chemical reaction that may take a million years to occur in nature. As Mark Twain wrote in *Life on the Mississippi*, "Nothing hurries geology."

Summary

Geology is the scientific study of the earth. Geological investigations indicate that the earth is changing due to internal and surficial processes. Internal processes are probably driven mostly by convection currents within the earth's mantle. Surficial processes are due to solar energy and gravity. Movement of the crust of the earth is caused by internal forces. Plate tectonic theory visualizes the crust and uppermost mantle (the lithosphere) as being broken into several major plates that are in motion relative to each other. The plates are moving *away* from spreading centers along mid-oceanic ridges, where new crust is being created. Plates are moving *toward* boundaries with other plates; continuous convergence may result in one plate's being overridden and forced back into the mantle while the other plate is deformed into mountains.

The earth's surface is constantly being altered by air and water in motion. The hydrologic cycle is rain falling on the land surface, flowing toward a sea, evaporating to the atmosphere and eventually precipitating once again, as rain (or snow).

The interaction between the internal and external forces of the earth is illustrated by the rock cycle, a conceptual device relating igneous, sedimentary, and metamorphic rocks to each other, to surficial processes such as weathering and erosion, and to internal processes such as tectonic forces. Changes take place because one or more processes will force earth's material out of equilibrium.

Although the earth is changing constantly, the rates of change are generally extremely slow by human standards. Geologists do not regard a million years as a very long period of time. The principle of uniformitarianism allows us to determine what happened in the past by understanding present-day processes.

Table 1.1

Some Important Ages in the Development of Life on Earth

Time in Millions of Years Before Present	Animal Life on Earth
3	First humans
65	First important mammals; extinction of dinosaurs
230	First dinosaurs
300	First reptiles
350	First land vertebrates
400	Fishes become abundant
600	First abundant fossils
3,500	Earliest single-celled fossils
4,500	Origin of the earth

Terms to Remember

asthenosphere	mantle
continental drift	metamorphic rock
convection	mid-oceanic ridge
convection current	physical geology
converging boundary	plastically
core	plate tectonics
crust	rock cycle
equilibrium	scientific method
erosion	sediment
geology	sedimentary rock
gravity	spreading center
ground water	(diverging boundary)
heat engine	subduction zone
hydrologic cycle	tectonic forces
hypothesis	theory
igneous rock	transform boundary
lithified	uniformitarianism
lithosphere	weathering
magma	

Questions for Review

1. Describe three different ways rocks are formed.
2. What is the distinction between weathering and erosion?
3. What is meant by tectonic activity?
4. What would the surface of the earth be like if there were no tectonic activity?
5. Explain why cavemen never saw a dinosaur.
6. What are the three types of plate boundaries described in this chapter and how do they differ from one another?
7. What is meant by *equilibrium*? What happens when rocks are forced out of equilibrium?
8. What are the relationships among the mantle, the crust, the asthenosphere, and the lithosphere?
9. What role does gravity play in each of the heat engines?

Questions for Thought

1. According to plate tectonic theory, where are crustal rocks created? Why doesn't the earth keep getting larger if rock is continually being created?
2. What evidence is there that geologic processes operated in the past at about the same rate and in about the same way as they do now?
3. What percentage of geologic time is accounted for by the last century?
4. What would the earth be like without solar heating?
5. What are some of the technical difficulties you would expect to encounter if you tried to drill a hole to the center of the earth?

Supplementary Readings

Adams, F. D. 1954. *The birth and development of the geological sciences.* New York: Dover Publications.

Fisher, R. B. 1975. *Science, man and society.* 2d ed. Philadelphia: W. B. Saunders.

Gardner, M. 1957. *Fads and fallacies in the name of science.* New York: Dover Publications.

McPhee, J. 1980. Annals of the former world. *The New Yorker,* Oct. 20 and 27, 1980. (In 1981, published as a book, *Basin and range.* New York: Farrar, Straus & Giroux.)

Pirsig, R. M. 1974. *Zen and the art of motorcycle maintenance.* New York: Bantam Books (paperback). This book contains an exceptionally good exposition of the scientific method as well as considerable insight into the philosophy of science.

Sullivan, W. 1974. *Continents in motion.* New York: McGraw-Hill.

Wegener, A. 1966. *The origin of the continents and oceans.* New York: Dover Publications (paperback reprint of the original translation from German).

Wyllie, P. J. 1976. *The way the earth works.* New York: John Wiley & Sons.

2
Atoms, Elements, and Minerals

Purpose

Knowing the names and important characteristics of the most common elements and minerals is essential to understanding how they combine to form the rocks of the earth. Familiarity with this basic information will help you throughout the rest of your study of geology.

Some basic principles of chemistry also are necessary to understand material covered in later chapters, such as the various types of rocks, weathering, and the composition of the earth's interior and the crust. You need to know what a mineral is; how each mineral is composed of certain chemical elements in a remarkably orderly arrangement; and how the arrangement and characteristics of atoms control the physical properties of minerals. You will learn how to readily determine physical properties and use them to identify common minerals. (Appendix A is a further guide to the identification of minerals.)

Rock is naturally formed, consolidated material composed of grains of one or more minerals (this definition has a few exceptions). Most of the earth is rock. What, then, is a *mineral*? Among other things, a mineral is crystalline. A **crystalline** substance is one in which the atoms are arranged in a regularly repeating, orderly pattern. The print by M. C. Escher (figure 2.1) expresses in a vivid way the principle of crystallinity. You can visualize what crystallinity is in nature by mentally substituting identical clusters of atoms for each fish and imagining the clusters packed together.

Rock salt is an example of a rock made of grains of only one mineral. Rock salt is an aggregate of consolidated grains of the mineral *halite,* familiar to everyone as table salt. Halite is composed of equal numbers of sodium (Na) and chlorine (Cl) atoms arranged in a simple, orderly, crystalline pattern. Each sodium atom is surrounded by 6 chlorine atoms and each chlorine atom is surrounded by 6 sodium atoms. Billions of each type of atom are necessary to form a salt crystal the size of a pinhead. Halite crystals tend to be cubic because of the particular orderly

Figure 2.1 "Depth," print by M. C. Escher.
© BEELDRECHT, Amsterdam/VAGA, New York 1981. Collection Haags Gemeentemuseum.

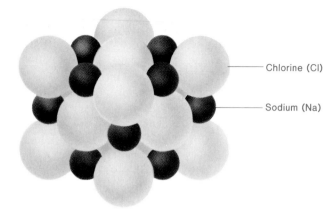

Figure 2.2 Model of the crystal structure of halite (or table salt).

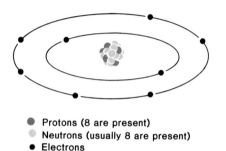

● Protons (8 are present)
○ Neutrons (usually 8 are present)
● Electrons

Figure 2.3 Schematic representation of an atom of oxygen. The electrons would be in spherical rather than circular orbits. The nucleus would be very much smaller relative to the size of the orbits.

way in which chlorine and sodium atoms are packed together (figure 2.2). This and other physical and chemical properties of halite are caused by (1) the pattern of repeating atoms, (2) the way the atoms are bonded to neighboring atoms, and (3) the characteristics of the elements chlorine and sodium.

Atoms and Elements

Halite (or table salt) crystals may be separated chemically into sodium and chlorine, both of which are elements. An **element** is a substance that cannot be broken down to other substances by ordinary chemical methods.

An **atom** is the smallest possible particle of an element that retains the properties of that element. All atoms of the element chlorine are essentially identical to all other chlorine atoms; the same is true for sodium. Water (H_2O) can be chemically broken down to the elements oxygen and hydrogen (two hydrogen atoms are present for every oxygen atom).

Atoms are far too small to see, even with the most powerful microscope. Our pictures of atoms are really models. A *model* in science is an image—graphic, mathematical, or verbal—that is consistent with the known data.

The picture of an atom that comes to most people's minds is one of tiny particles in orbit around a nucleus (figure 2.3). Although this model is now regarded by scientists as an oversimplification, it is perfectly adequate for an introductory geology course.

Models of atoms constructed by chemists and physicists show three types of subatomic particles—protons, neutrons, and electrons. A **proton** is a subatomic particle that contributes mass and a single positive electrical charge to an atom. A **neutron** is a subatomic particle that contributes mass to an atom but is electrically neutral. An **electron** is a single negative electric charge that contributes virtually no mass to an atom.

Protons and neutrons form the **nucleus** of an atom. Although the nucleus occupies a very tiny fraction of the volume of the entire atom, practically all the mass of the atom is concentrated in the nucleus. The **atomic mass number** is the total number of neutrons and protons in an atom. The atomic mass number of the oxygen atom in figure 2.3 is 16 (8 protons plus 8 neutrons). Heavier elements have more neutrons and protons than do lighter ones. For example, the heavy element gold has an atomic mass number of 197, whereas helium has 4.

The number of protons controls the "character" of an element to a greater extent than does the number of other subatomic particles. The **atomic number** of an element is the number of protons in each atom. We may refine our earlier definition of an element by adding that each atom of an element possesses the *same number of protons*. Gold has an atomic number of 80, or 80 protons per atom; oxygen always has 8 protons; hydrogen always has 1 proton; chlorine has 17; and sodium has 11. (Other atomic numbers are listed in Appendix C.)

The number of neutrons (and therefore the mass of an element) may vary within limits. **Isotopes** of an element are atoms containing different numbers of neutrons but the *same number of protons*. For example, the most common isotope of oxygen has 8 neutrons, but oxygen isotopes with 10 neutrons sometimes are detected. In geology, isotopes are important in radioactive dating of rocks (chapter 8).

An element's atomic weight is closely related to the mass number. **Atomic weight** is the weight of an *average* atom of an element, given in atomic mass units. Since sodium has only one isotope, its atomic mass number and its atomic weight are the same—23. On the other hand, chlorine has two common isotopes, with mass numbers of 35 and 37. The atomic weight of chlorine, which takes into account the abundance of each isotope, is 35.5 (the lighter isotope is more common than the heavier one).

Electrons, although possessing almost no mass, are visualized as occupying orbits around the nucleus. Virtually the entire volume of an atom is taken up by the space in which these tiny, electrically negative charges move. The number of electrons in an atom is related to the number of protons in the nucleus. Each electron is opposite in charge but equal in strength to a proton.

If the number of electrons in orbit around a nucleus is equal to the number of protons in the nucleus, the positive and negative charges balance each other and the atom is electrically neutral. Helium has 2 electrons, exactly balancing its 2 protons. Most elements, however, are not able to maintain an electric balance between protons and electrons within a single atom.

Chemical Activity

Many geological processes can be explained as chemical reactions. Some rocks form as a result of chemical reactions between substances. Chemical reactions also play a part in weathering. Understanding a few basic concepts of chemistry will clarify why and under what conditions chemical reactions occur.

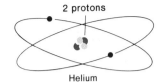

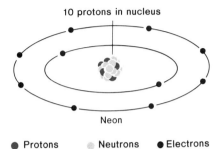

● Protons   Neutrons   ● Electrons

Figure 2.4 (A) Helium atom and (B) neon atom.

Atoms that are not electrically neutral tend to react (or combine) with other atoms to neutralize the electrical imbalance. Each atom not only seeks electrical neutrality, but also wants each of its orbit levels (or shells) to be full of electrons. The innermost shell is full when it possesses 2 electrons; outer shells each generally require 8 electrons to be complete.

Helium, for example, is a *stable* element because 2 protons are balanced by 2 electrons, and the 2 electrons exactly fill one shell. Neon similarly is stable; its 10 protons are balanced by 2 electrons in the inner shell and 8 electrons in the next shell (see figure 2.4). Neither of these elements normally reacts with other elements.

Ions

Chlorine and sodium are more typical elements, in that if an electron shell is complete, the atom is electrically out of balance. A sodium atom (figure 2.5) has a complete inner shell with 2 electrons and a second shell also filled with 8 electrons. One more electron would neutralize all 11 protons in the nucleus, but an eleventh electron alone in a shell is extremely unstable, so the sodium atom normally does without it. In each sodium atom, then, the eleven protons (11+) and 10 electrons (10−) sum up to a single excess positive charge (+1). Such an atom is an **ion**, an electrically charged atom or group of atoms. The sodium ion can be abbreviated as Na^+.

Chlorine, with an atomic number of 17, has a complete inner shell with 2 electrons and a complete second shell of 8 around this. A neutral chlorine atom would have only 7 electrons in the third shell; but since this shell requires 8 electrons, an extra electron is captured and incorporated in it. The chlorine ion then contains 18 electrons and 17 protons, and so has a single excess negative charge (Cl^-).

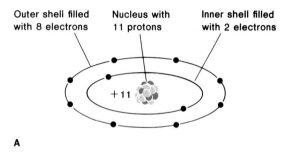

Outer shell filled with 8 electrons — Nucleus with 11 protons — Inner shell filled with 2 electrons

+11

A

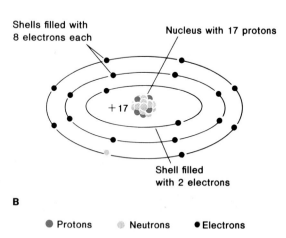

Shells filled with 8 electrons each — Nucleus with 17 protons

+17

Shell filled with 2 electrons

B

● Protons   ● Neutrons   ● Electrons

Figure 2.5 (A) Sodium (Na^+) ion. Ten electrons are in orbit about the nucleus, which contains eleven protons. (B) Chlorine (Cl^-) ion. Electron shown in color completes the outer shell of the chlorine atom, making it an ion.

Bonding

Ions may be regarded as tiny spheres that behave much like magnets. Positively charged ions attract negatively charged ions so that their electrical charges can be neutralized. In salt water, equal numbers of sodium ions (Na^+) and chlorine ions (Cl^-) move about freely. The electrical neutrality of the water is maintained because positive sodium ions exactly balance negative chlorine ions. If the water is evaporated, the sodium and chlorine are electrically attracted to one another and crystallize into halite. The crystal is the most orderly way in which chlorine and sodium ions can pack themselves together and neutralize their collective charges. The ions are *bonded* in the structure. **Bonding** is the attachment of an atom to one or more adjacent atoms; this commonly occurs in two ways, as figure 2.6 shows.

A chlorine ion and a sodium ion are fixed in place by their electrical attraction to one another. This is called **ionic bonding** because it is due to attraction between positively and negatively charged ions (figure 2.6*A*).

Ionic bonding is the most prevalent type of bonding in minerals. However, in most minerals the bonds between ions are not purely ionic. Atoms also are commonly bonded together by **covalent bonding,** or bonding in which adjacent atoms *share* electrons. Diamond is composed exclusively of covalently bonded carbon atoms (figure 2.6*B*). Carbon has an atomic number of 6, which means that the innermost shell is full with 2 electrons. Four more electrons are required to maintain electrical neutrality. In a diamond, each carbon atom has 4 electrons in the outer shell to maintain neutrality, while the need for 8 electrons

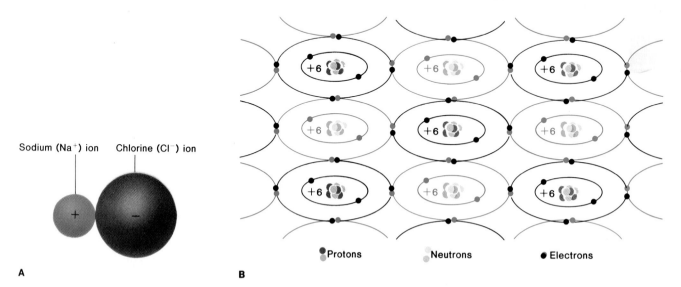

Sodium (Na^+) ion   Chlorine (Cl^-) ion

+   −

A

+6 +6 +6
+6 +6 +6
+6 +6 +6

● Protons   ● Neutrons   ● Electrons

B

Figure 2.6 (A) Ionic bonding between sodium (Na^+) and chlorine (Cl^-). (B) Carbon atoms covalently bonded, as in diamond.

in that shell is satisfied by electrons being shared with adjacent carbon atoms. Neighboring carbon atoms are close together, so that each of the outer-shell electrons spends half its time orbiting one atom and the other half orbiting an adjacent atom. Electrical neutrality is maintained, and each atom, in a sense, has 8 electrons in the outer shell (even though they are not all there at the same time). Covalent bonds in the diamond are extremely strong, and diamond is the hardest natural substance on earth. However, covalent bonds are not necessarily stronger than ionic bonds.

Chemical Composition of the Earth's Crust

Estimates of the chemical composition of the earth's crust are based on many chemical analyses that have been made of the rocks exposed on the earth's surface. (Models for the composition of the interior of the earth—the core and the mantle—are based on more indirect evidence.) Table 2.1 is the generally accepted estimate of the abundance of elements in the earth's crust. At first glance, the chemical composition of the crust (and, therefore, the average rock) may be quite surprising.

Most people think of oxygen in terms of the air we breathe. Yet most rocks are composed largely of oxygen, which is the most abundant element in the earth's crust. Unlike the oxygen gas in the air, oxygen in minerals is strongly bonded to other elements. By weight, oxygen ac-

counts for about half the crust, but it takes up 93 percent of the volume of an average rock. This is because the orbits of oxygen electrons take up a large amount of space relative to their weight. It is hardly an exaggeration to regard the crust as a mass of oxygen with the other elements occupying positions in crystal structures dictated by oxygen atoms. The relative number and size of oxygen and other atoms as a percentage of the earth's crust may be visualized from figure 2.7.

Silica is a term used for *oxygen plus silicon*. Because silicon is the second most abundant element in the crust, most minerals contain silica. The common mineral quartz (SiO_2) is pure silica that has crystallized. Quartz is one of many minerals that are **silicates,** substances that contain silica (as indicated by their chemical formulas). Most silicate minerals also contain one or more additional elements.

Note that the third most abundant element is aluminum, which is more common in rocks than iron. It might seem that aluminum should be less expensive than iron, but of course this is not the case. Common rocks are not mined for aluminum because it is so strongly bonded to oxygen and other elements. The amount of energy required to break these bonds and separate the aluminum make it too costly for commercial production. Aluminum is mined from the uncommon deposits where aluminum-bearing rocks have been weathered, producing compounds in which the crystalline bonds are not so strong.

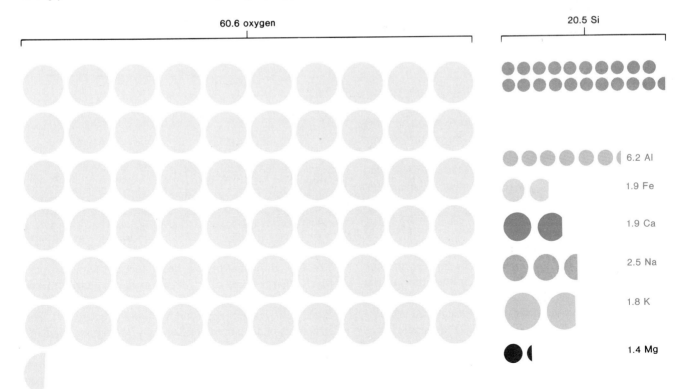

Figure 2.7 Composition of the average rock of the earth's crust. Each circle represents one percent of the rock. Circles are scaled to the size of respective ions.

Table 2.1

Crustal Abundance of Elements

Element	Symbol	Percentage by Weight	Percentage by Volume	Percentage of Atoms
Oxygen	O	46.6	93.8	60.5
Silicon	Si	27.7	0.9	20.5
Aluminum	Al	8.1	0.8	6.2
Iron	Fe	5.0	0.5	1.9
Calcium	Ca	3.6	1.0	1.9
Sodium	Na	2.8	1.2	2.5
Potassium	K	2.6	1.5	1.8
Magnesium	Mg	2.1	0.3	1.4
All other elements		1.5	—	3.3

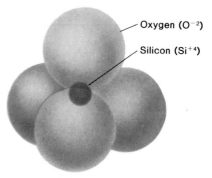

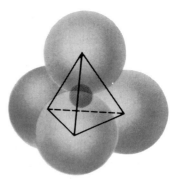

Figure 2.8 (*A*) The silica tetrahedron. (*B*) Corners of the tetrahedron coincide with centers of oxygen ions.

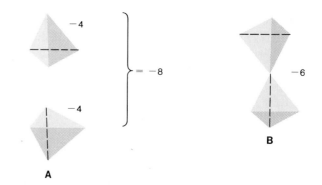

Figure 2.9 Single tetrahedrons (*A*) require more positively charged ions to maintain electrical neutrality than (*B*) tetrahedrons with shared oxygen atoms.

Collectively, the eight elements listed in table 2.1 account for more than 98 percent of the weight of the crust. All the other elements total only about 1.5 percent. Absent from the top eight elements are such vital elements as hydrogen (tenth by weight) and carbon (seventeenth by weight).

The element copper is only twenty-seventh in abundance, but our industrialized society is highly dependent on this metal. Most of the wiring in electronic equipment is copper, as are many of the telephone and power cables that crisscross the continent. However, the earth's crust is not homogeneous, and geological processes have created concentrations of elements such as copper in a few places. Exploration geologists are employed by mining companies to discover where, as well as why, ore deposits of copper and other metals occur.

The Silica Tetrahedron

The two most abundant elements, silicon and oxygen, combine to form the basic building block for most common minerals. In each "building block," four oxygen atoms are packed together around a single, much smaller, silicon atom, as shown in figure 2.8. The four-sided, pyramidlike, geometric shape called a *tetrahedron* is used to represent visually the four oxygen atoms surrounding a silicon atom. Each corner of the tetrahedron represents the center of an oxygen atom. This basic building block of a crystal is called a **silica tetrahedron.**

The bonds between the four oxygen atoms and the enclosed silicon atom are approximately 50 percent ionic and 50 percent covalent. This results in the atoms of the tetrahedron being very strongly bonded together. Within a silica tetrahedron the negative charges exceed the positive charges (see figures 2.8 and 2.9). A single silica tetrahedron would have a formula of SiO_4^{-4}, because silicon has an ionic charge of +4, and the four oxygen ions have 8 negative charges (-2 for each oxygen atom).

For the silica tetrahedron to be stable within a crystal structure, it must either (1) be balanced by sufficient positively charged ions or (2) share oxygen atoms with adjacent tetrahedrons (and therefore reduce the need for extra, positively-charged ions, as shown in figure 2.9). The structures of silicate minerals range from an *isolated silicate structure,* which depends entirely on positively charged ions to hold the tetrahedrons together, to *framework silicates* (quartz, for example), in which all oxygen atoms are shared by adjacent tetrahedrons.

Box 2.1
Our Largest Nuclear Power Plant—The Sun

The sun contains 99.8 percent of all the matter in the solar system (the sun and its planets). Although the planets are highly varied in size and composition (see chapter 22), they contribute little to the mass of the solar system. The composition of the solar system is essentially the composition of the sun.

Because so much mass is concentrated in the sun, you might suppose that it is made up mostly of heavy elements, but it is not. The sun is believed to be 98 percent hydrogen and helium— the two lightest elements. Obviously, then, each of the earth's eight most abundant elements must be minor constituents of the solar system.

Because of the sun's great size (it is 333,000 times the mass of the earth), its internal pressures are very high. Hydrogen atoms compressed together under this great pressure deep within the sun become involved in a nuclear reaction. Four hydrogen nuclei are compressed, or fused, into a single helium atom. Part of the original mass is converted to energy. This is the same nuclear reaction that takes place when a hydrogen bomb explodes. The energy released is awesome. The sun releases in one-millionth of a second more energy than the United States needs for a full year. (Of course, only a small fraction of this energy reaches the earth).

Even nuclear reactions consume fuel to produce energy. The sun is turning its hydrogen into helium at the rate of 4 million tons per second. But, even at this rate of consumption, there is enough hydrogen to keep the sun working at its present rate for another 5 billion years.

Isolated silicate structure Silicate minerals that are structured so that none of the oxygen atoms are shared by tetrahedrons have an **isolated silicate structure.** The individual silica tetrahedrons are bonded together by positively charged ions (figure 2.10). The common mineral **olivine,** for example, contains two ions of either magnesium (Mg^{+2}) or iron (Fe^{+2}) for each silica tetrahedron (figure 2.9); the formula for olivine is $(Fe,Mg)_2SiO_4$.

Chain silicates If two oxygen atoms of each tetrahedron are shared with adjacent tetrahedrons, the result may be a chain of tetrahedrons, a **chain silicate structure.** Each chain, which extends indefinitely, has a net excess of negative charges. The ratio of silicon to oxygen (as figure 2.11 shows) is 1:3; therefore, each mineral in this group (the *pyroxene* group) incorporates SiO_3^{-2} in its formula, and it must be electrically balanced by the positive ions that hold the parallel chains together.

One pyroxene mineral, for example, has a formula of $MgSiO_3$. This pyroxene may form in a cooling magma when earlier formed crystals of olivine, Mg_2SiO_4, react with silica (SiO_2) in the remaining melt. To accommodate the additional silica, olivine's isolated silicate structure is

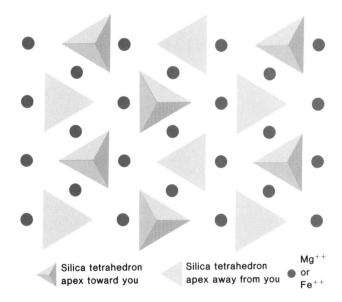

| Silica tetrahedron apex toward you | Silica tetrahedron apex away from you | Mg^{++} or Fe^{++} |

Figure 2.10 Diagrammatic representation of the crystal structure of olivine, as seen from one side of the crystal.

rearranged into the single chain silicate structure of pyroxene. In this case, Mg^{+2} ions would occupy the positive ion positions between chains shown in figure 2.11*A*.

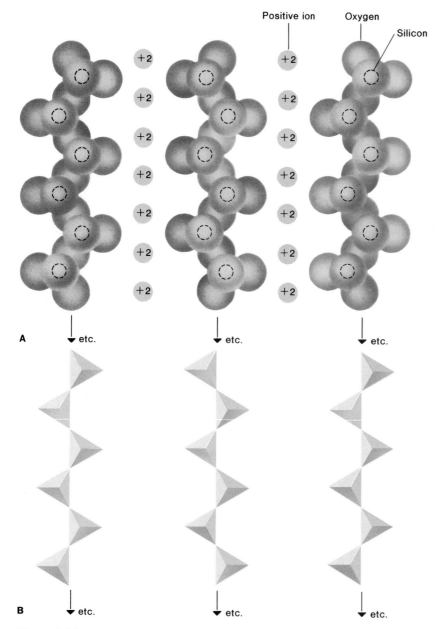

Figure 2.11 Single chain silicate structure. (*A*) Model of a single chain silicate mineral. (*B*) The same chain silicate shown diagrammatically as linked tetrahedrons: positive ions between the chains are not shown.

The *amphibole* group is characterized by *two* parallel chains in which every other tetrahedron along a chain shares an oxygen ion with the adjacent chain (figure 2.12). In even a small amphibole crystal, millions of parallel double chains are bonded together by positively charged ions.

Minerals with chain silicate structure are shaped like columns, needles, or even fibers. The long dimension of the external form is parallel to the long direction of the chain structure. Asbestos is a fibrous aggregate of certain chain silicate minerals.

The sheet silicates When each tetrahedron shares three oxygen ions, the result is a **sheet silicate structure,** characteristic of the *mica* group of minerals (figure 2.13). The positive ions that hold the sheets together are "sandwiched" between the silicate sheets.

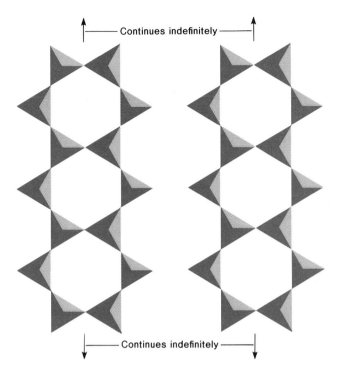

Continues indefinitely

Continues indefinitely

Figure 2.12 Double chain silicate structure shown diagrammatically by tetrahedrons. Positive ions (not shown) hold each double chain to adjacent double chains.

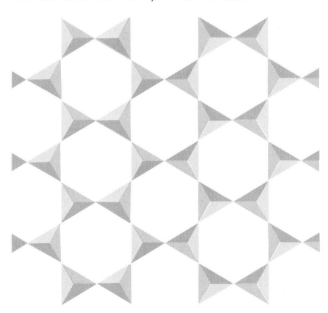

Figure 2.13 Sheet silicate structure as shown by tetrahedrons. Sheet structure is parallel to paper and linked to similar sheets (also parallel to the paper) by positively charged ions.

Framework silicates When all four oxygen ions are shared by adjacent tetrahedrons, a **framework silicate structure** is formed. Quartz is a framework silicate mineral. A feldspar is a framework silicate as well. However, the structure is complicated somewhat because aluminum

Figure 2.14 A framework silicate. All corners of the tetrahedrons are shared with adjacent tetrahedrons, and the structure extends indefinitely in three dimensions.
From *Crystallography and Crystal Chemistry* by F. D. Bloss. Copyright © 1971 Holt, Rinehart & Winston. Reprinted by permission of Holt, Rinehart & Winston.

substitutes for some of the silicon atoms in some of the tetrahedrons. The same kinds of substitutions also take place in pyroxenes, amphiboles, and micas, which helps account for the wide variety of silicate minerals.

Minerals

Although we have been discussing minerals, we have not fully defined what a mineral is. To be a **mineral** in the geological sense of the term, a substance must satisfy five conditions:

1. It must be a *crystalline solid*.
2. It must be *naturally occurring*.
3. It must be *inorganic*.
4. It must have a *definite chemical composition*.
5. It must possess *characteristic physical properties*.

The English language includes other meanings for the word *mineral* that conflict with the geologists' definition. The "minerals" listed on cereal boxes, for instance, have nothing to do with what geologists or chemists mean when they talk about minerals. Nor, for that matter, does the geologist's definition agree with the miner's definition of a mineral. To a miner, a "mineral" is anything of commercial value that is extracted from the ground.

In this book, the use of the term *mineral* is restricted to the strict geological definition.

Crystalline Solids

We have already mentioned that crystallinity, the first criterion for a mineral, is an orderly arrangement of atoms. Liquids are not crystalline, because the atoms are free to move about; nor is glass, because the atoms in glass are as randomly arranged as those in a liquid, except that they are "frozen" into place. The structure of glass is comparable to what would happen if fish like those in the Escher drawing (figure 2.1) were swimming freely and randomly distributed when the water suddenly froze. Nature is not always accommodating to definitions, however, and some substances exist that are not crystalline but otherwise meet the criteria for a mineral. For these not-quite-minerals, the term *mineraloid* is applied. An example of a mineraloid is *opal*.

Natural and Inorganic Substances

The second and third criteria need little explanation. Manmade crystalline compounds are not regarded as minerals. Substances that are part of plants or animals—that is, organic—are similarly excluded. Maple sugar that has crystallized from the sap of a maple tree is not a mineral, although it is crystalline and naturally occurring.

Definite Chemical Composition

The fourth criterion, definite chemical composition, is to be expected as a consequence of the inherent orderliness of crystalline substances. Essentially, this means that chemical analysis of any sample of a given mineral will always produce the same ratios of elements (in quartz, for example, two parts of oxygen for one part of silicon). In other words, the composition of any mineral can be expressed as a chemical formula. Quartz has a composition of SiO_2; halite, $NaCl$. Some leeway is allowed. For instance, we gave the formula for the mineral olivine as $(Mg,Fe)_2SiO_4$. Because magnesium and iron ions are about the same size, they can substitute freely for one another without distorting the crystal structure and significantly altering the properties of the mineral. Some chemical formulas appear much more complex than the crystal structures they represent because several such substitutions are permissible.

Chemical analysis can be used to aid in identification of minerals. But, for a variety of reasons, including the cost and difficulty of chemical analysis, physical properties (which reflect chemical composition) are more generally used for mineral identification.

Physical Properties

If two substances have identical chemical compositions and the same arrangement of atoms, it follows that they should possess the same physical properties. So the final condition is really a consequence of the conditions of definite chemical composition and of crystallinity.

Characteristic physical properties are the bases by which minerals are usually identified. Later in this chapter we will describe those properties that allow us to identify common minerals without using special equipment. The physical properties generally useful to the individual are color, streak, luster, hardness, external crystal form, fracture, cleavage, and specific gravity. Some occasionally helpful properties are taste, smell, magnetism, and striations.

To identify a sample of an unknown mineral, begin by systematically checking the physical properties of the mineral. By comparing the properties you find in an unknown mineral with a mineral identification table (such as Appendix A in this book), you should be able to identify the mineral. With a bit of experience, you may get to know the few diagnostic tests for each common mineral and no longer need to refer to an identification table.

The Important Minerals

It is useful to be able to associate the names of important minerals with the physical properties that can be used to identify them. Of course, what is an "important" mineral depends on your perspective. To a miner or prospector, an important mineral is one that is commercially valuable (and is, by implication, relatively uncommon). A "rockhound" is interested in collecting any mineral that is pretty or unusual. A gemologist specializes in those varieties of minerals that are of gem quality (diamonds, emeralds, etc.). A mineralogist is a scientist who studies the chemistry and crystallographic structure of minerals. In this book, the minerals we regard as important are those that help us understand the nature of the earth. We are particularly interested in the rock-forming minerals because they make up most of the rocks of the earth's crust.

Of the several thousand identifiable minerals that exist on earth, most are rare and not important to geology (many occur at only a single site on the globe). Only a few hundred are classified as rock-forming minerals. Even most of these are relatively uncommon in comparision with the few minerals that make up the vast bulk of the earth's crust. The five mineral groups named in part I of table 2.2 account for well over 90 percent of the earth's crust. These are the minerals whose names recur most often in this book. All are silicates.

Quartz may be the only familiar name among the most common minerals, unless you have already had some exposure to geology. The rest may seem like the names of strangers just met at a large party. However, like people, each mineral has its own character or physical properties. As you become more familiar with them, they will become more than just strange names.

As you may note from table 2.2, minerals having similar crystal structures and compositions are grouped under a common name. For instance, **feldspars**, the most common minerals in the crust, all have similar crystal

Table 2.2
Minerals of the Earth's Crust

Name	Chemical Composition	Type of Silicate Structure or Chemical Group
The most common rock-forming minerals. (These make up more than 90 percent of the earth's crust.)		
Feldspar group:		
Plagioclase	Ca and Na Al silicate	Framework silicate
Orthoclase	K Al silicate	Framework silicate
Pyroxene group (augite most common)	Fe, Mg silicate (some with Al, Na, Ca)	Single-chain silicate
Amphibole group (hornblende most common)	Complex Fe, Mg, Al silicate hydroxide	Double-chain silicate
Quartz	Silica	Framework silicate
Mica group:		
Muscovite	K Al silicate hydroxide	Sheet silicate
Biotite	K Fe Mg Al silicate hydroxide	Sheet silicate
Other common rock-forming minerals.		
Silicates		
Olivine	Mg, Fe silicate	Isolated silicate
Garnet group	Complex silicates	Isolated silicate
Clay minerals group	Complex Al silicate hydroxides	Sheet silicate
Nonsilicates		
Calcite	$CaCO_3$	Carbonate
Dolomite	$CaMg(CO_3)_2$	Carbonate
Gypsum	$CaSO_4 \cdot 2H_2O$	Sulfate
Much less common minerals having commercial value		
Halite	NaCl	Chloride
Diamond	C	Native element
Gold	Au (gold)	Native element
Hematite	Iron oxide	Oxide
Magnetite	Iron oxide	Oxide
Chalocopyrite	Cu, Fe sulfide	Sulfide
Sphalerite	Zn sulfide	Sulfide
Galena	Pb sulfide	Sulfide

structures of oxygen, silicon, and aluminum atoms. Minerals within the group are named according to whether potassium (**orthoclase** or **potassium feldspar**) or sodium and calcium (**plagioclase feldspar**) are incorporated into this basic crystal structure. A geologist doing field work cannot always distinguish the two varieties.

The **pyroxene group** and the **amphibole group**, which are single- and double-chain silicates, respectively, each contain a number of minerals. However, only one mineral from each group is important for our purposes. **Augite** is the most common pyroxene, and **hornblende** is the most common amphibole.

The **mica group** is characterized by minerals having a sheet silicate structure. The two most common micas are biotite and muscovite. **Biotite** is a dark-colored, iron/magnesium-bearing mica. **Muscovite** mica lacks iron and magnesium and is transparent or white.

The **clay minerals group** are also sheet silicates. Clays are abundant on the earth's surface and in sedimentary rocks, but make up only a minor percentage of the crust as a whole.

Nonsilicate minerals include *native elements,* which are minerals composed of only one element. Gold is a native element, as are diamond and graphite, both of which are composed solely of carbon. Other nonsilicates are classified according to the predominant negatively-charged ions in their crystal structures. For instance, halite is a chloride because the negatively charged ions in the crystal are Cl^-. If the mineral contains CO_3^{-2} ions, it is a *carbonate. Sulfides* have S^{-2} ions, *sulfates* SO_4^{-2}, and *oxides* O^{-2} (but without Si, S, or C bonded to the oxygen atoms).

Figure 2.15 Two samples of hematite; one is red, the other silver colored. They have identical streaks.

Figure 2.16 Fingernail (hardness of 2½) easily scratches gypsum (hardness of 2).

Nonsilicate minerals are also more abundant on the earth's surface than in the crust as a whole. **Calcite** (calcium carbonate or $CaCO_3$) is the most common nonsilicate mineral and is usually found at or near the earth's surface. Limestone and marble are rocks composed mainly of calcite.

Ore minerals or economic minerals are minerals having commercial value; most are not silicates. Among the ore minerals are iron oxides (the minerals magnetite and hematite) mined for iron and a copper-iron sulfide (the mineral chalcopyrite) that is the main source of copper. Lead and zinc come from galena (lead sulfide) and sphalerite (a zinc sulfide).

The Physical Properties of Minerals

The best approach to understanding physical properties of minerals is to obtain a sample of each of the most common rock-forming minerals named in table 2.2. The properties described can then be identified in these samples.

To identify an unknown mineral, you should first determine its physical properties, then match the properties with the appropriate mineral, using a mineral identification key or chart such as the ones included in Appendix A of this book.

Color

The first thing most people notice about a mineral is its color. Because color is so obvious, beginning students tend to rely too heavily on it as a key to mineral identification. Unfortunately, color also is apt to be the most ambiguous of physical properties. If you look at a number of quartz crystals, for instance, you may find specimens that are white, pink, black, yellow, or purple. Color is extremely variable in quartz and many other minerals because even minute chemical impurities can strongly influence it. Obviously, it is poor procedure to identify quartz strictly on the basis of color.

In some minerals, however, color is a useful property. Most of the **ferromagnesian minerals** (iron/magnesium-bearing), such as augite, hornblende, olivine, and biotite, are either green or black. Muscovite mica is white or colorless.

Streak

A pulverized mineral gives a color that usually is more reliable than the color of the specimen itself. An edge of a mineral sample is scraped across an unglazed porcelain plate. The resulting **streak**, color of a pulverized substance, may be diagnostic of the mineral. For instance, hematite always gives a reddish brown streak although the sample may be brown or red or silver-colored.

Unfortunately, few of the silicate minerals—the most common minerals—have a diagnostic streak, because most are harder than the porcelain streak plate.

Luster

The quality and intensity of *light* that is reflected from the surface of a mineral is termed **luster**. (A photograph cannot show this quality). The luster of a mineral is described by comparing it to familiar substances.

Luster is either *metallic* or *nonmetallic*. A **metallic luster** gives a substance the appearance of being made of metal. Metallic luster may be very shiny, like a chrome car part, or less shiny, like the surface of a broken piece of iron.

Diamonds—Expensive and Unscratchable

The value of diamonds is attributable both to their scarcity and to their physical properties of luster and hardness. The luster of diamond is almost unique in its brilliance. Most valuable is the colorless variety, which is cut into faceted gems. A rough diamond is split into smaller fragments along cleavage planes, and the facets are ground onto the gem by using diamond dust (no other substance would scratch the diamond). The facets enhance the luster, and the resulting brilliant play of light is an important reason why diamonds are highly prized as gems.

Most diamonds are not of gem quality and may be of several colors, including black, red, green, and brown. These minerals are nevertheless of great practical value because of diamond's extreme hardness. If Mohs' hardness scale indicated absolute hardness, quartz would still be 7, topaz 8, and corundum 9, but diamond would have a hardness of 40—more than four times the hardness of corundum.

Diamonds can be used in industry for cutting or drilling through rock. They are embedded in bits used to drill into the earth's crust.

South Africa is the world's principal producer of diamonds. Although most diamonds are very

Figure 2.17 Cut and uncut diamonds. Photos by Joel Arem.

small, the largest one found in South Africa weighed over half a kilogram. U.S. diamond production is minor. The only significant production was in Arkansas, where thousands of small diamonds were mined before commercial operations became unfeasible there.

Experiments have shown that extremely high pressures, such as those found near or below the base of the earth's crust, are needed to convert ordinary carbon into a diamond. The presence of diamond in a rock implies that the rock has moved from near the bottom of the crust to the surface of the earth. Artificial diamonds were first made, under very high pressure, in 1955 and are now being produced for industrial purposes. At high temperatures, a diamond will burn, combining with oxygen to form carbon dioxide.

Nonmetallic luster is more common. The most important type is **glassy** (also called **vitreous) luster,** which gives a substance a glazed appearance, like glass or porcelain. Most silicate minerals have this characteristic. The feldspars, quartz, the micas, and the pyroxenes and amphiboles all have a glassy luster.

Less common is an **earthy luster.** This resembles the surface of unglazed pottery and is characteristic of the various clay minerals. Some uncommon lusters include *resinous* luster (appearance of resin), *silky* luster, and *pearly* luster.

Hardness
The property of "scratchability," or **hardness**, can be tested fairly reliably. For a true test of hardness, the harder mineral must be able to make a groove or scratch on a smooth, fresh surface of the softer mineral. For example, quartz can always scratch calcite or feldspar. Substances can be compared to **Mohs' scale of hardness** (table 2.3), on which ten minerals are designated as standards of hardness. The softest mineral, talc (used for talcum powder because of its softness), is designated as 1. Diamond, the hardest natural substance on earth, is 10 on the scale.

Rather than carry samples of the ten standard minerals, a geologist doing field work usually relies on common objects to test for hardness (table 2.3). A fingernail usually has a hardness of about 2½. If you are able to scratch the smooth surface of a mineral with your fingernail, then the hardness of the mineral must be less than

Table 2.3
Mohs' Hardness Scale

1. Talc
2. Gypsum
    Fingernail
3. Calcite
    Copper coin
4. Fluorite
5. Apatite
    Knife blade
    Glass
6. Orthoclase feldspar
    File
7. Quartz
8. Topaz
9. Corundum
10. Diamond

A

B

2½. A copper coin, such as a penny, has a hardness between 3 and 4; however, the brown oxidized surface of most pennies is much softer, so using a penny for hardness tests requires caution. A knife blade generally has a hardness slightly greater than 5, but it depends on the particular steel alloy used for the blade. A geologist uses a knife blade to distinguish between softer minerals, such as calcite, and harder minerals similar in appearance, such as quartz. Ordinary window glass, usually slightly harder than a knife blade (although some glass, such as that containing lead, is much softer), can be used in the same way as a knife blade for hardness tests. A file (one made of tempered steel for filing metal, not a fingernail file) may be used for a hardness of between 6 and 7.

External Crystal Form

The **crystal form** of a mineral is a set of faces that have a definite geometric relationship to one another. If minerals were always able to develop their characteristic crystal forms, mineral identification would be a much simpler task. In rocks, however, most minerals grow while competing for space with other minerals. In fact, the orderly sets of faces that make up a crystal form can develop only under rather specialized conditions. Specifically, most minerals are able to develop their characteristic crystal faces only if they are surrounded by a fluid that can be easily displaced as the crystal grows. On the other hand, a few minerals, notably garnet, are able to overpower and displace surrounding solid material during growth, so that they almost always develop their characteristic crystal faces. Some well-developed crystals of common minerals are shown in figure 2.18. (The term **crystal** is used by some to mean a substance exhibiting crystal faces; others use the term interchangeably with "crystalline substance.")

C

Figure 2.18 Crystals. (*A*) Quartz. (*B*) Feldspar. (*C*) Garnet. Photo of garnet by W. C. Irvin.

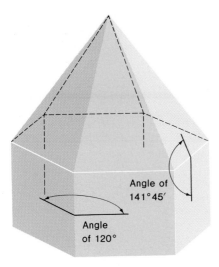

Figure 2.19 Quartz crystal showing two interfacial angles.

Crystals of minerals have played an important role in the development of chemistry and physics. Steno, a Danish naturalist living in the seventeenth century, first noted that the angle between two adjacent faces of quartz is always exactly the same, no matter what part of the world the quartz sample comes from or the color or size of the quartz crystal. As shown in figure 2.14, the angle between any two adjacent sides of the six-sided "pillar" (which is called a prism by mineralogists) is always exactly 120°, and that between a face of the "pillar" and one of the "pyramid" faces (actually part of a rhombohedron) is always exactly 141°45′.

To find such regularity in nature usually has profound implications. When minerals other than quartz were studied, they too were found to have sets of angles for adjacent faces that never varied from sample to sample. This observation became formalized as the *law of constancy of interfacial angles,* or *Steno's law.* Later the discovery of X-ray beams and their behavior in crystals vindicated Steno's theory about the structure of crystals.

Steno suspected that each type of mineral must be composed of many tiny, identical building blocks, with the geometric shape of the crystal being a function of how these building blocks are put together. If you are stacking rectangular bricks, there are only a few shapes that the stack can be. Likewise, stacking rhombohedrons in a three-dimensional pattern produces only a limited number of possible shapes (figure 2.21).

Steno's law was really a precursor of atomic theory, developed centuries later. Our present concept of crystals is that atoms are clustered into geometric forms—cubes, bricks, hexagons, etc.—and that a crystal is essentially an orderly three-dimensional stacking of these tiny geometric forms. Halite, for example, may be regarded as a series of cubes stacked in three dimensions (figure 2.22). Because of the cubic "building block," crystal faces on halite are at 90° angles to one another.

Figure 2.20 Quartz City on Mercury by science fiction artist Frank R. Paul. Crystals have been a recurring theme in science fiction. According to the story, this city on Mercury was built entirely of quartz crystals by insect men.
Amazing Stories, September 1941; reprinted by permission of Ultimate Publishing Company.

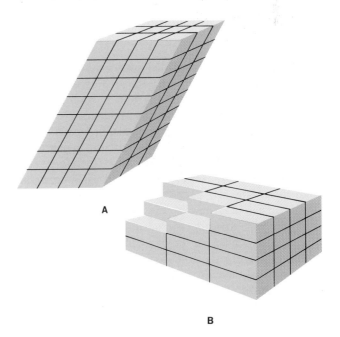

Figure 2.21 Geometric forms built by stacking of (A) rhombohedrons and (B) bricks.

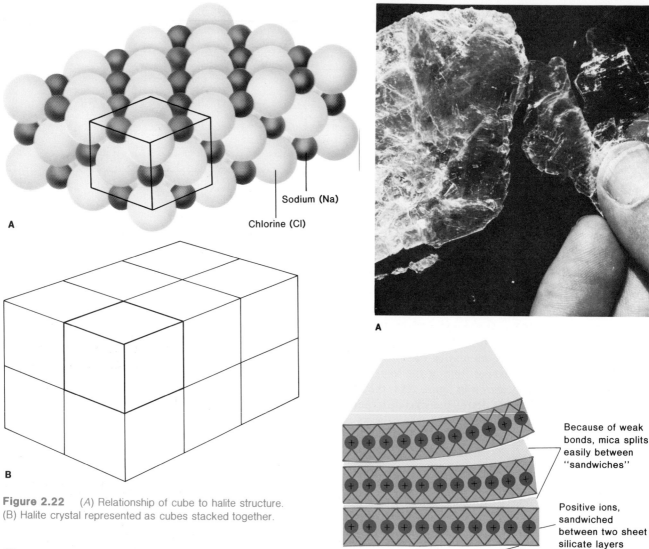

Figure 2.22 (A) Relationship of cube to halite structure. (B) Halite crystal represented as cubes stacked together.

Sodium (Na)

Chlorine (Cl)

A

B

A

Because of weak bonds, mica splits easily between "sandwiches"

Positive ions, sandwiched between two sheet silicate layers

Sheet silicate layer

B

Figure 2.23 (A) Mica pulled apart along cleavage planes. (B) Relationship of mica to cleavage. Mica crystal structure is simplified in this diagram.

Cleavage

The internal order of a crystal may be expressed externally by crystal faces, or it may be indicated by the tendency to split apart along certain preferred directions. **Cleavage** is the ability of a mineral to break along preferred planes.

A mineral tends to break along certain planes because the bonding between atoms is weaker there. In quartz, the bonds are equally strong in all directions; therefore quartz has no cleavage. The micas, however, are easily split apart into sheets (figure 2.23). If we were able to look at the arrangement of atoms in the crystalline structure of micas, we would see that the individual silica tetrahedrons are strongly bonded to one another *within* each of the silicate sheets. The bonding *between* adjacent sheets, however, is weak; therefore it is easy to pull the mineral apart parallel to the plane of the sheets.

Cleavage is one of the most useful diagnostic tools because it is identical from sample to sample of the same material. Cleavage is especially important for identifying minerals in rocks.

The wide variety of combinations of cleavage and *quality* of cleavage also increases the diagnostic value of this property. The cleavage of mica is regarded as a single direction of cleavage, and its quality is perfect. Other minerals may be characterized as having one, two, or more cleavage directions; the quality can range from perfect to poor (poor cleavage is very hard for anyone but a well-trained mineralogist to detect). In determining how many cleavage directions a mineral has, be sure that you are counting directions using a single grain or crystal of that mineral (a rock is composed of many grains or crystals).

Three of the most common mineral groups—the feldspars, the amphiboles, and the pyroxenes—have two directions of cleavage (figure 2.24). In feldspars, the two

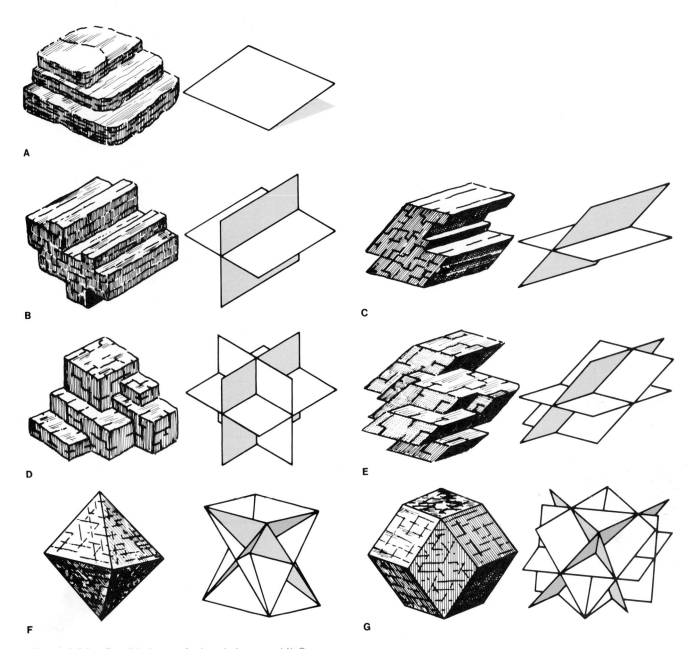

Figure 2.24 Possible types of mineral cleavage. (*A*) One direction of cleavage. (*B*) Two directions of cleavage which intersect at 90° angles. Feldspar is an example. (*C*) Two directions of cleavage which do not intersect at 90° angles. Amphibole is an example. (*D*) Three directions of cleavage which intersect at 90° angles. Halite is an example. (*E*) Three directions of cleavage which do not intersect at 90° angles. Calcite is an example. (*F*) Four directions of cleavage. Diamond is an example. (*G*) Six directions of cleavage. Sphalerite is an example.

Reprinted by permission from R. D. Dallmeyer, *Physical Geology Laboratory Manual,* Dubuque, Iowa: Kendall-Hunt Publishing Company, 1978.

Figure 2.25 Cleavage fragments of halite.

Figure 2.26 Conchoidal fracture.

directions are at angles of about 90° to each another, and both directions are of very good quality. In pyroxenes, the two directions also are at about right angles, but the quality is only fair. In amphibole, the two very good cleavage directions are at an angle of 56° (or 124° for the obtuse angle).

Halite is an example of a mineral with three excellent cleavage directions, all at 90° to one another. This is called *cubic* cleavage (figure 2.25).

Calcite also has three cleavage directions, each excellent. But the angles between them clearly are not right angles. Calcite's cleavage is known as *rhombohedral* cleavage.

Some minerals have more than three directions of cleavage. Diamond has very good cleavage in four directions (ironically, the hardest natural substance on earth can be easily shattered into small cleavage fragments). Sphalerite, the principal ore of zinc, possesses six directions.

Recognizing cleavage and determining angular relationships between cleavage directions takes some practice. Students new to mineral identification tend to try to ignore cleavage because it is not so immediately apparent to the unfamiliar eye as color. Proper determination of cleavage frequently is the key to identifying a mineral, so the small amount of practice needed to develop this skill is worthwhile.

Fracture

Fracture is the way a substance breaks where not controlled by cleavage. Minerals such as quartz, olivine, and garnet, which have no cleavage, usually have an irregular fracture. This is the most common type of fracture for minerals.

Some minerals may show **conchoidal fracture,** curved fracture surfaces (figure 2.26). These look rather like the inside of a clam shell (hence the name). This type of fracture is sometimes seen in quartz but is more common in noncrystalline substances, such as glass.

Specific Gravity

The density or "heaviness" of a mineral is generally given as a comparison to the weight of water. **Specific gravity** is defined as the ratio of the mass of a substance to the mass of an equal volume of water, determined at a specified temperature.

Liquid water has a specific gravity of 1. (Ice, being lighter, has a specific gravity of about 0.9.) Most of the common silicate minerals weigh about two and a half times as much as equal volumes of water: quartz has a specific gravity of 2.65; the feldspars range from 2.56 to 2.76. Special scales are required to determine specific gravity precisely. However, a person can easily distinguish by hand very heavy minerals such as galena (a lead sulfide with a specific gravity of 7.5) from the much lighter silicate minerals.

Figure 2.27 Panning gold during California's gold rush (circa 1849).
Courtesy California Division of Mines and Geology.

Gold, with a specific gravity of 19.3, is much heavier than galena. Because of its high specific gravity, gold can be collected by "panning." The lighter clay and silt particles in the pan may be sloshed out with the water, while the gold dust lags behind in the bottom of the pan (figure 2.27).

Other Properties

Properties that are useful in only a few instances include taste and smell. Halite obviously tastes salty; few other minerals have any taste at all. An "earthy" smell is characteristic of some clay minerals when they are moistened.

Plagioclase feldspar commonly exhibits **striations**—straight, parallel lines on the *flat* surfaces of one of the two cleavage directions (figure 2.28). The lines appear to be etched by a delicate scriber. In plagioclase, they are caused by a systematic change within the pattern of crystalline structure.

The mineral **magnetite** (an iron oxide) owes its name to its characteristic physical property of being attracted to a magnet. Where large bodies of magnetite are found in the earth's crust, compass needles point toward the magnetite body rather than to magnetic north. Airplanes navigating by compass have become lost because of the influence of large magnetite bodies. Some other minerals are weakly magnetic, but the magnetism cannot be detected except by specialized instruments.

A clear crystal of calcite exhibits an unusual property. If you place a calcite crystal over an image on paper, you will see two images (figure 2.29). This phenomenon is known as *double refraction* and is caused by light splitting into two components when it enters some crystalline materials.

Figure 2.28 Plagioclase striations.

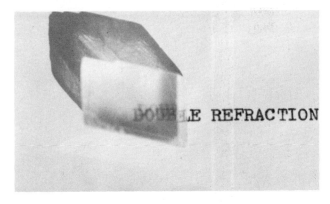

Figure 2.29 Double refraction in calcite. Two images of the letters are seen through the transparent calcite crystal.

Some properties require very specialized equipment to detect. Perhaps most important are the characteristic effects of minerals on X-rays, which we can explain only briefly here. X-rays are able to penetrate between the atoms in a crystal until they are reflected or "bounced off" planes of atoms within the crystalline pattern. The X-rays leave the crystal at precise and measurable angles controlled by the planes of atoms that make up the internal crystalline structure. The pattern of X-rays leaving the crystal may be recorded on photographic film or by various recording instruments. Each mineral has its own pattern of reflected X-rays, which serves as an identifying "fingerprint."

Simple Chemical Tests
One chemical reaction is routinely used for identifying minerals. The mineral calcite, as well as some other carbonate minerals (those containing CO_3^{-2}), reacts with a weak acid to produce carbon dioxide gas. In this test, a drop of dilute hydrochloric acid applied to the sample of calcite bubbles vigorously, indicating that CO_2 gas is being formed. Normally this is the only chemical test that geologists do during research.

Summary

Atoms are composed of *protons* (+), *neutrons,* and *electrons* (−). A given element always has the same number of protons. An atom in which the positive or negative electric charges do not balance is an *ion.*

Ions or atoms are bonded together in very orderly, three-dimensional structures called *crystals.*

A crystalline substance is considered a mineral (in geologic terms) if it is naturally occurring and inorganic, and has a definite chemical composition and characteristic physical properties.

The three most abundant elements in the earth's crust are oxygen, silicon, and aluminum. Most minerals are silicates, with the silica tetrahedron the basic building block.

Feldspars are the most common minerals in the earth's crust. The next most abundant minerals are quartz, the pyroxenes, the amphiboles, and the micas. All are silicates.

Minerals are usually identified by their physical properties. Cleavage is generally the most useful physical property for identification purposes. Other important physical properties are external crystal form, fracture, hardness, luster, color, streak, and specific gravity.

Terms to Remember

amphibole group
atom
atomic mass number
atomic number
atomic weight
augite
biotite
bonding
calcite
chain silicate structure
clay minerals group
cleavage
conchoidal fracture
covalent bonding
crystal
crystal form
crystalline
earthy luster
electron
element
feldspar group
ferromagnesian minerals
fracture
framework silicate structure
glassy (vitreous) luster
hardness
hornblende
ion

ionic bonding
isolated silicate structure
isotope
luster
magnetite
metallic luster
mica group
mineral
Mohs' hardness scale
muscovite
nonmetallic luster
neutron
nucleus
olivine
ore mineral
orthoclase
plagioclase
proton
pyroxene group
quartz
rock
sheet silicate structure
silica
silicates
silica tetrahedron
specific gravity
streak
striations

Questions for Review

1. Answer the following about quartz.
   What elements does it contain?
   What is its chemical formula?
   What type of silicate structure does it have?
   How many protons does each of its elements have? (see Appendix C.)
   Why is it regarded as a mineral?
2. Explain the difference between ionic and covalent bonding.
3. How do the various feldspars differ from one another chemically?
4. Distinguish among the following terms:
   silica
   silicon
   silicate
   silica tetrahedron
5. What is the distinction between cleavage and external crystal form?
6. How would you distinguish the following on the basis of physical properties (you might refer to Appendix A)?
   feldspar/quartz
   muscovite/feldspar
   calcite/feldspar
   amphibole/pyroxene
   pyroxene/feldspar
7. Using triangles to represent tetrahedrons, start with a single triangle (to represent isolated silicate structure) and, by drawing more triangles, build on the triangle to show a single-chain silicate structure. By adding more triangles, convert that to a double-chain structure. Turn your double-chain structure into a sheet-silicate structure.
8. What is the major factor controlling chemical activity between atoms?
9. What are the three most common elements (by number and approximate percentage) in the earth's crust?
10. What are the five next most common elements?

Questions for Thought

1. Why are there more nonsilicate minerals on the surface of the earth than within the crust?
2. How does oxygen in the atmosphere differ from oxygen in rocks and minerals?
3. Using Appendix A, can you make any generalization relating physical properties to chemical composition? (For instance, carbonate minerals tend to be softer than most silicate minerals.)
4. What happens to the atoms in water when it freezes? Is ice a mineral?
5. How would you expect the appearance of a rock high in iron and magnesium to differ from a rock with very little iron and magnesium?

Supplementary Readings

Bloss, F. D. 1970. *Crystallography and crystal chemistry: An introduction.* New York: Holt, Rinehart & Winston.

Ernst, W. G. 1969. *Earth materials.* Englewood Cliffs, N.J.: Prentice-Hall.

Hurlbut, C. S., Jr., and C. Klein. 1977. *Manual of mineralogy After J. D. Dana.* 19th ed. New York: John Wiley & Sons.

Mason, B., and L. G. Berry. 1968. *Elements of mineralogy.* San Francisco: W. H. Freeman.

Prinz, M., G. Harlow, and J. Peters. 1978. *Simon & Schuster's Guide to Rocks and Minerals.* New York: Simon & Schuster.

Saunders, B. C., and R. E. D. Clark. 1964. *Atoms and molecules simply explained.* New York: Dover Publications.

Vanders, I., and P. F. Kerr. 1967. *Mineral recognition.* New York: John Wiley & Sons.

Zim, H. S., and P. R. Shaffer. 1967. *Rocks and minerals.* New York: Golden Press.

3
Volcanism and Extrusive Rocks

Purpose

Volcanic eruptions, while awesome natural spectacles, also provide important information on the workings of the earth's interior. Volcanic eruptions vary in nature and in degree of explosive violence. A strong correlation exists between the chemical composition of the magma (or lava) involved in volcanic activity and the violence of an eruption. Also related to the chemistry of the lavas are the size and shape of volcanoes and lava flows and the patterns of their distribution on the earth's surface.

An understanding of volcanism provides a background for theories relating to mountain-building, the development and evolution of continental and oceanic crust, and how the crust is deformed. Our observations of volcanic activity fit nicely into plate tectonic theory. The kinds of eruptions that take place along spreading centers are radically different from those associated with converging plate boundaries. In the next chapter we complete the story of igneous rocks and what they tell us about the earth's interior by extending our discussion to rocks that form from magma solidifying underground.

The names and a classification scheme for the common extrusive rocks are introduced here. With practice, using real rocks, you should be able to identify the common extrusive rocks using the information in this chapter and the identification table in Appendix B.

The May 18, 1980 eruption of Mount St. Helens was a spectacular reminder of the energy that exists in the earth's interior. If plate tectonic theory is correct, parts of North America are overriding a portion of the Pacific ocean floor. Some of the mechanical energy is transformed to heat energy along the subduction zone (as described in chapter 1). At depth, high temperatures cause previously solid rock to melt. At least some of the **magma** (molten rock or liquid that is mostly silica) works its way upward to reach the earth's surface to erupt. Magma does not always reach the earth's surface before solidifying, but when it does, it is called **lava.**

Box 3.1
Eruption of Mount St. Helens, 1980

Until 1980 not many people living in Washington or Oregon thought that the volcanic cones of the Cascade Range might be hazardous. Peaks such as Mount Rainier, Mount Hood, and Mount Baker (and about ten others) were considered integral parts of the scenery. These picturesque snow-capped cones towering over evergreen forests seemed unlikely to change. Geologists felt otherwise. It would be exceedingly unlikely that volcanoes which had shown intermittent activity over hundreds of thousands of years would be dead. In fact, California's Lassen Peak at the southern extreme of the Cascade Range had erupted from 1914 to 1917.

Mount St. Helens, in southern Washington, had last erupted in 1857. Geologists were not surprised when Mount St. Helens erupted in 1980. Its inactivity had lasted little more than a century—trivial time to geology. Between March and May of 1980 Mount St. Helens was transformed from a serene, snow-covered cone to a darkened, gouged-out stump of a peak; from a thing of beauty to a killer.

The 1980 eruptions were preceded by thousands of small earthquakes. Geologists, alerted to the possibility of an eruption, swarmed over the area, setting up instruments and establishing observation posts. On March 27 ash and steam eruptions began and continued for the next six weeks. Water that had seeped into the ground became superheated steam at depth. As in an exploding boiler, the water vapor expanded suddenly and blasted its way through the overlying rock, carrying pulverized rock skyward. During this early stage of activity, geologists speculated on the location of the magma, which was the heat source for the volcanic boiler. The magma seemed to be working its way slowly upward beneath the volcano, as indicated by the pattern of earthquakes.

During this early stage of steam and ash eruptions, St. Helens provided a fine show. "Volcano fever" spread, particularly in Portland,

Figure 3.1 Mount St. Helens before the 1980 eruptions, as seen from the north.
Photo by Austin Post, U.S. Geological Survey.

Figure 3.2 A steam and ash eruption. Mount St. Helens April 10, 1980.
Photo U.S. Geological Survey.

Oregon, the largest city with a view of the eruptions. Ice cream dishes and cocktails made to look like volcanoes, T-shirts, and commemorative trinkets sold briskly to residents and tourists alike. At this time the most dangerous thing you could do was to fly over the mountain—not because of the eruptions, but because the air was crowded with light aircraft carrying geologists, television and press crews, and tourists. Seventy planes were in the air over the mountain at one time and near-collisions were common.

A team from the U.S. Geological Survey a few years earlier had completed a study of the potential hazards of renewed eruption, based on the peak's geologic record for the past 38,000 years. On the advice of the survey geologists, U.S. Forest Service and state officials blocked off the most potentially hazardous areas on and near the mountain. Geologists were concerned about the hazards of large mudflows during the steam and ash stage of the eruptions. Numerous small mudflows had already been observed. The mudflows were slurries of loose ash and water (from rainfall or melting glacier ice or snow) that flowed down the volcano. The concern was that a large mudflow might continue along a stream valley beyond the mountain and wipe out a populated area. For this reason, water levels were lowered in reservoirs on the flanks of the volcano, so that mudflows might be impounded.

The steam-driven eruptions continued. Geologists sensed from studying the patterns of earthquakes that magma was working its way slowly upward. But they could not determine exactly how deep beneath the surface the magma was, nor when (or if) it might break through to the surface. Another indication that the magma was moving upward was that the peak was swelling— like a balloon being inflated. The northern flank of the mountain bulged outward at a rate of 1.5 meters per day. Bulging continued until the surface of the northern slope was displaced outward over a hundred meters from its original position (see figure 3.3). The bulge was gravitationally unstable and the Geological Survey warned about another hazard—a truly large landslide.

Although geologists knew that the magma was responsible for the bulge, they considered the potential landslide to be far more dangerous than a magmatic eruption. They knew that it was possible that the magma could blast out of the north side of the volcano, but based on the past behavior of St. Helens, they felt that the first eruptions of magma would probably be through the summit, with the energy released relatively harmlessly skyward. But this wasn't what happened; the magma did blast its way out of the north flank of the volcano and with disastrous consequences.

The huge blast that marked the arrival of the magma at the surface on May 18 seemed to destroy the summit and north flank of St. Helens almost instantly. Within seconds after the eruption began, an area extending outward ten kilometers was stripped of all vegetation and soil. Downslope forests were leveled; leafless, scorched trunks, as seen from the air, seemed like thousands of jackstraws strewn on the ground.

Although the sequence of events was exceedingly rapid, it is now clear what happened. A fairly strong earthquake shook the bulging north slope loose. The resulting landslide stripped away the rock that sealed in the magma. With the protective lid removed, gases that had been dissolved in the magma were released suddenly. On a grand scale, it was comparable to what happens when a bottle of warm beer or pop is shaken and the top is removed. The magma exploded into a froth while blasting out of the north flank of the volcano. The mass of gases and volcanic rock fragments roared down the side of the volcano and continued beyond its base, destroying trees and all organic matter close to the volcano and knocking over forests farther downslope.

Exploding gases continued to propel frothing magma and volcanic ash vertically into the atmosphere. The dense, mushroom-shaped cloud of ash was blown northeastward by the winds aloft. Fallout of ash went on for days, causing serious damage as far away as Montana. In some towns, nightlike darkness occurred at midday. Crops were destroyed. Breathing became difficult. Automobile engines were destroyed by fine volcanic particles sucked into cylinders and wearing away working parts.

Damage was estimated to be in the hundreds of millions of dollars, and 63 people were killed or presumed dead. While the loss of any lives is lamentable, the death toll might have been much worse. For comparison, 30,000 people were killed

Box 3.1 *Continued*

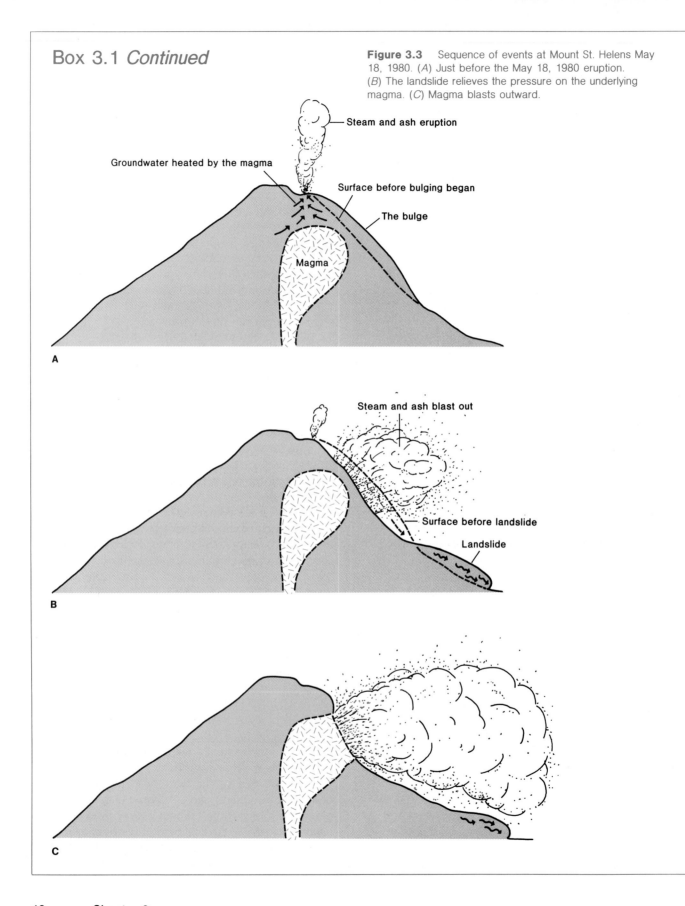

Figure 3.3 Sequence of events at Mount St. Helens May 18, 1980. (*A*) Just before the May 18, 1980 eruption. (*B*) The landslide relieves the pressure on the underlying magma. (*C*) Magma blasts outward.

Steam and ash eruption

Groundwater heated by the magma

Surface before bulging began

The bulge

Magma

A

Steam and ash blast out

Surface before landslide

Landslide

B

C

Figure 3.4 May 18, 1980. The side of the volcano has been blasted away as magmatic explosions continue. © 1980 Keith Ronnholm.

Figure 3.5 Vertical eruptions continue to blast volcanic ash high into the atmosphere.
Photo U.S. Geological Survey.

during an eruption of Mt. Pelée (described later in this chapter). Countless lives were saved, no doubt, by the U.S. Geological Survey advice to public officials. As important, the officials heeded the advice (perhaps it is significant that Washington's governor was a scientist) and resisted pressures from the public, notably the people that wanted access to the closed lands. Ironically, only two days before the catastrophic eruption, a group whose homes were in the area north of the peak staged a protest demanding access. They were escorted in and out of the area to pick up their belongings. We assume that they knew little about geology. They owe their lives to scientists whose knowledge kept them out of an area that would be utterly destroyed.

During the months that followed the May 18th eruption there were occasional new eruptions, but each of much less intensity than the first. At times a volcanic dome grew as magma welled upward into the floor of the new, large crater. Such domes are usually destroyed by a subsequent eruption. Based on the mountain's history, geologists believe that the current level of intermittent activity could continue for a decade or more, but it is unlikely that a single eruption in the near future will match the energy released and the violence of the May 18, 1980 one.

Lava may erupt quietly or, as in the case of Mount St. Helens, violently. Volcanic activity, or **volcanism,** is not restricted to the eruption of lava. Rock fragments may be erupted instead of lava (as happened during the early 1980 eruptions of Mount St. Helens). Gases also play an important role in volcanism. Gas explosions at Mount St. Helens were particularly violent; in other cases, the escaping gases merely force magma out of the ground as lava flows.

Material blown out of a volcano is called **pyroclastic debris** or **tephra**, both terms meaning rock fragments produced by volcanic explosions. Tephra, such as the volcanic ash that littered much of the Pacific Northwest in 1980, and rock formed from solidification of lava are collectively regarded as **extrusive rock,** surface rock resulting from volcanic activity.

The most obvious landform created by volcanism is a **volcano,** a hill or mountain constructed by the extrusion of lava or ejection of rock fragments from a vent. However, volcanoes are not the only landforms created by volcanism. Very fluid lavas may flow out of the earth and flood an area, solidifying into a nearly horizontal layer of extrusive rock. Successive layers of lava flows may accumulate into a lava plateau.

Volcanism

Volcanic activity is important to geology for several reasons. Landforms are constructed and portions of the earth's surface built up. Less commonly, landforms are destroyed by violent eruptions. Volcanoes are important to the science of geology because they provide clues to the nature of the inaccessible earth's interior and help us understand how the earth's internal processes work. By studying the magma, gases, and rocks from eruptions, we may make inferences on the chemical conditions as well as the temperatures and pressures within the earth's crust or underlying mantle.

Effects on Humans

Volcanism is also significant in human affairs. Its effects can be catastrophic or, surprisingly, beneficial.

Hawaii   One region where the overall effects of volcanism have been favorable to the human inhabitants is Hawaii. An occasional field or village may be overrun by outpourings of lava. Nevertheless the weathered volcanic ash and lava produce excellent fertile soil. Moreover, Hawaii's periodically erupting volcanoes (which are relatively safe to watch) are great spectacles that attract both tourists and scientists, benefiting the islands' economy (figure 3.6).

Figure 3.6   An eruption in Hawaii Volcanoes National Park. U.S. National Park Service Photo.

Were it not for volcanic activity, Hawaii would not exist. The islands are the crests of a series of volcanoes that have been built up from the bottom of the Pacific Ocean over millions of years (the vertical distance from the summit of Mauna Loa volcano to the ocean floor greatly exceeds the height of Mount Everest). Hawaii, quite literally, is growing as lava flows into the sea and solidifies, adding more land to the islands.

Geothermal energy   In some other areas of geologically recent volcanic activity, underground heat generated by volcanism is harnessed for human needs. In Italy, Mexico, New Zealand, and California, geothermal installations produce electric power. Steam or superheated water trapped in layers of hot volcanic rock is tapped by drilling and then piped out of the ground to provide power for turbines that generate electricity. Naturally heated geothermal fluids can also be tapped for space or domestic water heating or industrial use, as in paper manufacturing.

Volcanic catastrophes   While the eruption of Mount St. Helens in 1980 was indeed awesome, its effects were not nearly so disastrous as a number of historical eruptions elsewhere in the world. For instance, the Roman city of Pompeii and at least four other towns near Naples in Italy were destroyed in 79 A.D. when Mount Vesuvius erupted (figure 3.7). Before that time vineyards on the flanks of the apparently "dead" volcano extended to the summit. Pompeii was buried under five to eight meters of hot ash from the surprise eruption of Vesuvius. Seventeen centuries later the town was rediscovered. Excavation revealed molds of people suffocated by the ashfall, many with facial expressions of terror. This eruption was not

Figure 3.7 Pompeii with Mt. Vesuvius in background.
Editorial Photocolor Archives Photo.

the end of Vesuvius's activity. The volcano was active almost continuously from 1631 to 1944, with major twentieth-century eruptions in 1906, 1929, and 1944.

The island of Krakatoa in the western Pacific, comprising three apparently inactive volcanoes, erupted in 1883 with the force of several hydrogen bombs. This Indonesian island, which formerly rose 800 meters above sea level, was blown apart, and only one-third of the island remained after the eruption. An estimated 13 cubic kilometers of rock collapsed into the subsurface magma chamber that had been emptied by the eruption, leaving an underwater depression 300 meters deep where the major part of the island had been. The explosion was heard 5,000 kilometers away. On nearby Java, tens of thousands of people died as a result of the giant sea waves (tsunamis) that were generated.

A similar series of explosions in prehistoric time (about 6,600 years ago) was at least partially responsible for creating Crater Lake in Oregon. Volcanic debris that covers more than a million square kilometers in Oregon and neighboring states is traced to those eruptions. The original volcano, named Mount Mazama by geologists, is estimated to have been about 2,000 meters higher than the present rim of Crater Lake. Collapse of the volcano, as well as explosions, accounts for the depression the present-day lake occupies (figures 3.8 and 3.9).

The southern Cascade Mountains, where Crater Lake is located, have been built up by eruptions over the past 30–40 million years (figure 3.10). Only the youngest peaks (those built within the past two million years) such as Mount St. Helens, Mount Rainier, Mount Shasta, and Mount Hood still stand out as cones. As we know from Mount St. Helens, any of these could again become active.

Eruptive Violence and Physical Characteristics of Lava

What controls the degree of violence associated with volcanic activity? Why can we state confidently that active volcanism in Hawaii poses only slight danger to humans, yet have violent explosions in the Cascade Mountains, such as at Mount St. Helens? Whether eruptions are very explosive or relatively "quiet" is largely attributable to two factors: (1) the amount of gas in the lava or magma,

Figure 3.8 Crater Lake, Oregon.
Oregon Department of Transportation Photo.

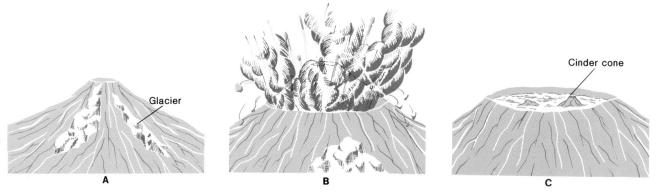

Figure 3.9 The development of Crater Lake. (After Howell Williams.) (*A*) Original volcano (Mt. Mazama.) (*B*) Violent explosion and collapse of summit area. (*C*) Renewed volcanism builds cinder cone in caldera.

and (2) the ease or difficulty the gas has in escaping to the atmosphere. The **viscosity,** or resistance to flow, of a lava determines how easily the gas can escape. The more viscous the lava and the greater the volume of gas trying to escape, the more violent the eruption is likely to be. Later we will show how these factors not only determine the degree of violence of eruption but also influence the shape and height of a volcano.

Scientific Investigation of Volcanism

Volcanoes and lava flows, unlike many other geologic phenomena, can be observed directly, and samples can be collected without great difficulty (at least for the quiet, Hawaiian type of eruption). We can measure the temperature of lava flows, collect samples of gases being given off, observe the lava solidifying into rock, and take rock samples into the laboratory for analysis and study. By comparing rocks observed solidifying from lava with similar ones found in other areas of the world (and even with samples from the moon) where volcanism is no longer

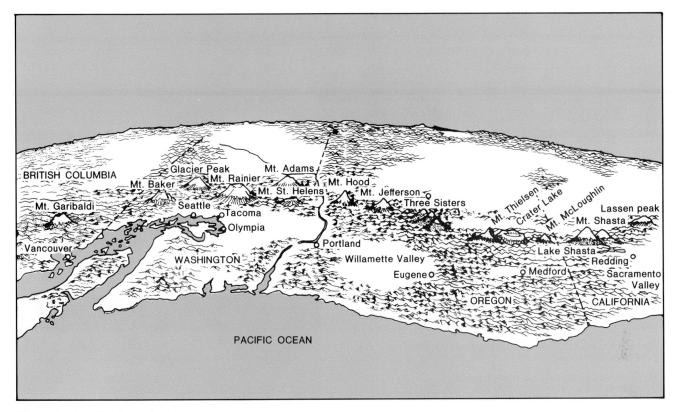

Figure 3.10 The Cascade volcanoes.
Map by Gary Rands, from *Fire and Ice, the Cascade Volcanoes* by
S. L. Harris, courtesy of the Mountaineers. Used by permission of
Charles E. Merrill Publishing Co.

active, we are able to determine the nature of volcanic activity that took place in the geologic past.

Gases From active volcanoes we have learned that most of the gas released during eruptions is water vapor, which condenses as steam. Other gases, such as hydrogen sulfide (which smells like rotten eggs), carbon dioxide, and hydrochloric acid, are given off in lesser amounts with the steam.

Chemistry of Volcanic Rocks
Chemical analyses show that silica (SiO_2) is the most abundant component of virtually all volcanic rocks. The amount of silica, however, can vary, from about 45 percent to about 75 percent of the total weight of volcanic rocks. The variations between these extremes account for striking differences in the appearance and mineral content of the rocks as well as in the behavior of the parent lava.

Mafic rocks Rocks having a silica content close to 50 percent (by weight) are considered *silica-poor*, even though silica is the most abundant constituent. Chemical analyses show that the remainder of these rocks is composed mostly of the oxides of aluminum (Al_2O_3), calcium

(CaO), magnesium (MgO), and iron (FeO and Fe_2O_3). (These oxides generally combine to form the silicate minerals described in chapter 2—they are not usually found as isolated oxides in a rock.) Rocks in this group are called **mafic**—silica-poor igneous rocks with a relatively high content of magnesium, iron, and calcium. (The term "mafic" comes from magnesium and ferric.) The most common mafic extrusive rock is **basalt,** which is dark in color.

Felsic rocks At the other extreme, the *silica-rich* (65 percent or more of silica) rocks tend to have only very minor amounts of the oxides of calcium, magnesium, and iron. The remaining 25 to 35 percent of these rocks is mostly aluminum oxide (Al_2O_3) and oxides of sodium (Na_2O) and potassium (K_2O). These are called **felsic rocks** and are defined as silica-rich igneous rocks with a relatively high content of potassium and sodium (the name comes from the generally high amount of *feldspar*, which crystallizes from the potassium, sodium, aluminum, and silicon oxides). *Rhyolite,* the most abundant volcanic rock with a felsic composition, is light in color because of the low iron and magnesium content.

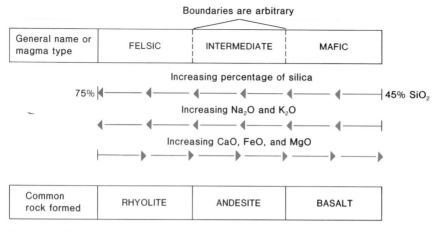

General name or magma type	FELSIC	INTERMEDIATE	MAFIC

Boundaries are arbitrary

Increasing percentage of silica

75% ◀————◀————◀————◀————◀————◀————◀ 45% SiO$_2$

Increasing Na$_2$O and K$_2$O

◀————◀————◀————◀————◀

Increasing CaO, FeO, and MgO

▶————▶————▶————▶————▶

Common rock formed	RHYOLITE	ANDESITE	BASALT

Figure 3.11 Relationship between volcanic rock names and composition of lava from which they formed.

Intermediate rocks Rocks with a chemical content between felsic and mafic are classified as **intermediate rocks.** *Andesite,* usually medium to dark gray in color, is the most common intermediate volcanic rock.

Relationship of minerals to chemistry The chemical composition of the magma determines which and how much of each mineral will crystallize to form an igneous rock. Therefore, mafic, intermediate, and felsic types of rock, being of different chemical compositions, are made up of quite different combinations of minerals (figure 3.11). How mineral content is used to identify extrusive rocks is described later in this chapter.

Viscosity of Lava

The degree of violence with which a volcano erupts is, as mentioned earlier, closely related to the viscosity of the lava. Two factors influence viscosity: (1) the temperature of the lava relative to the cooler temperature at which it solidifies, and (2) the silica content of the lava. If the lava being extruded is considerably hotter than its solidification temperature, the lava is less viscous (more fluid) than if it is at a temperature near its solidification point. Temperatures at which lavas solidify range from about 700°C for felsic rocks to 1,500°C for mafic rocks.

Mafic lavas, being low in silica, tend to flow easily. Conversely, felsic lavas, which are high in silica, are very viscous and flow sluggishly. Felsic lavas are more viscous because even before they have cooled sufficiently to allow crystallization of minerals, silica tetrahedrons have begun to form as small chains, sheets, and frameworks in the lava. Although too few atoms are involved for the structures to be considered crystals, the total effect of these silicate structures is to make the liquid lava more viscous, in much the same way that flour or cornstarch thickens gravy.

Figure 3.12 Crater on Cotopaxi volcano in Ecuador. Photo by Tom Simkin, Smithsonian Institution.

Types of Volcanoes

Volcanic material that is ejected from and deposited around a central vent produces the conical shape typical of volcanoes. The **vent** is the opening through which an eruption takes place. The **crater** of a volcano is a basin-like depression over a vent at the summit of the cone (figure 3.12). Material is not always ejected from the central vent. In a **flank eruption,** lava pours from a vent on the side of a volcano.

A **caldera** is a volcanic depression much larger than the original crater. (Ironically, the most famous caldera in the United States is called "Crater Lake" rather than "Caldera Lake.") A caldera may be caused when a volcano's summit is blown off by exploding gases, as occurred at Mount St. Helens in May 1980, or, as in the case of Crater Lake, when the crater floor collapses into a vacated magma chamber beneath the volcano (figure 3.9).

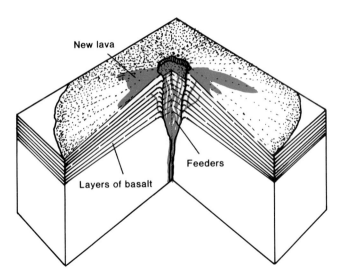

Figure 3.13 Cutaway view of a shield volcano.

New lava

Feeders

Layers of basalt

The three major types of volcanoes (shield, cinder cone, and composite) discussed below are markedly distinct from one another in size, shape, and composition. Although volcanic domes are not cones, they can be considered volcanoes and are also discussed in this section.

Shield Volcanoes

Shield volcanoes are broad, gently sloping cones constructed of solidified lava flows. Because the lava flows from a central vent, without building up much near the vent, the slopes are usually between 2° and 10° from the horizontal, producing a volcano in the shape of a flattened dome or "shield" (figure 3.13).

The islands of Hawaii are essentially a series of shield volcanoes built upward from the ocean floor by intermittent eruptions that have taken place over millions of years (figure 3.14). Although spectacular to observe, the eruptions are relatively nonviolent because the lavas are fairly fluid (less viscous). By implication, then, the shield volcanoes of the Hawaiian Islands are constructed of a series of layers of basalt (low in silica and relatively high in iron, magnesium, and calcium oxides).

There are two types of basalt flows, each of which solidifies with a characteristic surface. Both types have Hawaiian names. **Pahoehoe** (pronounced *pah-hoy-hoy*) is a lava flow characterized by a ropy or billowy surface (figure 3.15). The surface is formed by the quick cooling and solidification from the surface downward of a lava flow or pool of lava that was fully liquid. By contrast, flowing basalt that is cool enough to have partially solidified moves as a slow, pasty mass. Its largely solidified

Figure 3.14 Shield volcanoes in Hawaii's Volcanoes National Park. Mauna Loa is in the background. Kilauea and its caldera are in the foreground.
Air photo, U.S. Geological Survey.

Figure 3.15 Pahoehoe.
Photo by H. T. Stearns, U.S. Geological Survey.

Volcanism and Extrusive Rocks   53

Figure 3.16 An aa flow in Hawaii.
Photo by G. A. Macdonald, U.S. Geological Survey.

Figure 3.17 Spatter cone seen in a yard from the porch of a house in Hawaii.
Photo by G. A. Macdonald, U.S. Geological Survey.

front is shoved forward as a pile of rubble. A flow such as this is called **aa** (pronounced *ah-ah*), a lava flow that solidifies with a spiny, rubbly surface (figure 3.16). A minor feature which sometimes develops on the surface of a solidifying lava flow is a **spatter cone,** a small, steep-sided cone built from lava sputtering out of a vent (figure 3.17). When a small local pocket of gas is trapped in a cooling lava flow, the gas seeks to escape and belches the lava up out of a vent through the already hard surface of the flow. Falling lava plasters itself onto the developing cone and solidifies. The sides of a spatter cone can be very steep, but the height rarely exceeds 10 meters.

Cinder Cones

A **cinder cone** is a volcano constructed of loose rock fragments ejected from a central vent (figure 3.18). In contrast to the gentle slopes of shield volcanoes, cinder cones commonly have slopes of about 30°. Most of the ejected material lands near the vent during an eruption, building up the cone to a peak. Steepness of the slopes of accumulating loose material is limited by gravity to about 33°. Cinder cones tend to be very much smaller than shield volcanoes. Few cinder cones exceed a height of 500 meters.

The fragments of volcanic rock that make up the cinder cones are *pyroclastic* (from the Greek *pyro,* "fire," and *clastic,* "broken"). *Pyroclasts* or *tephra,* the fragments formed by volcanic explosion, can be almost any size. *Dust* and *ash* are the finest particles; *cinders* range from about 4 to 32 millimeters; *bombs* and *blocks* are large pyroclasts. When solid rock has been blasted apart by a volcanic explosion, the pyroclastic fragments are **angular,** with no rounded edges or corners. If lava is ejected into the air, a molten blob becomes streamlined during flight, solidifies, and falls to the ground as a **bomb,** a spindle- or lens-shaped pyroclast (figure 3.19).

Figure 3.18 Cerro Negro, a cinder cone in Nicaragua.
Photo by Mark Hurd Aerial Surveys Corp.; courtesy California Division of Mines and Geology.

Figure 3.19   Spindle-shaped bomb.

Local concentrations of gas in a magma cause eruptions that build cinder cones. Cinder cones are not necessarily related to the silica content of the extrusive rock or lava. Some cinder cones are found in Hawaii, perched on the flanks of the much larger shield volcanoes. Although numerous cinder cones may be seen in parts of the world where the crust is geologically active, such as in western North America, most of the cinder cones themselves are apparently extinct.

The life span of an active cinder cone tends to be short. The local concentration of gas is depleted rather quickly during the eruptive periods. Moreover, as landforms, cinder cones are temporary features in terms of geologic time. This is because they are made of unconsolidated material and can be eroded away relatively easily.

Composite Volcanoes

A **composite volcano** (also called **stratovolcano**) is one constructed of alternating layers of pyroclastics and rock solidified from lava flows. The slopes are intermediate in steepness, compared with those of cinder cones and shield volcanoes. Pyroclastic layers build up steep slopes as debris collects near the vent, just as in cinder cones. However, subsequent lava flows tend to subdue the profile of the cone as the downward flow builds up the height of the flanks more than the summit area. The solidified lava acts as a protective cover over the loose pyroclastic layers, making composite volcanoes less vulnerable to erosion than cinder cones (figure 3.20).

Composite volcanoes are built up over long spans of time. Eruption is intermittent, with hundreds or thousands of years of inactivity separating a few years of violent activity. During the quiet intervals between eruptions, composite volcanoes may be eroded by running water, landslides, or glaciers. These surficial processes tend to alter the surface, shape, and form of the cone. But because

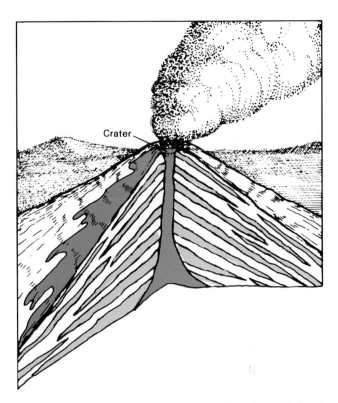

Figure 3.20   Cutaway view of a composite volcano. Colored layers are lava flows. Stippled layers are pyroclastics.

of their long lives and relative resistance to erosion, composite cones can become very large. Aconcagua, a composite volcano in the Andes, is 6,960 meters above sea level and the highest peak in the western hemisphere.

The extrusive material that builds composite cones is predominantly of intermediate composition, although minor felsic and mafic eruptions may be locally involved. Therefore, *andesite* is the most prevalent rock associated with composite volcanoes. If the temperature of an andesite lava is considerably above the temperature at which it would be completely solidified, the relatively nonviscous fluid flows easily from the crater down the slopes. On the other hand, if sufficient gas pressure exists, an explosion may litter the slopes with pyroclastic andesite, particularly if the lava has fully or partially solidified and clogged the volcano's vent.

There can be considerable variation in the composition as well as eruptive history of individual volcanoes. For instance, Mount Rainier is composed of 90 percent lava flows and only 10 percent pyroclastic layers. On the other hand, Mount St. Helens was built mostly from pyroclastic eruptions—reflecting a more violent history. As would be expected, the composition of the rocks formed during the 1980 eruptions of Mount St. Helens is somewhat higher in silica than average for Cascade volcanoes.

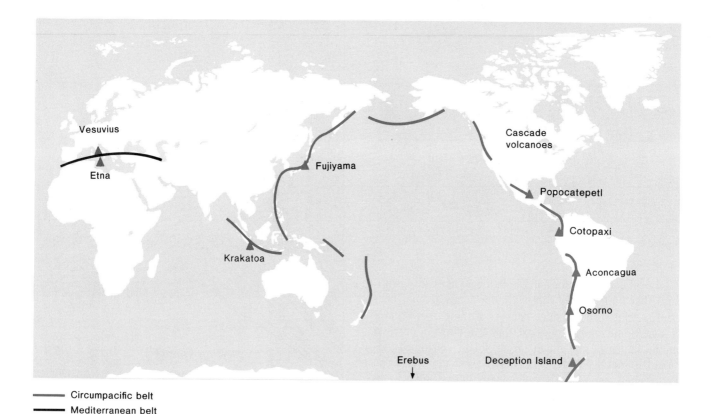

Vesuvius
Etna

Fujiyama

Cascade
volcanoes

Popocatepetl

Cotopaxi

Aconcagua

Osorno

Krakatoa

Erebus
↓

Deception Island

——— Circumpacific belt
——— Mediterranean belt

Figure 3.21 Map of the world showing the major
volcanic belts.

Distribution of composite volcanoes Nearly all the
larger and better known volcanoes of the world are composite volcanoes. They tend to be aligned along two major
belts on the earth (figure 3.21). The **circum-Pacific belt,**
or "Ring of Fire," is the larger. The Cascade Range volcanoes described earlier make up a small segment of the
circum-Pacific belt.

Several composite volcanoes in Mexico rise higher
than 5,000 meters, including Orizaba (third highest peak
in North America) and Popocatepetl. Cortez sent his men
to climb Popocatepetl during his conquest of Mexico in
1521. They were lowered into the smoking crater and
returned with sulfur needed to make gunpowder.

The circum-Pacific belt includes many volcanoes in
Central America, the west coast of South America, and
Antarctica. Deception Island in the Antarctic, a caldera
similar to Crater Lake, began erupting in 1967, causing
the evacuation of three scientific reasearch stations that
were set up on the island. Mount Erebus, also in Antarctica, is the southernmost active volcano in the world (figure 3.22).

The western portion of the Pacific belt includes volcanoes in New Zealand, Indonesia, the Philippines, and
Japan. The beautifully symmetrical Fujiyama, in Japan,
is probably the most frequently painted volcano in the

Figure 3.22 Mount Erebus, Antarctica, the southernmost
active volcano in the world.
Photo by Philip R. Kyle.

world. The northernmost part of the circum-Pacific belt
includes active volcanoes on Alaska's Aleutian Islands.

The second major volcanic belt is the **Mediterranean
belt,** which includes Mount Vesuvius. An exceptionally
violent eruption of Mount Thera, an island in the Mediterranean, may have destroyed an important site of early
Greek civilization. (Some archeologists consider Thera to
have been the original "lost continent" of Atlantis.)

Figure 3.23 Old Japanese print of Fujiyama.
Photo by The Bettmann Archive, Inc.

Figure 3.24 Volcanic dome growing in the caldera of Mount St. Helens July 1980.
Photo by Terry Leighley, U.S. Geological Survey.

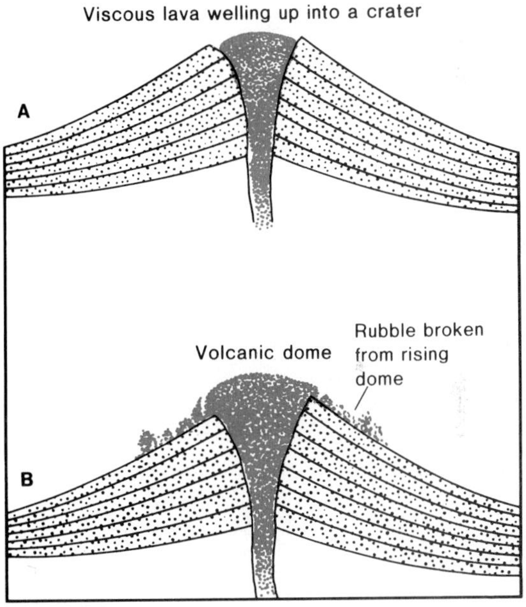

Volcanic Domes

Volcanic domes are steep-sided, dome- or spine-shaped masses of volcanic rock formed from viscous lava that solidifies in or immediately above a volcanic vent. A volcanic dome grew within the caldera of Mount St. Helens after the climactic eruption of May 1980 (figure 3.24). This was expected because of the exceptionally high viscosity of the lava associated with the St. Helens eruptions. Most of the viscous lavas that form volcanic domes are very high in silica (felsic). They solidify as *rhyolite* or *andesite* if minerals crystallize, or as *obsidian* (volcanic glass) if no minerals crystallize.

Because the thick, pasty lava that squeezes from a vent is too viscous to flow, it builds up a steep-sided dome or spine (figure 3.25). Some volcanic domes act like champagne corks, keeping gases from escaping. If the plug is removed or broken, the gas escapes suddenly and violently. Some of the most destructive volcanic explosions known have been associated with volcanic domes. However, volcanic domes are much less common than the three major types of volcanic cones.

Sometimes magma solidifies beneath a vent and clogs the throat of a volcano formed earlier, and the mass is shoved upward like a piston by the gas trapped beneath. The spine that grew during the 1902 eruption of Mount Pelée on the Caribbean island of Martinique is a famous example. A virtually solid plug of lava was pushed up out of the crater at speeds as rapid as 20 meters per day by gases trying to escape. As the rock mass rose, large chunks of hot rock broke off, carving the plug into a spine that attained a height of over 300 meters before collapsing into a pile of rubble (figure 3.26).

As the spine developed on Pelée, gas explosions blew out clouds of red-hot ash and dust called **nuées ardentes** (French for "glowing clouds"). The climax came with

Viscous lava welling up into a crater

Figure 3.25 A volcanic dome forming within the crater of a cinder cone.

great suddenness on the morning of May 8, when great flaming clouds descended like an avalanche down the mountainside, engulfing the port town of St. Pierre (figure 3.27) in minutes and incinerating everything in its path. Thirty thousand people were burned to death or suffocated (of the four survivors, one was a condemned prisoner in a poorly ventilated dungeon). The temperature of the blast was over 700°C during its sweep through the city.

Such a very hot flow of pyroclastics is called a **glowing avalanche.** Being heavier than air, a glowing avalanche,

Figure 3.26 The spine at Mount Pelée.
Historical Pictures Service, Chicago.

Figure 3.27 The ruins of St. Pierre in 1902. Mount Pelée is in the clouds.
Photo by Underwood & Underwood, courtesy Library of Congress.

composed of fiery debris mixed with hot gases, descends swiftly downward and outward. After it comes to a halt, the particles may weld together to form a hard rock called a **welded tuff.**

Lava Floods

Not all extrusive rocks are associated with volcanoes. Large regions of the continents are now covered by extrusive rock that did not originate in a volcano. This lava was apparently so fluid, or nonviscous, that it flowed almost as easily as water, building up no cone at all around the vents. Such lava is, of course, mafic (low in silica). It was extruded at a temperature well above the melting point of basalt, the rock that the lava formed as it solidified.

Plateau basalts were produced during the geologic past by outpourings of vast quantities of lava. The Columbia plateau area of Washington and Oregon (figure 3.28), for example, is constructed of layer upon layer of basalt, accumulating to thicknesses as great as 3,000 meters. Each individual flood of lava added to the pile a layer generally between 15 and 100 meters thick and hundreds of square kilometers in extent (figure 3.29).

Basalt layers give the landscape a striking appearance in most places where they are exposed. Instead of looking like stacked-up slabs or tablets of solid, unbroken rock, the individual layers appear to be formed of parallel, vertical columns, mostly six-sided. This characteristic of basalt is called **columnar structure** or **columnar jointing.** An explanation for the columns can be found in the way in which basalt contracts as it cools *after* solidifying Basalt becomes completely solid at temperatures below about 1200°C. The hot layer of rock then continues to cool to temperatures normal for the earth's surface. Like most solids, basalt contracts as it cools. The layer of basalt is easily able to accommodate the shrinkage in the narrow vertical dimension; but the cooling rock cannot "pull in" its edges, which may be hundreds of kilometers away. The tension created causes the rock to fracture into an orderly hexagonal pattern (figure 3.30).

Submarine Eruptions

Submarine eruptions, notably those occurring along mid-oceanic ridges, almost always consist of mafic lavas that create basalt. In fact, basaltic rock, thought to have been formed from lava erupting along mid-oceanic ridges, or solidifying underground beneath the ridges, makes up virtually the entire crust underlying the oceans. In a few places—Iceland, for example—volcanic islands rise above the otherwise submerged system (See Box 3.2).

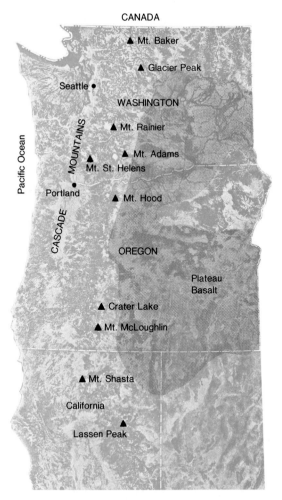

Figure 3.28 Locations of recently active Cascade volcanoes and areas covered by plateau basalts.

Figure 3.29 Basalt layers in the Columbia plateau, Washington.

A

B

Figure 3.30 Columnar jointing at Devil's Postpile, California. (*A*) Side view. (*B*) The columns as seen from above. (Scratches were caused by glacial erosion, as explained in chapter 12.)

Box 3.2
An Icelandic Community Battles a Volcano—And Wins

The inhabitants of Iceland are in daily contact with volcanism. Volcanic heat helps to mitigate the harsh cold of these sub-Arctic islands as geothermal water provides warmth for their homes.

In 1963 submarine eruptions resumed in this region after a period of no volcanic activity. Within a few months, the volcano Surtsey had built itself up above sea level, giving Iceland a new island.

Ten years later, in 1973, eruptions began on one of the tiny Vestmann Islands south of Iceland's main island. On Heimaey, one of Iceland's most important and prosperous fishing ports was nearly destroyed by the eruptions. First ash and then lava flows erupted from a new fissure on the edge of the town. The ashfall quickly buried nearby parts of the town and accumulated on the streets and houses. Flaming spatter ignited roofs, and houses burned. Within a week a cinder cone 150 meters high marked the edge of the town. Some residents were evacuated, but the townspeople who remained, along with rescue workers, worked hard to save the rest of the town. Ash was shoveled off roofs before a heavy accumulation could cause collapse. To prevent breakage from drifting ash, windows were sealed off with sheet metal. Despite the constant volcanic activity, water and electrical services were maintained. The greatest fear of the residents was that the harbor would be blocked by a 40-meter-high tongue of rubbly *aa* lava that began moving slowly away from the main flow and toward the harbor, engulfing twelve houses in one day. The town's livelihood depended on the survival of the harbor.

To halt the lava's advance, fire hoses and large pumps were put to work to cool down the lava with sea water. This unprecedented step apparently worked; the lava front hardened enough so that new lava was deflected elsewhere. The harbor was saved, but the town and its

A

B

Figure 3.31 (*A*) Town on Heimaey blanketed with ash. Lava flow in left background is moving toward sealing off the harbor. (*B*) Spraying the advancing flow with water. Photos from U.S. Geological Survey.

surroundings bore little resemblance to the place that had existed several months earlier.

Five months after they began, the eruptions stopped. Ash cleared from the streets and buildings was used to make an extension of the airport runway. Nearly all the evacuated residents returned to resume their lives on the volcano-built island.

Figure 3.32   Pillow basalt in the Sultanate of Oman.
Photo by E. H. Bailey, U.S. Geological Survey.

Pillow Basalts

Figure 3.32 shows **pillow structure**—rocks, generally basalt, occurring as pillow-shaped rounded masses closely fitted together. Observations of submarine eruptions by divers have revealed that pillow structure results when elongate blobs of lava break out of a thin skin of solid basalt over the top of a flow that is submerged in water. Each blob is squeezed out like toothpaste, and its surface is chilled to rock almost instantly. A new blob forms as more lava inside is able to break out. Each new pillow settles down on the pile, with little space left in between. When pillow basalts are found exposed in mountain ranges in various parts of the world, they are usually regarded as indications of submarine eruption in the geologic past followed, much later, by uplift.

Identification of Extrusive Rocks

Extrusive rocks are named and identified on the basis of their composition and texture.

Composition

The amount of silica in a lava strongly influences not only the viscosity of lava and the violence of eruptions, but also which particular rock is formed. Fortunately, we do not have to make a chemical analysis of a volcanic rock to determine whether it is a rhyolite, an andesite, or a basalt. For most igneous rocks, we can indirectly determine the approximate chemical composition by identifying the minerals present and the relative abundance of each mineral in the rock. Because extrusive igneous rocks are generally fine-grained, a microscope usually is needed for precise identification of the component minerals. In most cases, however, we can guess what the probable mineral content is by noting how dark or light in color an extrusive rock is. Most felsic rocks are light-colored because they contain more feldspar and quartz (which have a high percentage of silica) and fewer of the dark minerals (which contain iron and magnesium). Mafic rocks, on the other hand, tend to be dark because of their ferromagnesian component minerals.

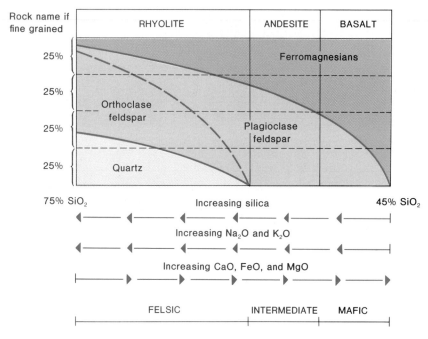

Rock name if fine grained

	RHYOLITE	ANDESITE	BASALT

25% Ferromagnesians

25% Orthoclase feldspar

25% Plagioclase feldspar

25% Quartz

75% SiO$_2$ Increasing silica   45% SiO$_2$

◀ ——— ◀ ——— ◀ ——— ◀ ——— ◀ ——— ◀ ———

Increasing Na$_2$O and K$_2$O

◀ ——— ◀ ——— ◀ ——— ◀ ——— ◀ ——— ◀ ———

Increasing CaO, FeO, and MgO

▶ ——— ▶ ——— ▶ ——— ▶ ——— ▶ ———

FELSIC   INTERMEDIATE   MAFIC

Figure 3.33 Classification of the common extrusive rocks. Rocks with names based entirely on texture (obsidian, breccia, pumice, tuff) are not included. Coarse-grained equivalent rocks are added to this diagram in the next chapter.

Rhyolite, a felsic rock, is usually cream colored, tan, or pink; it is made up mostly of feldspar but always includes some quartz. Note that the rhyolite portion of figure 3.33 is larger than the areas shown for andesite and basalt. Geologists commonly subdivide this portion of the classification system. For example, *dacite,* the rock associated with the 1980 St. Helens eruptions, contains more ferromagnesian minerals and plagioclase but less orthoclase and quartz than the average rhyolite. In our classification system, dacite corresponds to the right portion of the area in figure 3.33 assigned to rhyolite.

A **basalt** has a relatively low amount (about 50 percent by weight) of silica. Much of that silica is bonded to iron and magnesium to form ferromagnesian minerals, such as *olivine* or *augite,* which are dark green or black. The remaining silica plus aluminum is bonded predominantly with calcium to form calcium-rich *plagioclase feldspar* (which tends to be darker gray than the white or pink potassium or sodium feldspars associated with felsic rocks). Basalt does not contain quartz because no silica is left over after the other minerals have formed. Because of the preponderance of dark minerals in basalt, this rock is usually dark gray to black.

Andesite, which crystallizes from an intermediate lava, can be recognized on the basis of its moderately gray or green color. This is because a little over half the rock is composed of light- to medium-gray plagioclase feldspar,

and the rest of its components are ferromagnesian minerals. Rarely is there sufficient silica in the lava for quartz to form in an andesite.

The chemical and mineralogical relationships of the common extrusive igneous rocks are shown in figure 3.33. This classification chart can be used along with the rock identification table in Appendix B to identify extrusive rocks.

Textures

Grain size Some extrusive rocks (such as obsidian and pumice) are classified solely on the basis of their textures, but most are classified by composition *and* texture. *Grain size* is a rock's most important textural characteristic. For the most part, extrusive rocks are fine grained or else made of glass.

A **fine-grained rock** is one in which most of the mineral grains are smaller than 1 millimeter. In some, the individual minerals are distinguishable only with a microscope. **Obsidian** (figure 3.34) is volcanic glass and is also one of the few rocks that is not composed of minerals. A fine-grained or glassy texture distinguishes extrusive rocks from most intrusive rocks. Intrusive igneous rocks (chapter 4) solidify underground and generally are coarse grained.

Figure 3.34 Obsidian.

Figure 3.35 Porphyritic andesite.
Photo by W. C. Irvin.

Figure 3.36 Photomicrograph of tuff.
Photo by G. A. Izett, U.S. Geological Survey.

Two factors are critical in controlling grain size during the solidification of igneous rocks: rate of cooling and viscosity. If lava cools rapidly, the atoms have time to move only a short distance; they bond with nearby atoms, forming only small crystals. If extremely rapid or almost instantaneous cooling occurs, individual atoms in the lava are "frozen" in place, forming glass rather than crystals.

Grain size is controlled to a lesser extent by the viscosity of the lava. The atoms in a very viscous lava cannot move so freely as those in a very fluid lava. Hence, a rock formed from viscous lava is more likely to be obsidian or of finer grains than one formed from more fluid lava. Most obsidian, when chemically analyzed, has a very high silica content and is the chemical equivalent of rhyolite.

Porphyritic textures   Volcanic extrusive rock that does not have a uniformly fine-grained texture throughout is described as porphyritic. A **porphyritic rock** is one in which large crystals are enclosed in a *matrix* (or *ground mass*) of much finer grained minerals or obsidian. The large crystals are termed **phenocrysts.** A porphyritic rock is often described as looking rather like raisin bread; the matrix or ground mass is the bread, the phenocrysts are the raisins. In the porphyritic andesite shown in figure 3.35, phenocrysts of feldspar and ferromagnesian minerals are enclosed in a matrix of crystals too fine grained to distinguish with the naked eye but visible under a microscope.

Two stages of solidification are represented in porphyritic texture. Slow cooling takes place while the magma is underground. Minerals that form at higher temperatures crystallize and grow to form phenocrysts in the still partly fluid magma. If the entire mass is then erupted, the remaining liquid portion cools rapidly at the earth's surface and forms the fine-grained matrix.

Fragmental textures   When loose pyroclastic material (ash, bombs, etc.) is cemented or otherwise consolidated, the new rock is called *tuff* or *volcanic breccia,* depending on the size of the fragments. A **tuff** (figure 3.36) is a rock

Figure 3.37 Vesicular basalt.

Figure 3.38 Pumice.

composed of fine-grained pyroclastic particles (ash and dust). A **volcanic breccia** is a rock formed of larger pieces of volcanic rock (cinders, blocks, bombs).

How welded tuff is formed from a glowing avalanche was described earlier. A volcanic breccia is produced when pyroclastic debris on the flank of a volcano is overrun or engulfed by a lava flow that then solidifies.

Textures due to trapped gas A magma deep under ground is under high pressure, generally high enough to keep all its gases in a dissolved state. On eruption, the pressure is suddenly released and the gases come out of solution. This is analogous to what happens when a bottle of beer or soda is opened. Because the drink was bottled and capped under pressure, the gas (carbon dioxide) is in solution. Uncapping the drink relieves the pressure, and the carbon dioxide separates from the liquid as gas bubbles. If you froze the newly opened drink very quickly, you would have a piece of ice with small, bubble-shaped holes. Similarly, when a lava solidifies while gas is bubbling through it, holes are trapped in the rock, creating a distinctive *vesicular* texture. A **vesicle** is a cavity caused by gas in a lava. A vesicular rock has the appearance of Swiss cheese (whose texture also is caused by trapped carbon dioxide gas). Vesicular basalt is quite common (figure 3.37). **Scoria,** a highly vesicular basalt, actually contains more gas space than rock.

In more viscous lavas, where the gas cannot escape so easily, the lava is churned into a froth (like the head of a glass of beer). When cooled quickly, it forms **pumice,** a frothy glass that has so much void space that it can float in water (figure 3.38). Powdered pumice is used as an abrasive because it can scratch metal or glass.

The Source of Lava

Geologists agree that magma, which becomes lava if it reaches the earth's surface, is formed locally within the outer 100 kilometers or so of the earth. Pockets of magma form, apparently, from the melting of rock within the crust or the uppermost part of the mantle. Why do rocks within the crust or upper mantle melt? What controls the composition of the magmas and, by inference, the rocks that form from them?

Plate tectonics goes a long way toward explaining these and other questions. Any theory that deals with the origin and composition of magma must explain the data summarized in this chapter. Some of the important aspects of volcanism that must be accounted for are the following: (1) Basalt, which makes up virtually the entire oceanic crust, is the most abundant extrusive rock, but, as shown in the next chapter, felsic rocks are the most common intrusives. (2) Geologically young andesite volcanoes are remarkably aligned along the circum-Pacific and Mediterranean belts. (3) Most contemporary submarine volcanism tends to occur along the mid-oceanic ridges.

Geologists agree that most basaltic magma is produced by partial melting of the *asthenosphere*. The asthenosphere, as described in chapter 1, is the plastic zone of the mantle beneath the rigid *lithosphere* (the upper mantle and crust that make up a plate). **Partial melting** means that only the chemical components of the asthenosphere having the lowest melting temperatures become liquid while minerals requiring higher temperatures to melt remain crystalline.

The probable reason that the asthenosphere is plastic or "soft" is that the temperatures there are only slightly lower (or, perhaps, slightly higher) than the temperatures required for partial melting of mantle rock that is deeply buried. Partial melting may take place either because extra heat raises the temperature above the melting points for some of the components of the asthenosphere or because pressure is reduced. In general, the greater the pressure on a substance, the more the melting temperature is raised. The asthenosphere is solid because of the high pressures due to deep burial. However, if a crack develops through the overlying lithosphere, the localized reduction in pressure could be sufficient to permit partial melting of that part of the asthenosphere.

Geologists are not sure whether increased temperature or reduced pressure is the dominant factor in the generation of basaltic magma. If increased temperature is the critical factor, the extra heat could be provided either by convection currents or more localized hot **mantle plumes,** narrow columns of hot mantle rock that rise from deep within the earth and spread radially outward beneath the lithosphere (figure 3.39). Spreading centers may overlie upwelling convection currents or they may overlie a series of hot mantle plumes (or perhaps both).

If a reduction of pressure is the critical factor in causing partial melting of mantle material, plate tectonics can explain this easily. Where two plates are moving away from each other along a diverging boundary (spreading center), a crack or series of cracks would extend through the rigid lithosphere. If a fissure or crack system extends into the asthenosphere, pressure is reduced sufficiently to permit partial melting and the formation of a basaltic magma.

Part of the basaltic magma erupts along the surface of the spreading center (usually a mid-oceanic ridge crest) and part of the magma solidifies in the underlying fissures. As shown in figure 3.40, the process is relatively continuous as spreading keeps pulling the lithosphere apart to create new fissures.

In 1974 geologists in a remarkable program called project FAMOUS (an acronym for French American Mid-Ocean Underseas Study) made deep dives to the mid-Atlantic ridge in small research submarines. A submarine

Side view

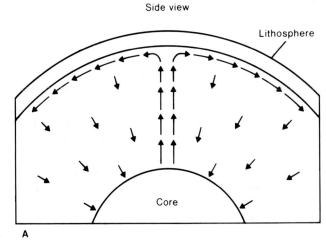

Top view

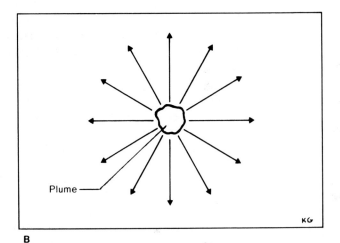

Figure 3.39 Mantle plume, showing schematic pattern of heat flow. (*A*) Side view. (*B*) Top view.

actually entered the fracture that splits the ridge, and scientists could observe pillow structure on the floor and walls of the rift (figure 3.41).

Great stacks of basalt layers on land, such as the plateau basalts of eastern Washington and Oregon, are believed to have formed because a spreading center developed and a continent began splitting. Fractures extended entirely through the continental lithosphere into the asthenosphere. Basaltic magma formed and rose through the fissures to flow over the surface of the continent. For some reason, after a few million years the process stopped. According to plate tectonics, the split between the present continents of North America and Europe began in a similar manner. However, unlike the incipient spreading of the Pacific Northwest, spreading continued for hundreds of millions of years, creating the present Atlantic Ocean basin. The spreading continues today, widening the Atlantic slightly each year.

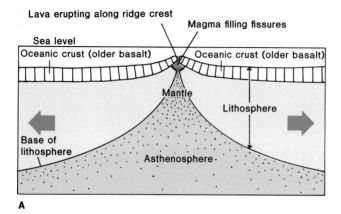

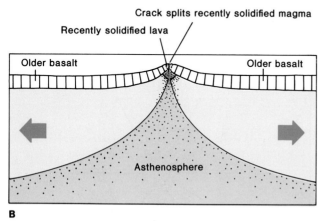

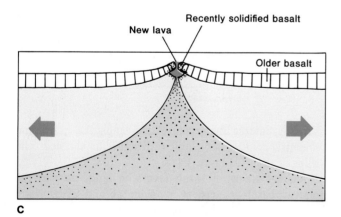

Figure 3.40 Basaltic crust is continuously being created along a spreading center. (*A*) A fissure develops due to sea-floor spreading. Magma fills the fissure and erupts on the sea floor. (*B*) Magma solidifies and a new fissure develops through the recently formed igneous rock. (*C*) Magma again fills the fissure and erupts on the sea floor.

Figure 3.41 Pillow basalt and tensional fracture in the mid-Atlantic ridge. Photo taken from submersible during Project FAMOUS's investigation of the ridge.
Photo by R. D. Ballard, Woods Hole Oceanographic Institution.

Not all basalt erupts along spreading centers. Hawaiian eruptions occur within the Pacific plate at considerable distance from a mid-oceanic ridge. Most geologists attribute the basaltic magma to a mantle plume or "hot spot" beneath the plate (figure 3.42). As the Pacific plate overrides the plume (currently beneath the island of Hawaii), magma is created in the asthenosphere and eventually erupts, adding new land to the Hawaiian islands.

Plate Tectonics and the Origin of Andesite

According to plate tectonic theory, the remarkable alignment of composite volcanoes along the circum-Pacific belt is due to subduction at converging plate boundaries. For example, the source of magma for Mount St. Helens and the other Cascade volcanoes is the Juan de Fuca Plate, a small plate whose spreading center is in the Pacific not far west of the Washington and Oregon coastline (figure 3.43). The Juan de Fuca plate moves eastward and is subducted beneath the North American continent, which is moving westward. The oceanic lithosphere, capped by basalt with a veneer of overlying marine sediment, sinks diagonally beneath the continental lithosphere (figure 3.44). As it descends, the upper portion of the oceanic plate comes in contact with progressively hotter material. Once it has slid beneath the continental lithosphere, it

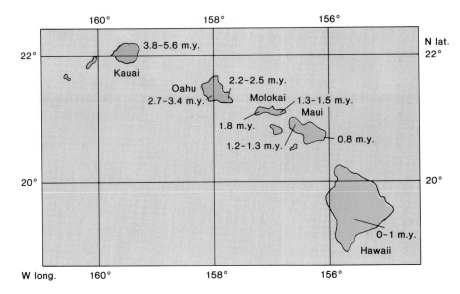

Figure 3.42 How plate motion over a "hot spot" has created the Hawaiian Islands. Map showing the sequence of ages of volcanic rocks in the Hawaiian Island group. (*1*) Kauai, the northernmost Hawaiian Island, formed 3.8–5.6 million years ago. (*2*) Plate motion over the "hot spot" continues for over 4 million years, creating the various volcanic islands. Present eruptions take place along the edge of the island of Hawaii. From I. McDougall, 1964, *Geological Society of America Bulletin.*

continues under the asthenosphere. Here temperatures are high enough to permit partial melting of the upper portion of the descending plate. The depth at which this happens is fairly uniform, as implied by the alignment of active volcanoes parallel to the Pacific coastline. The magma, being less dense than the surrounding rocks, rises toward the earth's surface, eventually erupting and building composite cones.

Although rhyolite and basalt eruptions sometimes take place when composite cones are built, the vast majority of eruptions involve andesitic lava or tephra. Geologists are not certain why andesite predominates. Perhaps the melt is a combination of basalt and silica-rich sedimentary material (subducted on top of the basalt of the oceanic crust). Alternatively, only part of the basaltic crust may melt, leaving behind a more ferromagnesian-rich residue. Or, perhaps, as a mafic magma ascends, it absorbs felsic material as it passes through the lower part of the continental crust.

To more thoroughly understand how magma is generated, we need to know about *intrusive rocks*, igneous rocks that solidify underground. In the next chapter we describe intrusive rocks and expand upon the topic of how magma forms.

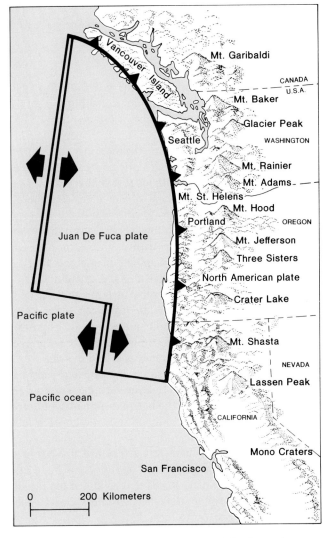

Figure 3.43 The Juan de Fuca plate and the Cascade volcanoes.

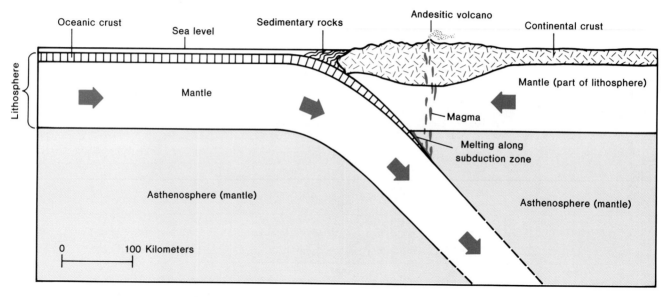

Figure 3.44 Magma forming at a converging plate boundary.

Summary

Lava is molten rock that reaches the earth's surface, having been formed as *magma* from rock within the earth's crust or from the uppermost part of the mantle.

Lava contains between 45 and 75 percent *silica* (SiO_2). The more silica present, the more viscous the lava. The temperature of a lava also affects its viscosity. Viscous lavas are associated with more violent eruptions than are more fluid lavas. *Volcanic domes* form from the extrusion of very viscous lavas.

A *mafic* lava, relatively low in silica, crystallizes into *basalt,* the most abundant extrusive igneous rock. Basalt, which is dark in color, is composed of minerals that are relatively high in iron, magnesium, and calcium.

Rhyolite, a light-colored rock, forms from *felsic* lavas that are high in silica but contain little iron, magnesium, or calcium. Because potassium and sodium are important elements in rhyolite, its constituent minerals are mostly potassium- and sodium-rich feldspars and quartz.

A lava with a composition intermediate between mafic and felsic crystallizes to *andesite,* a moderately dark rock. Andesite contains about equal amounts of ferromagnesian minerals and sodium- and calcium-rich feldspars.

Extrusive rocks characteristically are fine grained. *Porphyritic* rock contains some larger crystals in an otherwise fine-grained rock. Rocks that solidified too rapidly for crystals to develop are called *obsidian.* Gas trapped in rock causes *vesicles* to form.

Pyroclasts or *tephra* are the result of volcanic explosions. *Tuff* is volcanic ash that has been reconsolidated into a new rock. If large pyroclastic fragments have become reconsolidated, the rock is termed a *volcanic breccia.*

A *cinder cone* is composed of loose pyroclastic material that forms steep slopes as it falls back around the crater. Cinder cones are not so large as the other two major types of cones.

A *shield volcano* is built up by successive eruptions of mafic lava. Slopes are gentle, but the volume generally is great.

Composite cones are made of alternating layers of pyroclastic material and solidified lava flows; they are intermediate in steepness between cinder cones and shield volcanoes. Young composite volcanoes, predominantly composed of andesite, are aligned along the circum-Pacific belt and, less extensively, in the Mediterranean belt. These belts are located at converging plate boundaries, according to the theory of plate tectonics.

Plateau basalts and basalts formed at mid-oceanic ridges appear to be produced by magmas that originate in the upper mantle and follow fissures upward through the earth's crust. The *mid-oceanic ridges* are regarded in plate tectonic theory as present-day spreading centers, and the newly erupted basalt becomes part of the oceanic crust. Flood basalts may be due to incipient spreading centers on continental crust.

Terms to Remember

aa
andesite
angular pyroclasts
basalt
bomb
caldera
cinder cone
circum-Pacific belt
columnar structure
    (columnar jointing)
composite volcano
    (stratovolcano)
crater
extrusive rock
felsic rocks
fine-grained rock
flank eruption
glowing avalanche
intermediate rocks
lava
mafic rocks
magma
mantle plumes
Mediterranean belt
nuées ardentes

obsidian
pahoehoe
partial melting
phenocryst
pillow structure
    (pillow basalts)
plateau basalts
porphyritic rock
pumice
pyroclastic debris (tephra)
rhyolite
scoria
shield volcano
spatter cone
tuff
vent
vesicle
viscosity
volcanic breccia
volcanic dome
volcanism
volcano
welded tuff

Questions for Review

1. Name the minerals, and the approximate percentage of each, that you would expect to be present in each of the following rocks: andesite, rhyolite, basalt.
2. What clues would you look for if you were asked to predict whether or not a violent and disastrous eruption might occur in a volcanic area that is not active at the present time?
3. What property (or characteristic) of obsidian makes it an exception to the usual geologic definition for the term "rock"?
4. What factors control the viscosity of a lava?
5. What factors determine whether a series of volcanic eruptions builds a shield volcano, a composite volcano, or a cinder cone? Describe each type of volcanic cone.
6. What might be the origin of basalt found on the sea floor a thousand or more kilometers from an active mid-oceanic ridge?
7. Explain how a vesicular porphyritic andesite might have been formed.
8. What gases are liberated by volcanic action?
9. Why are extrusive igneous rocks fine grained?
10. Why is it that flood basalts do not build volcanic cones?

Questions for Thought

1. Why does only a small portion of the mantle rock melt, and why does the melting take place below fissures that extend upward through the crust?
2. Why are continental igneous rocks richer in silica than oceanic igneous rock?
3. If a hot mantle plume were under the interior of a continent, what might happen?

Supplementary Readings

Bullard, F. M. 1977. *Volcanoes of the earth.* 2nd ed. Austin: University of Texas Press.

Decker, R. W., and B. Decker. 1981. *Volcanoes.* San Francisco: W. H. Freeman.

Green, J., and N. M. Short. 1971. *Volcanic landforms and surface features: A photographic atlas and glossary.* New York: Springer-Verlag.

Harris, S. L. 1980. *Fire and ice, the Cascade volcanoes* (2nd ed.) Seattle: The Mountaineers, Pacific Search Books.

Macdonald, G. A. 1972. *Volcanoes.* Englewood Cliffs, N.J.: Prentice-Hall.

Macdonald, G. A., and A. T. Abbott, 1970. *Volcanoes in the sea.* Honolulu: University of Hawaii Press.

Sheets, P. D., and D. K. Grayson. 1979. *Volcanic activity and human ecology.* New York: Academic Press.

4

Intrusive Activity and the Origin of Igneous Rocks

Purpose

In this chapter we continue the discussion of igneous activity to include the rock-forming processes of magmas that do not reach the earth's surface but solidify underground. Although intrusive and extrusive rocks are similar in many ways, intrusive rocks cannot simply be thought of as underground equivalents of volcanic rocks. There are important differences between extrusive and intrusive rocks, both in distribution and in properties. As later chapters show (chapters 17–20), intrusive rocks are far more important to the continental crust and mountain belts, whereas extrusive rocks are more important to the oceanic crust.

An explanation of the structural relationships between bodies of intrusive rock and other rocks in the earth's crust begins this chapter. Intrusive rocks are then described and classified (the classification system is an elaboration of the one given in chapter 3), followed by a summary of theories on the origin of extrusive as well as intrusive rocks. You will be able to perceive how various hypotheses, some old, some new, relate to the theory of plate tectonics.

Intrusive rocks are rocks that appear to have crystallized from magma emplaced in surrounding rock. Bodies of intrusive rocks are exposed to us only after erosion and, usually, uplift have taken place.

Some intrusive rocks formed from magma that was solidifying underground while volcanic activity was taking place above. It would be a misconception, however, to regard all intrusive events as being subsurface counterparts of volcanism. If this were true, the intrusive equivalent of basalt (the most abundant extrusive rock) ought to be the predominant intrusive rock. Quite the opposite is true. **Gabbro,** a mafic, coarse-grained, igneous rock composed predominantly of ferromagnesian minerals and calcium-rich plagioclase feldspar, is the intrusive equivalent of basalt. But gabbro is not very abundant, whereas **granite,** a felsic, coarse-grained, igneous rock composed

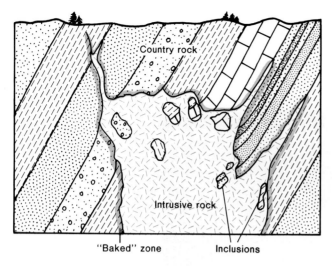

Figure 4.1 Igneous rock apparently intruded pre-existing rock (country rock) as a liquid.

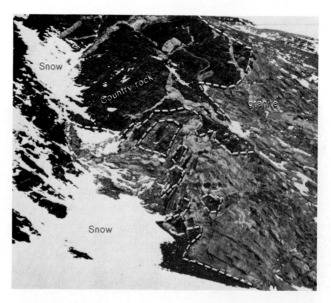

Figure 4.2 Granite (light-colored rock on the right) has intruded country rock (dark-colored rock). Part of contact has been outlined by the dashed line. Note the inclusions within the granite and offshoots of granite into fractures in the country rock (dikes). Ellsworth Land, Antarctica. Photo by P. L. Williams, U.S. Geological Survey.

mostly of potassium- and sodium-rich feldspars and quartz, is the most abundant intrusive rock. Coarse-grained granite is, in turn, chemically and mineralogically similar to rhyolite, a not-very-abundant extrusive rock. This striking contrast between the most abundant intrusive and extrusive igneous rocks has long puzzled geologists. Any comprehensive theory on the origin of magmas and igneous rocks must take this paradox into account.

What evidence suggests that large bodies of granite (and other intrusive rocks) might have formed from the underground solidification of magma? (1) Mineralogically and chemically, intrusive rocks are essentially identical to volcanic rocks (but are of different textures). (2) Experimental studies have confirmed that most of the minerals present in these rocks can form only at high temperatures. Other experimental studies indicate that some of the minerals could have formed only at high pressures, implying they were deeply buried. (3) In many places pre-existing solid rock, *country rock,* appears to have been forcibly broken by an intruding liquid, with the magma flowing into the fractures that developed (figures 4.1 and 4.2). **Country rock,** incidentally, is an accepted term for any older rock that was intruded by an igneous body. (4) The country rock adjacent to the intrusive rock is seen to have been "baked" ("metamorphosed" is the correct term) along the contact with the intrusive rock. (5) The rock types of the country rock match **inclusions,** fragments of rock which are distinct from the body of igneous rocks in which they are enclosed. (6) "Chill zones" in the intrusive rock adjacent to contacts with country rock indicate that the magma solidified more quickly here due to the rapid loss of heat to the cooler country rock.

Laboratory experiments have greatly increased our understanding of how igneous rocks form. However, geologists have not been able to create in the laboratory an artificial rock identical to granite. Only very fine-grained rocks containing the minerals of granite have been made from artificial magmas, or "melts." The temperature and pressure at which granite is presumed to form can be duplicated in the laboratory—but not the time element. Calculations indicate that a large body of magma requires over a million years to solidify completely. This very gradual cooling is thought to be responsible for the coarse-grained texture of most intrusive rocks.

Chemical processes involving silicates are known to take place exceedingly slowly. But another problem in trying to apply experimental procedures to real rocks is determining what roles water vapor and other gases play when rocks such as granite are crystallizing. Gases are not retained in rock crystallized underground from a magma, but large amounts of gas (especially water vapor) are released during volcanic eruptions. No one has seen an intrusive rock forming; hence we can only speculate on the role these gases might have played before they escaped. One example shows why the role of gases is important. Laboratory studies have shown that granite can melt at temperatures as low as 650°C if water (dissolved in the melt) is present and under high pressure. Without the water, the melting temperature is several hundred degrees higher. Not knowing how much water was present during crystallization makes accurate determination of temperatures difficult and speculative.

A

B

Figure 4.3 (*A*) Ship Rock in New Mexico. (*B*) Relationship to the former volcano.
Photo by D. A. Rahm, courtesy Rahm Memorial Collection, Western Washington University.

Intrusive Bodies

Intrusions or **intrusive structures** are bodies of intrusive rock. Their size and shape, as well as their relationship to surrounding rocks, are important aspects of the architecture of the earth's crust. The various intrusions are named and classified based on the following considerations: (1) Is the body large or small? (2) Does it have a particular geometric shape or not? (3) Did the rock form at a considerable depth or was it a shallow intrusion? (4) What is the geometric relationship of the intrusion to the country rock?

Shallow Intrusive Structures

Some igneous bodies apparently solidified near the surface of the earth (at depths probably less than 2 kilometers). These bodies probably represent clogging of the subsurface "plumbing systems" of volcanoes or lava flows. Shallow intrusive structures tend to be relatively small in comparison with those that formed at considerable depth. Because the country rock near the earth's surface generally is cool, intruded magma tends to chill and solidify relatively rapidly. Many shallow intrusive rocks are as fine grained as their volcanic counterparts, although some are slightly more coarse grained. If a rock is fine grained, even if it solidified underground, its name is the same as for the corresponding extrusive rock. For example, a fine-grained rock of intermediate composition is an andesite whether it formed from a lava flow or from rapid cooling within the throat of a volcano. A **volcanic neck** is an intrusive structure that apparently formed from magma that solidified within the throat of a volcano.

One of the best examples is Ship Rock in New Mexico (figure 4.3). Geologists interpret the history of this feature as follows: A volcanic cone was formed. As eruptions ceased, the throat beneath the vent became clogged with magma that solidified into a more or less cylindrical body. In time the volcano (probably a cinder cone) eroded away with relative ease; the more resistant plug remained and eroded more slowly into its present shape. Weathering and erosion are continuing (falling rock has been a serious hazard to rock climbers), and eventually Ship Rock will be reduced to the level of the desert floor.

Dikes and sills   Another, and far more common, intrusive structure can also be seen at Ship Rock. The low, wall-like ridge extending outward from Ship Rock is an eroded dike. A **dike** is a tabular (shaped like a table top), discordant, intrusive structure. **Discordant** means that the body is not parallel to any layering in the country rock. (Think of a dike as cutting across layers of country rock.) Dikes may form at shallow depths and be fine grained, such as those at Ship Rock, or at greater depths and be coarse grained. Dikes need not protrude from the ground like walls. The ones at Ship Rock do so only because they are more resistant to weathering and erosion than the country rock.

A **sill** is also a tabular intrusive structure, but it is **concordant.** That is, sills differ from dikes in being parallel to any planes or layering present in the country rock (figure 4.4). Typically, the country rock bounding a sill is layered sedimentary rocks. As magma squeezes into a crack between two layers, it solidifies into a sill.

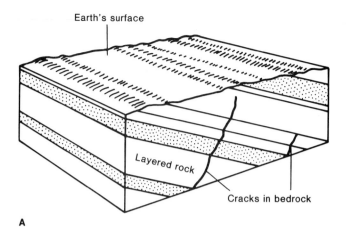

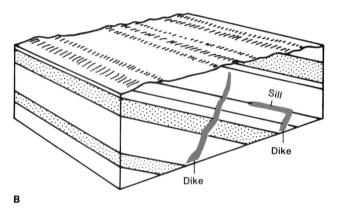

Figure 4.4 (A) Magma squeezing into cracks or planes of weakness solidifies into tabular intrusions. (B) The concordant intrusion where magma has intruded between sedimentary layers is a sill; the discordant intrusions are dikes.

A rarely found close relative of a sill is the blister-shaped structure called a **laccolith.** It also is a concordant intrusive body, but the central portion is thicker and domed upward.

Intrusions that Crystallize at Depth

Igneous rocks that formed at great depth—more than several kilometers—are called **plutonic rocks** (after Pluto, the Greek god of the underworld). Characteristically, these rocks are coarse grained, reflecting the slow cooling and solidification of magma. A **pluton** is an igneous body that crystallized deep underground. Most plutons are irregular in shape, unlike dikes and sills. The larger masses of magma had to break through country rock or shoulder it aside as they moved upward, and so developed in an irregular shape. Discordant plutons that have become exposed at the earth's surface because of erosion are arbitrarily distinguished by size. A **stock** is a small discordant pluton with an outcrop area (i.e., the area over which it is exposed to the atmosphere) of less than 100 square

Figure 4.5 A sill (light-colored rock above the man's head) that intruded layered sedimentary rock.
Photo by J. D. Vine, U.S. Geological Survey.

kilometers. If the outcrop area is greater than 100 square kilometers, the body is called a **batholith** (figure 4.6), a large discordant pluton.

Most batholiths crop out over areas vastly greater than the minimum 100 square kilometers. Although batholiths can be mafic, intermediate, or felsic, most are felsic; that is, they are composed of granite. Many major mountain ranges are carved largely from granite, examples being found in the Appalachians in the eastern part of North America and also in the ranges that parallel the West Coast. Over half the rock exposed in the Sierra Nevada of California is plutonic (figure 4.7). Geologists used to think that batholiths probably extended as continuous bodies from surface exposures to the base of the crust. Indirect evidence now suggests that few batholiths extend more than 20 kilometers below the surface.

Identification of Intrusive Igneous Rocks

Coarse-grained texture is the most significant difference between plutonic rocks and finer grained extrusive and shallow intrusive rocks. (For our purposes, **coarse-grained rocks** are defined as those in which most of the grains are larger than 1 millimeter.) The crystalline grains of plutonic rocks are commonly interlocked in a mosaic pattern (figure 4.8).

As with extrusive rocks, the names of plutonic rocks are based on texture and mineralogical composition. Because of the larger mineral grains, plutonic rocks are easier to identify than extrusive rocks. The physical properties of each mineral in a plutonic rock can be more readily determined. And, of course, knowing the minerals makes rock identification a simpler task. In figure 4.9, the classification chart presented earlier for extrusive rocks has been expanded to include intrusive rocks. Use this chart, along with the rock identification table in Appendix B, to identify common igneous rocks.

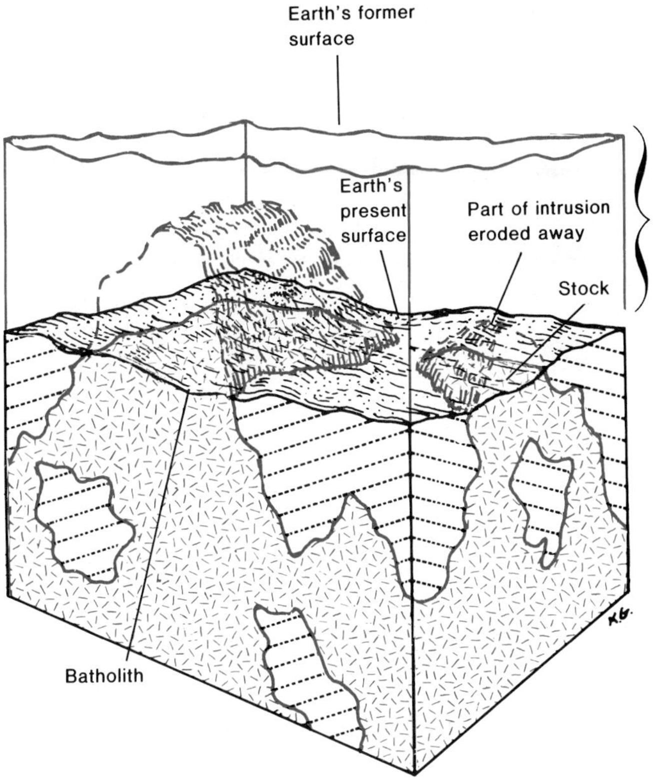

Earth's former surface

Earth's present surface

Part of intrusion eroded away

Portion removed by erosion

Stock

Batholith

Figure 4.6 A batholith and a stock. The cross-sectional view indicates that the stock and batholith are part of the same intrusion.

Figure 4.7 Part of the Sierra Nevada batholith. All light-colored rock shown here is granite.

A

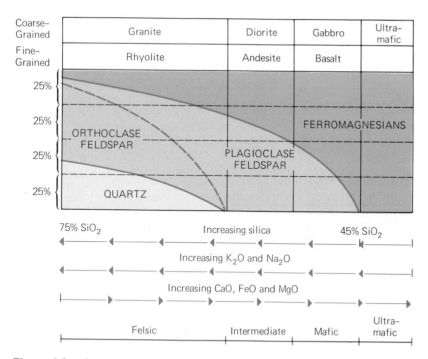

B

Quartz

Feldspar

Figure 4.8 (*A*) Coarse-grained texture characteristic of plutonic rock. (*B*) A similar rock seen through a polarizing microscope. Note the interlocking crystal grains of individual minerals.
Photomicrograph *B* by A. H. Koschman, U.S. Geological Survey.

Coarse-Grained	Granite		Diorite	Gabbro	Ultra-mafic
Fine-Grained	Rhyolite		Andesite	Basalt	

25%

25%   FERROMAGNESIANS

ORTHOCLASE FELDSPAR

25%   PLAGIOCLASE FELDSPAR

25%   QUARTZ

75% SiO₂   Increasing silica   45% SiO₂

Increasing K₂O and Na₂O

Increasing CaO, FeO and MgO

Felsic   Intermediate   Mafic   Ultra-mafic

Figure 4.9 Classification chart for the most common igneous rocks. Rock names based on special textures are not shown.

A

B

C

Figure 4.10   Plutonic rocks. (*A*) Granite. (*B*) Diorite. (*C*) Gabbro.

Box 4.1
Pegmatite—A Rock Made of Giant Crystals

Pegmatites are extremely coarse-grained igneous rocks. In some pegmatites, crystals are as large as 10 meters across. Strictly speaking, a pegmatite can be of diorite, gabbro, or granite. However, the vast majority of pegmatites are felsic, with very large crystals of orthoclase feldspar, sodium-rich plagioclase feldspars, and quartz plus very minor amounts, if any, of ferromagnesian minerals. Hence the term *pegmatite* generally implies that a rock is of granitic composition (if otherwise, a term like "gabbroic pegmatite" is used). Pegmatites are interesting both as geological phenomena and as minable resources.

The extremely coarse texture of pegmatites is attributed to both slow cooling and the low viscosity of the fluid from which they formed. As lava solidifying to rhyolite is very viscous, we would expect that magma solidifying to granite, being chemically similar, also would be viscous. Pegmatites, however, probably form from a fluid that is made mostly of water under high pressure. The water is saturated with dissolved ions derived from the granitic magma. Geologists believe the following sequence of events accounts for most pegmatites.

As a granite pluton cools, progressively more of the magma solidifies into the minerals of a granite. By the time the pluton is well over 90 percent solid, the residual magma contains a very high amount of silica and ions of elements that will crystallize into orthoclase and sodium plagioclase. Also present are elements that could not be accommodated into the crystal structures of the common minerals that formed during the normal solidification phase of the pluton. Fluids, notably water, that were in the original magma are left over as well, sometimes in considerable quantities. If no fracture above the pluton permits the fluids to escape as gases, they become sealed in, as in a pressure cooker. Although saturated with dissolved ions from the residual magma, the water prevents silica tetrahedrons in the melt from forming incipient structures, even

Figure 4.11 Pegmatite at the Etta Mine, South Dakota. The hat is on a single, large crystal that extends diagonally upward from the lower left of the photo.
Photo by S. Paige, U.S. Geological Survey.

those involving just a few tetrahedrons. When a crystal does start to form during slow cooling of the watery solution, the appropriate atoms within the melt are able to move freely in the fluid and become part of that growing crystal. The crystal adds more and more atoms and becomes very large.

Pegmatite bodies are generally quite small. Many are podlike structures, either within the upper portion of a granite pluton or within the overlying country rock near the contact with granite, the fluid body evidently having squeezed into the country rock before solidifying. Pegmatite dikes are fairly common, especially within granite plutons, where they apparently filled cracks that developed in the already solid granite. Some pegmatites form small dikes along contacts between granite and country rock, filling cracks that developed as the cooling granite pluton contracted.

Most pegmatites contain only quartz, feldspar, and perhaps mica. Minerals of considerable commercial value are found in a few pegmatites. Large crystals of muscovite mica are mined from pegmatites. These crystals are called "books" because the cleavage flakes (tens of centimeters across) look like pages. Because muscovite is an excellent insulator, the cleavage sheets are used in electrical devices, such as toasters, to separate uninsulated electrical wires. In some pegmatites, even the large feldspar crystals are mined for various industrial uses, most notably the manufacture of ceramics.

Many rare elements also are mined from pegmatites. These elements were not absorbed by the minerals of the main pluton and so were concentrated in the residual pegmatitic magma, where they crystallized as constituents of unusual minerals. Minerals containing the element lithium are mined from pegmatites. Lithium becomes part of a sheet silicate structure to form a pink or purple variety of mica (called lepidolite). Uranium ores, similarly concentrated in the residual melt of magmas, are extracted from pegmatites.

Some pegmatites are mined for gemstones. Emerald and aquamarine are varieties of the mineral beryl and occur in pegmatites that crystallized from a solution containing the element beryllium. A large number of the world's very rare minerals are found only in pegmatites, many of these in only one known pegmatite body. These rare minerals are mainly of interest to collectors and museums.

Hydrothermal veins (chapter 7) are closely related to pegmatites. Veins of quartz are common in country rock near granite. Many of these are believed to be caused by water that is able to escape from the magma. Silica dissolved in the very hot water cakes on the walls of cracks as the water cools while traveling surfaceward. Sometimes valuable metals such as gold, silver, lead, zinc and copper are deposited with the quartz in veins.

Ultramafic Rocks

As you may have noted in the chart (figure 4.9), ultramafic rocks do not have a fine-grained counterpart. This curious fact appears to indicate that ultramafic magma never reaches the surface. An **ultramafic rock** is composed entirely or almost entirely of ferromagnesian minerals. No feldspars are present and, of course, no quartz. Most ultramafics are composed of coarse-grained pyroxene and/or olivine. Chemically, these rocks contain less than 45 percent silica.

Experiments indicate that very high temperatures (almost 2,000°C) are required to melt ultramafic rocks. Such high temperatures could not be sustained by a magma traveling upward through the considerably cooler earth's crust. For this reason, geologists believe that most ultramafic rocks formed far below the surface, probably in the mantle. This view is supported by experimental studies that have found that some of the minerals in ultramafic rocks can only have formed at very high pressure. Where we find large bodies of ultramafic rocks, the usual interpretation is that a slice of the mantle has traveled upward as solid rock.

Varieties of Granite

Granite and rhyolite occupy a larger area in the classification chart than do the other rocks. This reflects granite's greater variation in composition. For instance, a granite whose composition corresponds to the right side of the field (that is, nearer to diorite/andesite) contains much more plagioclase than orthoclase and somewhat more ferromagnesian minerals than does a rock whose composition plots in the left side of the granite field. Geologists have arbitrarily subdivided the field of granite and named each of the varieties; a rock in the right portion of the field, for example, is called granodiorite.

Any classification system is, of course, a manmade device, and for this reason, classification systems differ somewhat between different groups of geologists. We define the boundary between granite and **diorite** (a coarse-grained rock composed of approximately equal amounts of plagioclase feldspar and ferromagnesian minerals) by the presence or absence of quartz; but we could just as easily have placed the boundary slightly to the left, so that a rock with 10 percent or less quartz would be diorite.

Abundance and Distribution of Plutonic Rocks

In comparison with the plutons that occupy large portions of the earth's crust, the shallow intrusive bodies are minor in extent and significance.

We mentioned earlier the paradox that basalt is the most abundant extrusive rock whereas granite is the most commonly found intrusive rock. We also pointed out that most basalt is associated with the oceanic crust (although plateau basalts cannot be ignored) and that granite is associated with mountain ranges.

Granite is not only the most abundant igneous rock in mountain ranges, but also the predominant igneous rock throughout the continental crust. In most of the non-mountainous parts of North America—the plains of the central interior, for instance—no igneous rock is exposed at the surface. But underneath a veneer of sedimentary rock only a few kilometers thick lies the much older "basement" rock, much of which was orginally plutonic. Some very old granite plutons are not covered over by sedimentary rocks, as, for example, in eastern Canada. Additionally, plutons have also been found in places like Grand Canyon where local erosion has cut through the sedimentary veneer and exposed the continental basement. These plutons have intruded metamorphic rocks that are even older. Some parts of the basement underlying the continent are thought to be mountain ranges that long ago were eroded to plains (as explained in chapter 18).

It is apparent that *granite* is the igneous rock of the continents, *basalt* of the oceans, and *andesite* (usually on or near continental margins) the building material of young volcanic mountains.

How Magma Forms

A rock melts and becomes a magma when the temperature is higher than the melting points of minerals present in a rock. A rock becomes entirely molten if the temperature is higher than the melting points of *all* the minerals in that rock. If the temperature has exceeded the melting points for only some of the minerals, only part of the rock melts. A complication of this is that the temperature at which a given mineral melts can vary. Pressure, amount of gas (particularly water) present, and the kind of neighboring minerals can all have an important influence on the melting point of a mineral. The factors that control melting of rocks are discussed below.

Sources of Heat for Melting

Geothermal gradient   The rate of temperature increase associated with increasing depth beneath the surface is the **geothermal gradient.** A miner descending a mine shaft notices that the temperature is rising. Recorded data show this rise to be about 2.5°C for each 100 meters (25°C/km) of descent in the outer part of the crust. The greater the depth, then, the more likely it is that temperatures will be high enough to melt rock. Because of the effects of pressure, however, the rock may remain solid at great depths where the temperature is very high.

Radioactivity   Some elements, such as uranium, produce heat through radioactive decay. These elements normally are present in rocks only in very minor amounts. The heat generated, however, raises the rock temperature above that expected from the geothermal gradient. Magma may form locally where the rock's melting temperature is exceeded.

Radioactive elements are present in greater amounts in felsic rocks than in mafic rocks. Heat from radioactivity is more likely to be significant in continental rocks, where granite predominates.

Friction   Rock grinding past rock may also generate heat. In regions where active mountain-building is taking place, the friction caused by the moving and shifting of large rock masses generates heat that may combine with heat from other sources and aid in melting rocks.

Hot mantle plumes   Otherwise unexplained "hot spots" on the earth's surface may be caused by hot mantle plumes, which, as described in chapter 3, are narrow upwellings of hot material within the mantle. Although their existence is hypothetical, hot mantle plumes could help account for some igneous activity, such as the midoceanic eruptions that built up the Hawaiian Islands. Volcanism in the middle of continents may be similarly attributable to mantle plumes. Yellowstone National Park has had considerable volcanic activity in the recent geologic past, and some geologists have suggested that a hot plume may be present in the mantle below the Park.

Factors That Control Melting Temperatures

Pressure   The melting points of minerals generally *increase* with increasing pressure. Pressure increases with depth in the earth's crust, just as temperature does. So a rock that melts at a given temperature at the surface of the earth requires a higher temperature to melt deep underground.

When confining pressure is high enough to keep rocks from melting, a reduction in that pressure can permit melting to occur. This seems to be what happens along mid-oceanic ridges when basalt erupts. A major fissure extends through the earth's crust. Pressure is reduced by the crack, rock melts, and a basalt magma wells up, erupting along the ridge.

Water under pressure   If sufficient gas, especially water vapor, is present and under high pressure, the effect of pressure is dramatically changed. Water vapor sealed in under high pressure by overlying rocks aids in breaking down crystal structures. High water pressure can significantly lower the melting points of minerals (figure 4.12).

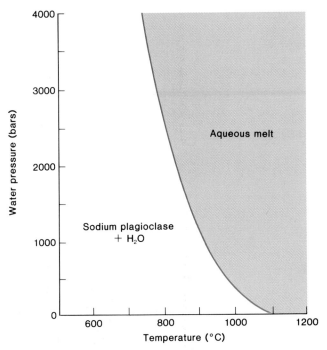

Figure 4.12 Melting temperature of a mineral relative to water pressure.

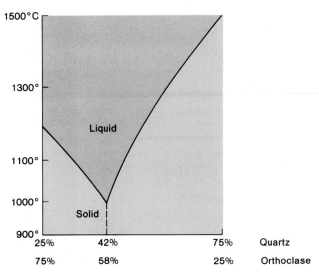

Figure 4.13 Melting temperatures for mixtures of quartz and orthoclase at atmospheric pressure.
Modified from Schairer and Bowen, 1956, V 254, p. 16, *American Journal of Science.*

Experiments have shown that, under moderately high pressure, water mixed with granite lowers the melting point of granite from about 900°C (when dry) to as low as 625°C when saturated with water under the pressure equivalent to that of 10,000 atmospheres or *bars.*

Effect of mixed minerals   Two metals—as in solder—can be mixed in a ratio so that their melting temperature is much lower than the melting points of the pure metals. Minerals behave similarly. Experiments have shown that in some cases, mixed fragments of two minerals melt at a lower temperature than either mineral alone. Figure 4.13 shows the melting temperatures for quartz and orthoclase mixed in various proportions. If the mixture is 42 percent quartz (58 percent orthoclase), melting takes place at a temperature just above 1000°C. On the other hand, if the mixture is 75 percent quartz and 25 percent orthoclase (corresponding to the right edge of the diagram), it will require 1500°C to turn that mixture into a liquid. Pure quartz would require even higher temperatures to melt.

Theories About the Origin of Magmas

Differentiation and Bowen's Reaction Theory
Differentiation is the process by which different ingredients separate from an originally homogenous mixture. An example is the separation of whole milk into cream and skimmed milk. In the early part of the twentieth century,

N. L. Bowen conducted a series of laboratory experiments demonstrating that differentiation is a plausible way both felsic and mafic rocks could be formed from a single parent magma.

Bowen's reaction series, shown in figure 4.14, is the sequence in which minerals crystallize from a cooling basaltic magma, as demonstrated by Bowen's laboratory experiments. In simplest terms, Bowen's reaction series shows that those minerals with the highest melting temperatures crystallize from the cooling magma before those with lower melting points. The concept is a bit more complicated than that, however.

Crystallization begins along two branches, the *discontinuous branch* and the *continuous branch.* In the discontinuous branch, changes from one mineral to another occur at discrete temperatures during cooling and solidification of the magma. Changes in the continuous branch occur gradationally through a range in temperatures and affect only the one mineral, plagioclase. Although crystallization takes place simultaneously along both branches, we must explain each separately.

Discontinuous branch   All the minerals in the discontinuous branch are ferromagnesian. In this branch, as the completely liquid basaltic magma slowly cools, it reaches the temperature at which *olivine* begins to crystallize from the magma. Olivine is a mineral with an exceptionally high proportion (2:1) of iron and magnesium to silicon—formula, $(Fe, Mg)_2SiO_4$. The liquid left after olivine has crystallized is relatively depleted in iron and magnesium and relatively enriched in silicon (because only one part of Si is used for two parts of Fe and Mg).

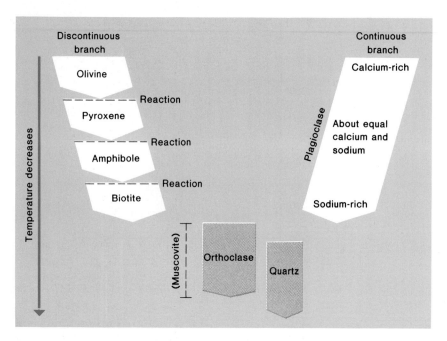

Figure 4.14 Bowen's reaction series.

As the melt cools further, the melting temperature for the next mineral of the series is reached, and *pyroxene* begins to crystallize. The olivine previously formed now *reacts* with the remaining melt, and the original crystal structure of olivine is rearranged into that of pyroxene (from isolated silica tetrahedrons to single chains of tetrahedrons). The crystal structure of pyroxene accommodates a higher amount of silicon relative to the iron and magnesium—a ratio of 1 to 1; formula $(Mg, Fe)SiO_3$. As the temperature decreases, more pyroxene crystallizes directly from the melt until the point is reached at which *amphibole* becomes stable.

Now pyroxene reacts with the melt. Its crystal structure is rearranged into amphibole's double chains of silica tetrahedrons. More of the silicon leaves the melt (along with aluminum and minor amounts of sodium and calcium) and is incorporated into the newly developing amphibole crystals.

If still more melt is left after amphibole has formed, on further cooling, amphibole reacts with the melt to produce *biotite* (which is a sheet silicate). Biotite is the last of the ferromagnesian minerals to crystallize. Any magma remaining after biotite has finished crystallizing contains neither iron nor magnesium.

Continuous branch Plagioclase feldspar is the only mineral in the continuous branch. As the completely liquid magma cools, the plagioclase with the highest melting point begins to crystallize. This plagioclase has a very high amount of calcium. Silicon and aluminum, which are part of all feldspars, combine with calcium to form the variety of plagioclase associated with mafic igneous rocks. Upon further cooling, plagioclase continues to grow at the expense of the magma. As the temperature slowly drops, the total amount of plagioclase increases, and progressively more sodium is incorporated into each growing plagioclase crystal. Plagioclase continues to crystallize during cooling until all the calcium and sodium in the magma are used up.

Any magma left after the crystallization is completed along the two branches is richer in silicon than the original magma and also contains potassium and aluminum. The potassium and aluminum combine with silicon to form *orthoclase feldspar*. If the water pressure is high, *muscovite* may also form at this stage. Any leftover melt is pure silica, which crystallizes as *quartz*.

Bowen used this experimentally determined reaction series to support the hypothesis that all magmas (mafic, intermediate, and felsic) are derived from a single parent magma (mafic) by differentiation. The early-developing minerals are separated from the remaining magma. Normally a newly erupted cooling basalt lava progresses only a short distance down the reaction series before all the ingredients are used up. Olivine develops, but only part of it reacts with the melt to form pyroxene before all the magma is used up. Simultaneously, calcium-rich plagioclase is growing and becoming progressively more sodic; but its growth ceases when the slight amount of sodium is used up. The rock becomes a completely solid aggregate of calcium-rich plagioclase, pyroxene, and olivine—in other words, what one expects to find in a basalt or gabbro.

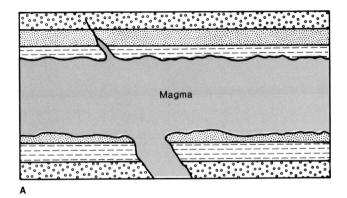

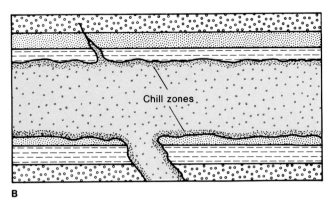

Chill zones

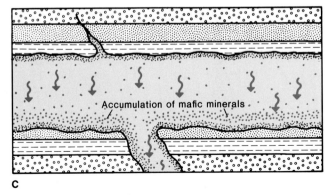

Accumulation of mafic minerals

C

Figure 4.15 Cross section showing the process of differentiation by crystal settling in a sill and dike. (A) Recently intruded magma is completely liquid. (B) Upon slow cooling, minerals such as olivine crystallize first. (C) The heavier crystals that formed early sink, leaving the remaining magma depleted in mafic constituents.

Crystal settling   Only if the original basaltic magma cools slowly, and the earliest-formed minerals are separated physically from the magma, can the minerals on the lower part of the reaction series crystallize. **Crystal settling** is the downward movement of minerals that are denser (heavier) than the magma from which they crystallized. What is pictured as happening is that, as the olivine crystallizes from the magma, the crystals settle to

the bottom of the magma chamber (figure 4.15). Calcium-rich plagioclase similarly settles as it forms. The remaining magma is, therefore, depleted of calcium, iron, and magnesium. Because these minerals were economical in their use of the relatively abundant silica, the remaining magma becomes richer in silica as well as in sodium and potassium. If sufficient mafic ingredients are removed in this manner, the remaining residue of magma eventually solidifies into a granite.

Undoubtedly this method of differentiation does take place in nature, although probably not to the extent that Bowen envisioned. The lowermost portions of some large sills are composed entirely of calcium-rich plagioclase and olivine, whereas upper levels are considerably less mafic. However, even in large sills differentiation has not progressed far enough to produce granite within the sill.

Even assuming that the mafic minerals settle ever deeper in large magma bodies, there is a problem in trying to explain the origin of granite by Bowen's theory. Calculations indicate that to produce a given volume of granite, about ten times as much mafic rock would first have to form and settle out. If this is true, we would expect to find far more mafic plutonic rock than granite in the earth's crust. But, as we have indicated, granite is far more abundant than gabbro. Unless the mafic rocks simply settled completely out of the crust, it seems unlikely that granite batholiths could have been produced by differentiation.

This is not to say that Bowen's work is discredited. Quite the opposite. Valuable insight has been gained that has led to other theories on the behavior of magmas. Moreover, differentiation does occur and can explain relatively minor compositional variations within intrusive bodies, even if it does not satisfactorily explain the origin of large granite bodies.

Assimilation

A very hot magma may melt some of the country rock and assimilate the newly molten material into the magma (figure 4.16). This is like putting a few ice cubes into a cup of hot coffee. The ice melts; the coffee cools as it becomes diluted. Similarly, if a hot basaltic magma, perhaps generated from the mantle, melts portions of the continental crust, the magma simultaneously becomes richer in silica and cooler. Possibly the intermediate magmas that are associated with circum-Pacific andesite volcanoes may have been derived through assimilation of some crustal rocks by the basalt.

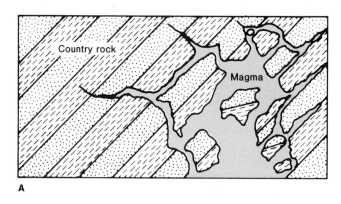

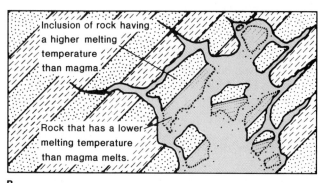

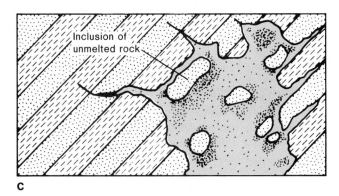

Figure 4.16 Assimilation. Magma formed is intermediate in composition between the original magma and the absorbed country rock. (*A*) Ascending magma breaks off blocks of country rock (the process is called stoping). (*B*) Inclusions of country rock having melting temperatures lower than the magma melt. (*C*) The molten country rock blends with the original magma, leaving unmelted portions as inclusions.

Very large amounts of silica-rich rock would have to be assimilated by a basalt magma for a granite batholith to form. It is unlikely that there would be sufficient extra heat in the basalt magma to melt so much rock. It would be like adding several cups of ice to a cup of coffee—the coffee would not have enough heat to melt that much ice.

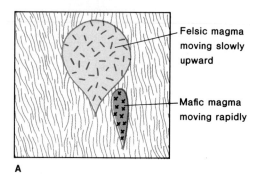

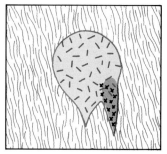

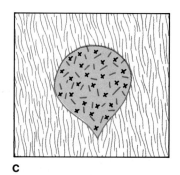

Figure 4.17 Mixing of magmas. (*A*) Two bodies of magma moving surfaceward. (*B*) The mafic magma catches up with the felsic magma. (*C*) The two magmas combine and become an intermediate magma.

Mixing of Magmas

The idea that some of our igneous rocks may be "cocktails" of different magmas is currently receiving more attention by geologists than it did in the past. The concept is quite simple. If two magmas meet and merge within the crust, the combined magma will be compositionally intermediate (figure 4.17). If you had approximately equal amounts of a granitic magma mixing with a basaltic magma, the resulting magma should consolidate underground as diorite or on the surface as andesite.

Partial Melting

A granitic magma could be created by partial melting of rock—visualize progressing *upward* through Bowen's reaction series (going from cool to hot). As might be expected, the first portion of a rock to melt as temperatures rise forms a liquid with the chemical composition of quartz and orthoclase. The silicon plus potassium and aluminum "sweated out" of the solid rock could accumulate into a pocket of felsic magma. If higher temperatures prevailed, more mafic magmas would be created. Small pockets of magma could consolidate and form a large mass.

The lower part of the continental crust is a very plausible source for granite batholiths. Partial melting of these rocks could be caused by combinations of the various heat sources and the other factors controlling melting. The magma created, being less dense than the surrounding rock, would well upward in large viscous blobs. The magma would make room for itself as it rises, either by shouldering aside the overlying country rock or by stoping. **Stoping** means fracturing country rock above the magma chamber. The blocks of rock would settle to the bottom of the magma chamber or perhaps be partially assimilated by the upward moving magma. Upon cooling, the magma eventually solidifies into granite plutons. Only rarely does the granitic magma reach the surface to erupt and form rhyolitic volcanic rock.

Many geologists regard basalt as the product of partial melting within the mantle, at temperatures hotter than those in the crust. As basaltic magma is much more fluid than rhyolitic magma, it travels rapidly and easily through fissures to the surface, rather than solidifying in the crust. (In the few places where basaltic magma does solidify as a pluton within the crust, gabbro forms.) The solid residue left behind in the mantle by a basaltic magma is ultramafic rock.

Explaining Igneous Activity by Plate Tectonics

The Origin of Basalt and Ultramafic Rocks

One of the appealing aspects of the theory of plate tectonics is that it can account reasonably well for the variety of igneous rocks and their distribution patterns. As explained in chapter 3, most basalt erupts along spreading centers, most notably along the mid-oceanic ridge system. The basaltic magma originates from partial melting of the underlying mantle (figure 4.18). Probably the fissures resulting from the separation of oceanic plates cause reduced pressure in this part of the upper mantle and allow the already very hot rock to melt at least partially. Local high temperatures in the mantle under the ridge system may be due to hot mantle plumes, which add heat to that expected from the geothermal gradient. Some of the basaltic magma erupts along the submarine ridge to form pillow basalt, while some fills the fissures as dikes. The dikes are pulled apart by spreading plates; and more magma fills the new fracture and erupts on the sea floor. Solidified basalt is carried away from the ridge as newer basalt is added. Sediments slowly cover the older basalt as it moves farther from the ridge.

As material erupts from the ridge and basalt is removed, the mantle beneath the ridge becomes depleted. The unmelted residue (olivine and pyroxene) becomes ultramafic rock. The rigid ultramafic rock, the overlying basalt, and any sediment that may have deposited on the basalt comprise the lithosphere of an oceanic plate, which moves away from a spreading center over the asthenosphere.

The Origin of Granite and Andesite

Intermediate and felsic magmas are thought to be products of convergence between two plates (figure 4.19). A cool slab of oceanic lithosphere (mostly basalt and ultramafic rock that probably formed millions of years earlier,

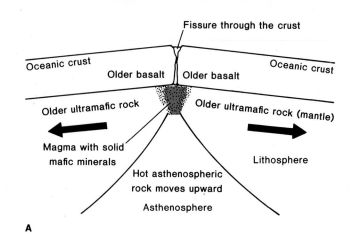

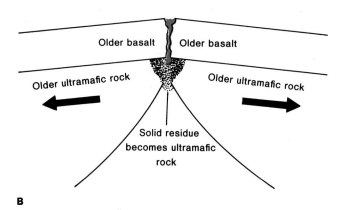

Figure 4.18 Schematic representation of how basaltic oceanic crust and the underlying ultramafic mantle rock form at a spreading center. The process would be more continuous than the two-step diagrammatic representation implies. (A) Partial melting of asthenosphere takes place beneath a spreading center. (B) The magma squeezes into the fissure system. Solid mafic minerals are left behind as ultramafic rock.

plus younger overlying sedimentary rock) descends beneath the continental crust. The descending slab gets hotter with increasing depth. Some extra heat is created by friction between the descending plate and the overriding continent. Water trapped in the descending oceanic crust probably helps a magma form by lowering the melting temperatures for the rocks. Melting (more likely, partial melting) of the rocks takes place.

Exactly how intermediate magmas are created in one place and felsic magmas in another is uncertain. A number of hypotheses have been proposed. There is general agreement that the composite volcanoes aligned along the circum-Pacific belt are tapping into magma being generated at a fairly uniform depth beneath the earth's surface.

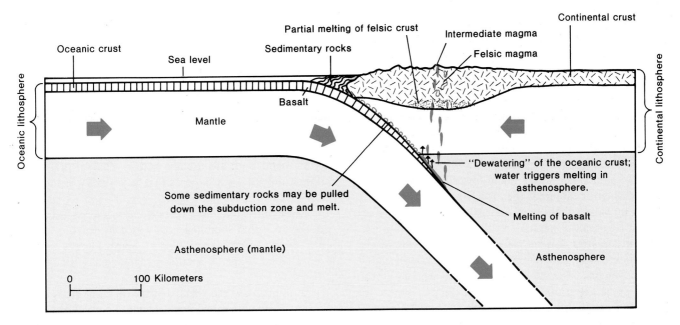

Figure 4.19 Some processes that may contribute to magma generation at a converging boundary.

But why is the intermediate magma created at such a level? And what are the processes by which the two plates form granitic magma? Several hypotheses dealing with these questions are currently being debated and are briefly described below.

Partial melting of basalt As temperature increases with the descent of the oceanic slab, the basalt begins to melt. The initial melt is less mafic than basalt. The resulting magma is of felsic or, more likely, intermediate composition. Many geologists feel that this is how the andesite of the composite volcanoes forms. However, because this process could create only a minor amount of granitic melt, it is not regarded as the cause of the great granite batholiths.

Differentiation of mantle Figure 4.19 shows part of the mantle, asthenosphere, wedged between the descending oceanic crust and the overlying continental lithosphere.

Initial melting of this part of the asthenosphere might produce a minor amount of felsic magma, but probably not enough to account for the great volumes of granitic plutonic rocks in the continental crust. It seems more likely that if significant volumes of melt are produced from this part of the asthenosphere, they would be either basaltic or andesitic in composition.

Melting of sedimentary rock The sedimentary rock that rests on the basalt of the descending oceanic plate is much richer in silica than the basalt itself. The sedimentary rock therefore melts at a lower temperature than the basalt and forms a felsic magma. (It is doubtful whether this alone could account for the huge volume of granitic batholiths in the continental crust.)

Assimilation of crustal rocks Rocks of the overlying continental crust are more felsic than those of the descending oceanic plate. A mafic magma is generated in the mantle or oceanic crust beneath the continental lithosphere. While moving upward into the overriding continental crust, the more mafic magma can absorb some of the more silica-rich rocks, thus becoming intermediate in composition.

Partial melting of the lower crust Continental crust is thicker under the mountains on the edge of the continent. Because of the lower level of this "root" zone of mountains, the rock is hotter. If a sufficiently high temperature is reached, partial melting occurs, creating a very felsic magma. (This process was regarded as a likely source for granitic magmas even before plate tectonics became a popular theory.)

Heating by transient magma Intermediate or mafic magma formed beneath the continent would travel relatively quickly to the earth's surface. Perhaps a large number of fissures lead it through the lower continental crust (like a radiator heating system in which hot-water pipes disperse heat to surroundings), and the already hot rocks of the lower continental crust are triggered into melting into granitic magma. The granitic magma, being more viscous, wells up much more slowly than the rapidly moving andesite or basalt magma.

Combinations of processes None of these hypotheses alone seems able to account for the observed granitic and andesitic igneous phenomena. Most hypotheses currently being considered combine two or more concepts to account for what may happen.

Some things that might happen are as follows. Perhaps the subducted basaltic crust melts as it slides under the hot, asthenosphere which underlies the continental lithosphere. Alternatively, the descending slab releases the water collected in the crustal rocks while they were beneath an ocean. The water would lower melting temperatures when it entered the overlying asthenosphere, triggering partial melting of that part of the mantle and generating basaltic magma. As the basaltic magma ascends, differentiation takes place and some mafic minerals are removed from the magma, which results in an intermediate magma. The intermediate magma works its way relatively quickly through the continental lithosphere to erupt and help build an andesitic composite volcano. An alternative to differentiation would be for the basaltic magma to become contaminated by felsic material when it reaches the lower part of the continental crust. Contamination may be due to assimilation of felsic rocks by the basaltic magma or due to mixing of a felsic magma (generated from the continental crust) with the basaltic magma that had formed at a lower level. In either case, the resulting magma would be intermediate in composition.

In order to explain the great volumes of granitic plutonic rocks, most geologists feel that partial melting of the lower crust must take place. Perhaps the more mafic magmas created in the underlying asthenosphere act as a transient heat source as they move upward through the lower continental crust. Since the felsic rocks of the continental crust have relatively low melting temperatures, partial melting of the lower continental crust would be quite plausible.

We should emphasize that the picture we have presented is not an observation, but a plausible interpretation of available data. There are a number of other variations possible for the picture based on different interpretations of the data. Plate tectonics has not provided final answers to the problems raised by igneous phenomena. Rather, it has provided a broad framework in which to work toward solutions to the problems.

Summary

Intrusive rocks are igneous rocks that formed underground. Some intrusive rocks have solidified near the surface as a direct result of volcanic activity. Volcanic *necks* solidified within volcanoes. Fine-grained *dikes* and *sills* may also have formed in cracks during local extrusive activity. A sill is *concordant*—parallel to the planes within the country rock. A dike—which is *discordant*—cuts across them. Both are tabular bodies. Coarser grains in either a dike or a sill indicate that it probably formed at considerable depth.

Most intrusive rock is *plutonic*—that is, coarse-grained rock that solidified slowly at considerable depth. Most plutonic rock is in *batholiths*—large plutons having no particular shape. A smaller irregular body is called a *stock*.

Plutonic rocks are, like extrusive rocks, named on the basis of their mineral content, which in turn reflects the chemical composition of the magmas from which they formed. *Granite, diorite,* and *gabbro* are the coarse-grained equivalents of *rhyolite, andesite,* and *basalt,* respectively. *Ultramafic* rocks, made entirely of ferromagnesian minerals, have no fine-grained equivalent, and most of them probably originate in the mantle.

The pattern of worldwide distribution of intrusive rock contrasts sharply with the distribution of extrusive rocks. Basalt strongly predominates in the oceanic crust. Granite strongly predominates in the continental crust. Younger granite batholiths occur mostly within younger mountain belts. Andesite is largely restricted to narrow zones along convergent plate boundaries.

Each mineral within a rock has a different melting temperature. Minerals within a basalt or a gabbro have higher melting points than those within a granite or a rhyolite. If the temperature rises, not all of a rock melts at once; a magma forms from only the components of the rock that can melt at that particular temperature. Water dissolved in a magma and kept there by high pressure can reduce the melting temperature. High pressure without water present has the opposite effect: if very hot rock without water is solid under high pressure, reducing the pressure may allow the rock to melt partially or totally.

Heat for melting of rocks comes from several sources. The *geothermal gradient* is the increase in temperature with increased depth beneath the surface. *Friction* from rocks sliding past other rocks can generate heat, as can *radioactive decay* of certain elements. Hot *mantle plumes*, from the lower mantle, may bring in more heat along the mid-oceanic ridges and perhaps elsewhere.

No single process can satisfactorily account for all igneous rocks. Each of several hypotheses may contribute adequate explanations for some igneous rocks. In the process of *differentiation*, based on *Bowen's reaction series*, a residual magma more felsic than the original mafic magma results as the early-forming minerals separate out of the magma. In *assimilation*, a hot, original magma is contaminated by picking up and absorbing rock of a different composition. *Magma mixing* produces a magma intermediate in composition between the two types of magma that are mixed.

Partial melting produces a felsic magma from more mafic rocks because the temperature attained is insufficient to cause the mafic minerals to melt.

The theory of *plate tectonics* incorporates various parts of previous theories. Basalt is generated where hot mantle rock partially melts. The fluid magma rises easily through fissures that may have previously caused a reduction in pressure and so allowed the partial melting. The ferromagnesian portion that stays solid remains beneath the oceanic crust as ultramafic rock. Granite and andesite are produced due to the effects of an oceanic plate descending beneath a continental plate. Differentiation, assimilation, partial melting, and mixing of magmas may each play a part in creating the appropriate rocks.

Terms to Remember

assimilation	granite
batholith	inclusion
Bowen's reaction series	intrusion (intrusive structure)
coarse-grained rocks	intrusive rock
concordant	laccolith
country rock	pegmatite
crystal settling	pluton
differentiation	plutonic rock
dike	sill
diorite	stock
discordant	stoping
gabbro	ultramafic rock
geothermal gradient	volcanic neck

Questions for Review

1. Why do mafic magmas tend to reach the surface much more often than do felsic magmas?
2. If basalt is subjected to differential melting, what would you expect the magma to be composed of? What would be retained as solid material?
3. What rock would probably form if magma that was feeding composite volcanoes solidified at considerable depth?
4. Why is a higher temperature required to form magma at the oceanic ridges than in the continental crust?
5. What is the difference between feldspar found in gabbro and feldspar found in granite?
6. What is the difference between a dike and a sill?
7. How are most ultramafic rocks believed to have formed?
8. Describe the differences between the continuous and the discontinuous branches of Bowen's reaction series.

Questions for Thought

1. In parts of major mountain belts, sequences of rocks are found which geologists interpret as slices of ancient oceanic lithosphere. Assuming that such a sequence formed at a spreading center and plate motion moved it toward a converging boundary, what rock types would you expect to make up this sequence going from the top downward?
2. What would happen, according to Bowen's reaction series, under the following circumstances: olivine crystals form and only the surface of the crystals reacts with the melt to form a coating of pyroxene that prevents the interior of olivine from reacting with the melt?

Supplementary Readings

Bayly, B. 1968. *Introduction to petrology*. Englewood Cliffs, N.J.: Prentice-Hall.

Ernst, W. G. 1969. *Earth materials*. Englewood Cliffs, N.J.: Prentice-Hall.

Hyndman, D. W. 1972. *Petrology of igneous and metamorphic rocks*. New York: McGraw-Hill.

Zim, H. S., and P. R. Shaffer. 1967. *Rocks and minerals*. New York: Golden Press.

5
Weathering and Soil

Purpose

In this chapter, you will study several visible signs of weathering in the world around you, such as the rounded edges of boulders and the cliffs and slopes of the Grand Canyon. As you study these features, keep in mind that weathering processes prepared the planet for human use. From the weathering of rock came, in the course of time, the development of soil, on which depends the world's food supply.

How has this transformation come about? You learned in chapters 3 and 4 that the minerals making up igneous rocks crystallize at relatively high temperatures and sometimes at high pressures as magma and lava cool. Although these minerals are stable when they form, most of them are not stable during prolonged exposure at the earth's surface. In this chapter you see how minerals and rocks are changed when they are subjected to the physical and chemical conditions existing at or near the earth's surface. Materials formed at depth are no longer in equilibrium when they are exposed to the much lower and more variable temperatures and pressures at the surface. The rocks are susceptible to mechanical weathering (physical disintegration) and chemical weathering (decomposition) as they are attacked by various atmospheric agents. (A review of the discussion of the chemical composition and atomic structure of minerals in chapter 2 will help you understand the reactions that occur during chemical weathering.)

A knowledge of weathering processes is necessary to understand the origin of sediments (primarily mud and sand) and the development of soil. Sedimentary rocks, which are formed from sediments, are discussed in chapter 6. In a general sense, weathering prepares earth materials for erosion and is a fundamental part of the rock cycle, transforming rocks into the raw material that eventually becomes sedimentary rocks.

How Weathering Alters Rocks

Rocks exposed at the earth's surface are constantly being altered by water, air, changing temperature, and other environmental factors. The term **weathering** refers to the group of destructive processes, both mechanical and chemical, that change the character of rock at or near the earth's surface.

Mechanical weathering (or physical disintegration) includes several processes that break rock into smaller pieces. The change in the rock is physical, with little or no chemical change involved. For example, water freezing and expanding in cracks can cause rocks to disintegrate physically. **Chemical weathering** is the decomposition of rock resulting from exposure to water and atmospheric gases (principally carbon dioxide and water vapor). As rock is decomposed by these agents, new chemical compounds are formed.

Mechanical weathering breaks up rock but does not change the composition. A large mass of granite may be broken into smaller pieces by frost action, but its original crystals of quartz, feldspar, and mica are unchanged. On the other hand, if the granite is being chemically weathered, some of the original minerals are chemically changed into different minerals. In nature, mechanical and chemical weathering usually occur together, and the effects are interrelated.

Weathering is a relatively long, slow process. Typically, joints or fractures are enlarged gradually by frost action or plant growth (as roots pry into rock crevices), and as a result more surfaces are exposed to attack by chemical agents. Chemical weathering initially works along contacts between mineral grains. Tightly bound crystals are loosened as weathering products form at their contacts. Mechanical weathering can then proceed, until a once tough rock slowly crumbles into individual grains. Which process is more important? Most geologists feel that, overall, the processes of chemical weathering are more effective and pervasive than the forces of mechanical weathering.

Consider the example of granite broken into smaller pieces (that are still granite) by mechanical weathering. If enough time is available for complete chemical weathering, the feldspar crystals of the granite will no longer be identifiable. They will have been changed into clay minerals (with an internal crystalline structure similar to that of the micas). Since the rock no longer contains feldspar, it is not really granite any more.

Solid minerals are not the only products of chemical weathering. Some minerals—calcite, for example—dissolve when chemically weathered. We can expect limestone, a sedimentary rock consisting mainly of calcite, to weather chemically in quite a different way than does granite.

Figure 5.1 Chemical weathering in a humid climate has pitted and discolored this marble tombstone since it was erected in 1859.

Effects of Weathering

The results of chemical weathering are easy to find. Look along the edges or corners of old stone structures (figure 5.1) for evidence. The inscriptions on statues and tombstones that have stood for several decades may no longer be sharp. Building blocks of limestone or marble exposed to rain and atmospheric gases may show solution effects of chemical weathering in a surprisingly short time. Granite buildings may also show the effects of weathering, although it may take centuries for the effects to become apparent. Mineral grains in granite may be loosened, cracks enlarged, and the surface discolored and dulled by the products of weathering. Surface discoloration is also usual on bedrock outcrops. That is why field geologists carry rock hammers—to break rocks in order to examine unweathered surfaces.

We tend to think of weathering as destructive because it mars statues and building fronts. As rock is destroyed, however, valuable products can be created. The major components of soil are products of rock weathering. The growth of land plants and the production of food for most animals therefore depend upon weathering. Some metallic ores, such as those of copper and aluminum, are concentrated into economic deposits by chemical weathering. Marine organisms are nourished by dissolved products of weathering carried in solution to the sea.

The interesting patterns of weathered rock can provide clues about the kind of processes that have been at work on the rocks. A **spheroidally weathered boulder** is a

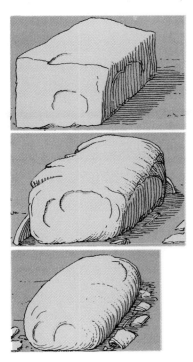

Figure 5.2 Spheroidal weathering. Edges and corners retreat faster than flat rock faces, so angular boulders become rounded.

A

B

Figure 5.3 Spheroidal weathering. (*A*) Concentric layers spall off weathering rock. (*B*) Desert boulders rounded by spheroidal weathering, Arizona.
Photo *A* by W. T. Schaller, U.S. Geological Survey. Photo *B* by F. L. Ransome, U.S. Geological Survey.

Figure 5.4 Pedestal rocks in Monument Park, Colorado. The caps are formed of a resistant rock that weathers more slowly than the softer rock of the pedestals.
Photo by W. H. Jackson, U.S. Geological Survey.

rock that has been rounded by weathering from an initial blocky shape. It is rounded because chemical weathering acts more rapidly or intensely on the corners and edges of a rock than on the smooth rock faces (figures 5.2 and 5.3).

Differential weathering is the term for varying rates of weathering that result when some rocks in an area are more resistant to weathering than others. The harder (more resistant) material weathers more slowly and eventually stands higher or protrudes above the softer parts. Figures 5.4, 5.5, and 5.6 show some striking landforms produced by erosion of rocks that weather at differing rates.

Mechanical Weathering

Of the numerous processes that cause rocks to disintegrate, the most effective are frost action, abrasion, and pressure release.

Figure 5.5 Differential weathering effects at Bryce Canyon
National Park, Utah.
Photo by R. G. Luedke, U.S. Geological Survey.

Figure 5.6 Sedimentary rocks in Grand Canyon National
Park, Arizona. Some layers of rock are resistant to weathering
and form cliffs. Less resistant rock layers weather to form
gentler slopes between cliffs.
Photo by N. W. Carkhuff, U.S. Geological Survey.

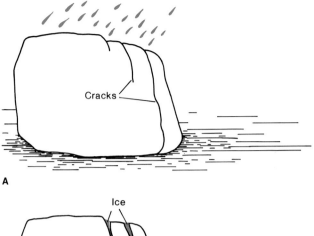

A

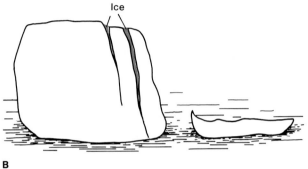

B

Figure 5.7 Frost wedging occurs when (*A*) water fills cracks in a rock and then freezes. (*B*) Expanding ice wedges the rock apart.

Figure 5.8 Frost wedging. This granite has broken as ice expanded in its cracks.
Photo by F. E. Matthes, U.S. Geological Survey.

Frost Action

Frost action—the mechanical effect of freezing water on rocks—commonly occurs as frost wedging or frost heaving. **Frost wedging** is a type of frost action in which the expansion of freezing water pries rock apart. Most rock contains a system of cracks (chapter 15). Water that has trickled into a crack in a rock freezes and expands when the temperature drops below 0°C. The expanding ice

wedges the rock apart, extending the crack or even breaking the rock into pieces (figures 5.7 and 5.8). Frost wedging is most active in regions with many days of freezing and thawing. Partial thawing allows new water to be added to the ice in the crack; refreezing adds new ice to the old ice. The pressure of the expanding ice wedge is the most effective agent of mechanical weathering.

In **frost heaving** a layer of loose rock or soil is lifted by the expansion of freezing water. An ice layer may form just below the surface of the ground. Rain and melting snow add new water to the soil, and when this water freezes, the ice layer thickens. As the thickening ice layer expands, the ground bulges upward. Frost heaving can break up road surfaces and leave lawns spongy and misshapen after the ice thaws in spring.

Abrasion

Abrasion, the grinding away of rock by friction and impact during transportation, is another process that can mechanically weather rock. (Not all geologists agree that this is a weathering process, however.) As loose fragments of rock are picked up and moved by a stream, they are tumbled against one another and bounced against rocks on the stream bottom. The fragments gradually grind and break themselves into smaller and smaller pieces, and also grind away the bedrock of the stream bottom. Glaciers, waves, and even wind are other agents that can carry and abrade rock.

It is important to distinguish between *weathering, erosion,* and *transportation.* Weathering, both physical and chemical, can affect rocks that are either stationary or moving. **Erosion** is the *physical removal* of rock by an agent such as running water or glacial ice. Weathering helps loosen rock fragments so that they are more easily eroded (this is the usual sequence), but rock can be eroded before it has weathered at all. Streams and glaciers can erode weathered or unweathered rock. After a rock fragment has been picked up (eroded), it is usually transported. **Transportation,** then, is the movement of eroded particles by agents such as rivers, waves, glaciers, or wind. Weathering processes continue during transportation. A boulder being transported by a stream can be mechanically weathered by abrasion and chemically weathered by the water in the stream.

Pressure Release

The reduction of pressure on a body of rock can cause it to crack; **pressure release** is a significant type of mechanical weathering. For example, a large mass of rock, such as a batholith, originally forms under great pressure from the weight of several kilometers of rock above it. This

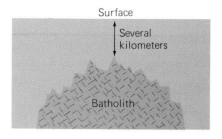

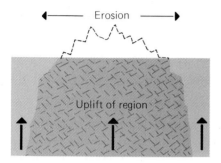

Figure 5.9 A granite batholith is exposed by regional uplift and erosion of the overlying rock. Unloading causes a reduction of pressure on the granite.

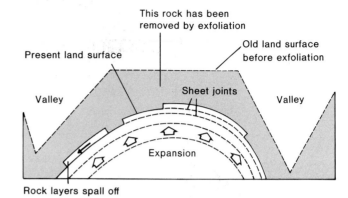

Figure 5.10 Exfoliation, caused by pressure release and rock expansion, can form rounded domes.

Figure 5.11 Exfoliation layers on top of Half Dome, Yosemite National Park, California.
Photo by F. C. Calkins, U.S. Geological Survey.

Figure 5.12 Exfoliation dome, Sierra Nevada, California.
Photo by G. K. Gilbert, U.S. Geological Survey.

batholith is gradually exposed by uplift of the region and erosion of the overlying rock (figure 5.9). The removal of the great weight of rock above the batholith (usually termed **unloading**) allows the granite to expand upward. The outer part of the rock expands more than the inner part, and cracks develop parallel to the outer surface. This is **sheet-jointing.** (Sheet joints, of course, can be expanded by frost action; weathering processes interact.) On slopes, gravity may cause rock between such joints to spall off or break loose in concentric slabs from the underlying granite mass (figures 5.10 and 5.11). This process of spalling off is called **exfoliation. Exfoliation domes** (figure 5.12) are large, rounded landforms developed in massive rocks, such as granite, by this process.

Several other processes mechanically weather rock but are generally less effective than frost action, abrasion, and pressure release. *Plant growth,* particularly roots growing in cracks, can break up rocks, as can *burrowing animals.* Such activities help to speed up chemical weathering by enlarging passageways for more water and air. The *pressure of salt crystals* formed as water evaporates inside small spaces in rock also helps to disintegrate the rock. *Extreme changes in temperature,* like those during a forest fire, may cause a rock to expand or contract until it cracks. Whatever processes of mechanical weathering are at work, as rocks disintegrate into smaller fragments, the total surface area increases (figure 5.13), allowing more extensive chemical weathering by water and air.

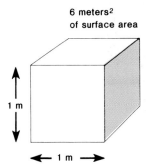

6 meters² of surface area

1 m

1 m

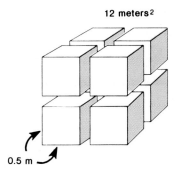

12 meters²

0.5 m

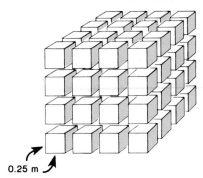

24 meters²

0.25 m

Figure 5.13 Mechanical weathering can increase the surface area of a rock, causing increased chemical weathering. As a cube breaks up into smaller pieces, its volume remains the same but its surface area increases.

Chemical Weathering

The processes of chemical weathering, or *rock decomposition,* transform rocks and minerals exposed to water and atmospheric gases into new chemical combinations. A mineral that crystallized deep underground from a water-deficient magma may eventually be exposed at the earth's surface, where it may react with the abundant water there to form a new, different mineral. A mineral containing very little oxygen may react with oxygen in the air, extracting oxygen atoms from the atmosphere and incorporating them into its own crystal structure, thus forming a different mineral. These new minerals are weathering products. They have adjusted to physical and chemical conditions at (or near) the earth's surface. Minerals change gradually at the surface until they come into *equilibrium* or balance with the surrounding conditions. Once in equilibrium, they do not change further, unless the surface conditions change.

For an example, refer again to the batholith in figure 5.9. The large body of granite (upper diagram), which forms several kilometers deep in the earth, is in equilibrium with the conditions there—namely, high pressure, high temperature, and the absence of abundant water and atmospheric gases. The minerals within the granite are *stable* under these conditions and do not change as long as the conditions do not change. But if the granite is eventually exposed at the earth's surface by uplift and erosion (as in the lower diagram), the rock is exposed to new conditions—lower temperatures and pressures and the presence of atmospheric gases and water. Some of the minerals in granite, such as the ferromagnesian minerals and the feldspars, are *unstable* in the new environment. They gradually weather, forming new chemical combinations—in this case, clay minerals and soluble products carried off in solution—that are stable under surface conditions.

Different minerals weather at different rates. The ferromagnesian minerals in granite, for example, may weather faster than the feldspars. Many rocks exposed at the earth's surface are only partially weathered—some minerals have come into equilibrium with surface conditions, but other minerals have not.

Role of Oxygen

Oxygen is abundant in the atmosphere and quite active chemically, so it often combines with minerals or with elements within minerals that are exposed at the earth's surface.

The rusting of an iron nail exposed to dampness and air is a simple example of chemical weathering. Oxygen from the atmosphere combines with the iron to form iron oxide, the reaction being expressed as follows:

$$4Fe + 3O_2 \rightarrow 2Fe_2O_3$$
iron + oxygen → iron oxide

Iron oxide formed in this way is a weathering product of numerous minerals containing iron, such as the ferromagnesian group. This type of iron oxide (Fe_2O_3) is the mineral **hematite,** which has a brick-red color when powdered. If water is present, as it usually is at the earth's surface, the hematite combines with water to form **limonite,** which is yellowish-brown when powdered. Its formula is $Fe_2O_3 \cdot nH_2O$ (the n representing a variable amount of water). The brown, yellow, or red color of soil and many kinds of sedimentary rock commonly is the result of small amounts of hematite and limonite released by the weathering of iron-containing minerals.

Table 5.1

Chemical Equations Important to Weathering

A. Solution of Carbon Dioxide in Water to Form Acid

$$CO_2 + H_2O \rightleftharpoons H_2CO_3 \rightleftharpoons H^+ + HCO_3^-$$

| carbon dioxide | water | carbonic acid | hydrogen ion | bicarbonate ion |

B. Solution of Calcite

$$CaCO_3 + CO_2 + H_2O \rightleftharpoons Ca^{++} + 2HCO_3^-$$

| calcite | carbon dioxide | water | calcium ion | bicarbonate ion |

C. Solution of Calcite

$$CaCO_3 + H^+ + HCO_3^- \rightleftharpoons Ca^{++} + 2HCO_3^-$$

D. Chemical Weathering of Feldspar to Form Clay Mineral

$$2\ KAlSi_3O_8 + 2\ H^+ + 2\ HCO_3^- + H_2O \rightarrow Al_2Si_2O_5(OH)_4 + 2\ K^+ + 2\ HCO_3^- + 4\ SiO_2$$

| feldspar (orthoclase) | (from CO_2 and H_2O) | | | clay mineral | (soluble salt) | | silica in solution or as fine solid particles |

Role of Acid

Weak acid is a very effective agent of chemical weathering, particularly the hydrogen ion (H^+) that is present in acid. The most important natural source of acid for rock weathering at the earth's surface is dissolved carbon dioxide (CO_2) in water. Other natural sources are acids given off by plants during growth and decay, acidic waters from hot springs and volcanic gases, and the strongly acidic water that drains from some mines. Surface water readily dissolves these acids and becomes slightly acidic itself.

Some carbon dioxide is dissolved in rain as it falls through the atmosphere, so that most rain is slightly acidic when it hits the ground. Carbon dioxide dissolved in water forms *carbonic acid* (H_2CO_3), which dissociates into the hydrogen ion and the bicarbonate ion (see equation *A* in table 5.1).

Large amounts of carbon dioxide also dissolve in water that percolates through soil. The openings in soil are filled with a mixture of gases that differs from air. Soil gas has a much higher content of carbon dioxide than does air because of decaying organic matter and the respiration of soil organisms.

Industrial air pollution from the burning of coal and petroleum adds a great deal of carbon dioxide to an urban atmosphere. Because of the increased carbon dioxide, as well as the presence of oxides of sulfur and nitrogen, which also form acids in water, the acidity of rain is greater in urban areas. Chemical weathering rates are substantially higher in urban areas than in rural areas.

The hydrogen ion (H^+) of acids is a prime weathering agent. Because of its electrical charge and its small size, this ion is very active chemically. Hydrogen ions attack the crystal lattices (orderly arrangements of atoms) of minerals and substitute for other ions in the lattices. The mineral lattices are disrupted, and the original minerals decompose.

Solution Weathering

Some minerals are completely dissolved by chemical weathering. *Calcite*, for instance, goes into solution under the influence of carbon dioxide and water, as shown in equation *B* in table 5.1. The carbon dioxide and water combine to form carbonic acid, which dissociates into the hydrogen ion and the bicarbonate ion, as you have seen, so the equation for the solution of calcite can also be written as equation *C* in table 5.1.

There are no solid products in the last part of the equation, indicating that complete solution of the calcite has occurred. In regions underlain by limestone (which is mostly calcite), solution features such as caves may be formed by the removal of the soluble calcite, especially if the climate is humid and water is plentiful.

Chemical Weathering of Feldspar

The weathering of the mineral feldspar is an example of the alteration of an original crystal lattice to an entirely different type of lattice in the weathered product. When feldspar is attacked by the hydrogen ion of carbonic acid (from carbon dioxide and water), it forms clay minerals.

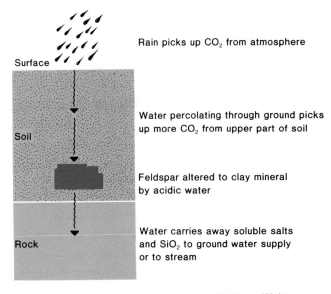

Rain picks up CO₂ from atmosphere

Water percolating through ground picks up more CO₂ from upper part of soil

Feldspar altered to clay mineral by acidic water

Water carries away soluble salts and SiO₂ to ground water supply or to stream

Figure 5.14 *Chemical weathering of a feldspar. Water percolating through the soil alters the feldspar to a clay mineral and carries away soluble salts and silica.*

In general, a **clay mineral** is a hydrous aluminum silicate with a sheet silicate structure like that of mica. The entire silicate structure of the feldspar thus is altered by weathering: feldspar is a framework silicate, but the weathered clay mineral is a sheet silicate, differing both chemically and physically from feldspar. Partly because of the complexity of the reaction, the chemical weathering of feldspar proceeds at a much slower rate than the solution weathering illustrated by calcite.

Let us look in more detail at the weathering of feldspar (equation *D* in table 5.1). Rainwater percolates down through soil, picking up carbon dioxide from the atmosphere and the upper part of the soil. The water, now slightly acidic, comes in contact with feldspar in the lower part of the soil (figure 5.14), as shown in the first part of the equation. The acidic water reacts with the feldspar and alters it to a clay mineral.

The hydrogen ion (H^+) attacks the feldspar structure, becoming incorporated into the clay mineral product (the hydrogen ion shows up as the H in the OH at the end of the clay mineral formula). When the hydrogen moves into the crystal structure, it releases potassium (K) from the feldspar. The potassium is carried away in solution as a dissolved ion (K^+). The bicarbonate ion from the original carbonic acid does not enter into the reaction; it reappears on the right side of the equation. The potassium ion and the bicarbonate ion, which form a *soluble salt,* are carried away in solution by the moving water.

All the silicon from the feldspar cannot fit into the clay mineral, so some is left over and is carried away as silica (SiO_2) by the moving water. This excess silica may be carried in solution or as extremely small solid particles.

The weathering process is the same regardless of the type of feldspar: K-feldspar (orthoclase) forms potassium salts; Na-feldspar and Ca-feldspar (plagioclase) form sodium salts and calcium salts, respectively. The ions that result from the weathering of Ca-feldspar are calcium ions (Ca^{++}) and bicarbonate ions (HCO_3^-), both of which are very common in rivers and in underground water, particularly in humid regions.

The weathering of Ca-feldspars (plagioclase) into clay minerals can supply small amounts of both silica (SiO_2) and the ions Ca^{++} and HCO_3^- to underground water. Under ordinary chemical circumstances, the Ca^{++} and HCO_3^- can combine to form $CaCO_3$, the mineral calcite (calcium carbonate). This is significant because calcite and silica are the most common materials precipitated as sedimentary rock *cement,* which binds loose particles of sand, silt, and clay into solid rock (see chapter 6). The weathering of feldspars and other minerals is a likely source for such cement.

If the soluble salts and silica are not precipitated as solids, they remain in solution and may eventually find their way into a stream and then into the ocean. Enormous quantities of dissolved material are carried by rivers into the sea (one estimate is 4 billion tons per year). This is the main reason that sea water is salty.

Chemical Weathering of Other Minerals
The weathering of ferromagnesian or dark minerals is much the same as that of feldspars. Two additional products are found on the right side of the equation—magnesium salts and iron oxides (hematite and limonite). Micas also weather in much the same way (biotite, of course, is both a mica and a ferromagnesian mineral).

In general, the rock-forming minerals weather at rates that are proportional to their positions in Bowen's reaction series. A high-temperature mineral, such as pyroxene, forms under conditions that differ greatly from surface conditions. When exposed to surface conditions, it is farther out of equilibrium than a low-temperature mineral, such as orthoclase, so pyroxene weathers faster than orthoclase. Similarly, a Ca-rich plagioclase weathers faster than a Na-rich plagioclase.

Quartz is quite stable at the earth's surface. It does not weather chemically, although it is subject to mechanical weathering over very long periods of time. According to Bowen's reaction series (chapter 4), quartz is the last mineral to form, crystallizing at a lower temperature than other minerals. Quartz is resistant to chemical weathering for two reasons: (1) It originally formed at a relatively low temperature. (2) Quartz (SiO_2) lacks ions such as Ca^{++}, K^+, and Na^+ that are easily attacked and replaced by H^+. Most other common minerals, which do weather chemically, contain at least one of these ions.

"Hard water" is water that contains relatively large amounts of dissolved calcium (often from the chemical weathering of Ca-feldspar) or magnesium (from the ferromagnesian minerals). Water withdrawn from the ground-water supply or from a stream for drinking and other purposes may contain enough of these ions to prevent soap from lathering. Calcium ions in hard water form gray curds with soap. The curd continues to form until all the calcium ions are removed from the water and bound up in the curd. Only then will soap lather and clean laundry. Cleaning laundry in hard water therefore takes an excessively large amount of soap.

Hard water may also precipitate a scaly deposit inside tea kettles and hot-water tanks and pipes (figure 5.15). The entire hot-water piping system of a home in a hard-water area eventually can become so clogged that the pipes must be replaced.

"Soft water" may carry a substantial amount of ions in solution, but not the ions that prevent soap from lathering. Water softeners in homes replace calcium ions with sodium ions, which do not affect lathering or cause scale. However,

Figure 5.15 Scale in hot-water pipes caused by hard water.
Photo by Hauser Water Conditioning, Inc.

water containing a large amount of sodium ions, whether from a softener or from natural sources, may be harmful if used as drinking water by persons who need to restrict salt in their diet for health reasons.

Table 5.2 summarizes weathering products for the common minerals. Note that quartz and clay minerals commonly are left after complete chemical weathering of a rock. Sometimes other solid products, such as iron oxides, also are left after weathering.

Soil

In engineering and construction usage, "soil" is apt to be the designation for any kind of loose or unconsolidated earth material; but most geologists commonly use the term **soil** for a layer of weathered, unconsolidated material on top of bedrock. Soil scientists and some geologists further restrict the use of the term to layers of weathered, unconsolidated material that contains organic matter and is capable of supporting plant growth. (If this definition is used, then the term *regolith* can be applied to any loose surface sediment. Soil would then be thought of as the upper part of the regolith.)

The common gardening term *loam* is a soil of approximately equal amounts of sand, silt, and clay along with a generous amount of organic matter. Such soils can be well drained and very fertile. They are the best gardening soils. *Topsoil,* which is basically the same thing as loam, is the upper part of the soil, and is more fertile than the underlying *subsoil,* which is often stony and lacks organic matter.

In many cases the soil minerals and plant nutrients come from the weathering of the rock beneath the soil, but sometimes the parent, or source, materials have been transported from a considerable distance. A mature, fertile soil is the product of centuries of growth and decay of plants and other organisms, combined with the results of long-continued mechanical and chemical weathering of rock.

Box 5.2
Clay Minerals and Plant Growth

Clay minerals are hydrous aluminum silicates that occur as platelike flakes of microscopic size with a sheet silicate structure. Because of ion substitution within the crystal lattice, most clay minerals have a negative electrical charge on the flat faces of the flakes.

This negative charge is important to life on earth because it holds water in the soil and helps retain plant nutrients in soil.

The water molecule, made up of two hydrogen atoms and one oxygen atom, is neutral in charge but has a positive end and a negative end. The negative charge on the clay mineral face attracts the positive ends of the water molecules to the clay flake (figure 5.16). The clay holds the water loosely enough that most of it is available for uptake by plant roots.

Plant nutrients, such as Ca^{++} and K^+, commonly supplied by the weathering of minerals such as feldspar, are also held loosely on the surface of clay minerals. A plant root is able to exchange its own H^+ for the Ca^{++} and K^+ that the plant needs for healthy growth (figure 5.17).

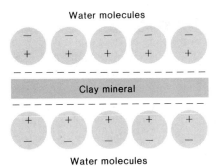

Figure 5.16　Negative charges on a clay mineral attract positive ends of water molecule.

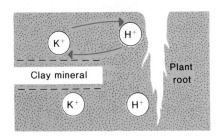

Figure 5.17　Ion exchange between plant root and clay mineral.

Table 5.2
Weathering Products of Common Minerals

Original Mineral	Under Influence of CO_2 and H_2O	Main Solid Product		Other Products (Mostly Soluble)
Feldspar	⟶	Clay mineral	+	Salts, SiO_2
Ferromagnesian minerals (including biotite mica)	⟶	Clay mineral	+	Salts, SiO_2, Fe oxides
Muscovite mica	⟶	Clay mineral	+	Salts, SiO_2
Quartz	⟶	Quartz grains (Sand)		
Calcite	⟶	—		Salts

Clay minerals and quartz, the two minerals usually remaining after complete weathering of rock (table 5.2), have important roles in soil development and plant growth. Quartz crystals form sand grains that help keep soil loose and aerated, allowing good water drainage. (Partially weathered crystals of feldspar and other minerals can also form sand-sized grains.) Clay minerals help to hold water in a soil. Since most plants need both air and water in a soil for optimum growth, the best soils for plant growth have a balance between clay minerals and sand.

Soil Horizons

As soils develop toward maturity, a distinct layering becomes apparent (figure 5.18). Layers of soil distinguishable by characteristic physical or chemical properties (including organic content) are termed **soil horizons.** Boundaries between soil horizons are usually transitional rather than sharp.

The **A horizon,** or **zone of leaching,** is the top layer of soil and is characterized by the downward movement of water. Part of the rain falling on the ground percolates downward through the soil. This tends to leach, or wash down, some of the soil materials to lower levels. In a wet or humid climate, clay minerals, iron oxides, and dissolved calcite are most typically leached downward. Leaching may make the A horizon pale and sandy, but the uppermost part often is darkened by plant humus that collects on the top of the soil. (This is the loamy topsoil.)

The **B horizon,** or **zone of accumulation,** is a soil layer characterized by the accumulation of material leached downward from the A horizon above. This layer is often quite clayey and stained red or brown by hematite and limonite. Calcite may also build up in B horizons.

The **C horizon** is incompletely weathered parent material, lying below the B horizon. The parent material is commonly the underlying bedrock, which is subjected to mechanical and chemical weathering from frost action, roots, plant acids, and other agents. In such a case, the C horizon is transitional between unweathered bedrock below and developing soil above.

Residual and Transported Soils

A **residual soil** is one that develops directly from weathering of the rock below. Figure 5.18 is a diagram of a residual soil developing in a humid climate from a bedrock source. Although this is a typical situation, a number of important agricultural regions in the United States and elsewhere have developed on **transported soils,** which did not form from the local rock but from parent material brought in from some other region and deposited, usually by running water, wind, or glacial ice. For example, mud deposited by a river during times of flooding can form an excellent agricultural soil next to the river after floodwaters recede. The soil-forming mud was not weathered from the rock beneath its present location but was carried downstream from regions perhaps hundreds of kilometers away. Transported wind deposits called *loess* (chapter 13) are the parent material for some of the most valuable food-producing soils in the Midwest and the Pacific Northwest.

Soils, Parent Rock, and Time

The character of a soil depends partly upon the parent rock it develops from. A soil developing on weathering

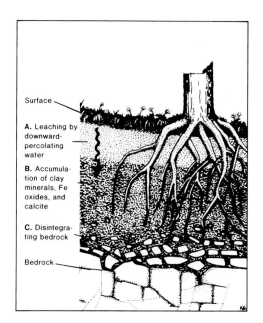

Figure 5.18   Soil horizons that form in a humid climate.

granite will be sandy, as sand-sized particles of quartz and partially-weathered feldspar are released from the granite. As time passes, the partially-weathered feldspar grains weather completely, forming fine-grained clay minerals. The quartz does not weather, so the resulting soil has both sand and clay (and perhaps silt) in it.

A soil forming on basalt may never be sandy, even in its early stages of development (this depends upon the relative rates of chemical weathering versus mechanical weathering). The fine-grained feldspars and pyroxenes in the basalt weather to fine-grained clay minerals. Since the parent rock had no coarse-grained minerals and no quartz to start with, the resulting soil may lack sand. Such a soil may not drain well, although it can be quite fertile.

Note that the character of a soil changes with time. A soil developing from granite begins as a sandy soil and becomes more clayey with time. Over very long periods of time, the type of parent rock becomes less and less important. Given enough time, soils forming from many different kinds of igneous, metamorphic, and sedimentary rocks can become quite similar (in the same climate). The presence or absence of coarse grains of quartz in the parent rock becomes the only characteristic of the parent rock to have long-term significance.

Soils and Climate

In addition to parent material and time, some other factors that cause soils to vary in character are climate and the slope of the land surface. Climate is by far the most important.

Soils in humid regions, as in the eastern United States, are generally characterized by downward move-

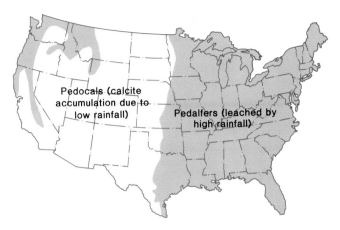

Figure 5.19 Distribution of pedalfer and pedocal soils in the United States.
U.S. Department of Agriculture.

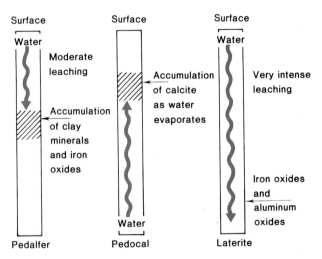

Figure 5.20 Water movement within the major soil groups.

ment of water through the earth materials. (figure 5.18 shows such a soil). Such soils are called **pedalfers** (figure 5.19). They are marked by effective downward leaching, due to high rainfall and to the acids produced by the decay of abundant humus.

In dry or arid climates, like those in many parts of the western United States, soils called **pedocals** form (figure 5.19). These soils are characterized by little leaching, scant humus, and the upward movement of soil water beneath the land surface. The water is drawn up by subsurface evaporation and capillary action.

The evaporation of water beneath the land surface can cause the precipitation of salts within the soil (figure 5.20). These salts are usually calcium salts such as calcite (which is the origin of the term pedo*cal*). An extreme example of salt build-up can be found in desert **alkali soils,** in which heavy concentrations of toxic sodium salts may prevent plant growth.

Hardpan In popular usage, "hardpan" is a term applied loosely to any relatively hard layer of earth material that is difficult to excavate or drill. Geologists, however, use the term *hardpan* specifically to designate a relatively hard, often clayey, layer in soil, produced by cementation of soil particles. Such a layer is usually too hard to dig or drill through without blasting. Hardpan layers in humid regions are generally formed of clay minerals, silica, and iron compounds that have accumulated in the B horizon. In arid climates a different type of hardpan, called *caliche,* may form from the cementing of soil by calcium carbonate and other salts that precipitate in the soil as water evaporates. Both types of hardpan are really layers of rock within loose soil. A hardpan layer can break plows, prevent water drainage through the soil, and act as a barrier to plant roots. Tree roots may grow laterally along rather than down through hardpan; such shallow-rooted trees are easily uprooted by wind.

Laterites In tropical regions where temperatures are high and rainfall is abundant, highly leached soils called **laterites** form. Under such conditions weathering is deep and intense. Laterites are usually red and are composed almost entirely of iron and aluminum oxides, generally the least soluble products of rock weathering in tropical climates (figure 5.20). If hematite is present in sufficient quantities, it can be mined as iron ore. But tropical rainfall usually hydrates hematite to limonite, which is seldom rich enough to make mining feasible. Although tropical soils cannot usually be mined for iron, aluminum is sometimes found in nearly pure layers of **bauxite** $(Al_2O_3 \cdot nH_2O)$, the principal ore of aluminum. Because bauxite is formed under conditions of tropical weathering, the United States has very little aluminum ore and depends almost entirely on tropical countries for its aluminum supply. A small percentage of our aluminum supply has come from bauxite deposits in Arkansas which formed on an igneous rock with a high aluminum content approximately 50 million years ago when the region had a tropical climate.

Laterites are relatively nonproductive soils. This may seem strange when you think of the lush jungle growth that often exists on lateritic soils. Jungle vegetation, though, is nourished largely by a layer of humus on top of the soil. If the jungle and the humus layer are cleared away—an increasingly common practice in tropical regions—the laterite quickly becomes incapable of sustaining plant growth, making tropical agriculture very difficult. Laterite exposed to the sun is apt to bake into a permanent, brick-like layer that makes digging nearly impossible. This hard layer can be quarried, however, and then it makes a durable building material.

Summary

When rocks that formed deep in the earth become exposed at the earth's surface, they are altered by *mechanical* and *chemical weathering.*

Mechanical weathering, largely caused by *frost action, abrasion* during transportation, and *sheet-jointing* after unloading, disintegrates (breaks) rocks into smaller pieces.

By increasing the exposed surface area of rocks, mechanical weathering helps speed chemical weathering.

Weathering processes form spheroidally weathered boulders, differentially eroded landforms, and exfoliation domes.

Chemical weathering results when a mineral is unstable under surface conditions; i.e., low temperature and pressure and the presence of water and atmospheric gases. As chemical weathering proceeds, the mineral's components recombine into combinations in equilibrium with surface conditions.

Weak acid, primarily from the solution of carbon dioxide in water, is the most effective agent of chemical weathering.

Calcite dissolves when it is chemically weathered. Most of the silicate minerals form *clay minerals* when they chemically weather. Quartz is very resistant to chemical weathering.

Soil develops by chemical and mechanical weathering of a parent material. Some definitions of soil require that it contain organic matter and be able to support plant growth.

Soils, which can be *residual* or *transported,* usually have distinguishable layers or *horizons,* in part from water movement within the soil.

Climate is the most important factor determining soil type.

Laterites form under conditions of intense tropical weathering. Bauxite, the ore of aluminum, occurs as a component of laterite.

Terms to Remember

abrasion
A horizon (zone of leaching)
alkali soil
bauxite
B horizon (zone of accumulation)
chemical weathering
C horizon
clay mineral
differential weathering
erosion
exfoliation
exfoliation dome
frost action
frost heaving
frost wedging
hematite
laterite
limonite
mechanical weathering
pedalfer
pedocal
pressure release
residual soil
sheet-jointing
soil
soil horizon
spheroidally weathered boulder
transportation
transported soil
unloading
weathering

Questions for Review

1. Why are some minerals stable several kilometers underground but unstable at the earth's surface?
2. Describe what happens to each mineral component during the chemical weathering of granite in a humid climate.
3. Explain what happens chemically when calcite dissolves.
4. Why do stone buildings tend to weather more rapidly in cities than in rural areas?
5. Describe at least three processes that mechanically weather rock.
6. How can mechanical weathering speed up chemical weathering?
7. Name at least three natural sources of weak acid in solution. Which one is most important for chemical weathering?
8. What is the difference between a residual soil and a transported soil?
9. What is a laterite and how does it form?

Questions for Thought

1. Consider Bowen's reaction series. Which mineral weathers at a faster rate—orthoclase or olivine? Why?
2. Why do soils develop internal layers or horizons?
3. In a humid climate, is a soil formed from granite the same as one formed from gabbro? Discuss the similarities and possible differences with particular regard to mineral content and soil color.
4. Discuss the effects of climate on chemical weathering and soil development.

Supplementary Readings

Carroll, D., 1970. *Rock weathering.* New York: Plenum Press.

Hunt, C. B., 1972. *The geology of soils.* San Francisco: W. H. Freeman.

Keller, W. D., 1957. *The principles of chemical weathering.* Columbia, Mo.: Lucas Brothers.

———. 1969. *Chemistry in introductory geology.* Columbia, Mo.: Lucas Brothers.

Kellogg, C. E., 1950. Soil. *Scientific American* (July 1950). Offprint #821. San Francisco: W. H. Freeman.

McNeil, M., 1964. Lateritic soils. *Scientific American* (November 1964). Offprint #870. San Francisco: W. H. Freeman.

Ollier, C. D., 1969. *Weathering.* New York: American Elsevier.

U. S. Department of Agriculture, 1957. *Soil: Yearbook for 1957.* Washington, D.C.: U. S. Government Printing Office.

6

Sediments and Sedimentary Rocks

Purpose

The rock cycle (chapter 1) is a theoretical model of the constant recycling of rocks as they form, are destroyed, and then reformed. We began our discussion of the rock cycle with igneous rock (chapters 3 and 4), and we now discuss sedimentary rocks. Metamorphic rocks, the third major rock type, are the subject of the next chapter.

You saw in the previous chapter how weathering produces sediment. In this chapter we explain more about sediment origin, as well as the erosion, transportation, sorting, deposition, and eventual lithification of sediments to form sedimentary rock. Because they have such diverse origins, sedimentary rocks are difficult to classify. We make a general division into clastic, chemical, and organic sedimentary rocks, but this classification is not entirely satisfactory. Furthermore, despite their great variety, only three sedimentary rocks are very common—shale, sandstone, and limestone.

Sedimentary rocks contain numerous clues as to their origin and the environmental conditions that prevailed at the time of sediment deposition. Geologists find out this information from the size and shape of rock units and from sediment grains and the sedimentary structures such as fossils, cross-beds, ripple marks, and mud cracks that are contained in the rock.

The widespread distribution of sedimentary rocks is what makes them important. About three-fourths of the continents' land surfaces are blanketed with a thin skin of sedimentary rocks, and yet these rocks make up only a small percentage of the total volume of continents. Concentrated in sedimentary rocks are many of the important geologic resources such as petroleum and coal. Because of their economic importance, and because they are the rocks most likely to be "underfoot," sedimentary rocks have been studied in very great detail.

Some Lengthy Definitions

Sediment

The kinds of sediments that form sedimentary rocks are, for the most part, quite familiar. Sediment includes such particles as sand on beaches, mud on a lake bottom, boulders frozen into glaciers, pebbles in streams, and dust particles settling out of the air onto the furniture in your home. An accumulation of clam shells on the sea bottom offshore would be called sediment, as would coral fragments broken from a reef by large storm waves. Salt crystals forming as individual suspended grains during the evaporation of sea water are also sediment.

Obviously, a geologic definition of sediment must be broad to include such a wide variety of substances. **Sediment** is the collective name for loose, solid particles that can originate in one of three ways:

1. Weathering and erosion of pre-existing rocks.
2. Chemical precipitation from solution, usually in water.
3. Secretion by organisms.

These particles usually collect in layers on the earth's surface.

An important part of the definition is that the particles are loose. Sediments are said to be **unconsolidated,** which means that the grains are separate, or unattached to one another.

Lithification

Lithification is the general term for a group of processes that convert loose sediment into sedimentary rock. Most sedimentary rocks have been lithified (or *consolidated*) by the precipitation of *cement* around sediment particles. The cement binds the loose sediment into a firm, coherent rock. Lithification includes not only cementation but other processes such as compaction and crystallization, which are described later in the chapter.

Sedimentary Rock

Most sedimentary rocks form from lithified sediment, but some sedimentary rocks form without going through the sediment stage; that is, without being a pile of loose, unconsolidated grains. Some precipitated rocks are in this category. The sedimentary rock *limestone,* for instance, can form by the precipitation of calcite within a coral reef by corals and algae. A limestone formed in this way has been precipitated directly as a solid rock. The definition of the term sedimentary rock, therefore, must be broader than "a rock formed from lithified sediment."

Sedimentary rock is rock that has formed from (1) lithification of any type of sediment; (2) precipitation from solution; or (3) consolidation of the remains of plants or animals.

Note that the distinction between sediment and sedimentary rock is sometimes subtle. A tiny crystal of halite (salt) suspended in evaporating sea water is a sediment grain precipitated from solution, but a sedimentary rock chemically precipitated from the waters of a hot spring was never sediment. Broken pieces of a coral reef are sediment, but a solid unbroken core of the reef is a sedimentary rock that has never been sediment.

Coal is a sedimentary rock formed from the compression of plant remains, such as moss, leaves, roots, twigs, and even tree trunks. Geologists disagree as to whether to call a piece of moss or a tree trunk a sediment grain. Those who would not consider plant materials to be sediment would say that coal did not form from sediment. Coal is of interest for another reason. It is clearly a rock but is *not* formed of minerals (except for scattered mineral grains trapped within the original mat of plant material). The existence of coal complicates any definition of the term *rock*.

Volcanic ash and *tuff* can be considered sedimentary because "ash" consists of rock fragments and tuff is consolidated ash. Some geologists prefer to call tuff a "fragmental volcanic rock."

Sedimentary rocks are broadly classified as *clastic* (formed from fragments of pre-existing rocks), *chemical* (formed by precipitation from solution), or *organic* (formed from the remains of organisms). These terms are not mutually exclusive, however. A rock can be both chemical and organic if it is made up of minerals, such as calcite, precipitated from solution by organisms. The three categories, in common use among geologists, are referred to with appropriate qualifications throughout this book when we discuss sedimentary rocks.

Sediment

Sediment particles are classified and defined according to the size of individual fragments. Table 6.1 shows the precise definitions of particles by size.

The term **gravel,** which includes all particles coarser than sand, generally implies that the particles are rounded on their edges and corners rather than sharp and angular. **Rubble** is made up of angular fragments coarser than sand. **Sand** has visible grains that feel gritty between your fingers. **Silt** is finer grained than sand; individual grains are not visible to the unaided eye. Silt does not feel gritty between your fingers, but if you bite into a sediment composed of silt-sized fragments, you can feel the grit between your teeth. (A geologist often does this with an unknown

Table 6.1

Definitions of Sediment Particles (in Terms of Size)

Particle Name		Diameter of Fragment	
		(mm)	(inches)
Boulder	⎫	Greater than 256	Greater than 10
Cobble	⎬ Gravel (if rounded)	64–256	2.5–10
Pebble	⎭ Rubble (if angular)	2–64	0.08–2.5
Sand		0.062–2	0.0025–0.08
Silt	⎫ Mud	0.004–0.062 (4–62 microns)	0.00015–0.0025
Clay	⎭	less than 0.004 (less than 4 microns)	Less than 0.00015

sediment to test its grain size. You might try it, even though the grating of silt on your teeth may send an unpleasant chill up your back.) **Clay** is the finest grained sediment, so fine that it does not feel gritty to either fingers or teeth. **Mud** is a term loosely used for silt and clay, usually wet.

Geologists do not agree on the upper size limit of clay. Many accept 4 microns as the upper limit, but others prefer 2 microns, particularly those who work extensively with soils and clay minerals (a *micron* is .001 millimeter).

Note that we now have two different uses of the word *clay*—a *clay-sized particle* (table 6.1) and a *clay mineral* (chapter 5). A clay-sized particle can be composed of any mineral at all, provided its diameter is less than 4 microns. A clay mineral, on the other hand, is one of a small group of silicate minerals with a sheet silicate structure. Clay minerals are often so fine-grained that they fall into the clay-size range, but sometimes clay minerals are coarse enough to be called silt.

Quite often the composition of sediment in the clay-size range turns out to be mostly clay minerals, but this is not always the case. Because of its resistance to chemical weathering, quartz may show up in this fine-size grade. Intense mechanical weathering can break down a wide variety of minerals to clay size, and these extremely fine particles may retain their mineral identity for long periods of time if chemical weathering is slow. The great weight of glaciers is particularly effective at grinding minerals down to the clay-size range, producing "rock flour," which gives a milky appearance to glacial meltwater streams (chapter 12).

Weathering, erosion, and transportation are some of the processes that affect the character of sediment (chapter 5). Both weathered and unweathered rock and sediment can be eroded, and weathering does not stop after erosion has taken place. Sand being transported by a river

also can be actively weathering, as can mud on a lake bottom. The character of sediment can also be altered by *rounding* and *sorting* during transportation, and by eventual *deposition*.

Transportation

Rounding is the grinding away of sharp edges and corners of rock fragments during transportation. Grinding is particularly effective in sand and gravel as rivers, glaciers, or waves cause particles to hit and scrape against one another or against a rock surface, such as a rocky stream bed. Boulders in a stream may show impressive rounding in less than one kilometer of travel. Because rounding during transportation is so rapid, it is a much more important process than spheroidal weathering (chapter 5), which also tends to round sharp edges.

Sorting is a process in which sediment grains are selected and separated according to grain size (or grain shape or specific gravity). Because of its high viscosity and manner of flow, a glacier does not sort the sediment it carries. Glaciers deposit all sediment sizes in the same place, so glacial sediment is usually an unsorted mixture of clay, silt, sand, and gravel. A river, however, sorts its sediment, separating sand from gravel, and silt and clay from sand. Sorting takes place because of the greater weight of larger particles. Boulders weigh more than pebbles, so they are more difficult for the river to transport. Similarly, it takes more of the river's energy to transport pebbles than sand, and more for sand than for silt or clay.

Figure 6.1 shows a river transporting all sizes of sediment as it flows out of steep mountains onto a gentle plain, where it loses energy and slows down. As the river loses energy, the heaviest particles of sediment are deposited. The boulders come to rest first. As the river continues to slow down, cobbles and then pebbles are deposited. Sand comes to rest as the river loses still more energy. Finally the river is carrying only the finest sediment—silt and clay. The sediment sizes were originally mixed, but the river has sorted the sediment by grain size.

Deposition

When transported material settles or comes to rest, **deposition** occurs. The term is also used to refer to the accumulation of chemical and organic sedimentary rocks.

Sediment is deposited when running water, glacial ice, waves, or wind lose energy and can no longer transport their load. Deposition of chemically precipitated sedimentary rocks occurs when chemical changes take place in a water solution affected by evaporation, a change in temperature, a change in pressure, or the action of organisms. Deposition of organic material occurs as organisms die and their remains accumulate.

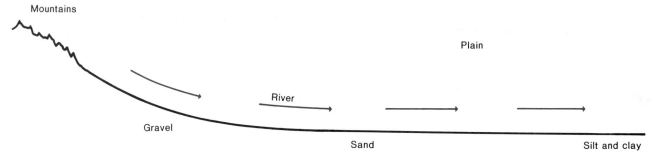

Figure 6.1   Sorting of sediment by a river. The coarse sediment is deposited first, and the finest sediment is carried the farthest.

The **environment of deposition** is the location in which deposition occurs. It is usually marked by characteristic physical, chemical, or biological conditions. A few examples of environments of deposition are the deep-sea floor, a desert valley, a river channel, a coral reef, a lake bottom, and a beach. You would expect the mud on the sea floor to differ in some ways from the mud on a desert valley, or even from mud on a lake bottom. Sand on a beach may differ from sand in a river channel. Some differences are due to varying sediment sources and transporting agents, but many are the result of conditions in the environment of deposition itself.

An important part of the job of geologists studying sedimentary rocks is to try to determine the ancient environment of deposition of the sediment that formed the rock. Factors that can help in this determination are the general rock relationships in the field, the features (including fossils) found within the rock, the mineral composition of the rock, and the size, shape, and surface texture of the individual sediment grains. Later in the chapter we present a few examples of interpretation of sedimentary rocks.

Types of Sedimentary Rocks

Clastic Sedimentary Rocks

A **clastic sedimentary rock** is a rock composed of fragments of pre-existing rock. The term **detrital** is generally used as a synonym for *clastic*. The rock fragments can be from igneous, sedimentary, and metamorphic rocks and can result from erosion, mechanical weathering, and chemical weathering. In most cases the sediment has been eroded and transported before being deposited. During transportation the grains may have been rounded and sorted.

Clastic sediment is lithified to form a clastic rock mainly by **cementation,** the chemical precipitation of material in the spaces between sediment grains. The precipitated material binds the grains together into a hard rock (figure 6.2).

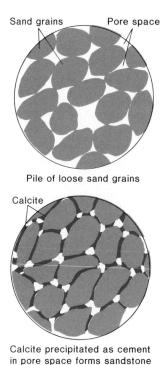

Figure 6.2   Lithification of sandstone by cementation of loose sand grains. (*A*) Pile of loose sand grains. (*B*) Calcite precipitated as cement in pore space forms sandstone.

When a clastic sediment is deposited, the grains fit fairly well together. Because sediment grains have irregular shapes, however, many small openings, called *pores,* are left between the grains even if they are packed very tightly together. The total amount of space taken up by openings between sediment grains is called **pore space.** (Some *rocks,* particularly sedimentary and volcanic rocks, also contain significant amounts of pore space.)

Underground water can move through the pore space of a thick sequence of sediments. Because underground water usually contains dissolved ions from the chemical weathering of minerals, it is possible for some of these ions to precipitate out of the water as solid material if the chemical conditions are right.

Table 6.2

The Common Clastic Sedimentary Rocks[1]

Sediment		Clastic Sedimentary Rock
Rubble	——→	Sedimentary breccia
Gravel	——→	Conglomerate
Sand	——→	Sandstone
Clay and silt	——→	Shale

1. These rocks can be readily recognized and named in the field. Appendix B describes several varieties of these common clastic rocks.

Cement is the term given to the solid material that precipitates in the pore space of sediments and binds the grains together to form solid rock. As the cement precipitates, it attaches itself very tightly to the sediment grains, holding them in a rigid framework. The cement partially fills the pores, reducing the total amount of pore space. Sedimentary rock cement is often composed of the mineral calcite or other carbonate minerals. Silica is another common cement. Iron oxides may act as cement, but are less common than calcite or silica.

A clastic sedimentary rock has a **clastic texture,** that is, an arrangement of rock fragments bound by cement into a rigid network (figure 6.2). A rock with a clastic texture generally still has some pore space; cement rarely fills the pores completely.

The most common types of clastic sedimentary rocks are listed in table 6.2, along with the sediment types that form them. Sedimentary rocks are also listed and described in Appendix B, which is designed to help you identify the sedimentary rocks.

Breccia and conglomerate   Sedimentary breccia is a coarse-grained sedimentary rock formed by the cementation of coarse, angular fragments of rubble. Because rocks are rounded so rapidly during transport, geologists conclude that the angular fragments within breccia must not have moved very far from their source. Sedimentary breccia might form, for example, from fragments that have accumulated at the base of a steep slope of rock that is being mechanically weathered. Landslide deposits also might lithify into sedimentary breccia. This type of rock is not particularly common.

Conglomerate is a coarse-grained sedimentary rock formed by the cementation of rounded gravel. It can be distinguished from breccia by the definite roundness of its particles (figure 6.3). Because conglomerates are coarse grained, geologists conclude that the original sediment did not travel far; some transport, however, was necessary to round the particles. Angular fragments that fall from a

Figure 6.3   Conglomerate.
Photo by W. C. Irvin.

cliff and then are carried a few kilometers by a river or by waves would become rounded. Such fragments could lithify to form conglomerate.

Sandstone   Sandstone is a medium-grained sedimentary rock formed by the cementation of sand grains. Any deposit of sand can lithify to sandstone. Rivers deposit sand in their channels, and wind piles up sand into sand dunes. Waves deposit sand on beaches and in shallow water. Deep-sea currents spread sand over the sea floor. As you might imagine, sandstones show a great deal of variation in grain size, grain shape, mineral composition, degree of sorting, and degree of rounding.

Sandstones, conglomerates, and sedimentary breccias can all contain a substantial amount of **matrix,** a fine-grained material found in the space between larger grains (figure 6.4). Matrix in a conglomerate is commonly a mixture of sand, silt, and sometimes clay. In sandstone, silt and clay may form the matrix.

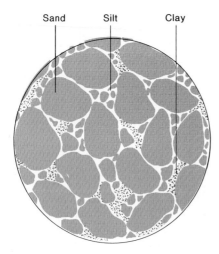

Sand   Silt   Clay

Figure 6.4 A poorly sorted sediment made of sand, silt, and clay grains. Lithification of such a sediment would produce a "dirty sandstone."

Shale   Shale is a fine-grained sedimentary rock notable for its splitting capability (called *fissility*). Splitting takes place along the surfaces of very thin layers within the shale. Most shales appear *laminated;* that is, the very thin layers are visible to the unaided eye. The silt and clay deposits that lithify as shale accumulate on lake bottoms, at the ends of rivers in deltas, beside rivers in flood, and on quiet parts of the deep ocean floor.

Clastic sedimentary rocks are lithified primarily by cementation, but in fine-grained rocks (such as shale) *compaction* is also important. **Compaction** is the loss in overall volume and pore space as sedimentary particles are packed closer together by the weight of overlying material. As a thick sequence of sediment builds up, the sediment at the bottom is compacted by the weight of the new sediment constantly being added to the top. Compaction is most pronounced in shale and other fine-grained rocks but occurs to a lesser extent in sandstones and even conglomerates.

Figure 6.5 shows the role of compaction in the lithification of shale from wet mud. Before compaction, as much as 80 percent of the volume of the wet mud may have been pore space, the pores being filled with water. The flakelike clay minerals were randomly arranged within the mud. Pressure from overlying material packs the sediment grains together and reduces the overall volume by squeezing water out of the pores. The clay minerals are reoriented perpendicular to the pressure, becoming parallel to one another like a deck of cards. The fissility of shale is due to splitting between these parallel clay flakes.

Compaction by itself does not generally lithify sediment into sedimentary rock. It does help consolidate clayey sediments by pressing the microscopic clay minerals so close together that attractional forces at the atomic level tend to bind them together. Even in shale, however, the primary method of lithification is cementation.

Chemical and Organic Sedimentary Rocks

Chemical and organic sedimentary rocks are discussed together because often the distinction between them is not clear. (Appendix B lists and describes the common chemical and organic sedimentary rocks and also includes information on how to identify them.)

A **chemical sedimentary rock** is a rock composed of material precipitated directly from solution. Precipitation may be *inorganic;* that is, caused by a pressure or temperature change, or by evaporation, or by the mixing of two solutions. Rock salt and gypsum, which form when water evaporates, are examples of inorganically precipitated chemical rocks. Precipitation can also be *organic,* as when calcium carbonate is extracted from sea water and precipitated by corals and algae in the stony core of a coral reef. Such a deposit would be an organically precipitated chemical limestone.

Organic sedimentary rocks are rocks composed mostly of the remains of plants and animals. Coal is clearly an organic rock, having formed from compacted plant remains. A limestone composed almost entirely of clam shells could also be called organic.

As must be evident, chemical and organic sedimentary rocks may form in a number of different ways or combinations of ways. Rock salt and gypsum form from the evaporation of water. Limestone, dolomite, and chert all have several different possible origins. Chalk, coquina, diatomite, and coal form from the accumulation of organic material (appendix B).

Evaporites   Rocks formed from crystals that precipitate during evaporation of water are called **evaporites.** They form from the evaporation of sea water or a saline lake (figure 6.6), such as Great Salt Lake in Utah. Rock salt and gypsum are the most common evaporites. Other examples of evaporites are some types of limestone, some dolomite, and layers of rarer minerals such as borates and potassium and magnesium salts.

Evaporites have a **crystalline texture,** an arrangement of interlocking crystals that develops as crystals grow and interfere with one another. Igneous rocks generally have crystalline textures that develop as crystals grow in cooling magma; the crystalline textures of evaporites are due to crystal growth during precipitation from solution.

Box 6.1
Pore Space, Water, and Oil

Part of the pore space in rocks such as sandstone or conglomerate ordinarily is not completely filled with cement (figure 6.2). The open pore space of a sandstone, for instance, may be as much as 20 percent of its volume.

In many regions, the pores in sandstones and conglomerates serve as reservoirs for underground water, which fills the open space in the rock. To tap underground water in such a region, a well is drilled into a sandstone containing water, which then flows from the pores into the well. From the well, the water can be pumped to the surface as needed. Petroleum and natural gas, which can also fill pores in rocks, are recovered by similar techniques.

The more open pore space a rock contains, the more water or oil it can hold. Clean, well sorted sandstone is an ideal rock for holding water or oil. A poorly sorted sandstone ("dirty sandstone") contains much silt and clay along with the sand grains. This matrix of silt and clay grains fills more of the pore space (figure 6.4), lowering the ability of a rock to hold fluids.

Other rock types, including fractured limestone and volcanic rocks, can also hold water and oil in their openings. More information about water and oil is in chapters 11 and 21, and box 15.1.

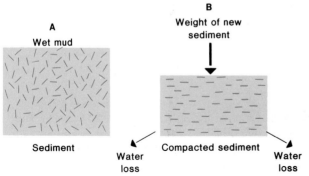

Figure 6.5 Compaction of wet mud. Cementation forms shale from compacted mud. (*A*) Randomly oriented silt and clay particles in water. (*B*) Particles reorient, some water is lost, and pore space decreases. (*C*) Splitting planes form parallel to oriented mineral grains.

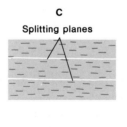

Figure 6.6 Salt deposited on the floor of a dried-up desert lake, Death Valley, California.
Photo by J. R. Stacy, U.S. Geological Survey.

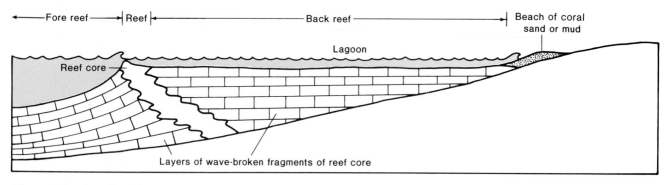

Fore reef → | Reef | ← Back reef → | Beach of coral sand or mud

Lagoon

Reef core →

Layers of wave-broken fragments of reef core

Figure 6.7 A reef and its wave-eroded sediments are a common source of limestone. Only the reef core is made of living coral. The fore reef and back reef are mostly broken fragments of dead coral.

When used in connection with sedimentary rocks, the term **crystallization** refers to crystal development and growth by precipitation from solution, usually in water. It is a process of lithification. Rocks, such as the evaporites, that form by crystallization may never have been sediments. Crystalline rocks usually lack cement and are held together by the interlocking of crystals. Pore space is lacking because the crystals have grown until they filled all available space. Underground water and petroleum are seldom found in crystalline rocks unless the rocks are highly fractured.

Limestone **Limestone** is a sedimentary rock composed mainly of calcite. Because limestones are formed by both organic and inorganic processes, many different kinds exist. Some are clearly *chemical*. Thin beds of limestone, often interlayered with evaporites, may have a crystalline texture, indicating that the limestones are evaporites as well. As was noted earlier, a limestone made up of clam shells could be classified as *organic*. Many limestones are *clastic*, exhibiting a definite clastic texture caused by cementation of individual grains. The grains may be shell fragments or broken pieces of coral from a reef.

Limestones, with few exceptions, generally have a marine origin. The calcite within most limestones precipitated originally from sea water. Coral reefs create much limestone, both by organic precipitation of limestone directly in the reef core and by the production of extensive layers of calcite sediment as storm waves break fragments from the living reef (figure 6.7). These layers of broken fragments may extend for several kilometers on either side of a reef. Most of the sand grains on the beaches of tropical islands are shell and coral fragments broken from reefs far offshore. Some of the sand on the beaches of southernmost Florida has a similar origin.

Limestones are particularly susceptible to **recrystallization,** the process by which new crystals, often of the

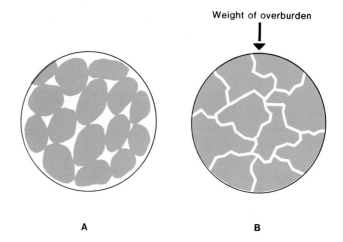

Weight of overburden

A   B

Figure 6.8 Recrystallization of clastic grains to form new crystals. (*A*) Before recrystallization (clastic texture). (*B*) After recrystallization (crystalline texture).

same composition as the original grains, develop in a rock. Calcite grains recrystallize easily, particularly in the presence of water and under the weight of overlying sediment. During recrystallization the grains may form new crystals that are smaller or larger than the original grains. Figure 6.8 shows small rounded grains in a clastic limestone recrystallizing to form large, interlocking calcite crystals. The original clastic texture of the rock has been destroyed and a new crystalline texture has formed. Because recrystallization usually destroys the original texture and sometimes the fossils of the limestone, it is very difficult to determine the geologic history of such a rock.

Dolomite The term **dolomite** is used both for a sedimentary rock and for the mineral that composes it, $CaMg(CO_3)_2$. (Some geologists use *dolostone* for the rock.) Dolomite often forms from limestone as calcium is replaced by magnesium, usually as water solutions move through the limestone. These solutions also tend to cause recrystallization of the rock. Dolomite is known to precipitate directly from sea water or saline lakes. It seems likely to many geologists, however, that most thick dolomite layers were formed by a postdepositional replacement of limestone.

Chert   A hard, compact, fine-grained sedimentary rock formed almost entirely of silica, **chert** occurs in two principal forms—as irregular, lumpy nodules within other rocks and as layered deposits like other sedimentary rocks. The nodules, often found in limestone, probably formed from inorganic precipitation as underground water replaced part of the original rock with silica. The layered deposits may also have formed from inorganic precipitation or from the accumulation of shell-like hard parts of microscopic marine organisms on the sea floor, or from a combination of both.

   Microscopic fossils composed of silica are abundant in some cherts. But because chert is susceptible to recrystallization, the original fossils are easily destroyed, and the origin of many cherts remains doubtful.

Coal   A sedimentary rock formed from the consolidation of plant material, **coal** is rich in carbon and is usually black; it burns readily. Many types of plant material can go into making coal—leaves, roots, woody tree trunks, and stems have been found as fossils in coal. It is likely that coal develops most often from **peat,** a brown, lightweight, unconsolidated or semiconsolidated deposit of plant remains that accumulates in swampy bogs. Since *peat moss* is a major constituent of peat, coals that formed from peat probably had a high proportion of peat moss as their original organic matter. Peat is transformed into coal largely by compaction after it has been buried by sediments. Several different varieties of coal are recognized, based on the type of original plant material and the degree of compaction (chapter 21).

Sedimentary Structures
Sedimentary structures are features that are found within sedimentary rock. They usually formed during or shortly after deposition of the sediment, but before lithification.

   One of the most prominent structures, seen in almost all large bodies of sedimentary rock, is **bedding,** an arrangement of layers or beds of rock (figure 6.9). Most bedding is horizontal because the sediments from which the sedimentary rocks formed were originally deposited as horizontal layers. The law of **original horizontality,** a general principle of geology, states that most water-laid sediment is deposited in horizontal or near-horizontal layers that are essentially parallel to the earth's surface. In many cases this is also true for sediments deposited by ice or wind. Sedimentary rocks formed from such sediments preserve the horizontal layering in the form of beds. A **bedding plane** is a nearly flat or planar surface of deposition, separating two beds of rock. A change in grain size or composition of particles being deposited, or a pause during deposition, can create bedding planes.

A specialized type of bedding that is not horizontal is **cross-bedding,** an arrangement of relatively thin layers of rock within a larger bed of rock. The thin layers are inclined at an angle to the more nearly horizontal bedding planes of the larger rock unit (figure 6.10). Cross-bedding is found most often in sandstone. It develops as sand is deposited on steep, local slopes (figure 6.11). The distinctive patterns of cross-bedding can be formed in many

Figure 6.9 Bedding in sedimentary rocks in Capitol Reef National Monument, Utah.
Photo by J. R. Stacy, U.S. Geological Survey.

Figure 6.10 Cross-bedded sandstone in Zion National Park, Utah. This cross-bedding was probably formed in sand dunes.
Photo by J. K. Hillers, U.S. Geological Survey.

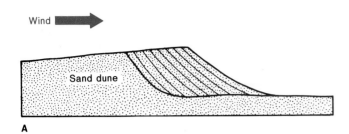

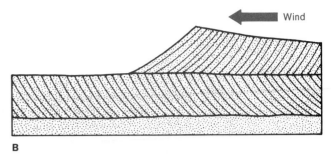

A

B

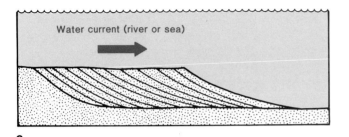

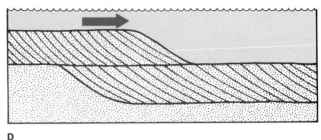

C

D

Figure 6.11 The development of cross-bedding in wind-blown sand (*A* and *B*) and current-deposited sand (*C* and *D*). (*A*) Sand deposits in inclined layers on the downwind side of a dune. (*B*) Second dune covers first. Cross-bedding may change places—in sand dunes deposited by wind; in sand ridges deposited by ocean currents on the sea floor; in sediment bars and dunes deposited by rivers in their channels; and in deltas that form at the mouths of rivers.

orientation if wind direction shifts. (*C*) Current fills in a depression on river bottom or sea floor with sediment. (*D*) Continued sedimentation may cover first set of cross-beds with another.

Graded bedding is an arrangement in which particle sizes vary gradually within a single bed, from coarse grains at the bottom of the bed to progressively finer grains toward the top. A single bed may have gravel at its base and grade upward through sand and silt to fine clay at the top. Graded bedding may build up as sediment is deposited by a gradually slowing current. This seems particularly likely to happen during deposition by a **turbidity current,** a flowing mass of sediment-laden water that is heavier than clear water and so flows downslope along the bottom of the sea or a lake. Figure 6.12 shows the development of a graded bed by turbidity current deposition.

Mud cracks are polygonal cracks formed in very fine-grained sediment as it dries (figure 6.13). As drying requires air, mud cracks form only in sediment exposed above water. Mud cracks may form in lake-bottom sediment as the lake dries up; in flood-deposited sediment as a river level drops; or in marine sediment exposed to the air, perhaps temporarily by a falling tide. Cracked mud can lithify to form shale, preserving the cracks. The filling of mud cracks by sand can form casts of the cracks in an overlying sandstone.

Figure 6.12 Development of a graded bed of sediment deposited by a turbidity current.

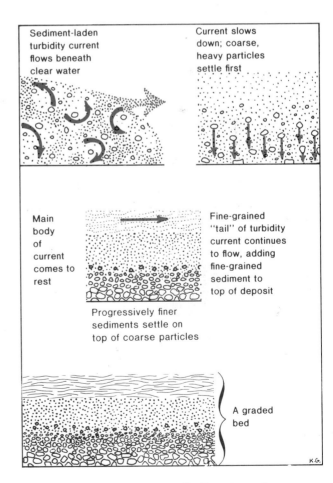

Sediment-laden turbidity current flows beneath clear water

Current slows down; coarse, heavy particles settle first

Main body of current comes to rest

Fine-grained "tail" of turbidity current continues to flow, adding fine-grained sediment to top of deposit

Progressively finer sediments settle on top of coarse particles

A graded bed

A

B

Figure 6.13 (A) Mud cracks in recently dried mud. (B) Mud cracks preserved in shale; they have been partially filled with sediment.

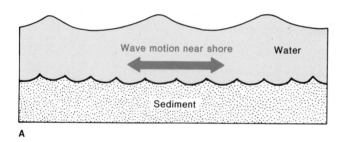

A

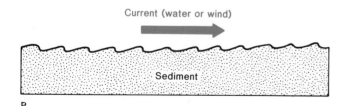

B

Figure 6.14 Development of ripple marks in loose sediment.
(A) Symmetric ripple marks form beneath waves.
(B) Asymmetric ripple marks forming beneath a current are steeper on their downcurrent sides.

Ripple marks are small ridges formed on the surface of a sediment layer by moving wind or water. The ridges form perpendicular to the motion. Ripple marks, found in gravel, sand, or silt, can be caused by either waves or currents of water or wind (figure 6.14). Wave-caused ripple marks are symmetric ridges; current-caused ripple marks are asymmetric, with steeper sides in the downcurrent direction. Either type can be preserved in rock (figure 6.15).

Fossils, traces of plants or animals preserved in rock, are relatively common sedimentary structures. The hard parts of organisms are most likely to be fossilized. If a bone or shell is covered by sediment before it decays, its imprint in the rock becomes a fossil (figures 6.16 and 6.17). The bone or shell itself is seldom preserved, having been dissolved away by ground water, but new matter precipitates in place of the original material and gives a durable cast of the original shape. A preserved footprint or trail of an organism is also a fossil, as is the impression of a leaf. Because many limestones are composed of shell and coral debris, fossils are particularly common in limestones, but they also occur in shales and sandstones. Because coal and petroleum are both formed from ancient organic matter, they are sometimes called *fossil fuels.*

Figure 6.16 Fossil fish in a rock from western Wyoming.
Photo by W. T. Lee, U.S. Geological Survey.

Figure 6.15 Ripple marks preserved in sandstone near Morrison, Colorado.
Photo by J. R. Stacy, U.S. Geological Survey.

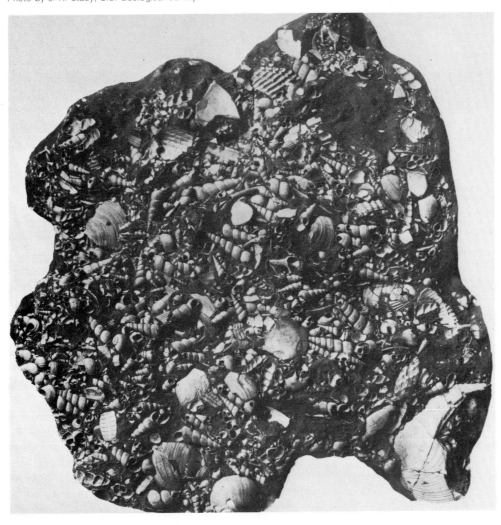

Figure 6.17 Fossil shells of clams and snails in a rock from eastern Virginia.
Photo by W. T. Lee, U.S. Geological Survey.

Box 6.3
Naming of Rock Units

A **formation** is a body of rock of considerable thickness with recognizable unity or similarity that makes it distinguishable from adjacent rock units. Although a formation is usually composed of one bed or several beds of sedimentary rock, units of metamorphic and igneous rock are also called formations. It is a convenient unit for mapping, describing, or interpreting the geology of a region.

Formations are often based on rock type. A formation may be a single thick bed of sandstone. A sequence of several thin sandstone beds could also be called a formation, as could a sequence of alternating limestone and shale beds.

The main criterion for distinguishing and naming a formation is some visible characteristic that makes a section of rock into a recognizable unit. This characteristic may be rock type or sedimentary structures or both. For example, a thick sequence of shale may be overlain by basalt flows and underlain by sandstone. The shale, the basalt, and the sandstone would each be a different formation. Or a sequence of thin limestone beds, with a total thickness of hundreds of meters, may have recognizable fossils in the lower half and distinctly different fossils in the upper half. The limestone sequence may then be divided into two formations on the basis of its fossil content.

Formations are given proper names, with the first name usually a geographic location where the rock is well exposed, followed by a name of a rock type, such as Navajo Sandstone, Austin Chalk, Baltimore Gneiss, Onondaga Limestone, or Chattanooga Shale. If the formation has a mixture of rock types, so that one rock name does not accurately describe it, it is called simply "formation," as in the Morrison Formation or the Martinsburg Formation.

A **contact** is the boundary surface between two different rock types or ages of rocks. In

Interpretation of Sedimentary Rocks

Sedimentary rocks contain many clues to the conditions that prevailed at the time of their deposition. In general, when geologists study sedimentary rocks, they try to identify and reconstruct the character of the sediment's *source area,* the region's *geography* at the time of deposition, and the sediment's *environment of deposition.*

Source Area

The source area of a sediment is the locality that was eroded to provide the sediment. It is characterized by its rock type, climate, and relief.

The *type of rock* in the source area has an important influence on the resulting sediment. Erosion of a basaltic volcano, for example, may yield several types of sediment (gravel, sand made of partially weathered fragments of basalt, and clay), but *not* sand-sized quartz grains because quartz is not present in the source rock. A quartzose sandstone cannot be interpreted, therefore, as coming from a basaltic source area. Weathering of granite or many sandstones, however, *does* produce quartz sand. Thus the source area of a quartz-containing sandstone probably included granite, pre-existing sandstones, or both.

The *climate* of the source area has a pronounced effect on the resulting sediment. A region of moderate rainfall and distinct seasons, with repeated cycles of freezing and thawing, may yield sediment that is more influenced by mechanical weathering than chemical weathering. A granitic source area in such a climate yields angular blocks of unaltered granite from frost action, sand grains formed of quartz and partially weathered feldspar and mica, and a minor amount of clay minerals from chemical weathering.

The same granite in a tropical region, with high temperature, high rainfall, and no frost action, may yield quite different sediment. Chemical weathering is much more intense than mechanical weathering in such a region. Feldspars and micas weather completely, forming fine-grained clay minerals, and the only sand-sized particles are grains of unweathered quartz. Large angular blocks of granite rubble may not form at all.

Relief is the vertical distance between the tops of hills and the bottoms of valleys. Rugged mountains have high relief, and a gently sloping plain has low relief. Since relief controls the rate of erosion to a great extent, it can influence the character of the resulting sediment. Low relief

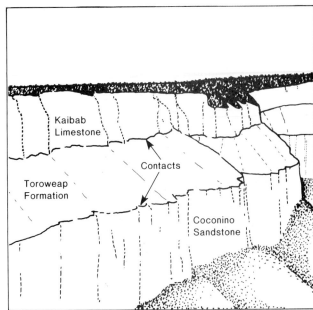

Figure 6.18 The upper three formations in the cliffs of the Grand Canyon, Arizona.
Photo by R. Arnold, U.S. Geological Survey.

sedimentary rock formations, the contacts are usually bedding planes.

Figure 6.18 shows the three formations that make up the upper part of the canyon walls in Grand Canyon National Park in Arizona. The contacts between formations are also shown.

means slow erosion, so in a flat region chemical weathering may go to completion before erosion removes the sediment. As a result, the sediment from low-relief areas usually contains a considerable amount of clay minerals. This can be true even in climates where chemical weathering is slow.

High relief means rapid erosion. Erosion can outpace chemical weathering in such a region, so both weathered and unweathered sediment can be eroded from a high-relief area. This can be true even in a tropical region where chemical weathering is very rapid.

Note that a geologist is interested in the *ancient* relief, climate, and rock type of the source area, not the present conditions. A conglomerate that was deposited 150 million years ago may indicate that its source area was granitic, influenced by a moderate climate, and of high relief. Yet the *modern* region surrounding the conglomerate may be sedimentary, tropical, and of low relief. The interpreted conditions of the ancient source area may show little relationship to modern conditions in that region.

Geologists cannot always be sure that they have interpreted the source area correctly. A sandstone containing much unweathered feldspar could have come from a region of moderate relief and moderate climate, where erosion outstripped chemical weathering. A region of very high relief in the tropics could also have been the source. A very cold climate could also have existed in the source area, however, for chemical weathering is extremely slow when the temperature is low and any water is in the form of ice that never thaws. A desert, with little water present, could also produce a feldspar-rich sandstone. Sometimes there are additional clues about the source area from such features as the surface textures of grains and the presence of transported fossils, but in some cases the precise nature of the source area cannot be determined.

Paleogeography

The term *paleogeography* means "ancient geography." Geologists study sedimentary rocks to try to reconstruct the surface configuration of the land in the past. Of particular interest are the *location* of the source area and its *distance* from the site of sediment deposition. To help determine these things, geologists study the size and shape

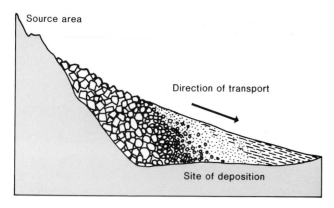

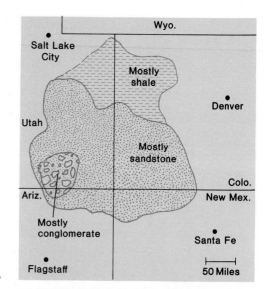

Figure 6.19 Sediment deposits usually become thinner in the direction of transport away from the source area, and sediment grains become finer and more rounded. See Appendix E for rock symbols.

of rock units (beds or formations), the size and roundness of sediment particles, and any clues to old current directions that the rock may contain, such as cross-beds or ripple marks made by currents.

Figure 6.19 shows how several of these characteristics vary with distance from the source area. As a general rule, sediment deposits get thinner away from the source, and the sediment grains themselves become finer and (for coarse particles) more rounded. Refer back to figure 6.11 and notice how the inclination of cross-bedding is an indication of old current direction. Asymmetric ripple marks can also be used to determine current direction (figure 6.14).

Figure 6.20 shows how three of these characteristics were used to determine the location of the source area for a particular rock unit in the southwestern United States. The unit is the Salt Wash Member of the Morrison Formation. (*Formation* is defined in box 6.3; a *member* is a subdivision of a formation.) It is an important rock unit, for it contains a great deal of uranium, deposited within the rock by ground water long after the rock formed. The unit thickens and coarsens to the southwest, and cross-beds show that the old currents that deposited the sediment came from the southwest. These three facts strongly suggest that the source area was to the southwest. This information can help prospectors search for uranium within the Salt Wash.

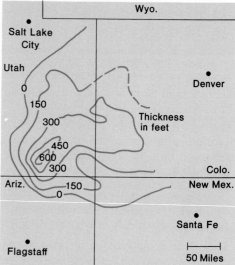

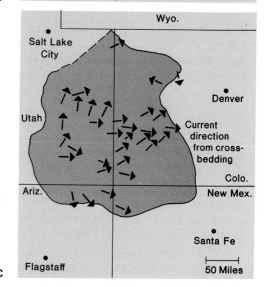

Figure 6.20 Characteristics of the Salt Wash Member of the Morrison Formation that help locate its source area. (*A*) The sediment grains become coarser to the southwest. (*B*) The deposit becomes thicker to the southwest. (*C*) Cross-bedding shows that the depositing currents came mostly from the southwest (arrows point downcurrent).
Redrawn and simplified from Craig and others, 1955, *U.S. Geological Survey Bulletin.*

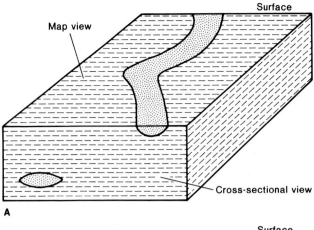

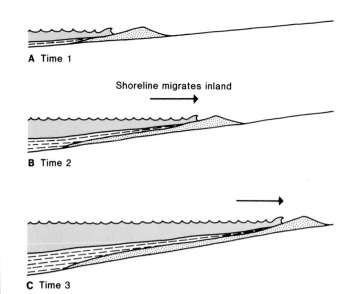

Figure 6.22 A blanket sandstone can form from beach sand as a shoreline migrates inland due to land subsidence or sea-level rise.

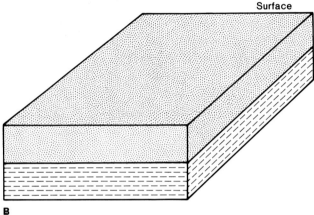

Figure 6.21 Two different shapes for sandstone units. (*A*) "Shoestring" sandstones are narrow and elongate. A buried shoestring sandstone is shown surrounded by shale. (*B*) "Blanket" sandstone are thick and widespread. This one overlies a shale bed.

Environment of Deposition

Clues to the environment of sediment deposition come from the size and shape of a sedimentary rock unit, the sedimentary structures such as mud cracks and fossils contained in rock, the vertical sequence of beds, and many other characteristics.

The *size and shape of the rock unit* can help indicate its environment of deposition. A sandstone bed may be fairly thin and narrow in cross section (figure 6.21*A*) but very elongated in map view (a "shoestring" sandstone). It is often surrounded by shale. Such a shape may indicate an old river channel filled with sand, a channel on the deep sea floor, or a barrier island (chapter 14). Or the sandstone may be tens to hundreds of meters thick and extend horizontally for hundreds of kilometers (a "blanket" or "sheet" sandstone—figure 6.21*B*). Such sands can form from enormous fields of sand dunes on land or from beach sediments migrating inland as the land subsides or the sea level rises (figure 6.22), or perhaps in other ways.

Sedimentary structures, including fossils, can often narrow the choice of environment. A blanket sandstone may be cross-bedded and may contain fossil footprints of lizards on bedding planes, in which case it was almost surely deposited as dune sand on land. If it contains symmetric ripple marks and fossil clam shells, it is probably a beach or near-shore sand that migrated onshore (or perhaps offshore).

The *sequence of beds* may be more diagnostic than a single bed. Unfossiliferous shale is difficult to interpret, but if shale beds alternate with evaporite beds such as gypsum, the entire sequence can be interpreted as forming either on land or in a very shallow marine basin where water can evaporate. Mudcracks and dinosaur footprints in shale indicate that the shale was formed as wet mud on land, and if sandstones are interbedded with such shale, the sandstones are undoubtedly continental, too.

In many parts of the eastern and midwestern United States, coal beds occur within a distinctive sequence of sedimentary rocks. The sequence, which may be repeated many times vertically, usually contains both coal and limestone (along with sandstone, shale, and other rocks). Widespread coal beds, formed of land plants, are generally interpreted as continental deposits. Limestone is usually marine. Thus the sequence implies that the environment changed from continental to marine, and the repetition of the sequence shows that these conditions alternated many times. Vast low-lying deltas that periodically flooded with sea water are a logical choice of environment (for part of the sequence; its complete interpretation is more complicated).

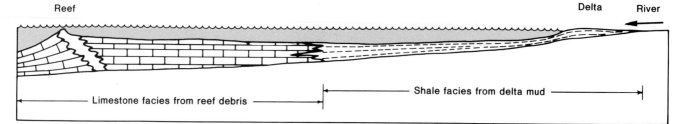

Figure 6.23 Two rock facies forming from two different sources. Within the limestone facies are the reef facies shown in figure 6.7.

Sedimentary Facies

An important concept in the study of sedimentary rocks is the idea of **sedimentary facies,** which are lateral variations in rock type or fossil content within a single rock unit. These variations are often controlled by the environment of deposition of the sediment.

Refer to figure 6.20A, which shows variations in rock type within a rock unit, the Salt Wash Member of the Morrison Formation. The Salt Wash Member is considered a single rock unit because all parts of it were deposited at approximately the same time and were derived largely from a single source area to the southwest. Within the Salt Wash, however, the grain size of the sediment varies with distance from the source area. These variations are facies. They are given names based on rock type, such as sandstone facies and shale facies.

A different type of facies variation is shown in figure 6.7. Here the rock is all limestone, but the limestone can be subdivided into fore-reef, reef, and back-reef facies. Each facies is clearly distinguishable from the others by such factors as presence or absence of bedding, angle of bedding, and fossil content.

Facies can differ in their source areas. A coral reef far offshore can provide limy sediment at the same time that rivers are depositing mud in deltas closer to shore (figure 6.23). The resulting rocks include a limestone facies from one source and a shale facies from another source.

Summary

Sediment forms from fragments of pre-existing rocks, chemical precipitation, and organisms.

Sedimentary rock forms by *lithification* of sediment *(clastic), precipitation* from solution *(chemical),* or *consolidation* of the remains of organisms *(organic).*

Sand, silt, and *clay* are sediment particles defined by grain size. *Gravel* and *rubble* are defined by grain size and roundness.

The composition of clastic sediment is governed by the rates of chemical weathering, mechanical weathering, and erosion. During transportation, grains can become rounded and sorted.

The *environment of deposition* helps determine the character of a sediment and the features found in the resulting sedimentary rock.

Clastic rocks form mostly by *cementation* of grains. *Matrix* may partially fill the pore space of clastic rocks. *Compaction* is important in fine-grained clastic rocks.

Breccia and *conglomerate* form from coarse sediment grains that have been transported only a short distance, perhaps by a river.

Sandstone forms from sand deposited by rivers, wind, waves, or ocean currents.

Shale forms from river, lake, or ocean mud.

Chemical rocks include the *evaporites,* notably rock salt and gypsum, which form as sea water or a saline lake dries up. Evaporites form by crystallization of minerals from solution, which leads to a crystalline texture of interlocking grains.

Limestone (composed of calcite) and *chert* (composed of silica) have a variety of origins. Some are clastic, some chemical, and some organic; and many result from a combination of these three origins. *Recrystallization* often destroys the original texture. It is likely that marine organisms contribute most of the material in most limestones and cherts.

Dolomite usually forms from alteration of limestone by magnesium-bearing solutions.

Coal, a major fuel, is consolidated plant material.

The most common sedimentary rocks are shale, sandstone, and limestone.

Sedimentary rocks are usually found in *beds* separated by *bedding planes* because the original sediments are deposited in horizontal layers.

Cross-bedding forms where sediment is deposited on a sloping surface in a sand dune, delta, or river bar.

Graded bedding forms as coarse particles fall from suspension before fine particles, perhaps in a turbidity current.

Mud cracks form in drying mud. *Ripple marks* form beneath waves or currents.

Fossils are the traces of an organism's hard parts or tracks preserved in rock.

A *formation* is a convenient rock unit for mapping and describing rock. Formations are distinguishable from adjacent rocks; their boundaries are *contacts*.

Geologists study the character of the sediment grains and sedimentary structures, the size and shape of rock units, and the sequence of beds in order to interpret the sediment's *source area* and *environment of deposition*, and the region's *paleogeography*.

Sedimentary facies are lateral variations in rock type or fossil content within a single rock unit.

Terms to Remember

bedding	limestone
bedding plane	lithification
boulder	matrix
cement	mud
cementation	mud cracks
chemical sedimentary rock	organic sedimentary rock
chert	original horizontality
clastic (detrital)	peat
sedimentary rock	pebble
clastic texture	pore space
clay	recrystallization
coal	ripple marks
cobble	rounding
compaction	rubble
conglomerate	sand
contact	sandstone
cross-bedding	sediment
crystalline texture	sedimentary breccia
crystallization	sedimentary facies
deposition	sedimentary rock
dolomite	sedimentary structure
environment of deposition	shale
evaporites	silt
formation	sorting
fossils	turbidity current
graded bedding	unconsolidated
gravel	

Questions for Review

1. Quartz is a common mineral in sandstone. Under certain circumstances, feldspar can be common in sandstone, even though it normally weathers rapidly to clay. What conditions of climate, weathering rate, and erosion rate could lead to a feldspar-rich sandstone? Explain your answer.

2. Describe with sketches how wet mud compacts before it becomes shale.
3. What do mud cracks tell about the environment of deposition of a sedimentary rock?
4. How does graded bedding form?
5. List the clastic sediment particles in order of decreasing grain size.
6. How does a sedimentary breccia differ in appearance and origin from a conglomerate?
7. Describe three different origins for limestone.
8. How does dolomite usually form?
9. What is the origin of coal?
10. Sketch the cementation of sand to form sandstone.
11. How do evaporites form? Name two evaporites.
12. Name the three most common sedimentary rocks.
13. What is a formation?
14. Sketch two ways that cross-bedding might form.

Questions for Thought

1. Describe as completely as you can the origin, transportation, and environment of deposition of the sediment that formed the following sedimentary rocks:
   A. Interbedded layers of shale and gypsum.
   B. A poorly sorted, graded sandstone interbedded with shales containing microscopic marine fossils.
   C. A shale with very thin beds, a high content of organic matter, and fossil fish skeletons.
   D. A poorly sorted conglomerate containing fossils of logs and grains from clay size to rounded boulders 3 meters across.
   E. A red shale with dinosaur footprints and mud-cracks.

2. How might graded bedding be used to determine tops and bottoms of sedimentary rock layers in an area where sedimentary rock is no longer horizontal? What other sedimentary structures can be used to determine tops and bottoms of tilted beds?

Supplementary Readings

Dunbar, C. O., and J. Rogers. 1957. *Principles of stratigraphy*. New York: John Wiley & Sons.

Ernst, W. G. 1969. *Earth materials*. Englewood Cliffs, N.J.: Prentice-Hall.

Krumbein, W. C., and L. L. Sloss. 1963. *Stratigraphy and sedimentation*. San Francisco: W. H. Freeman.

Laporte, L. F. 1968. *Ancient environments*. Englewood Cliffs, N.J.: Prentice-Hall.

Pearl, R. M. 1965. *How to know the minerals and rocks*. New York: McGraw-Hill.

Pettijohn, F. J. 1975. *Sedimentary rocks*. 3d ed. New York: Harper & Row.

7

Metamorphism, Metamorphic Rocks, and Hydrothermal Rocks

Purpose

Metamorphic rocks, the third major category of rocks in the rock cycle (chapter 1), complete our description of earth materials (rocks and minerals). Your knowledge of igneous and sedimentary processes obtained from previous chapters should aid you in understanding metamorphic rocks, which are formed from *pre-existing* rocks.

If you have read about weathering in chapter 5, you saw how rocks are altered when exposed at the earth's surface. Metamorphism (a word from Latin and Greek that means literally "changing of form") also involves alterations, but the changes are due to deep burial, tectonic forces, and high temperature rather than surface conditions.

As you study this chapter, try to keep clearly in mind how the chemical composition of a rock and the temperature, pressure, and water present each contribute to the metamorphic process and the resultant metamorphic rock.

We also discuss hydrothermally deposited rocks, which are found in association with both igneous and metamorphic rocks. Hydrothermal ore deposits, while not volumetrically significant, are of great importance to the world's supply of metals (chapter 21).

Because nearly all metamorphic rocks form deep within the earth's crust, they provide geologists with many clues about conditions at depth. Therefore an understanding of metamorphism will help you when, beginning with chapter 15, we return to consider geologic processes involving the earth's internal forces. Metamorphic rocks are a feature of the major mountain belts (chapter 18). They are especially important in providing evidence of what happens during subduction.

Appendix B will help you in identifying the most common metamorphic rocks.

From your study so far of earth materials and the rock cycle, you know that rocks change, given enough time, when their physical environment changes radically. **Metamorphism** is the transformation of pre-existing rock into texturally or mineralogically distinct new rock as a result of high temperature, high pressure, or both, but without the rock melting in the process.

The new rock, the **metamorphic rock,** in nearly all cases has a texture clearly different from that of the *original* rock, or **parent rock.** When limestone is metamorphosed to marble, for example, the fine grains of calcite coalesce and recrystallize into larger calcite crystals. The calcite crystals are interlocked in a mosaic pattern that gives marble a texture distinctly different from that of the parent limestone. If the limestone is composed entirely of calcite (without impurities), then metamorphosis into marble involves no new minerals, only a change in texture.

More commonly, the various elements of a parent rock react chemically and crystallize into new minerals, thus making the metamorphic rock distinct both mineralogically and texturally from the parent rock. This is because the parent rock is unstable in its new environment. The old minerals recrystallize into new ones that are at equilibrium in the new environment. For example, clay minerals form and are stable under low temperature and pressure conditions, such as we find at the earth's surface. When subjected to the temperatures and pressures deep within the earth's crust, the clay minerals of a shale can recrystallize into coarse-grained mica. Another example is that under appropriate temperature and pressure conditions, a quartz sandstone with a calcite cement would be metamorphosed as follows:

$$CaCO_3 \;+\; SiO_2 \;\rightarrow\; CaSiO_3 \;+\; CO_2$$

| (calcite) | (quartz) | (a mineral called wollastonite) | (carbon dioxide gas) |

No one has observed metamorphism taking place, just as no one has ever seen a granite pluton form. What, then, leads us to believe that metamorphic rocks form in a solid state (i.e., without melting) at high pressure and temperature? Many metamorphic rocks found on the earth's surface exhibit contorted banding (figure 7.1). These rocks, now hard and brittle, would shatter if smashed with a hammer. But they must have been **plastic** (capable of being bent and molded under stress) to have been folded into such contorted patterns. Because high temperature and pressure are necessary to make rocks plastic, a reasonable conclusion is that these rocks formed at considerable depth, where such conditions exist. Had the rocks melted, however, the banding would have been destroyed.

Laboratory experiments provide further support for the concept that metamorphic rocks form in an environment of high temperature and pressure. Certain minerals found only in metamorphic rocks have been made artificially under the kind of temperature and pressure conditions that exist five or more kilometers below the earth's surface.

Figure 7.1 An outcrop of metamorphic rock in British Columbia. The bent and deformed rock layers indicate that the rock was plastic during metamorphism.
Photo courtesy of Geological Survey of Canada.

The role of hot water in forming *hydrothermal rocks* (discussed later in this chapter) furnishes some indirect evidence regarding metamorphic processes, although hydrothermal rocks are not true metamorphic rocks. Large amounts of hot water that pass through fractures in rocks and deposit material (veins of quartz and other minerals) produce hydrothermal rocks in the process. We can infer from this (and other evidence) that water is important in metamorphism because of its capacity for dissolving elements from one mineral and carrying them to other minerals with which they may react.

Factors Controlling the Characteristics of Metamorphic Rocks

A metamorphic rock owes its characteristic texture and particular mineral content to several factors, the most important being (1) the composition of the parent rock before metamorphism, (2) temperature and pressure during metamorphism, and (3) the effects of fluids, such as water.

Composition of the Parent Rock

Usually no new elements or chemical compounds are added to the rock during metamorphism, except perhaps water. (Metasomatism, discussed later in this chapter, does involve addition of other elements.) The mineral content of the metamorphic rock is therefore controlled by the chemical composition of the parent rock. For example, most metamorphic rocks have a fairly high amount of silica, which indicates that their parent rocks were also high in silica. A basalt would always be metamorphosed into a rock in which the new minerals could collectively accommodate the approximately 50 percent silica and relatively high amounts of the oxides of iron, magnesium, calcium, and aluminum in the original rock. On the other hand, a limestone, composed essentially of calcite ($CaCO_3$), could not be metamorphosed into a silica-rich rock.

Temperature

A mineral is said to be *stable* if, given enough time, it does not react with or convert to a new mineral or substance. Any mineral is stable only within a given temperature range. The stability temperature range of a mineral varies with factors such as pressure and the presence or absence of other substances. Some minerals are stable over a large range of temperature. Quartz, if not mixed with other minerals, is stable at atmospheric pressure (i.e., at the earth's surface) up to about 800°C. At higher pressures, quartz remains stable to even higher temperatures. Other minerals may be stable over a temperature range of only 100 or 200°C. By knowing the particular temperature range in which a mineral is stable, a geologist may be able to deduce the temperature of metamorphism for a rock that includes that mineral.

Minerals stable at higher temperatures tend to be less dense (or have a lower specific gravity) than chemically identical minerals stable at lower temperatures. This is because as temperature increases, the ions vibrate more within their sites in the crystal structure. A more open (less tightly packed) crystal structure allows greater vibrations of ions; high-temperature minerals tend to have such a structure. (If the heat and resulting vibrations become too great, the crystal breaks apart and the substance becomes liquid.)

Heat is also important because higher temperatures speed chemical reactions. If the temperature in an oven is raised a few degrees, a roast cooks much faster. Similarly, a chemical reaction proceeds much faster at higher temperature, provided that is is possible for a reaction to take place. Because of the slowness of reaction rates, metamorphism rarely takes place below about 200°C, even though minerals may be unstable at these temperatures.

The upper limit on temperature in metamorphism is the melting temperature of the rock involved. For an ultramafic rock containing only ferromagnesian silicate minerals, this could be over 1,000°C; for a granite or rhyolite under high water pressure, it could be as low as 700°C.

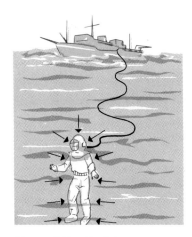

Figure 7.2   Confining pressure.

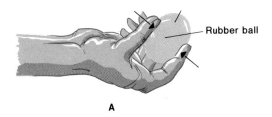

A

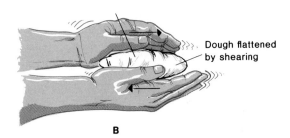

B

Figure 7.3   (*A*) Compressive directed pressure, and (*B*) shearing.

Pressure

Pressure involved in metamorphism is of two types—confining (static) pressure (figure 7.2) and directed (dynamic) pressure (figure 7.3).

Confining pressure   Pressure applied equally on all surfaces of a body is **confining** (or static) **pressure.** A diver senses confining pressure proportional to the weight of the water above. The pressure uniformly squeezes the diver's entire body surface. Likewise, an object buried deep within the earth's crust is compressed by strong confining pressure, which forces grains closer together and eliminates pore space.

Any new mineral that has crystallized under high pressure conditions tends to occupy less space than did the mineral or minerals from which it formed. The new mineral is denser than its low-pressure counterparts because the pressure forces atoms closer together in the crystal structure.

Directed pressure   Pressure applied unequally on the surfaces of a body is **directed** (or dynamic) **pressure.** Directed pressure tends to deform objects into spindle-shaped or flattened forms. If you squeeze a rubber ball between your thumb and forefinger, you are exerting **compressive directed pressure** on the ball. If you squeeze a ball of dough, it will remain flattened after you stop squeezing, because dough is plastic.

Directed pressure is also caused by **shearing,** when parts of a body move or slide relative to one another and parallel to the forces being exerted. If you flatten a ball of dough by rolling a rolling pin over it, this involves shearing. Note in the figure that shearing flattens the object *parallel* to the applied pressure, whereas directed compressive pressure flattens the object *perpendicular* to the applied pressure.

A rolling pin exerts shearing force to crush crackers into crumbs. Similarly, intense shearing caused by movements within the earth's crust (tectonic forces) grinds pre-existing minerals into finer grains. The increased amount of surface area on which reactions may take place facilitates chemical reactions. Shearing also tends to mix the ground-up fragments by moving grains past one another. Two mineral grains whose elements can react to form a new mineral are likely to be moved into contact with each other, thus allowing a new mineral to form.

Foliation

Directed pressure has a very important influence on the texture of a metamorphic rock because it forces the constituents of the rock to become parallel to each other. The parallel alignment of textural and structural features of

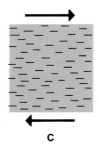

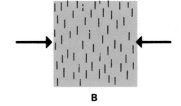

Figure 7.4   Orientation of platy minerals in metamorphic rocks. (*A*) Platy minerals randomly oriented. No directed pressure involved. (*B*) Platy minerals developed under the influence of compressive directed pressure. (*C*) Platy minerals developed under the influence of shearing.

a rock is called **foliation.** Foliation is manifested in various ways. If a platy mineral (such as mica) is crystallizing within a rock that is undergoing directed pressure, the mineral grows in such a way that it remains parallel to the direction of shearing or perpendicular to the direction of directed compression (figure 7.4). Any platy mineral attempting to grow against shearing is either ground up or forced into alignment. Minerals that crystallize in needlelike shapes (for example, hornblende) behave in a similar manner, growing with their long axes parallel to the plane of shearing or perpendicular to directed

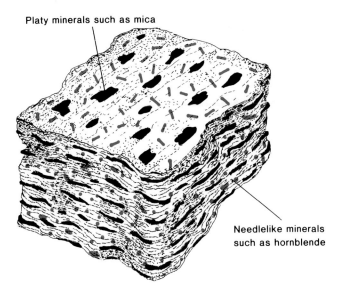

Platy minerals such as mica

Needlelike minerals such as hornblende

Figure 7.5 Schistose texture.

compression. The three very different textures described below are all variations of foliation and are important in classifying metamorphic rocks:

1. If the rock splits easily along nearly flat and parallel planes, indicating that pre-existing, microscopic, platy minerals were pushed into alignment during metamorphism, we say the rock is **slaty,** or that it possesses **slaty cleavage.**
2. If visible platy or needle-shaped minerals have grown essentially parallel to each other while under the influence of directed pressure, the rock is **schistose** (figure 7.5).
3. If the rock became very plastic and the new minerals separated into distinct (light and dark) layers or lenses, the rock has a layered or **gneissic** texture, such as in figure 7.1.

Engineers and builders must take foliation into account because bedrock can be moved with relative ease when a force is exerted parallel to foliation planes. Rockslides onto highways are a common hazard where roads built on slopes have been cut into foliated rock (see chapter 9).

Effects of Fluids

Water (as vapor) is by far the most important fluid involved in metamorphic processes, although other gases, such as carbon dioxide, sometimes play a role in metamorphism.

The only evidence in the rocks to indicate that water was present during metamorphism is that water is part of the crystal structures of many metamorphic minerals, whereas the presumed parent minerals were water-free. Water is thought to aid in triggering metamorphic chemical reactions. Apparently water under high pressure forces its way between grains, dissolves ions from one mineral, and then carries these ions elsewhere in the rock, where they can react with the ions of a second mineral. A new mineral forms that is stable under the existing conditions. Water can be thought of as a sort of intra-rock rapid transit for ions.

Time

The effect of time on metamorphism is hard to assess. Most metamorphic rocks are composed predominantly of silicate minerals, and silicate compounds are notorious for their sluggish chemical reaction rates. Many laboratory attempts to duplicate metamorphic reactions that are believed to occur in nature have been frustrated by the time element. The million or more years during which a particular combination of temperature and pressure may have prevailed in nature is a period of time even the most patient of researchers is unable to duplicate.

Classification of Metamorphic Rocks

As we noted before, the kind of metamorphic rock that forms is determined by the metamorphic environment (primarily the particular combination of pressure and temperature) and by the chemical constituents of the parent rock. A great variety of metamorphic rocks exists because of the numerous possible combinations of these factors. Classification of these rocks involves grouping them into categories based on similarities. (Appendix B contains a systematic procedure for identifying common metamorphic rocks.)

Box 7.1
Failure of the St. Francis Dam—
A Tragic Consequence of Geology Ignored

In 1928 the St. Francis Dam near Los Angeles, California broke, only a year after it had been completed. The concrete dam was about 60 meters (200 feet) high, and the wall that roared down the valley killed about 400 people in two counties.

The eastern edge of the dam had been built against a metamorphic rock with foliation planes parallel to the sides of the valley. Landslide scars in the valley should have been ample warning to the builders that the metamorphic rock moved, even under only the force of gravity. A competent engineer worries as much about the stability of the rock against which a dam is built as about the strength of the dam itself. Water pressure at the base of the dam exerted a force of 5.7 tons per square foot against the dam. With pressure such as this, the dam and part of the bordering foliated rock could easily slide. Movement would be parallel to the weak foliation planes, just as if the dam had been anchored against a giant deck of cards.

Ironically, investigators never found out for sure whether this was what caused the failure of the dam. Many other blunders had been made in construction, and any one of them could have caused the dam to break. The base of the dam was on a fault with ground-up rock; and, incredibly, the other side of the dam was built against rock that disintegrates in water. This is but one of many instances in which ignorance of geology cost lives and money. Had professional geological advice been sought, the dam probably would not have been built in that spot.

A

B

Figure 7.6 (*A*) The St. Francis Dam before failure (looking upstream). (*B*) The St. Francis Dam after failure (looking downstream). Note pieces of the dam carried downstream and the high-water mark in the standing segment of the dam.
Photos by California Department of Water Resources.

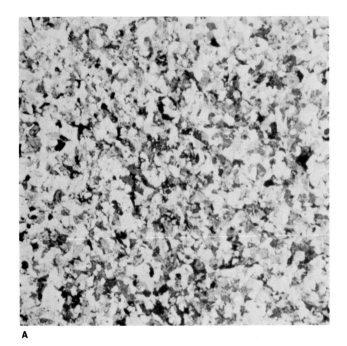

A

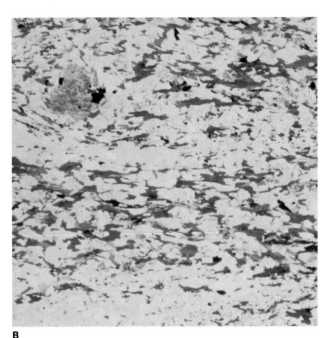

B

Figure 7.7 Photomicrographs of (A) nonfoliated rock and (B) foliated rock.

First consider the texture of a metamorphic rock. Is it *foliated* or *nonfoliated* (figure 7.7)? If the rock is nonfoliated, it is named on the basis of its composition. For example, a nonfoliated quartz-rich metamorphic rock is a *quartzite;* one composed almost entirely of calcite is a *marble.*

If the rock is foliated, you must determine what type of foliation is present. For example, a schistose rock is called a *schist.* But this name tells us nothing about what minerals are in this rock; so we add adjectives to describe the composition. Thus, a *garnet-mica schist* (whose parent was shale) is easily distinguishable from a *hornblende schist* (a metamorphic product of basalt). The relationship of texture to rock name is summarized in table 7.1.

Types of Metamorphism
The two most common types of metamorphism are contact or thermal metamorphism and regional or dynamothermal metamorphism. These are discussed below. Hydrothermal metamorphism, where hot water plays a major role, is discussed later in this chapter.

Contact (Thermal) Metamorphism
Contact or **thermal metamorphism** is metamorphism in which high temperature is the dominant factor. Confining pressure may influence which new minerals crystalize, but directed pressure is not involved in thermal metamorphism. Therefore, these rocks are nonfoliated.

Table 7.1
Classification and Naming of Metamorphic Rocks

Nonfoliated

Name Based on Mineral Content of Rock

Usual Parent Rock	Rock Name	Predominant Minerals
Limestone	Marble	Calcite
Dolomite	Dolomitic marble	Dolomite
Quartzose sandstone	Quartzite	Quartz
Shale	Hornfels	Fine-grained micas
Basalt	Hornfels	Fine-grained ferromagnesian minerals, plagioclase

Foliated

Name Based Principally on Kind of Foliation Regardless of Parent Rock. Adjectives are Used to Describe the Composition (e.g. biotite-garnet schist)

Texture	Rock Name
Slaty	Slate
Intermediate between slaty and schistose	Phyllite
Schistose	Schist
Gneissic	Gneiss

Usually the intense heat required for this process comes from magma intruding into the country rock. We can think of most instances of thermal metamorphism as the "cooking" of country rock in contact with an intrusion; hence, the common term *contact metamorphism.*

During contact metamorphism, shale is changed into the fine-grained metamorphic rock **hornfels.** Characteristically, microscopic micas develop. Sometimes a few minerals grow large enough to be seen—minerals that are especially capable of crystallizing under the particular temperature attained during metamorphism. Hornfels may also form from basalt, in which case hornblende or a related amphibole, rather than mica, is the predominant fine-grained mineral produced.

Limestone recrystallizes during metamorphism into **marble,** a coarse-grained rock composed of interlocking calcite crystals. Less commonly, dolomite recrystallizes into a **dolomitic marble.** Marble has long been valued as a building material and as a material for sculpture, partly because it is easily cut and polished and partly because it reflects light in a shimmering pattern, a result of the excellent cleavage of the individual calcite crystals. Marble is, however, highly susceptible to chemical weathering (chapter 5).

Quartzite is produced when grains of quartz in sandstone are welded together while the rock is subjected to high temperature. The boundaries are as hard as the individual grains. Quartzite, being as hard as a single quartz crystal, is therefore difficult to crush or break. It is the most durable of common rocks used for construction, both because of its hardness and because quartz is not susceptible to chemical weathering.

(Marble and quartzite can also form under conditions of regional metamorphism. These may be distinguished from their contact metamorphosed counterparts because they are foliated, as in a schistose marble.)

Regional (Dynamothermal) Metamorphism

The great majority of the metamorphic rocks found on the earth's surface are products of **regional** or **dynamothermal metamorphism,** which is metamorphism caused by relatively high temperature and pressure (directed and confining). Metamorphic rocks are prevalent in the most intensely deformed portions of mountain ranges. They are visible where once deeply buried cores of mountain ranges are exposed by erosion. Furthermore, large regions of the continents are underlain by metamorphic rocks, thought

Figure 7.8   Marble.

Table 7.2
Regional Metamorphic Rocks That Form under Approximately Similar Pressure and Temperature Conditions

Parent Rock	Rock Name	Predominant Minerals
Basalt	Amphibole schist (amphibolite)	Hornblende, plagioclase, garnet
Shale	Mica schist	Biotite, muscovite, quartz, garnet
Quartzose sandstone	Schistose quartzite	Quartz
Limestone or dolomite	Schistose marble	Calcite or dolomite
Ultramafic rock	Talc, chlorite schist	Magnesium amphibole, talc, chlorite

to be the roots of ancient mountains long since eroded down to plains or rolling hills. Because dynamothermal metamorphic rocks cover large areas, the term *regional metamorphism* is generally regarded as synonymous with dynamothermal metamorphism.

The high temperature associated with regional metamorphism is due to the great depth of burial, the heat generated by the friction of earth movements, and heat radiated from nearby magma bodies. The high confining pressure is due to burial under perhaps 10 or more kilometers of rock. The high directed pressure is a result of tectonism; that is, the constant movement and squeezing of the crust that takes place during mountain-building episodes.

Depending on the pressure and temperature conditions during metamorphism, a particular parent rock may recrystallize into one of several metamorphic rocks. For example, if basalt is metamorphosed at relatively low temperatures and pressures, it will recrystallize into a *greenschist,* a schistose rock containing chlorite (a green sheet-silicate), actinolite (a green amphibole), and sodium-rich plagioclase. At higher temperatures and pressures, the same basalt would recrystallize into an *amphibole schist* (also called *amphibolite*), a rock composed of hornblende, plagioclase feldspar, and, perhaps, garnet. Metamorphism of other parent rocks under conditions similar to those which produce amphibole schist from basalt should produce the metamorphic rocks shown in table 7.2.

Metamorphism of Shale

To show how rocks are changed by regional metamorphism, we look at what happens to shale during *progressive metamorphism*—that is, as progressively greater pressure and temperature act on a rock type with increasing depth in the earth's crust.

The metamorphic rock associated with the lowest pressure and temperature conditions of regional metamorphism is **slate,** a fine-grained rock that splits easily along flat, parallel planes (figure 7.9). Slate develops under temperatures and pressures only slightly greater than those found in the sedimentary realm. The temperatures are not high enough for the rock to recrystallize. The important controlling factor is intense shearing or compressive directed pressure. Shale, the parent rock, is formed largely of submicroscopic, platy, clay minerals. These minerals are simply realigned by the directed pressure, creating slaty cleavage in the rock. Sedimentary bedding may still be visible after metamorphism. Figure 7.9*B* shows slaty cleavage developed at an angle to the bedding. A slate indicates that a relatively cool and brittle rock has been subjected to intense tectonic activity.

Because of the ease with which it can be split into thin, flat sheets, slate is used for making blackboards, pool tables, and roofs.

Phyllite is a rock in which some of the clay minerals have recrystallized into microscopic micas. This requires a further increase in temperature and pressure. The extremely fine-grained mica imparts a silky sheen to the rock, which may otherwise closely resemble slate (figure 7.10). However, the slaty cleavage may be destroyed in the process of conversion of slate to phyllite.

A **schist** is characterized by coarse-grained, approximately parallel-oriented, minerals. Platy or elongate minerals that crystallize from the parent rock are clearly

A

B

Figure 7.9 (*A*) Slate outcrop in Antarctica. (*B*) Slaty cleavage that is nearly vertical developed at a high angle to bedding. (Light and dark layers are former sedimentary beds.)
Photo *A* by P. D. Rowley, U.S. Geological Survey.
Photo *B* by G. K. Gilbert, U.S. Geological Survey.

Figure 7.10 Phyllite, exhibiting a crinkled, silky-appearing surface.

Figure 7.11 Gneiss.
Photo by W. C. Irvin.

visible to the naked eye. Shale may recrystallize into several mineralogically distinct varieties of schist. Which minerals form depends upon the particular combination of temperature and pressure prevailing during recrystallization. For instance, if the rock is a *mica schist,* metamorphism probably took place at only slightly higher temperatures and pressures than those at which a phyllite would have formed. A *garnet-mica schist* indicates that a somewhat greater temperature and pressure prevailed than was necessary for a mica schist to form.

In a **gneiss,** a rock consisting of light and dark mineral layers or lenses, the highest temperatures and pressures have changed the rock so that minerals have separated into layers. Platy or elongate minerals (such as mica or amphibole) in dark layers alternate with layers of light colored minerals of no particular shape. In addition, coarse feldspars have crystallized and form part of the light-colored layers. In composition, a gneiss may resemble granite or diorite, but it is distinguishable from those plutonic rocks because of its foliation (figure 7.11).

Temperature conditions under which a gneiss develops approach those at which granite solidifies. It is not surprising, then, that the same minerals are found in gneiss and in granite. In fact, a previously solidified granite can be converted to a gneiss under high pressure and temperature conditions.

If the temperature becomes sufficiently high, partial melting of rock may take place, and a magma is sweated out into layers within the foliation planes of the solid rock. After the magma solidifies, the rock becomes a **migmatite,** a mixed igneous and metamorphic rock. A migmatite may be thought of as a "twilight zone" rock that is neither fully igneous nor entirely metamorphic. Migmatites may also be formed by metasomatism, as described later in this chapter.

Metamorphic facies   Because rocks such as schist are metamorphosed over a wide range of conditions, it has been useful to subdivide the various combinations of pressure and temperature into *stability fields,* such as is shown in figure 7.12. Each such field is called a metamorphic facies. Combinations of minerals in a rock are the bases for determining the **metamorphic facies** to which a rock belongs. Each metamorphic facies has a name (for example, *greenschist facies*). The diagram shows the relationships of the various facies to each other and to temperature and pressure. (A beginning geology student does not need to learn the names and compositions of all the facies, but he or she should understand the concept.)

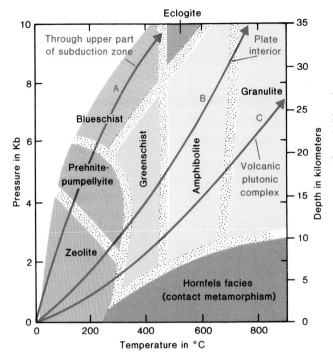

Figure 7.12 The metamorphic facies. Facies are named after minerals (prehnite, zeolite, pumpellyite) or rock types (e.g., blueschist, granulite). Boundaries between facies are approximate. The arrows represent increases in temperature with depth for the three lines shown in figures 7.13 and 7.14. From W. G. Ernst, *Metamorphism and Plate Tectonic Regimes.* Stroudsberg, Pa.: Dowden, Hutchinson & Ross, 1975; p. 425. Reprinted by permission of the publisher.

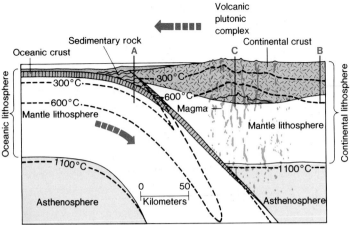

Figure 7.13 The 300°, 600°, and 1100° isotherms across a converging plate boundary. From W. G. Ernst, *Metamorphism and Plate Tectonic Regimes.* Stroudsberg, Pa.: Dowden, Hutchinson & Ross, 1975; p. 425. Reprinted by permission of the publisher.

By identifying the metamorphic facies of rocks presently cropping out on the surface, geologists can infer, within broad limits, the depth at which metamorphism took place. They may also be able to determine the corresponding temperature, again, within broad limits.

The concept of metamorphic facies is analogous to defining climatic zones by the combinations of plants found in each zone. A place where ferns, palm trees, and vines flourish would correspond to a climate with warm temperatures and abundant rainfall. On the other hand, a combination of palm trees, cactus, and sagebrush would imply a hot, dry climate. By way of analogy, assume that we have two specimens of schist, *A* and *B*; the parent rock of both is basalt. Schist *A* contains the minerals actinolite, chlorite, and epidote (all green minerals), that indicate (by metamorphic standards) low pressures and temperatures within the range of temperature and pressure combinations under which schist can crystallize. Schist *A* therefore belongs in the greenschist facies. In schist *B*, garnet and hornblende, also derived from basalt, imply a combination of higher pressure and higher temperature within the schist stability range. The presence of these minerals indicates that schist *B* belongs in the amphibolite facies.

Geothermal gradients Why do we get such wide ranges of temperature and pressure combinations? The main reason is that the *geothermal gradient* (the increase in temperature with depth, as described in chapter 4) is not the same everywhere in the world. Each of the three arrows (*A, B,* and *C*) in figure 7.12 represents a possible geothermal gradient. If you were somehow able to push a thermometer through the lithosphere, you would find the rock is hotter at shallower depths in areas with higher geothermal gradients than at places where the geothermal gradient is low. As indicated in figure 7.12, the geothermal gradient is higher progressing downward through an active volcanic-plutonic complex (for instance, the Cascade Mountains of Washington and Oregon) than it is in the interior of a plate (beneath the Great Plains of North America, for example).

Plate Tectonics and Metamorphism

The observed characteristics of metamorphic rocks are explainable in the context of plate tectonic theory. To demonstrate the relationship between regional metamorphism and plate tectonics, we will look at what is believed to take place at a converging boundary in which oceanic lithosphere is subducted beneath continental lithosphere, as shown in figures 7.13 and 7.14.

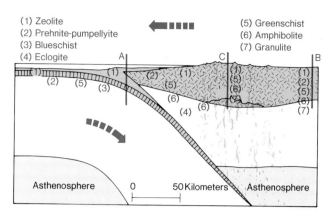

(1) Zeolite
(2) Prehnite-pumpellyite
(3) Blueschist
(4) Eclogite

(5) Greenschist
(6) Amphibolite
(7) Granulite

Figure 7.14 Schematic representation of the distribution of facies across a converging plate boundary.
From W. G. Ernst, *Metamorphism and Plate Tectonic Regimes.* Stroudsberg, Pa.: Dowden, Hutchinson & Ross, 1975; p. 426. Reprinted by permission of the publisher.

Table 7.3

Role of Water	Name of Process
No water	"Dry" metamorphism
Water merely transporting ions between grains in a rock	"Wet" metamorphism
Water brings ions from outside the rock, and they are added to the rock during metamorphism. Other ions may be dissolved and removed.	Metasomatism
Water passes through cracks or pore spaces in rock and precipitates minerals on the walls of cracks and within pore spaces.	Hydrothermal rocks

Directed pressure, which is responsible for foliation, would occur wherever rocks are being squeezed between the two plates or wherever rocks are sliding past one another. Shearing would be expected in, for example, the zone where the oceanic crust slides beneath the continental lithosphere. Compressive directed pressure would be present throughout wide zones in which rocks were caught, as if in a vise, between the continental and the oceanic crusts.

Confining pressure is directly related to depth (as shown in figure 7.12). For this reason, we would expect the same pressure at a depth of 20 kilometers beneath a volcanic area as beneath the relatively cool rocks of a plate's interior.

Heat is the most variable of the controlling factors of metamorphism. Figure 7.13 shows the temperatures calculated for a converging boundary. Lines connecting equal temperatures are called **isotherms.** Note how the 300°C, 600°C, and 1100°C isotherms change depth radically across the subduction zone. This is because rocks that were cool because they were relatively near the earth's surface have been transported rapidly to depth. The oceanic lithosphere along a subduction zone has not had time to heat up and come into thermal equilibrium with the relatively hot rocks elsewhere at these depths. On the top of the subducted oceanic slab, the extra heat provided by friction along with the heat that is normal for the overlying continental lithosphere and asthenosphere cause the isotherms to rise sharply toward the surface. The isotherms are bowed upward somewhat in the region beneath the volcanic zone because magma created along the lower levels of the subduction zone works its way upward and brings heat from the asthenosphere into the mantle and crust of the continental lithosphere.

If one were to determine the geothermal gradient at the three lines marked *A, B,* and *C* on figures 7.13 and 7.14, the temperatures for particular depths should plot on the corresponding arrows shown in figure 7.12. Follow arrow *A* in figure 7.12. This means that if you were able to drill vertically downward along line *A,* you would find, beneath unmetamorphosed rocks, rocks of the zeolite facies. At a greater depth would be the boundary between the zeolite and prehnite-pumpellyite facies. You would reach this boundary at a depth corresponding to 4 kilobars, and the temperature would be approximately 150°C. Your drill would penetrate rocks of the prehnite-pumpellyite facies until you reached the blueschist facies. In hole *B,* in the interior of the plate, the progression should be from zeolite facies to prehnite-pumpellyite facies to greenschist facies to amphibolite facies to granulite facies. Hole *C,* in the volcanic-plutonic complex, would not pass through the prehnite-pumpellyite facies but would go from zeolite facies to greenschist facies to amphibolite facies to granulite facies.

Hydrothermal Rocks

Rocks that have precipitated from hot water or have been altered by hot water passing through are hard to classify. As explained earlier, hot water is involved to some extent in most metamorphic processes. However, when rocks have been formed entirely by precipitation of ions derived from hydrothermal solutions, we cannot really call them metamorphic rocks. For this reason we prefer the term **hydrothermal rocks** for rocks formed by precipitation from solution in hot water.

Many gradations exist between hydrothermal rocks and rocks in which water merely assists the metamorphic process. These are summarized in table 7.3. The "dry" metamorphism referred to is relatively rare. Most of the examples given so far in this chapter probably took place with water present and so would be classed as "wet" metamorphism.

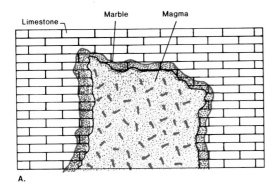

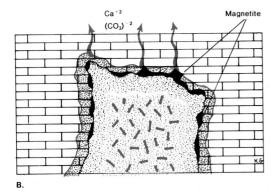

Figure 7.15 Development of a contact metasomatic deposit of iron (magnetite). (*A*) Magma intrudes country rock (limestone) and marble forms along contact. (*B*) As magma solidifies, gases bearing ions of iron leave the magma, dissolve some of the marble, and deposit iron as magnetite.

Metasomatism

Metasomatism is metamorphism coupled with the introduction of *ions* from an external source. The ions are brought in by water from outside the immediate environment and are incorporated into the newly crystallizing minerals. At the same time, the hot water may dissolve minerals that were part of the rock and carry them away.

If metasomatism is associated with contact metamorphism, the ions are introduced from a cooling magma. Some important commercial deposits of iron and other materials are of metasomatic origin (figure 7.15). Ions of the metal are transported by water and react with minerals in the host rock. Elements within the host rock are simultaneously dissolved out of the host rock and replaced by the metal ions brought in by the fluid. Because of the solubility of calcite, marble commonly serves as a host for metasomatic ore deposits.

Metasomatism that takes place during regional metamorphism produces quite different effects. When very hot water travels through a rock while gneiss or schist is crystallizing, ions (typically K^+, Na^+, Si^{+4}, and O^{-2}) carried by the water participate in metamorphic reactions. Large feldspar crystals may develop in schist due to addition of potassium or sodium ions. At the same time, magnesium

Figure 7.16 Migmatite in the North Cascades of Washington. Light layers are granitic.

and iron (the mafic components of the rock) may be removed by solution. Entire layers within a schist or gneiss may become granitic (composed predominantly of feldspar and quartz), forming a *metasomatic migmatite* (figure 7.16). The culmination of this process is conversion of the entire rock to predominantly feldspars and quartz. This process is called **granitization,** the metasomatic process by which granite is created from other rock without a melt being involved.

Hydrothermal Rocks

The most commonly found hydrothermal rocks are in veins. Veins consisting only of quartz are the most widespread, although some quartz veins contain other minerals. Veins having no quartz are less common; they may be composed of calcite or other minerals.

Quartz veins are especially common where igneous activity has occurred. These veins may form from hot water given off by a cooling magma; but probably they are mostly produced by ground water heated by the pluton and circulated by convection, as shown in figure 7.17. Where the water is hottest, more material is dissolved. As water vapor continues upward through progressively cooler rocks during its journey toward the earth's surface, it loses heat. The cooler water vapor can carry fewer ions in solution, and so the silicon and oxygen leave the water and cake onto the walls of the crack as silica (SiO_2), forming a quartz vein.

Hydrothermal veins are very important economically. They are the primary source of zinc, lead, silver, gold, and other metals on which industrialized civilization depends. Ore minerals containing these metals are found in quartz veins. Veins containing commercially extractable amounts of metals are by no means common (and might even be regarded as freaks of nature).

Metamorphism,
Metamorphic Rocks,
and Hydrothermal Rocks

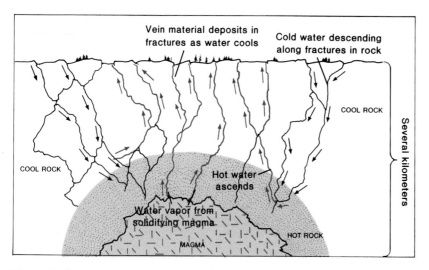

Figure 7.17 How veins form. Cold water descends, is heated, dissolves material, ascends, and deposits material as it cools upon ascending.

Some ore-bearing solutions percolate upward between the grains of the rock and deposit very fine grains of ore mineral throughout. These are called *disseminated ore deposits* and account for some of the largest mines in the world (see box 7.2).

Sources of Water

Where does the water come from? A logical explanation would be as follows. *Ground water* (the topic of chapter 11) seeps downward from the earth's surface through pores and fractures in rocks; however, the depth to which surface-derived water can penetrate is quite limited. Plate tectonics can account for water at deeper levels in the lithosphere as sea water trapped in the oceanic crust can be carried to considerable depths through subduction (figure 7.19). Water trapped in sediment and in sedimentary rocks lying on the basaltic oceanic crust is carried down with the descending crust. However, recent studies indicate that most of the water is carried by the basalt during its long journey from a mid-oceanic ridge to its plunge beneath a continent. When the water becomes sufficiently hot, it can work its way upward through the overlying continental lithosphere through fissures. In the process of ascending, water assists in the metamorphism of rocks, dissolves minerals, and carries the ions to interact during metasomatism, or it deposits quartz and other minerals in fissures as veins. The water can also play a role in lowering the melting points of rocks at depth, allowing magma to form. It later would be boiled off as the magma worked its way upward, cooled, and solidified.

Box 7.2
The United States' Largest Man-made Hole—The Bingham Canyon Copper Mine

The biggest man-made hole in North America is located at Bingham Canyon near Salt Lake City, Utah. The 800-meter-deep open pit mine is more than 3.5 kilometers wide at the top and is being continuously enlarged. The reason for this hole is copper. About half a million tons of rock are blasted apart and moved each day. Power shovels take a five-ton gulp of rock at a time to load railroad cars. The railway, owned by the mining company, weaves its way up the spiral of 15-meter-high terraces and leaves the pit through tunnels. The trains travel over 150 kilometers of track out of the pit to ore-processing plants nearby.

About 40,000 kilograms of explosives are used per day to blast apart over 100,000 tons of ore (copper-bearing rock) and three times that amount of waste rock.

Mining began here as a typical underground operation in the last century. The shafts and tunnels of the mine followed a series of veins. Originally ores of silver and lead were mined. Later it was discovered that fine-grained, copper-bearing minerals (chalcopyrite and other copper sulfide minerals) were disseminated in tiny pore spaces throughout a granite stock rather than restricted to the veins. Although the percentage of copper in the rock was small, the total volume of copper was recognized as huge. With efficient earth-moving techniques, large volumes of ore-bearing rock can be moved and processed. Today mining is still going on, and the company is able to make a profit even though less than 0.4 percent of the rock being mined is copper. Since 1904, 11 million tons of copper have been mined, processed, and sold. The mine has also produced

Figure 7.18 Bingham Canyon Copper Mine in Utah. Courtesy of Kennecott Copper Company.

impressive amounts of gold, silver, and other metals.

Obviously, such an operation is not without environmental problems. Many people regard the huge hole in the mountains as an eyesore. Disposing of the waste—over 99 percent of the rock material mined—creates problems. Wind stirs up dust storms from the piles of finely crushed waste rock unless it is kept constantly wet. The smelters that extract the pure copper from the sulfide minerals emit a toxic smoke containing sulfuric acid fumes. The prevailing winds blow the smoke away from Salt Lake City for all but a few days each year. A 360-meter-high smokestack was built as part of an emission control program that cost the company $280 million to meet federal health-related air standards.

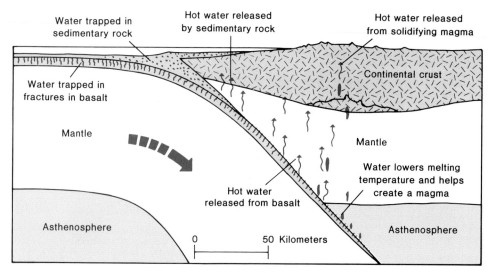

Figure 7.19 Behavior of water in a subduction zone. Sea water trapped in the oceanic crust is carried downward and released upon heating at various depths within the subduction zone.

Summary

Metamorphic rocks form from other rocks that are subjected to high temperature, generally accompanied by high pressure. Recrystallization takes place in the solid state although water, generally present, is an aid to metamorphic reactions. Pressure may be *confining pressure* or *directed pressure* or, more often, both. Directed pressure, either shearing or directed compressive pressure, is implied for foliated rocks (slate, phyllite, schist, gneiss).

Contact (or *thermal*) *metamorphic* rocks are produced during metamorphism without significant directed pressure but with high temperature. Generally contact metamorphism occurs in rocks immediately adjacent to intruded magmas.

Regional (or *dynamothermal*) *metamorphism,* which involves heat, confining pressure, and directed pressure, has created most of the metamorphic rock of the earth's crust. The concept of *metamorphic facies* is used to subdivide the widely varying combinations of pressure and temperature under which metamorphism can take place. Combinations of minerals found in a metamorphic rock indicate the metamorphic facies in which that rock recrystallized.

Hydrothermal rocks are formed when hot water precipitates material that crystallizes into minerals. During *metasomatism,* hot water introduces ions into a rock being metamorphosed, and so the chemical composition of the metasomatized rock is changed from that of the parent rock. *Migmatites* may be produced by metasomatism or by partial melting of a rock. *Granitization* is the process whereby a rock becomes granitic through metasomatism.

Plate tectonic theory accounts for the features observed in metamorphic rocks and relates their development to other activities in the earth. In particular, plate tectonics explains: (1) the deep burial of rocks originally formed at or near the earth's surface; (2) intense squeezing necessary for the directed pressure, implied by foliated rocks; (3) the presence of water deep within the lithosphere; and (4) the wide variety of pressures and temperatures believed to be present during metamorphism.

Terms to Remember

compressive directed pressure
confining pressure
contact (thermal) metamorphism
directed pressure
foliation
gneiss
gneissic
granitization
hornfels
hydrothermal rock
isotherm
marble; dolomitic marble
metamorphic facies
metamorphic rock
metamorphism
metasomatism
migmatite
parent rock
phyllite
plastic
quartzite
regional (dynamothermal) metamorphism
schist
schistose
shearing
slate
slaty
slaty cleavage

Questions for Review

1. What are the various sources of heat for metamorphism?
2. How do regional metamorphic rocks differ in texture from contact metamorphic rocks?
3. Why is it possible to get such a variety of combinations of pressure and temperature environments during metamorphism?
4. How would you distinguish:
   a. schist and gneiss
   b. slate and phyllite
   c. quartzite and marble
   d. granite and gneiss
5. Why do regional metamorphic rocks present hazards that should be taken into account by builders and engineers?
6. Why would an edifice built with blocks of quartzite be more durable than one built of marble blocks?

Questions for Thought

1. What happens to originally horizontal layers of sedimentary rock when they are subjected to the deformation associated with regional metamorphism?
2. What metamorphic and hydrothermal effects would be expected in the vicinity of a spreading center?
3. Why is it unlikely that a batholith would form through granitization?
4. Where in the earth's crust would you expect most migmatites to form?

Supplementary Readings

Ernst, W. G. 1969. *Earth materials.* Englewood Cliffs, N.J.: Prentice-Hall.

Ernst, W. G., ed. 1975. *Metamorphism and plate tectonic regimes.* Stroudsburg, Pa.: Dowden, Hutchinson & Ross, Inc.

Hyndman, D. W. 1972. *Petrology of igneous and metamorphic rocks.* New York: McGraw-Hill.

Zim, H. S., and P. R. Shaffer. 1967. *Rocks and minerals.* New York: Golden Press.

8

Time and Geology

Purpose

The immensity of geologic time is hard for humans to perceive. We find it unusual when someone lives a hundred years, but a person would have to live 10,000 times that long to observe a geologic process that takes a million years. In this chapter we try to help you develop a sense of the vast amounts of time over which geologic processes have been at work. As mentioned in chapter 1, the principle of *uniformitarianism* helped radically to change our view of life and the universe. Acceptance of this principle made people aware of the vast amounts of time involved in the earth's history.

To determine what those time spans are—how many years ago a rock formed—requires special techniques of radioactive dating, also described in this chapter. To geologists, however, being able to assign years (absolute age) to a process, significant as it is, is less important than establishing relative time and the sequence in which events have occurred. This chapter explains how to apply several basic principles to decipher a sequence of events responsible for geologic features. These principles can be applied to many aspects of geology—as, for example, in understanding geologic structures (chapter 15). The complex history of mountain belts (chapter 18) also assumes a knowledge of the techniques for determining relative ages of rocks.

Correlation—determining age relationships between geographically widely separated rock units—is necessary to gain an understanding of the geologic history of a region, a continent, or the whole earth. Substantiation of the plate tectonics theory depends on intercontinental correlation of rock units and geologic events, piecing together evidence that the continents were once one great body.

Widespread use of fossils for correlation led to the development of the standard geologic time scale. Originally based on relative age relationships, the subdivisions of the standard geologic time scale have now been assigned absolute ages through radioactive dating. Think of the geologic time scale as a sort of calendar to which events and rock units can be referred. Its major subdivisions are referred to frequently in this book.

The Key to the Past

We who live in the twentieth century are not so resistant to the concept of the immensity of geologic time as were those who lived two or three centuries ago. Then everyone in the western world believed that the earth was only a few thousand years old (although apparently the Chinese had a better concept of the age of the universe). In early Christendom, geologic events were placed within a biblical chronology, and catastrophic happenings were believed to account for features of the landscape. When rocks several thousand meters above sea level seemed to have been formed of sediment deposited in water (even to containing fossils similar to modern marine organisms), the explanation was that a worldwide inundation had simply drowned all the earth's mountains in a matter of days. Because no known physical laws could account for such events, processes of divine intervention were invoked. In the late 1700s, however, a Scottish naturalist, James Hutton (mentioned in chapter 1), proposed the radical idea that features observed on earth could be explained by natural processes that were still going on in the present. This idea became known as the principle of **uniformitarianism,** meaning that the geological processes operating at present are the same processes that have operated in the past. More succinctly: "The present is the key to the past."

For example, we may see silt and clay settling out of ocean or lake water, and we may also observe the processes of compaction and cementation that turn such sediment into the rock *shale*. If we find a similar layer of shale at a mountain top or exposed near the bottom of Grand Canyon (figure 8.1), we may, according to the concept of uniformitarianism, presume that the shale was formed through a similar process.

What made the idea of uniformitarianism so difficult for eighteenth-century scholars to accept was the vast amount of time that it implied. Layers of shale more than 2,000 meters thick are visible at many places on earth, yet our observations tell us that in most places silt and clay settle on ocean floors at rates of less than a millimeter a year. The time required to form a thousand meters of shale, then, would be more than a million years—far longer than the few thousand years Hutton's contemporaries believed the earth had existed.

The principle of uniformitarianism can be applied too rigidly if common sense is ignored. We cannot use uniformitarianism to claim that exactly the same *amount* of volcanic activity went on during the geologic past as at present. But by examining older rocks and comparing them with rocks being formed now by active volcanoes,

Figure 8.1   Grand Canyon, Arizona.

we can get a reasonably accurate picture of volcanism in the distant geologic past. In short, the principle of uniformitarianism provides assurance that physical and chemical laws were operative in the past as well as the present, and that, moreover, we need not invoke "magical" processes to explain geological features.

Acceptance of the principle of uniformitarianism led, of course, to the realization that geology involves time periods much greater than a few thousand years. But how long? Were the rocks near the bottom of Grand Canyon, for instance, formed closer to 10,000 or 100,000 or 1,000,000 or 1,000,000,000 years ago? What geologists needed was some "clock" that began working when rocks formed. Such a "clock" was found when radioactivity was discovered. Radioactive dating (discussed later in this chapter) allows us to determine a rock's **absolute age** (age given in years or some other unit of time). Geologists, however, usually are more concerned with **relative time,** the *sequence* in which events took place, rather than the number of years involved.

The difference between absolute age and relative time is shown in these statements:

"Uncle George planted the plum tree sometime between the time when little Oscar was born and the time when the house across the street burned down." This statement gives the time of an event (planting a tree) relative to other events.

But speaking in terms of absolute age: "Let's see, Uncle George planted that plum tree about four and a half, maybe five, years ago." Note that absolute age does not mean *exact* age, merely age given in units of time. Because most geologic problems are concerned with the sequence of events, we discuss relative time first.

Relative Time

The geology of an area may seem, at first glance, to be hopelessly complex. A nongeologist might think it impossible to decipher the sequence of events that created such a geologic pattern. However, a geologist has learned to approach seemingly formidable problems by breaking them down to a number of simple problems. As an example, the geology of Grand Canyon, shown in figure 8.1, may be analyzed in four parts: (1) horizontal layers of rock; (2) inclined layers; (3) rock underlying the inclined layers (plutonic and metamorphic rock); and (4) the canyon itself, carved into these rocks. Each part of the problem can be analyzed and interpreted. Ultimately the regional sequence of geologic events can be determined by piecing together the history of the individual parts.

Principles Used to Determine Relative Age

Most of the individual component parts of the larger problem are solved by applying several simple principles (or laws, as some prefer to call them) while studying the exposed rock. In this way the sequence of events or the relative time involved can be determined.

Generally we start with the last, or youngest, event to affect the geology of an area of interest and then work toward older events. The block diagram shown in figure 8.2 is similar to the geology of the Grand Canyon area. What sequence of events can you think of that might be responsible for the rock patterns? (You might briefly study the block diagram and see how much of the geologic history of the area you can decipher before reading further.)

To determine the relationship of geologic events to one another, three basic principles are applied one at a time. These are the principles of (1) *original horizontality,* (2) *superposition,* and (3) *cross-cutting relationships.* These three principles will be used in interpreting figure 8.2. (All the layers in the drawing represent sedimentary rock originally deposited in a marine environment.)

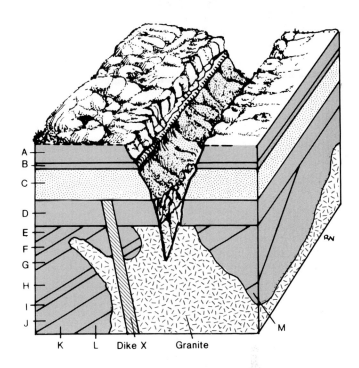

Figure 8.2 Block diagram representing an area somewhat similar to the Grand Canyon.

Original horizontality The principle of **original horizontality** states that beds of sediment deposited in water formed as horizontal or nearly horizontal layers (as described in chapter 6). The few exceptions (such as cross-bedding associated with deltas) are easily identifiable as such by the geologist and can be ignored in this discussion.

Note that beds *A* through *D* in figure 8.2 are horizontal. Evidently their original horizontal attitude has not changed since they were deposited. Beds *E* through *M*, however, must have been tilted after they were deposited as horizontal layers. By applying the principle of original horizontality, we have determined that a geologic event—tilting of bedrock—occurred after beds *E* through *M* formed. We can also see that the tilting event did not affect beds *A* through *D*.

Superposition The principle of **superposition** states that within a sequence of undisturbed sedimentary rocks, the layers get younger going from bottom to top.

It is obvious that if sedimentary rock is formed by sediment settling onto the sea floor, then the first (or bottom) layer must be there before the next layer can be deposited on top of it. The principle of superposition also applies to layers formed by multiple lava flows, where one lava flow is superposed on a previously solidified earlier flow.

Applying the principle of superposition, we can determine that *A* in figure 8.2 is the youngest layer of sedimentary rock, *B* the next youngest, and *D* the oldest of the still horizontal sedimentary layers. Similarly, we assume that layers *E* through *M* were originally horizontal (by the first principle). By mentally restoring them to their horizontal position, we can see that the youngest bed of that sequence is *E* and that beds *F* through *M* are progressively older.

Cross-cutting relationships The third principle can be applied to determine the remaining age relationships in figure 8.2. The principle of **cross-cutting relationships** states that a disrupted pattern is older than the cause of disruption. A layer cake (the pattern) has to be baked (established) before it can be sliced (the disruption).

To apply this principle, look for disruptions in patterns of rock. Note that the valley in figure 8.2 is carved into the horizontal rocks as well as into the underlying granite. The sedimentary beds on either side of the valley appear to have been sliced off, or *truncated*, by the valley. (Undisturbed sedimentary beds would normally become thinner toward the edges rather than stop abruptly.) So the event that caused the valley must have come after the sedimentation responsible for beds *A* through *D*. That is, the valley is younger than these layers.

We can also apply the principle of cross-cutting relationships elsewhere in the figure. The igneous dike *X*, which formed when magma filled a crack and solidified, is truncated at the bottom of layer *C* (it is very unlikely that the intrusion would have ended abruptly along a straight line there), which tells us that layer *C* is younger than the dike. On the other hand, dike *X* truncates layers *D* through *I* and also extends through the granite body. Therefore, dike *X* must have intruded after layer *D* was deposited. The base of layer *D* truncates layers *E* through *M* as well as the top of the granite body. Therefore, layer *D* is younger than both layers *E* through *M* and the granite. The granite has, in turn, truncated layers *M* through *G*; therefore, the granite is younger than those units.

From what we have learned through application of the three principles, we can now describe a geological history of the area represented in figure 8.2. Figures 8.3 through 8.11 show what the area was like going backward in time. Normally, progressing from youngest to oldest makes it easier to decipher events that took place. The last, or most recent, event to occur was the carving of the valley because, as can be seen, the valley sides truncate the youngest layers of rock.

The principle of *superposition* tells us that layer *A* is the youngest sedimentary rock unit (figure 8.3). Layer *A* and its predecessors, *B* and *C*, were deposited as horizontal layers beneath the sea (figure 8.4).

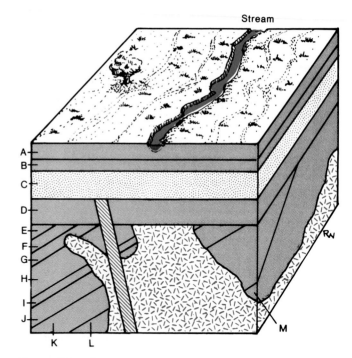

Figure 8.3 Same area as shown in figure 8.2 but before valley was carved into rock.

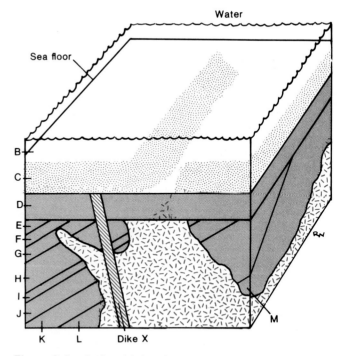

Figure 8.4 Sediment being deposited which will become part of layer *C*.

The principle of *cross-cutting relationships* tells us that dike *X* formed before layer *C* was deposited. Therefore, there was a break in sedimentation between layers *D* and *C*. The dashed and colored rocks at the tops of figures 8.5 and 8.6 represent an undeterminable amount

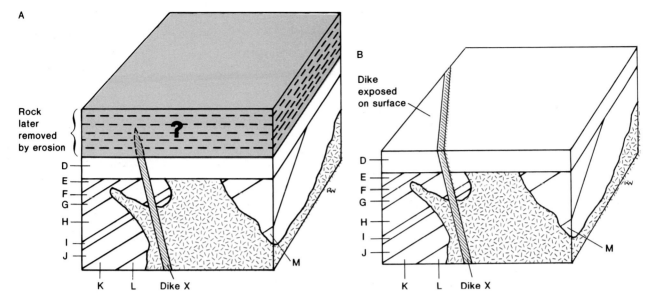

Figure 8.5 (A) Dike intruded into layer D and pre-existing overlying layers of indeterminable thickness. (B) The area after the rock layers above layer D were removed.

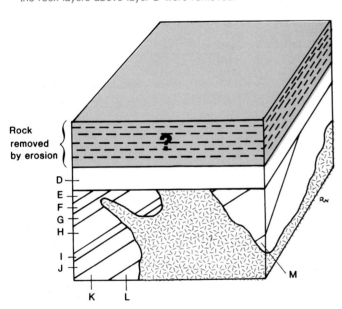

Figure 8.6 Area before intrusion of dike. Thickness of layers above D is indeterminable.

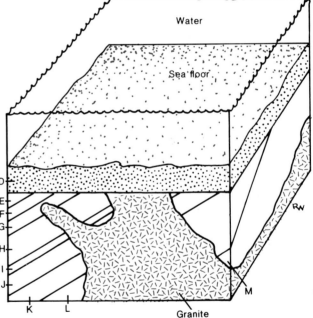

Figure 8.7 The area at the time layer D was being deposited.

of rock that was formed *after* layer D was deposited. These sedimentary layers were intruded by the dike (figure 8.5A). Then erosion removed the layers and part of the dike (figure 8.5B) *before* sedimentation began again, and layer C was deposited.

Figure 8.7 shows layer D being deposited. But before layer D could have been deposited, the surface on which it lies must have developed. That surface truncates the inclined layers and the granite body (figure 8.8) by cross-cutting relationships. It therefore has to be younger than either the granite or the inclined layers. The most likely cause of the truncation and the surface development is erosion.

From the principle of *original horizontality,* we infer that layers E through M must have been tilted after they formed. Figure 8.9 shows them in their original horizontal position.

The truncation of layers G through M by the granite tells us that the granite intruded sometime after layer G was deposited. Figure 8.10 shows the sequence of rocks E through M before the intrusion of granite.

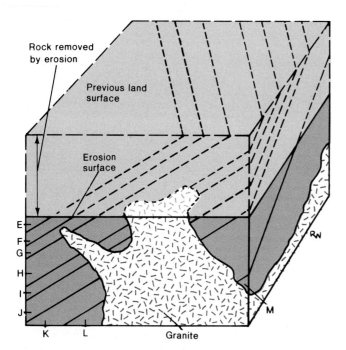

Figure 8.8 Area before deposition of layer *D*. Dashed lines show rock probably lost through erosion.

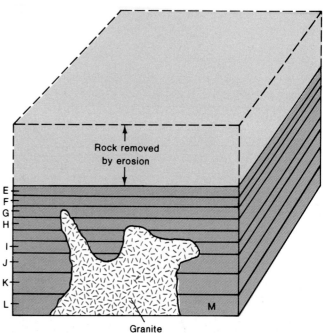

Figure 8.9 The area before layers *E* through *M* were tilted.

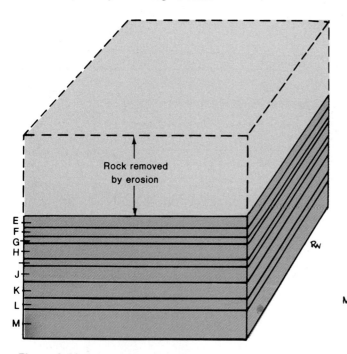

Figure 8.10 Area before the intrusion of the granite body.

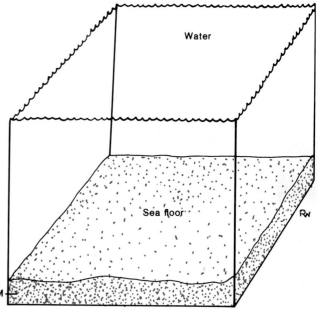

Figure 8.11 Area during deposition of the initial sedimentary layer.

By *superposition,* we know that layer *M*, the lowermost rock unit in the tilted sequence, must be the oldest rock shown in the diagram. Figure 8.11 shows the initial step in the entire rock sequence—the deposition of sediment that will form layer *M*.

Note that there are limits on how precisely we can determine the relative age of the granite body. It definitely intruded *before* unit *D* was deposited and *after* unit *G* was deposited. As no cross-cutting relationships can be observed between layers *E* or *F* and the granite, we cannot say whether the granite is younger or older than *E* or *F*. Nor, for that matter, can we determine whether the granite formed before, during, or after the tilting of the lower sequence of sedimentary rocks.

When combined with common sense and a knowledge of geology, several aids can be used in addition to the three basic principles to determine relative time. For example, we can look for signs of *contact metamorphism* (chapter 7) in the rocks of layers *G* through *M* immediately adjacent to the granite body, to see if they have been baked by the heat of the granitic magma. (The base of *D* in contact with granite would not be baked because *D* was deposited after the granite had cooled.)

We must also point out some special circumstances under which these three principles do not apply. For example, intense deformation by tectonic forces can overturn or disrupt beds to such an extent that the principle of superposition cannot be used (see chapter 15). A geologist must avoid being dogmatic in applying principles.

Correlation

In geology, **correlation** usually means the determination of *age relationships* between rock units or geologic events in separate areas.

A geologist may want to tie in the geology of an area he or she has investigated with adjacent areas studied by others. Or a geologist may want to correlate rocks and events in distant parts of the world to understand better how the earth has evolved. Part of the evidence in support of the theory of plate tectonics (and its predecessor, continental drift) depends on correlation of rocks in South America and Africa to see whether rock units of the same age could once have been continuous units. Various methods of correlation are described below.

Physical continuity Finding **physical continuity**—that is, being able physically to trace the course of a rock unit—is one way to correlate rocks between two different places. In figure 8.12 the prominent white layer of cliff-forming rock exposed along the upper part of Grand Canyon can be seen all the way across the photograph. You can physically follow this unit for several tens of kilometers, thus verifying that, wherever it is exposed in Grand Canyon, it is the same rock unit. Grand Canyon is an ideal location for correlation of rock units by physical continuity. However, it is not possible to follow this rock unit from the Grand Canyon into another region because it is not continuously exposed. We usually must use other methods to correlate rock units between regions.

Similarity of rock types Under some circumstances, correlation between two regions can be made by assuming that similar rock types in two regions formed at the same time. This method must be used with extreme caution, especially if the rocks being correlated are common ones.

To show why correlation by similarity of rock type does not always work, we can try to correlate the thick, white, cliff-forming layer in Grand Canyon (shown in figure 8.12) with a rock unit of similar appearance in Zion National Park about a hundred kilometers away. Figure 8.13 shows that both units are white sandstone. Cross-

Figure 8.12 The upper layers of sedimentary rock in Grand Canyon.

A

B

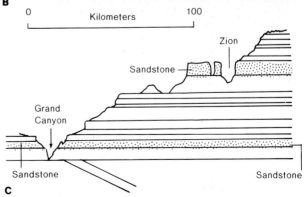

C

Figure 8.13 (*A*) Sandstone unit in Grand Canyon. (*B*) Sandstone unit in Zion National Park. (*C*) Schematic cross section through the Colorado plateau.

Box 8.1
Sedimentary Rock Layers That Transgress Time

Being able physically to follow a single prominent layer of sedimentary rock over a long distance is not a guarantee that the entire unit was deposited at exactly the same time period. An apparently continuous rock layer in which different portions formed at different times is called a **time-transgressive rock unit.** Figure 8.14 illustrates how one may form.

Sand is deposited along the shoreline of a beach while the land slowly subsides. In time the entire region has subsided. The sand layer, which is younger to the right and older to the left, is buried by more sediment. Ultimately the time-transgressive sand becomes lithified into sandstone.

No break in time occurs during the forming of time-transgressive rock units, and the difference in age between the younger and older portions of the layer generally is not great, geologically speaking. In some cases there may be no evidence to indicate that a rock unit is time-transgressive, and the geologist usually regards the entire rock unit as essentially of one age.

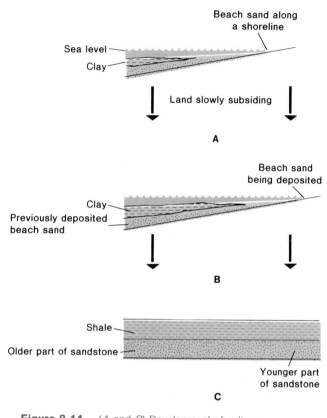

Figure 8.14 (*A* and *B*) Development of a time-transgressive sandstone bed. (*C*) Magnified view of layers after lithification.

bedding indicates that both were once a series of sand dunes. It is tempting to correlate them and conclude that both formed at the same time. But by piecing together the geology between the two units through a combination of physical continuity *and* use of the principle of superposition, it becomes clear that the sandstone in Zion is younger than that in Grand Canyon.

Correlation by similarity of rock types is more reliable if a very unusual sequence of rocks is involved. If you find in one area a layer of green shale on top of a red sandstone that, in turn, overlies basalt of a former lava flow, and then find the same sequence in another area, you probably would be correct in concluding that the two sequences formed at essentially the same time.

Correlation by fossils Fossils are common in sedimentary rock, and their presence is important for correlation. Plants and animals that lived at the time the rock formed were buried by sediment, and their fossil remains are preserved in sedimentary rock. Most of the fossil species found in rock layers are now extinct. (The same definition of *species* is used in geology as in biology.)

In a thick sequence of sedimentary rock, the fossils nearer the bottom (that is, in the older rock) are more unlike today's plants and animals than are those near the top. As early as the beginning of the nineteenth century, biologists began to notice that fossils in one layer of sedimentary rock often differ markedly from fossils in the layer above (or below). It became clear that many species of plants or animals existed only during the time that certain sedimentary layers were being deposited. Some species survived through the time interval represented by rock layers thousands of meters thick. Other species, confined to thin sequences of rock, apparently became extinct after a relatively short existence on earth. These observations, verified around the world, became formalized into the principle of **faunal succession:** Fossil species succeed one another in a definite and recognizable order. In general, fossils in progressively older rock show increasingly greater differences from species now living. Plants and animals have tended to evolve from simpler to more complex species through geologic time. The regularity of changes in species of fossils through successive layers is one of the very strong lines of evidence supporting the theory of evolution.

Historical geology is concerned with the study of life and changes in life forms throughout geologic time as well as with the physical evolution of the earth. *Paleontologists,* specialists in the study of fossils, have patiently and meticulously over the years identified thousands of species of fossils and determined which plant and animal species lived during which subdivision of geologic time. They have also been able to describe the physical environment in which the fossil species lived.

No matter where on earth they are found, individual fossil species always occur in the same sequence relative to one another. By comparing fossils found in a layer of rock in one area with similar fossils in another area, we can correlate the two rock units. More accurately, we can say that both rock units formed during the span of time that the species existed on the earth.

Ideally, a geologist hopes to find an **index fossil,** a fossil from a very short-lived species known to exist during a specific period of geologic time. A single index fossil allows the geologist to correlate the rock in which it is found with all other rock layers in the world containing that fossil.

Many fossils are of little use in time determination because the species thrived during too large a portion of geologic time. Sharks, for instance, have been in the oceans for a long time so discovering a shark's tooth in a rock would not be very helpful in determining the rock's relative age.

A geologist is likely to find several different fossils in a rock. Such a **fossil assemblage** is generally more useful for dating rocks than a single fossil would be, for the sediment must have been deposited at a time when all the species represented existed (figure 8.15).

Some fossils are restricted in geographic occurrence, representing organisms adapted to special environments. However, many formerly living organisms apparently lived over most of the earth, and fossil assemblages from these may be used for worldwide correlation. Fossils in the lowermost horizontal layers of Grand Canyon (figure 8.16) are comparable to ones collected in Wales, Great Britain, and a number of other places in the world. We may, therefore, correlate these rock units and say they formed during the same general span of geologic time.

The Standard Geologic Time Scale
Geologists can use fossils in rock to refer the age of the rock to the **standard geologic time scale,** a worldwide relative time scale. Based on fossil assemblages, the geologic time scale subdivides geologic time. On the basis of fossils found, a geologist may say, for instance, that the rocks of the lower portion of horizontal layers in Grand Canyon formed during the *Cambrian Period.* This implicitly correlates these rocks with certain rocks in Wales (in fact, the period takes its name from Cambria, the Latin name for Wales) and elsewhere in the world where similar fossils occur.

The geologic time scale, shown in a somewhat abbreviated form in table 8.1, has had tremendous significance as a unifying concept in the physical and biological sciences. The working out of the evolutionary chronology by successive generations of geologists and other scientists has been a remarkable human achievement. The geologic time scale, representing an extensive fossil record, consists of three **eras,** which are subdivided into **periods,** which are, in turn, divided into **epochs.** (Remember that this is a relative time scale.)

Precambrian denotes the vast amount of time that preceded the Paleozoic Era (which begins with the Cambrian Period). The **Paleozoic Era** (meaning "old life") began with the appearance of abundant and complex life, as indicated by fossils. Rocks older than Paleozoic contain few fossils. This is because creatures with shells or other hard parts, which are readily preserved in fossils, did not evolve until the beginning of the Paleozoic.

The **Mesozoic Era** (meaning "middle life") followed the Paleozoic. On land, reptiles were the dominant animals of the Mesozoic (this was the time when dinosaurs lived). We live in the **Recent** (or **Holocene) Epoch** of the **Quaternary Period** of the **Cenozoic Era** (meaning "new life"). The Quaternary also includes the most recent ice ages, which were part of the **Pleistocene Epoch.**

Absolute Age
Only within the few decades since the discovery of radioactivity have scientists been able to determine absolute ages of rock units. From these data we have been able to assign absolute values to the geologic time scale and so determine how many years ago the various eras, periods, and epochs began and ended. We can now state with a high degree of confidence that the Cenozoic Era began some 63 million years ago, the Mesozoic Era started about 240 million years ago, and the Precambrian ended (or the

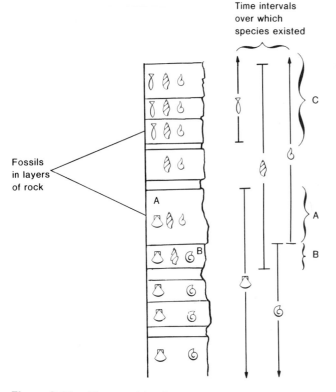

Time intervals
over which
species existed

Fossils
in layers
of rock

Figure 8.15 The use of fossil assemblages for determination of relative ages. Rock *A* contains 🝁 🝂 🝃. Therefore, it must have formed during time interval *A*. Rock *B* contains 🝄 🝅 🝆. Therefore, it must have formed during time interval *B*. Rock *C* contains 🝇 🝈 🝉. Therefore, it must have formed sometime during time interval *C*.

Figure 8.16 A trilobite several centimeters long. Fossils similar to this are found in the lowermost horizontal layers of Grand Canyon.
Photo by National Park Service, Grand Canyon National Park.

Paleozoic began) about 570 million years ago. The Precambrian includes most of geologic time, because the age of the earth is commonly regarded to be about 4.5 billion years. (Soviet geologists feel that 6 billion years is a better estimate.) The oldest rocks found on earth have been dated at about 3.8 billion years old. The 4.5-billion-year estimated age of the earth comes from various lines of evidence, mostly worked out by astronomers and planetary geologists who feel that all the planets formed about this long ago.

Radioactive Dating

Radioactivity can, under certain conditions, be used as a clock that began working when certain types of rocks formed. We can compare the amount of radioactive elements present with the amount of their radioactive decay products present and thereby determine how much time has elapsed since the rocks formed because we know the rate of radioactive decay or change.

Isotopes and radioactive decay As discussed in chapter 2, every atom of an element possesses the same number of protons in its nucleus. The number of neutrons, however, need not be the same in all atoms of the same element. The **isotopes** of a given element have different numbers of neutrons (but the same number of protons).

Uranium, for example, commonly occurs as two isotopes, U-238 and U-235. The former has 238 protons and neutrons in its nucleus, whereas the latter has 235 (figure 8.17). Of these particles, 92 (the atomic number of uranium) must be protons and the rest neutrons. U-238 weighs slightly more than U-235 and may be separated from it by special equipment because of the difference in mass.

Radioactive decay is the spontaneous nuclear disintegration of certain isotopes. As protons and neutrons leave these atoms, energy is produced. The particles departing from radioactive elements can be detected by a Geiger counter or similar device.

When protons are lost during radioactive decay, the atom becomes a different element. When a uranium-238 atom disintegrates radioactively, it loses a total of 32 protons and neutrons, in a complex series of steps, before becoming a nonradioactive, stable atom. Having lost 32 subatomic particles (out of 238), the now-stable atom has 206 neutrons and protons left. Ten of the lost particles are protons; so the atomic number has changed from 92 to 82, and the atom is now the element lead (abbreviated Pb) (figure 8.18). Specifically, it is the Pb-206 isotope. Lead-206 is the **daughter product,** the isotope produced by radioactive decay, of U-238.

An isotope of potassium, K-40, converts to argon, A-40, through a different process. From time to time a K-40 nucleus captures one of its orbiting electrons. The negative charge of the electron neutralizes a single positively charged proton. The proton becomes a neutron. Since there is one less proton in the nucleus, that atom no longer is a potassium atom (atomic number 19), but an argon atom (atomic number 18).

Table 8.1
Geologic Time Scale

Era	Period	Epoch
Cenozoic	**Quaternary**	Recent (Holocene) Pleistocene
	Tertiary	Pliocene Miocene Oligocene Eocene Paleocene
Mesozoic	**Cretaceous** **Jurassic** **Triassic**	
Paleozoic	**Permian** **Pennsylvanian** **Mississippian** **Devonian** **Silurian** **Ordovician** **Cambrian**	

Precambrian Time

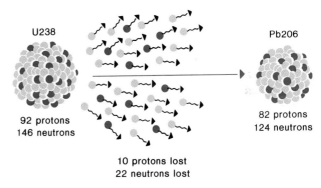

92 protons
146 neutrons

10 protons lost
22 neutrons lost

82 protons
124 neutrons

Figure 8.18 U-238 disintegrates radioactively to Pb-206 (intermediate daughter products are not shown).

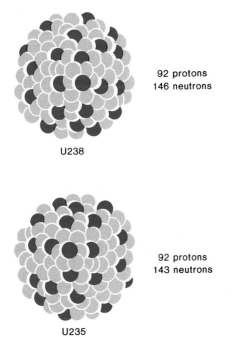

92 protons
146 neutrons

U238

92 protons
143 neutrons

U235

Figure 8.17 Nuclei of isotopes of U-238 and U-235.

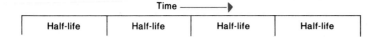

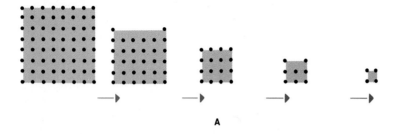

A

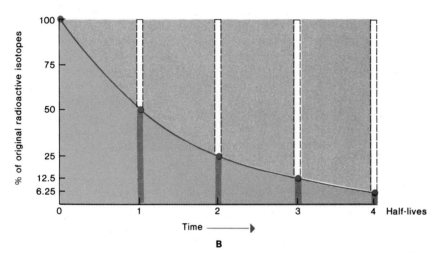

B

Figure 8.19 The curve used to determine the age of a rock by comparing the percentage of radioactive isotope left to the original amount. Heavy bars show the amount left after each half-life. Dashed bars show the amount disintegrated into daughter product and lost nuclear particles. The numbers of dots in the squares above the graph are proportional to the numbers of atoms.

Radioactive elements are useful for determining age because in a large number of atoms of a radioactive element, the *rate* of radioactive decay is nearly constant. Even a rock possessing a small fraction of a percent of uranium contains millions of uranium atoms. The rate at which atoms periodically decay is apparently unaffected by the high pressures and high temperatures of the earth's interior.

The decay rate for isotopes is given in terms of **half-life,** the time it takes for a given amount of a radioactive isotope to be reduced by one-half. (The other half would have disintegrated into daughter products.) The half-lives of some elements are measured in fractions of seconds. K-40, however, has a half-life of 1.3 billion years. If you began with one milligram of K-40, 1.3 billion years later one-half milligram of K-40 would remain. After another

1.3 billion years, there would be one-fourth of a milligram, and after another half-life only one-eighth of a milligram. (Note that two half-lives do not equal a whole life.)

To determine the age of a rock by using K-40, the amount of K-40 in that rock must first be determined by chemical analysis. The amount of A-40 (the daughter product) must also be determined and then used to calculate how much K-40 was present when the rock formed. By knowing how much K-40 originally was present in the rock and how much is still there, we may calculate the age of the rock on the basis of its half-life by simple mathematics. The graph shown in figure 8.19 demonstrates the mathematical relationship between a radioactively decaying isotope and time.

Table 8.2

Radioactive Isotopes Commonly Used for Determination of Ages of Rocks

Isotope	Half-Life	Daughter Product
K-40	1.3 billion years	Ar-40
U-238	4.5 billion years	Pb-206
U-235	713 million years	Pb-207
Th-232	14.1 billion years	Pb-208
Rb-87	49 billion years	Sr-87

Uses of radioactive dating Some problems must be dealt with if a meaningful and accurate date is to be obtained from a rock. Laboratory technicians must be highly skilled to operate the sophisticated equipment used in radioactive dating. Most successfully dated rocks are igneous, which, since they solidified from a melt, are unlikely to be contaminated by previously formed daughter products. Sedimentary rock cannot usually be dated by radioactive means. Inaccurate ages may be calculated for metamorphic rock because heat during metamorphism may have driven out some of either the daughter product or the radioactive isotope. In addition, chemically weathered rocks cannot be dated because of the material lost during weathering.

The potassium-argon (K-Ar) method is effective for dating a wide range of ages (from a few hundred thousand years to several billion years) because of its long half-life and because potassium is common in a wide variety of rocks. The disadvantage of the potassium-argon method is that argon is a gas and can be easily lost from rocks.

Table 8.2 shows the commonly used isotopes for dating rocks. U-238/Pb206, U-235/Pb-207, and Th-232/Pb-208 are used mainly for dating older geologic events (millions or billions of years). The two U-Pb systems are particularly useful if used together, since they provide internal cross-checks on the ages and can be used to get more accurate results.

Radiocarbon dating Because of its short half-life of 5,730 years, radiocarbon dating is useful only in dating things and events back to about 50,000 years (about 9 or 10 half-lives). The technique is most useful in archaeological dating and for very young geologic events (Recent, or Holocene, volcanic and glacial features for instance).

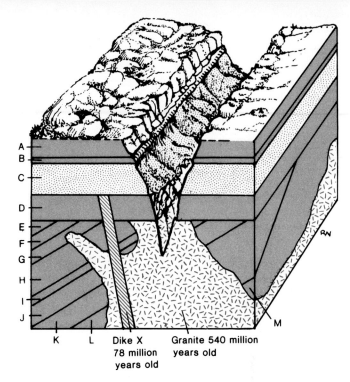

Figure 8.20 Same area as shown in figure 8.2 but with radioactive dates for igneous rocks indicated.

Most of the carbon in the air is carbon-12, but a minute fixed amount is radioactive carbon-14. Living matter incorporates C-12 and C-14 into its tissues; the ratios of C-12 and C-14 in the new tissues are usually the same as in the atmosphere. On dying, the organism ceases to build new tissue. The C-14 disintegrates radioactively at the fixed rate of its half-life (5,730 years). The radioactive emissions per gram of carbon from the plant or animal remains are determined. The greater the radioactivity, the younger the sample. By comparing the radioactivity per gram to previously determined standards, we may indirectly determine the ratio of C-12 to radioactive C-14 in organic remains, and we can determine the time elapsed since the death of the organism.

Combining Relative and Absolute Ages

Radioactive dating can be used to provide absolute time brackets for events whose relative ages are known. Figure 8.20 adds radioactive dates for each of the two igneous bodies to the diagram in figure 8.2. The date obtained for the granite is 540 million years B.P. (before present), while dike X formed 78 million years ago. We can now state that the tilted layers G through M formed before 540 million years ago (though we cannot say how much older they are). We still do not know whether layers E and F are older or younger than the granite because of the lack of cross-cutting relationships. Layer D's age is bracketed by the age of the granite and the age of the dike. That is, it is between 540 and 78 million years old. Layers A through C are younger than 78 million years old; how much younger we cannot say.

Through combining many radioactive dates from sites carefully selected for well-known relative age relationships, geologists have been able to assign absolute ages to the geologic time scale (table 8.3). Radioactive dating has also allowed us to extend the time scale back into the Precambrian. The Proterozoic and the Archean are the two major subdivisions of Precambrian time. There is, of course, a margin of uncertainty in each of the given dates, reflected in their being rounded off. The beginning of the Paleozoic, for instance, might be off by some 30 million years. The uncertainty is because of inherent limitations on the dating techniques as well as problems in selecting the ideal rock for dating. For instance, if you wanted to obtain the date for the end of the Paleozoic Era and the beginning of the Mesozoic Era, the ideal rock would be one found where there is no break in deposition of sediments between the two eras, as indicated by fossils in the rocks. But the difficulties in dating sedimentary rock make it unlikely that you would be able to date such rocks, even if you found them. Therefore, you must find and date igneous rocks that seem to have solidified, according to cross-cutting relationships or other evidence, at *about* the time of transition between the two eras.

Table 8.3
Geologic Time Scale

Era	Period	Epoch	Approximate Age in Millions of Years Before Present
Cenozoic	Quaternary	Recent (Holocene)	.01
		Pleistocene	2
	Tertiary	Pliocene	5
		Miocene	24
		Oligocene	38
		Eocene	55
		Paleocene	63
Mesozoic	Cretaceous		138
	Jurassic		205
	Triassic		240
Paleozoic	Permian		290
	Pennsylvanian		330
	Mississippian		360
	Devonian		410
	Silurian		435
	Ordovician		500
	Cambrian		570
Precambrian Time Proterozoic Eon			
Archean Eon			2,500
Formation of Earth			4,500

Box 8.2

The Longest Movie Never Shown—The Earth's Story

One way of trying to visualize and comprehend geologic time is to compare it to a motion picture. A movie is projected at a rate of 16 frames per second; that is, each image is flashed on the screen for only 1/16 of a second, giving the illusion of continuous motion. But suppose that each frame represented 100 years. If you lived a hundred years, one frame would represent your whole lifetime.

If we were able to show the movie on a standard projector, each 100 years would flash by in 1/16 of a second. It would take only ⅛ of a second to go back to the signing of the Declaration of Independence. The 2,000-year-old Christian era would be viewed for 1¼ seconds. A section showing all time back to the last major ice age would only be 11¼ seconds long. However,

you would have to sit through more than 11 hours of film to view a scene at the close of the Mesozoic Era (perhaps you would see the last dinosaur die). And it would take more than four days of continuous showing of this epic film to give a complete record from the beginning of the Paleozoic Era. You would have to spend over a month (32½ days) in the theater, without even a popcorn break between reels, to see a movie entitled "The Complete Story of Earth, from Its Birth to Modern Civilization."

Thinking of our lives as taking less than a frame of such a movie can be very humbling. From the perspective of that one frame, geologists would like to know what the whole movie is like or, at least, get a synopsis of the most dramatic parts of the film.

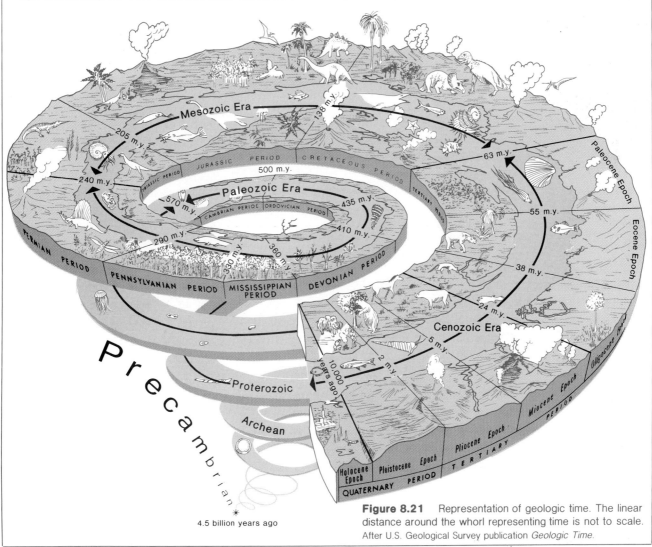

4.5 billion years ago

Figure 8.21 Representation of geologic time. The linear distance around the whorl representing time is not to scale. After U.S. Geological Survey publication *Geologic Time.*

Summary

The *principle of uniformitarianism,* a fundamental concept of geology, states that the present is the key to the past.

Relative time, or the sequence in which geologic events occur in an area, may be determined by applying the principles of *original horizontality, superposition,* and *cross-cutting relationships.*

Rocks in separate areas may be correlated by determining physical continuity of rocks between the two areas (generally this works only for a short distance). A less useful means of correlation is similarity of rock types (which must be used cautiously).

Similarity of *fossil assemblages* is used for worldwide correlation of rocks. Sedimentary rocks are assigned to the various subdivisions of the *geologic time scale* on the basis of fossils they contain, which are arranged according to the principle of *faunal succession.*

Absolute age—how many years ago a geologic event took place—is generally obtained by using *radioactive dating* techniques. Absolute ages have been determined for the subdivisions of the geologic time scale.

Terms to Remember

absolute age	Paleozoic Era
Cenozoic Era	periods
correlation	physical continuity
cross-cutting relationships	Pleistocene Epoch
daughter product	Precambrian
epochs	Quaternary Period
eras	radioactive decay
faunal succession	Recent (Holocene) Epoch
fossil assemblage	relative time
half-life	standard geologic time scale
index fossil	superposition
isotope	time-transgressive rock unit
Mesozoic Era	uniformitarianism
original horizontality	

Questions for Review

1. Suppose you had a radioactive isotope X whose half-life in disintegrating to daughter product Y is 10,000 years. By calculating how much it took to make the present amount of $Y,$ you determine that, originally, the rock contained 8 grams of isotope X. At present only ¼ gram of X is in the rock. How old is the rock?
2. What percentage of the earth's history is Precambrian?
3. Why is it desirable to use more than one fossil in a rock unit to determine its relative age?
4. By applying the various principles, draw a cross-section of an area in which the following sequence of events occurred:
    (a) Several layers of sedimentary rocks were deposited in the Cambrian through Devonian Periods on a much older Precambrian basement of metamorphic rock.
    (b) No record exists of Mississippian through Triassic rocks.
    (c) Intrusion of a stock occurred in Jurassic time.
    (d) Tilting and erosion to a flat plain preceded deposition of a sedimentary layer in late Cretaceous.
    (e) In the Tertiary Period, more and steeper tilting affected the entire area.
    (f) Erosion during the Quaternary Period created slightly hilly terrain.
    (g) Following erosion, a volcano with a feeder dike erupted in recent time.

Questions for Thought

1. Moon rocks have been dated that are considerably older than any dated on earth. Give a hypothesis to explain this.
2. As indicated by fossil records, why have some ancient organisms survived through very long periods of time whereas others have been very short-lived?
3. To what extent would a composite volcano (chapter 3) be subject to the three principles described in this chapter?
4. Suppose a sequence of sedimentary rock layers were tilted into a vertical position by tectonic forces. How might you determine (a) which end was originally up, and (b) the relative ages of the layers?
5. Note that in table 8.3 the epochs are given only for the Cenozoic Era (as is commonly done in geology textbooks). Why are the epochs for the Mesozoic and Paleozoic considered less important and not given?
6. Why would you not be able to use the principle of superposition to determine the age of a sill (defined in chapter 4)?

Supplementary Readings

Eicher, D. L. 1976. *Geologic time.* 2nd ed. Englewood Cliffs, N.J.: Prentice-Hall.

Harbaugh, J. W. 1968. *Stratigraphy and geologic time.* Dubuque, Iowa: Wm. C. Brown Company Publishers.

9

Mass Wasting

Purpose

When material on a hillside has weathered (the process described in chapter 5), it is likely to move downslope because of the pull of gravity. Such movement of soil and rock at the earth's surface is called mass wasting. Mass wasting is one of several erosion processes. Other processes of erosion (and deposition), involving streams, glaciers, wind, and ocean waves, are discussed in separate chapters.

Landsliding is probably the best known type of mass wasting, for sudden landslides can destroy towns and kill people. While these disasters involve *rapid* movement of debris and rock, mass wasting can also be very slow. A type of mass wasting too slow to be classed as a landslide is called creep.

In this chapter we describe how different types of mass wasting shape the land and alter the environment and what factors control the rapidity or slowness of the process. Understanding mass wasting and its possible hazards is particularly important in hilly or mountainous regions.

You may recall from previous chapters that mountains are products of tectonic forces. If tectonism were not at work, the surfaces of the continents long ago would have been reduced to featureless plains due to weathering and erosion. We consider the material on mountain slopes or hillsides to be out of equilibrium with respect to gravity. Because of the force of gravity, the various agents of erosion (moving water, ice, and wind) work to make slopes gentler and, therefore, increasingly more stable. The process of erosion discussed in this chapter is mass wasting.

Mass wasting (also called mass movement) is movement in which bedrock, rock debris, or soil moves downslope because of the pull of gravity. Mass wasting includes movement so slow as to be almost imperceptible (called *creep*) as well as **landslides,** a general term for the slow-to-very-rapid descent of rock or soil.

Mass wasting affects humans in many ways. Its effects range from the devastation of a killer landslide (see box) to the nuisance of having a fence slowly pulled apart

Box 9.1
Disaster in the Andes

As a result of a tragic combination of geological conditions, one of the most devastating landslides in history caused the destruction of the town of Yungay in Peru in 1970. Yungay was one of the most picturesque towns in the Santa River Valley, which runs along the base of the highest peaks of the Peruvian Andes. Heavily glaciated Nevado Huascaran, 6,663 meters (21,860 feet) above sea level, rises steeply above the populated narrow plains along the Santa River.

In May 1970 a sharp earthquake occurred. The earthquake was centered offshore from Peru about 100 kilometers from Yungay. Although the tremors in this part of the Andes were no stronger than those of some earthquakes that have done only light damage to cities in the United States, many poorly constructed adobe homes collapsed. Because of the steepness of the slopes thousands of small rockfalls and rockslides were triggered.

The greatest tragedy began when a slab of glacier ice about 800 meters wide, perched near the top of Huascaran, was dislodged by the shaking. (A few years earlier American climbers returning from the peak had warned that the ice looked highly unstable. The Peruvian press briefly noted the danger to the towns below, but the warning was soon forgotten.)

The mass of ice rapidly avalanched down the extremely steep slopes, breaking off large masses of rock debris, scooping out small lakes and loose

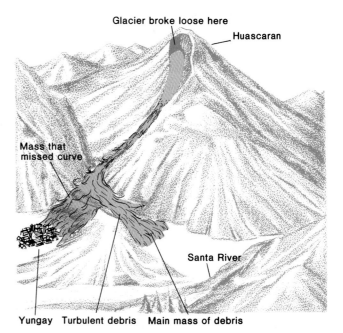

Figure 9.1 Diagram showing how the town of Yungay was destroyed.

rock that lay in its path. Eyewitnesses described the mass as a rapidly moving wall the size of a 10-story building. The sound was deafening. More than 50 million cubic meters of muddy debris fell 3.7 kilometers (12,000 feet) vertically and traveled 14.5 kilometers (9 miles) horizontally in less than 4 minutes, attaining speeds between 200 and 435 kilometers per hour (125 to 270

A

B

Figure 9.2 (*A*) Yungay buried beneath muddy debris and large boulders. Arrow shows where the mass of debris became airborne going over the ridge. Huascarán is in the background. (*B*) Yungay three years later. Tops of palm trees mark the site of the former town square.
Photo A by U.S. Geological Survey.

miles per hour). Some geologists believe that for the debris to travel that fast, a cushion of air must have formed under the moving mass to minimize friction between the debris and the land surface. In places the mass shot over ridges into the air like a huge cannonball. The main mass of material traveled down a steep valley until it came to rest blocking the Santa River and burying about 1,800 people in a small village. A relatively small part of the mass of mud and debris overtopped the valley sidewall, or ridge, as it came to a curve in the valley. The mass was airborne for a moment before it fell upon the town of Yungay below, completely burying it under several meters of mud and loose rock. Only the church steeple and the tops of palm trees could still be seen.

It was estimated that 17,000 people were killed in Yungay. This was far more than the town's normal population, for it was Sunday, a market day, and many families had come in from the country.

For several days after the slide the debris was too muddy for people to walk on, but within three years grass had grown over the site. Except for the church steeple and the tops of palm trees that still protrude above the ground, and the crosses erected by families of those buried in the landslide, the former site of Yungay would appear to be a scenic meadow overlooking the Santa River. The U.S. Geological Survey and Peruvian geologists found evidence showing that Yungay itself had been built on top of debris left by an even bigger slide in the recent geologic past. More slides will almost surely occur here in the future. Forewarned, the Peruvian government will not allow the building of a new town in the danger area.

Table 9.1

Some Types of Mass Wasting[1]

Type of Movement	Slowest	Increasing Velocities		Fastest
	Less than 1 cm/year	1 mm./day to 10 km/hour	1 to 5 km/hour	Velocities generally greater than 4 kilometers per hour
Flow	Creep (Debris)	Earthflow without slumping	Mudflow (Water-saturated debris)	Rock avalanche (Bedrock) Debris avalanche (Debris)
Slip		Earthflow (Debris) Earthflow with slumping	Rockslide (Bedrock) Debris Slide (Debris)	
Fall				Rockfall (Bedrock) Debris Fall (Debris)
		"Landslides"		

1. The type of material at the start of movement is shown in parentheses. Rates given are typical velocities for each type of movement.

by soil creep. In many cases of mass wasting, a little knowledge of geology, along with appropriate preventive action, could have averted destruction.

Whether slow, fast, or somewhere in between, the various kinds of mass wasting play an important role in the wearing away of the earth's surface.

Classification of Mass Wasting

A number of systems are used by geologists, engineers, and others for classifying mass wasting, but none has been universally accepted. Some are very complex and useful only to the specialist.

The classification system used here and summarized in table 9.1 is based on (1) rate of movement, (2) type of material, and (3) nature of the movement.

Rate of Movement

A landslide like the one in Peru clearly involved rapid movement. Just as clearly, movement of soil at a rate of less than a centimeter a year is slow movement. Between these extremes is a wide range. Some of the factors controlling the speeds at which mass movement takes place are discussed later in this chapter.

Type of Material

Mass wasting processes are usually distinguished on the basis of whether the descending mass started as bedrock (as in a rockslide) or as debris. The term **debris,** as applied to mass wasting processes, means any unconsolidated material at the earth's surface, such as soil and rock fragments (weathered or unweathered) of any size.

The amount of water (or ice and snow) in a descending mass strongly influences the rate and type of movement. This influence is explained later in this chapter.

Type of Movement

In general, the type of movement in mass wasting can be classified as mainly flow, slip, or fall (figure 9.3). A **flow** implies that the descending mass is moving downslope as a viscous fluid. **Slip** means the descending mass remains relatively coherent, with movement taking place along one or more well-defined surfaces. A **fall** occurs when material free-falls or bounces down a cliff (figure 9.3).

Two kinds of slips are shown in figure 9.3. In a **slide,** the descending mass moves along a plane approximately parallel to the slope of the surface. A **slump** involves movement along a curved surface, the upper part moving downward while the lower part moves outward.

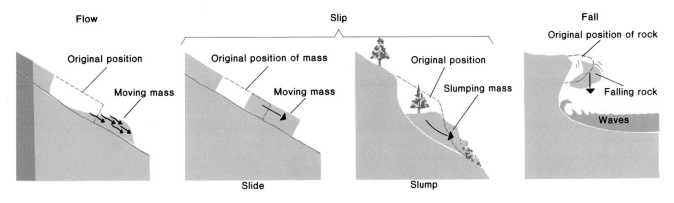

Figure 9.3   Flow, slip (slide and slump), and fall.

Table 9.2
Summary of Controls of Mass Wasting

Driving Force: Gravity		
Contributing Factors	**Most Stable Situation**	**Most Unstable Situation**
Slope angle	Gentle slopes or horizontal surface	Steep or vertical
Local relief	Low	High
Thickness of debris over bedrock	Slight thickness (usually)	Great thickness
Orientation of planes of weakness in bedrock	Planes at right angles to hillside slopes	Planes parallel to hillside slopes
Climatic factors		
Ice	Temperature stays above freezing	Freezing and thawing for much of the year
Water in soil or debris	Film of water around debris particles	Oversaturation of debris with water
Precipitation	Frequent but light rainfall or snow	Long periods of drought with rare episodes of heavy precipitation
Vegetation	Heavily vegetated	Sparsely vegetated

Triggering Mechanisms: 1. earthquakes; 2. weight added to upper part of a slope.

Controlling Factors in Mass Wasting

Table 9.2 summarizes the factors that influence the likelihood and the rate of movement of mass wasting. The table makes readily apparent some of the reasons why the landslide in Peru (box 9.1) occurred and why it moved so rapidly. (1) The slopes were exceptionally steep, and (2) the **relief** (the vertical distance) between valley floor and mountain summit was great, allowing the mass to pick up speed and momentum. (3) Water and ice not only added weight to the mass of debris, but also acted as lubricants. (4) Much loose rock and debris were available in the course of the slide. (5) Where the slide began, there were no plants with roots to anchor loose material on the slope. Finally, (6) the area was and is earthquake prone. Although the slide would have occurred eventually even without an earthquake, the earthquake acted as a trigger.

Other factors also influence susceptibility to mass wasting as well as rate of movement. The orientation of planes of weakness in bedrock (bedding planes, foliation planes, etc.) is important if the movement involves bedrock rather than debris. Fractures or bedding planes oriented so that slabs of rock can slide easily along these surfaces greatly increase the likelihood of mass wasting.

Table 9.2 indicates that climatic controls inhibit some types of mass wasting and aid others. Climate influences how much and what kinds of vegetation grow in an area and what type of weathering occurs. Infrequent but heavy rainfall aids mass wasting because it quickly saturates debris that lacks the protective vegetation found in wetter climates. By contrast, rain that drizzles intermittently much of the year tends to inhibit mass wasting. In cold climates, freezing and thawing contribute to downslope movement.

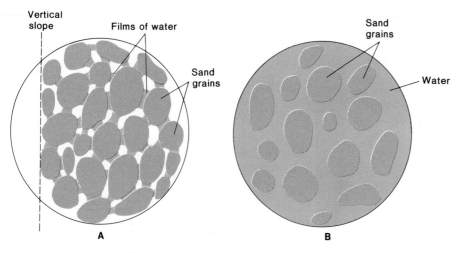

Figure 9.4 The effect of water in sand. (*A*) Unsaturated sand held together by surface tension of water. (*B*) Saturated sand grains forced apart by water; mixture flows easily.

Water

Water is a critical factor in downslope movement. When debris is saturated with water (as from heavy rain, or melting snow), it becomes heavier and is more likely to flow downslope. The added gravitational force due to the increased weight, however, is probably less important than the effect of water forcing grains of debris apart. This means that water is a very effective lubricant in debris that is sufficiently wet.

Paradoxically, a small amount of water in soil may actually prevent downslope movement. When water does not completely fill the pore spaces between the grains of soil, it forms a thin film around each grain (as shown in figure 9.4). Loose grains adhere to one another because of the *surface tension* created by the film of water. Surface tension of water between sand grains is what allows you to build a sand castle. The sides of the castle can even be vertical because surface tension holds the moist sand grains in place. Dry sand cannot be shaped into a sand castle because the sand grains slide back into a pile that generally slopes at an angle of about 30° to 35° from the horizontal. On the other hand, an experienced sand castle builder also knows that it is impossible to build anything with sand that is too wet. In this case the water completely occupies the pore space between sand grains, forcing them apart and allowing them to slide easily past one another. When the tide comes in, or someone pours a pail of water on your sand castle, all you have is a puddle of wet sand.

Similarly, as the amount of water in debris increases, rate of movement also tends to increase. Damp debris may not move at all, whereas moderately wet debris moves slowly downslope. Slow types of mass wasting, such as creep, are generally characterized by a relatively low ratio of water to debris. Earthflows tend to have and mudflows always have high ratios of water to debris. A mudflow that continues to gain water eventually becomes a muddy stream.

Box 9.2
Preventing Downslope Movement of Soil

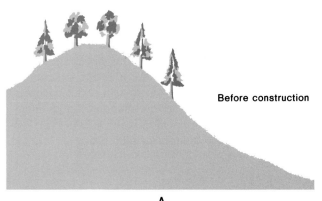

Before construction

A

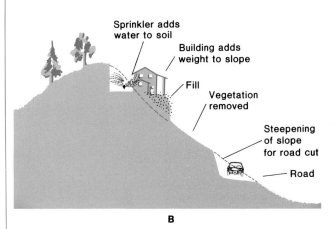

Sprinkler adds water to soil

Building adds weight to slope

Fill

Vegetation removed

Steepening of slope for road cut

Road

B

Figure 9.5 A hillside becomes vulnerable to mass wasting due to construction activities.

A Water trapped in soil causes movement, pushing down retaining wall.

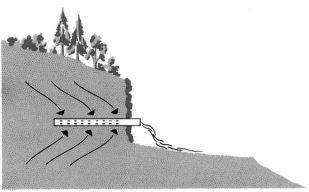

B Water drains through pipe, allowing wall to keep slope from moving.

Figure 9.6 Use of drains to aid in preventing mass wasting. (*A*) Water trapped in soil causes movement, pushing down retaining wall. (*B*) Water drains through pipe allowing wall to keep slope from moving.

Usually mass movements of debris can be prevented. Proper engineering is essential when the natural environment of a hillside is upset by construction activities. As shown in figure 9.5, construction activities generally make a slope more susceptible in several ways to mass wasting of debris. (1) The base of the slope is undercut, removing the natural support for the upper part of the slope. (2) Vegetation is removed during construction. (3) Buildings constructed on the upper part of a slope add weight to the potential slide. (4) Extra water may be allowed to seep into the debris.

Some preventive measures can be taken during construction. A retaining wall usually is built where a cut has been made in the slope, but this alone is seldom as effective a deterrent to downslope movement as people hope. If, in addition, drain pipes are put through the retaining wall and into the hillside, water can percolate through and drain away rather than collecting in the debris behind the wall (figure 9.6). Without drains, excess water may overcome the surface tension between grains. In this case, the trapped water acts as a lubricant and also adds weight to the debris, and eventually the whole soggy mass bursts through the wall.

Box 9.2 *Continued*

Another practical preventive measure is to avoid oversteepening the slope. The hillside can be cut back in a series of terraces rather than in a single steep cut. Besides removing much of the material that could add to the weight of a potential slide, this procedure prevents loose material (such as boulders dislodged from the top of the cut) from rolling to the bottom, knocking off more stones and debris during descent. Road cuts constructed in this way are usually reseeded with rapidly growing grass or plants whose roots can aid in anchoring the slope. A vegetation cover also minimizes erosion from running water.

Building a heavy structure high on a slope demands special precautions. To prevent movement of both the slope and the building, pilings may have to be sunk through the debris, perhaps even into bedrock. Developers may have to settle for fewer buildings than planned because too many structures will make the slope unsafe. If a thorough geologic study of conditions indicates that safe construction is not possible, the builders should be required by law to abandon the planned project. Even better would be zoning laws that prohibit construction in hazardous areas.

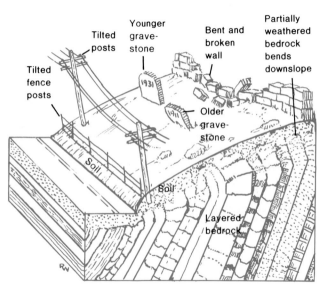

Figure 9.7 Indicators of creep.
After C. F. S. Sharpe.

Figure 9.8 Soil developed from vertical rock layers has crept downslope.
Photo by S. W. Lohman, U.S. Geological Survey.

Common Types of Mass Wasting

The common types of mass wasting were shown in table 9.1. Here we will describe each type in detail.

Creep

Creep is very slow, continuous, downslope movement of soil or unconsolidated debris. The rate of movement is usually less than a centimeter per year and can be detected only by observations taken over months or years. When conditions are right, creep can take place along nearly horizontal slopes. Some indicators of creep are illustrated in figures 9.7 and 9.8.

Two factors that contribute significantly to creep are water in the soil and daily cycles of freezing and thawing.

As we have said, if the ground is saturated with water, friction between grains is reduced and movement of soil downhill is facilitated. What keeps downslope movement from becoming more rapid in most areas is the presence of abundant grass or other plants that anchor the soil. Understandably, sloping pastures can be severely damaged by overgrazing.

Although creep does take place in year-round warm climates, the process is more active where the soil freezes and thaws during part of the year. During the winter in regions like the northeastern United States, the temperature may rise above and fall below freezing once a day or several times daily. When moisture is present in the soil, each freeze-thaw cycle moves soil particles a minute amount downhill, as shown in figure 9.9.

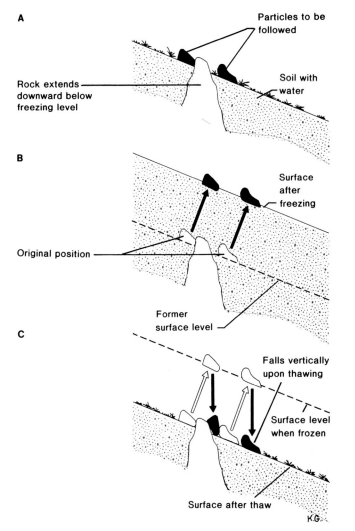

Figure 9.9 Movement downslope of soil as illustrated by following two particles during a freeze-thaw cycle.

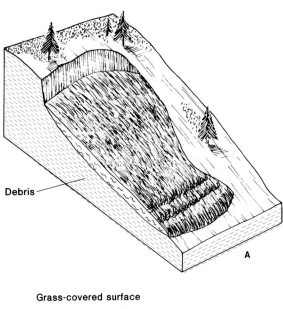

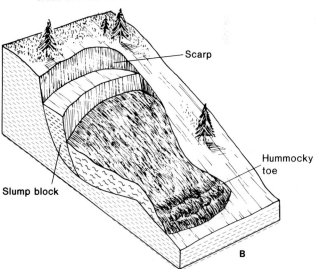

Figure 9.10 Earthflow. (*A*) Earthflow involving only flow. (*B*) Earthflow combining slip and flow.

Earthflow

In an **earthflow,** debris moves downslope as a viscous fluid; the process may be slow or rapid. Earthflows usually occur on hillsides that have a thick cover of debris, often after heavy rains have saturated the soil. Typically, the flowing mass remains covered by a blanket of vegetation, with a *scarp* (steep cut) developing where the moving debris has pulled away from the upper slope, which remains stationary.

An earthflow may be only a flow, with soil movement roughly parallel to the slope. Most earthflows, however, involve both slipping and flowing. Figure 9.10*B* shows how the upper part of an earthflow slumps downward as a relatively coherent block, shoving the lower part outward and causing the debris to flow downhill. Meanwhile, a hummocky lobe forms at the toe or front of the earthflow. An earthflow may be active over a period of hours, days, or months; in some earthflows intermittent slow movement continues for years.

A

B

Figure 9.11 Earthflows. (A) A small earthflow in California
(B) Earthflows in the Horse Heaven Hills, Washington. Lobes are
encroaching on the highway.
Photo A by G. K. Gilbert, U.S. Geological Survey.
Photo B by D. A. Rahm; courtesy Rahm Memorial Collection, Western
Washington University.

Figure 9.12 Earthflow at a coastal community in California. Photo by California Division of Mines and Geology.

Human activity can trigger earthflows by adding too much water to soil by septic tank systems or overwatering of lawns. In one case, in Los Angeles, a man departing on a long trip forgot to turn off the sprinkler system for his hillside lawn. The soil became saturated, and both house and lawn were carried downward on an earthflow whose lobe spread out over the highway below.

Earthflows, like other kinds of landslides, may be triggered by undercutting at the base of a slope. The undercutting may be caused by waves breaking along shorelines or streams eroding and steepening the base of a slope. Along coastlines, destruction of buildings by mass wasting is surprisingly common. Entire housing developments and expensive homes built for a view of the ocean are lost. A home buyer who knows nothing of geology is not likely to realize that the sea cliff is there entirely because of the relentless erosion of waves along the shoreline. Nor is the person likely to be aware of the potential for landslides that a steepened slope creates.

Bulldozers can undercut the base of a slope more rapidly than wave erosion, and such oversteepening of slopes by human activity has caused many landslides. Unless careful engineering measures are taken at the time a cut is made, roadcuts or platforms carved into hillsides for houses may bring about disaster.

Box 9.3
Solifluction and Permafrost

One variety of earthflow is usually associated with colder climates. **Solifluction** is the flow of water-saturated debris over impermeable material. Because the impermeable material beneath the debris prevents water from draining freely, the debris between the vegetation cover and the impermeable material becomes saturated (figure 9.13). Even a gentle slope is susceptible to movement under these conditions.

The impermeable material beneath the saturated soil may be either impenetrable bedrock or, as is more common, **permafrost**, ground that remains frozen over a period of many years. Most solifluction takes place in areas of permanently frozen ground, such as are found in Alaska and northern Canada. Permafrost occurs at depths ranging from a few centimeters to a few meters beneath the surface. The ice in permafrost acts as a cementing agent for the debris. When all the pores are filled with ice, the ground becomes a concretelike mass.

Above the permafrost is a zone that, if the debris is saturated, is frozen during the winter and so is indistinguishable from the underlying permafrost. When this zone thaws during the summer, the water, along with water from rain and runoff, cannot seep downward through the permafrost, and so the slopes become susceptible to solifluction.

Since solifluction movement is not rapid enough to break up the overlying vegetation cover into blocks, the water-saturated debris flows downslope, pulling vegetation along with it and forming a wrinkled surface. Gradually the debris collects at the base of the slope, where the vegetated surface bulges into a hummocky lobe.

Permafrost creates problems other than solifluction for those who build in the far north. In arctic and subarctic regions, great expanses of flat terrain become swampy during the summer because of permafrost, making overland travel very difficult. Building anything on permafrost terrain presents serious problems. In the preliminary stages of planning the Alaska pipeline, a road was bulldozed across permafrost terrain during the winter, removing the vegetation from

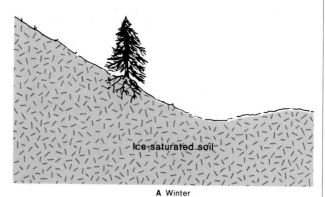

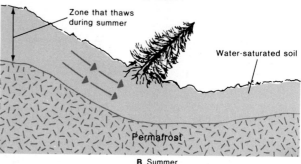

A Winter

B Summer

Figure 9.13 Solifluction due to thawing of ice-saturated soil.

Figure 9.14 A railroad built on permafrost terrain in Alaska.
Photo by Lynn A. Yehle, U.S. Geological Survey.

the rock-hard ground. It was an excellent truck route during the winter, but when summer came, the road became a quagmire several hundred kilometers long (see figure 1.8). The strip will never be usable to vehicular traffic as planned, nor will the vegetation return for many decades.

Figure 9.15 A dried mudflow in the Peruvian Andes.

Mudflow

A **mudflow** is a flowing mixture of debris and water, usually moving down a channel. It can be visualized as a stream with the consistency of a thick milkshake. Usually after a heavy rainfall a slurry of soil and water forms and begins moving down a slope. Most mudflows quickly become channeled into valleys. They then move downvalley like a stream except that, because of the heavy load of debris, they are more viscous. Mud moves more slowly than a stream but, because of its high viscosity, is capable of transporting boulders, automobiles, and even locomotives. Houses in the path of a mudflow will be filled with mud, if not broken apart and carried away.

Mudflows are more likely to occur in arid regions than in wet climates where a dense cover of vegetation protects soil and debris. A hillside in a desert environment, where it may not have rained for many years, may be covered with a blanket of loose material. With sparse desert vegetation offering little protection, a sudden thunderstorm with drenching rain can saturate the loose debris so rapidly that a mudflow is created in minutes.

Lack of vegetation can be the cause of mudflows in other situations. Mudflows frequently occur on young volcanoes that are littered with ash. Heavy rains or rapid melting of snow may provide the water. Alternatively, a mudflow can be triggered by renewed volcanic activity on a glaciated volcano, as occurred at Mount St. Helens in 1980 (figure 9.16). The heat from fresh, hot ash or a new lava flow melts glacial ice, mixing meltwater with loose pyroclastic debris and starting a mudflow. Mudflows also occur after forest fires have destroyed slope vegetation that normally anchors soil in place. Burned-over slopes are extremely vulnerable to mudflow if heavy rains fall before the vegetation is restored.

Figure 9.16 This 75-meter-long bridge on Washington state highway 504 across the North Fork of the Toutle River was washed out by mudflow during the May 18, 1980 eruption of Mount St. Helens. The steel structure was carried about .5 kilometers downstream and partially buried by the mudflow. R. L. Schuster, U.S. Geological Survey.

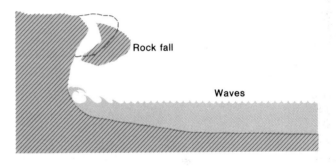

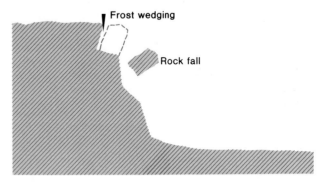

Figure 9.17 Two examples of rockfall.

Rockfall

In the movement called **rockfall**, rock falls freely or bounces down a cliff (figure 9.17). When a steep slope or cliff is being undercut, as by a river or wave erosion or highway construction, large blocks of rock tend to break off along cracks in the bedrock or along planes of weakness, such as bedding planes. Blocks of rock commonly break off through frost wedging (a type of mechanical

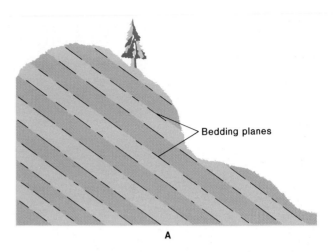

Figure 9.18 Talus slope in British Columbia.

weathering). Most cliffs have an apron of fallen rock at their bases that are the result of rockfall. An accumulation of broken rock (from rockfalls) at the base of a cliff is called **talus** (fig. 9.18).

Rockslide

A **rockslide** is, as the term suggests, the rapid sliding of a mass of bedrock along an inclined surface of weakness, such as a bedding plane, a major fracture in the rock, or a foliation plane (figs. 9.19 and 9.20). Once sliding begins, a rock slab usually breaks up into rubble. Like rockfalls, rockslides can be caused by undercutting at the base of the slope, due to erosion or construction activities.

Some rockslides travel only a few meters before halting at the base of a slope. In country with high relief, however, a rockslide may travel hundreds or thousands of meters before reaching a valley floor. If movement becomes very rapid, the rockslide may break up and become a rock avalanche. A **rock avalanche** is a very rapidly moving, turbulent mass of broken-up bedrock. Movement in a rock avalanche is flowage on a grand scale.

Some geologists have suggested that in very rapidly moving rock avalanches, air trapped under the rock mass may create an air cushion that reduces friction. This could explain why some landslides reach speeds of several hundred kilometers per hour. On the other hand, other geologists have contended that the rock mass would be too turbulent to permit such an air cushion to form.

Ultimately, a rockslide or rock avalanche comes to rest as the terrain becomes less steep. Sometimes the mass of rock fills the bottom of a valley and creates a natural dam. If the rock mass suddenly enters a lake or bay, it may create a huge wave that can destroy lives and property far beyond the area of the original landslide.

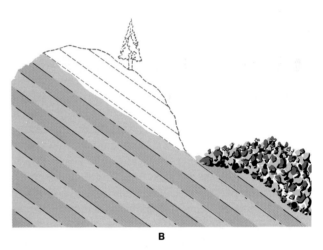

Figure 9.19 A rockslide along bedding planes. (*A*) Before slide, a steep slope with bedding planes undercut. (*B*) After slide.

As in slower mass movements, water can play an important role in causing a rockslide. In 1925 exceptionally heavy rains in the Gros Ventre Mountains of Wyoming caused water to seep into a layer of shale (figure 9.21). The shale, along with other layers of sedimentary rock above and below it, was inclined roughly parallel to the hillside. With the wet shale acting as a lubricant, the overlying sedimentary rock and its soil cover slid into the valley, blocking the river. The slide itself merely created a lake, but the subsequent breaking of the natural dam resulted in a flood that destroyed the small town of Kelly several kilometers downstream and killed several residents who were standing on a bridge watching the floodwaters come down the valley.

Figure 9.20 A rockslide in southern California. Sliding took place along steep fractures in the rock.
Photo by California Division of Mines and Geology.

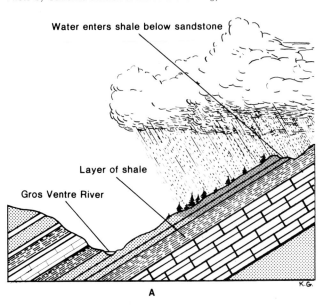

Water enters shale below sandstone

Layer of shale

Gros Ventre River

A

K.G.

Sliding along wet shale layer,
which acts as a lubricant

Slide debris dams river

B

K.G.

C

Figure 9.21 (*A* and *B*) Diagrammatic representation of the Gros Ventre, Wyoming, slide. (*C*) Photo of Gros Ventre Slide.
A and *B* after W. C. Alden, U.S. Geological Survey.

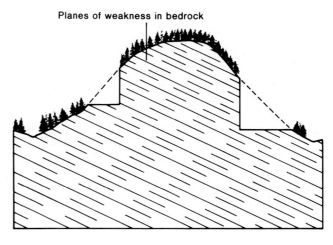
Debris Slides, Falls, and Avalanches

Landslides composed of debris or rock fragments rather than bedrock have names preceded by the word "debris" rather than "rock." A **debris slide** is rapid movement of debris as a coherent mass. A **debris fall** is a free-falling mass of debris. A **debris avalanche** is debris moving very rapidly and turbulently downslope.

Summary

Mass wasting is the movement of a mass of debris (soil and loose rock fragments) or bedrock toward the base of a slope. Movement may take place as flow, slip, or fall. Gravity is the driving force. A number of factors determine whether movement will occur and, if it does, the rate of movement.

The slowest type of movement, *creep,* occurs mostly on relatively gentle slopes, usually aided by water in the soil. In colder climates repeated freezing and thawing of water within the soil contributes to creep.

Landsliding is a general term for more rapid mass wasting of rock, debris, or both. Some types of landslides are earthflow, mudflow, rockfall, rockslide, debris fall, debris slide, rock avalanche, and debris avalanche.

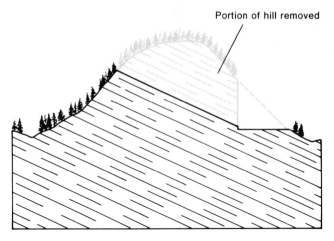

Figure 9.23 The same hazardous roadcut shown in figure 9.22, but showing removal of rock that might slide.

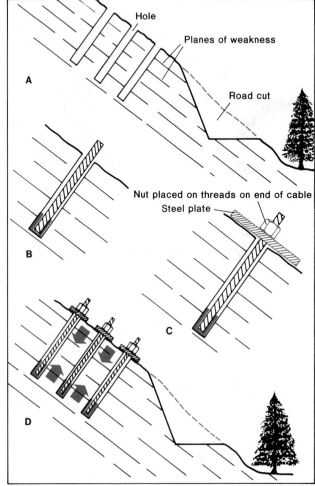

Figure 9.24 "Stitching" a slope to keep bedrock from sliding along planes of weakness. (A) Holes are drilled through unstable layers into stable rock. (B) Expanded view of one hole. A cable is fed into the hole and cement is pumped into the bottom of the hole and allowed to harden. (C) A steel plate is placed over the cable and a nut tightened. (D) Tightening all the nuts pulls unstable layers together and anchors them in stable bedrock.

Earthflows vary greatly in velocity. Debris *flows*, and often *slips* as well. Usually the upper part of the moving mass slumps downward while the lower part flows outward. Water within the pore spaces of the debris is an important factor contributing to earthflow. *Solifluction*, a special variety of earthflow, usually takes place in arctic or subarctic climates where the ground is permanently frozen *(permafrost)*.

A *mudflow* is a slurry of debris and water. Most mudflows flow in channels much as streams do.

Rockfall is the fall of broken rock down a vertical or near-vertical slope. A *rockslide* is a slab of rock sliding down a less-than-vertical surface. *Debris falls* and *debris slides* involve unconsolidated material rather than bedrock. A *rock* or *debris avalanche* is a turbulent mass of rock fragments or soil moving very rapidly downslope.

Terms to Remember

creep	relief
debris	rock avalanche
debris avalanche	rockfall
debris fall	rockslide
debris slide	slide
earthflow	slip
fall	slump
flow	solifluction
landslide	talus
mass wasting	
mudflow	
permafrost	

Questions for Review

1. How does a slump differ from a slide?
2. What is the distinction between solifluction and creep?
3. What role does water play in each of the types of mass wasting?
4. Why is solifluction more common in colder climates than in temperate climates?
5. List and explain the key factors that control mass wasting.

Questions for Thought

1. How would you classify the types of mass wasting if the amount of water involved were a criterion?
2. If you were building a house on a cliff, what would you look for to ensure that your house would not be destroyed through mass wasting?
3. Why isn't the land surface of the earth flat after millions of years of erosion by mass wasting as well as by other erosional agents?
4. Can any of the indicators of creep be explained by processes other than mass wasting?

Supplementary Readings

Eckel, E. B., ed. 1958. *Landslides and engineering practice.* Highway Research Board Special Report 29. National Academy of Sciences–National Research Council Publication 544.

Ericksen, G. E., G. Plafker, and J. Fernandez Concha. 1970. *Preliminary report on the geologic events associated with the May 31, 1970, Peru earthquake.* U.S. Geological Survey Circular 639.

Legget, R. F. 1973. *Cities and geology.* New York: McGraw-Hill.

Ritter, D. F. 1978. *Process geomorphology.* Dubuque, Iowa: Wm. C. Brown Company Publishers.

Sharpe, C. F. S. 1938. *Landslides and related phenomena.* New York: Columbia University Press. Reprinted 1960 by Pageant Press.

Tank, Ronald W. 1973. *Focus on environmental geology.* New York: Oxford University Press.

Washburn, A. L. 1973. *Periglacial processes and environments.* London: Edward Arnold Ltd.

10
Streams, Stream Action, and Landscape Development

Purpose

Running water, in conjunction with mass wasting, is the most important geologic agent in eroding, transporting, and depositing sediment. Almost every landscape on earth shows the results of these processes. Although other agents—ground water, glaciers, wind, and waves—can be locally important in sculpturing the land, stream action and mass wasting are the dominant processes of landscape development.

The first part of this chapter deals with the various ways that streams erode, transport, and deposit sediment. We then examine landforms produced by stream action, such as valleys, flood plains, deltas, alluvial fans, and terraces, in terms of how each of these is related to changes in stream characteristics. The chapter concludes with a discussion of the factors that control slope angle and the appearance of stream-eroded landscapes.

In September 1977, over Missouri, a mass of cold air from Canada met a mass of warm, moist air moving north from the Gulf of Mexico. The ensuing cold front created a severe thunderstorm system that dumped 30 centimeters (12 inches) of rain on Kansas City in less than 24 hours. This phenomenally heavy rain, which could be expected only once every 500 years, quickly overfilled local streams and storm sewers. A two-meter wall of water roared down normally peaceful Brush Creek beside a major shopping center, and muddy waters rose as high as four meters up the sides of nearby stores. Floating automobiles were carried down streets by the surging water. As the waters receded, leaving a blanket of mud and wreckage behind, the toll became apparent—24 dead, 1,200 homeless, and damage of more than $30 million. The Kansas City flood was a vivid reminder that streams are effective agents of erosion and sediment transportation and deposition, occasionally with devastating results to people and property.

The term **stream** refers to a body of running water that is confined in a channel and moves downhill under the influence of gravity. In some parts of the country,

Figure 10.1 Ohio River in flood in Rockport, Indiana, 1937. The river's channel is in the right third of the photograph. Lines of trees mark the banks of the river during normal flow.
Photo by L. L. Ray, U.S. Geological Survey.

stream implies size: rivers are large, streams somewhat smaller, and brooks or creeks even smaller. Geologists, however, use the word for any body of running water, from a small trickle to a huge river.

Channel Flow and Sheet Flow

A stream more or less fills its **stream channel,** a long, narrow depression shaped by the stream, usually on the floor of a broader valley. The channel may be cut into solid rock, or, more commonly, into loose sediment which is periodically moved by the flowing water. The stream *banks* are the sides of the channel; the stream *bed* is the bottom of the channel. During a flood the waters of a stream may rise to the point where they spill over the banks and out of the channel onto the valley floor (figure 10.1). During normal flow, however, the stream stays in its channel.

Not all water that moves over the land surface is confined to channels. Sometimes, particularly during heavy rains, water runs off as **sheetwash,** a thin layer of unchanneled water flowing downhill (figure 10.2). Although this type of runoff occurs in humid regions, it is much more common in arid regions, where the lack of vegetation allows more water to spread over the surface

Figure 10.2 Sheetwash. Colored arrows represent sheet of water washing downslope.

as a thin film. Sheetwash, along with the violent impact of raindrops, can produce considerable *sheet erosion,* in which a thin layer of surface material, usually topsoil, is removed by the flowing sheet of water. This gravity-driven movement of sediment is a process intermediate between mass wasting and stream erosion.

Overland sheetwash becomes concentrated in small channels, forming tiny streams called *rills.* Rills merge to form small streams, and small streams join to form larger streams. Most regions are drained by networks of coalescing streams.

Box 10.1
Preventing Sheet Erosion on Farms

Tilled fields are particularly susceptible to sheet erosion because plowing and cultivating during the planting season remove the vegetation cover. Sheet erosion can remove as much as 60 tons of topsoil per acre in a single year. Farmers use several techniques to slow sheet erosion in their fields (figure 10.3).

In *contour plowing,* the furrows are plowed along contours (lines of equal elevation), rather than up and down the slopes. Furrows that run directly down a slope channelize sheet flow into small rivulets that increase the velocity of the water and thus wash down more soil. If the furrows run along contour lines, however, they are perpendicular to the direction of sheet flow. Each ridge and groove tends to retard the water, thereby reducing sheet erosion of topsoil.

In *strip planting,* two different crops are grown in alternating bands along contour lines. For example, a strip of hay might be planted downhill from a strip of corn. The dense growth and root systems of the hay slow any sheet flow moving downhill from the more widely spaced corn.

Terracing the land involves cutting or building flat surfaces, again parallel to the contours. The terraces may be so narrow as to hold only one row of plants, or wide enough for an entire field. The flat surfaces of the terraces slow the downhill flow of water and so decrease soil erosion.

Combinations of contour plowing, strip planting, terracing, and other techniques such as shallow and infrequent plowing can be very effective in slowing sheet erosion of topsoil. A recent development that looks very promising in further controlling sheet erosion is to mulch fields with organic matter to reduce raindrop impact and sheet flow. Mulching sometimes is done on untilled land into which seeds have been drilled. Such protection can essentially eliminate topsoil loss by sheet erosion.

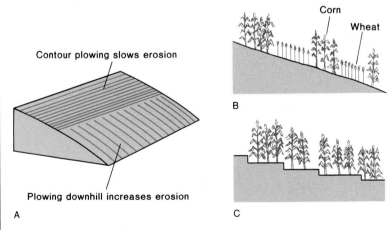

Figure 10.3 Methods of preventing sheet erosion. (*A*) Contour plowing. (*B*) Strip planting. (*C*) Terracing.

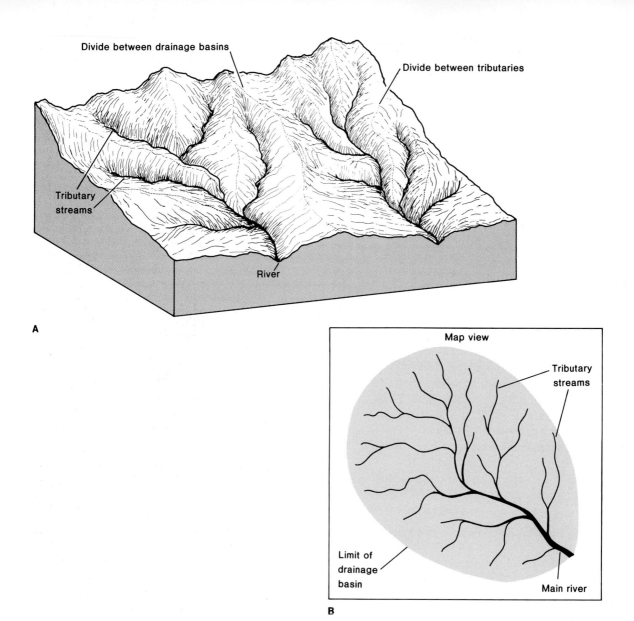

Figure 10.4 A drainage basin is the area drained by a river and its tributaries. (*A*) Two drainage basins separated by a drainage divide. (*B*) Map view of a drainage basin. This is a dendritic drainage pattern, which develops on uniform rock.

Drainage Basins

A **drainage basin** is the total area drained by a stream and its tributaries (a **tributary** is a small stream flowing into a larger one). A drainage basin can be outlined on a map by drawing a line around the region drained by all the tributaries to a river (figure 10.4). The Mississippi River's drainage basin, for example, includes all the land area drained by the Mississippi River itself and by all its tributaries, including the Ohio and Missouri Rivers. This great drainage system includes approximately half the land area of the contiguous 48 states.

A ridge or strip of high ground dividing one drainage basin from another is termed a **drainage divide** (figure 10.4). The best known in the United States is the Continental Divide, an imaginary line separating streams that flow to the Pacific Ocean from those that flow to the Atlantic and the Gulf of Mexico. The Continental Divide, which extends from the Yukon Territory down into Mexico, crosses Montana, Wyoming, Colorado, and New Mexico in the United States. Signs indicating the crossing of the Continental Divide have been placed at numerous points where major highways intersect the divide.

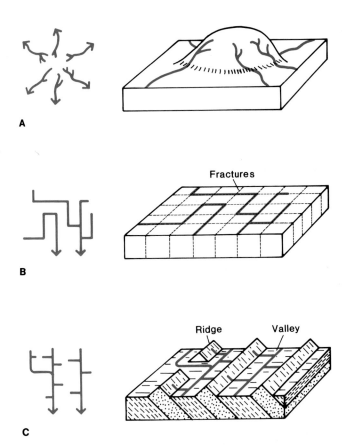

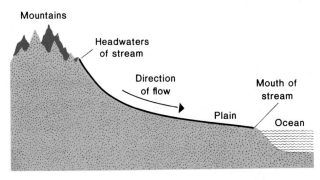

Figure 10.6 Longitudinal profile of a stream originating in mountains and flowing over a plain to the sea. Note the steep slope in the mountains and the gentler slope across the plain. (Steepness of slopes is exaggerated.) This concave-upward profile is common to most streams.

Figure 10.5 Drainage patterns can tell something about the rocks underneath. (A) A radial pattern develops on a conical mountain or dome. (B) A rectangular pattern develops on regularly fractured rock. (C) A trellis pattern develops on alternating ridges and valleys caused by the erosion of resistant and nonresistant tilted rock layers.

Drainage Patterns

The arrangement, in map view, of a river and its tributaries is a **drainage pattern.** A drainage pattern can in many cases reveal the nature and structure of the rocks underneath it.

Most tributaries join the main stream at an acute angle, forming a V pointing downstream. If the pattern resembles branches of a tree or veins in a leaf, it is called **dendritic** (figure 10.4). Dendritic drainage patterns develop on uniformly erodible rock, usually horizontal sedimentary rocks or unfractured crystalline rock, such as igneous rock in a batholith. A **radial pattern,** in which streams diverge outward like spokes of a wheel, forms on high conical mountains, such as composite volcanoes and domes (figure 10.5A). A **rectangular** drainage **pattern,** in which tributaries have frequent ninety-degree bends and tend to join other streams at right angles, develops on regularly fractured rock (figure 10.5B). A network of fractures meeting at right angles forms pathways for streams because fractures are eroded more readily than unbroken

rock. A **trellis pattern** consists of parallel main streams with short tributaries meeting them at right angles (figure 10.5C). A trellis pattern forms in a region where tilted layers of resistant rock such as sandstone alternate with nonresistant rock such as shale. Erosion of such a region results in a surface topography of parallel ridges and valleys.

Longitudinal Profile

On maps, streams are usually depicted as curving, bending, or wiggly blue lines, as if seen from above. Another useful way of looking at a stream is to draw a **longitudinal profile,** which is a line drawn to show a stream's slope as if it were viewed from the side. Figure 10.6 shows the longitudinal profile of a stream that begins in steep mountains and flows out over a gentle plain into the ocean. The **headwaters** of a stream are the upper part near the source. The **mouth** is the place where the stream enters the sea, a large lake, or a larger stream.

Factors Affecting Stream Erosion and Deposition

Stream erosion and deposition are controlled primarily by a river's velocity and, to a lesser extent, by its turbulence and discharge. These factors in turn are closely related to the stream gradient, channel shape, and channel roughness.

Velocity

The speed at which water in a stream travels is called the **stream velocity.** A moderately fast river flows at about 5 kilometers per hour. Rivers during flood flow much faster, however, sometimes with velocities of 25 kilometers per hour or more.

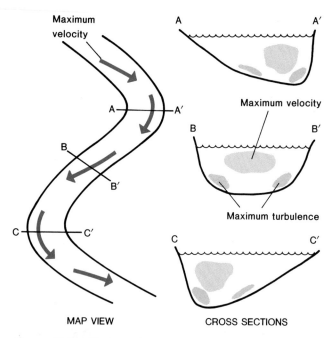

MAP VIEW   CROSS SECTIONS

Figure 10.7 Regions of maximum velocity and turbulence in a stream. Arrows on the map show how the maximum velocity shifts to the outside of curves. Sections show maximum velocity and greater turbulence on outside of curves.

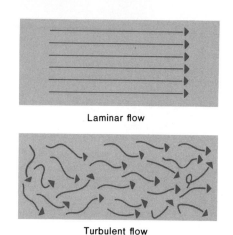

Laminar flow

Turbulent flow

Figure 10.8 Laminar flow and turbulent flow. Arrows show paths of water drops (streamlines).

The cross-sectional views of a stream in figure 10.7 show that a stream reaches its maximum velocity near the middle of the channel. Near the stream's banks and bed, friction between the water and the stream channel slows the water. When a stream goes around a curve, the region of maximum velocity is displaced by centrifugal force toward the outside of the curve. Velocity is the key factor in a stream's ability to erode, transport, and deposit. High velocity generally results in erosion and transportation; deposition occurs when a river slows down. Slight changes in velocity can cause great changes in the sediment load carried by the river.

Turbulence

Water can be described as flowing in two ways: laminar flow and turbulent flow (figure 10.8). **Laminar flow** is a smooth, slow flow in which each drop of water travels a smooth path parallel to neighboring drops. Laminar flow often occurs underground, when water slowly trickles down into the ground, but it is not the dominant type of flow in streams. **Turbulent flow** contains swirls and eddies. The drops of water do not flow parallel to one another but travel along erratically curved paths that cross those of neighboring drops. The velocity of flow at any one point varies with time. Turbulent flow is the type of water motion that occurs in most parts of streams.

The amount of turbulence in a stream varies from place to place and from minute to minute, depending on the stream's velocity, channel roughness, and other factors. This variability affects the stream's ability to erode and transport sediment. The region of maximum turbulence in a stream—where most erosion takes place—lies near the stream bed on a straight stretch of stream. It is displaced toward the outside corner of the channel where the stream's path curves (figure 10.7).

Gradient

One factor that controls a stream's velocity is the **stream gradient,** the downhill slope of the bed (or of the water surface, if the stream is very large). A stream gradient can be measured in meters per kilometer (although in the United States stream gradients usually have been expressed in feet per mile, the units most common on U.S. maps). A gradient of 5 m/km means that the river drops 5 meters vertically for every kilometer it travels horizontally. The lower Mississippi River, for example, has a very gentle gradient, 0.1 m/km or less. Mountain streams may have gradients as steep as 10–40 m/km, or occasionally even steeper.

Two streams of equal size (and with similar channel shape and cross-sectional area) will have different velocities if they have different gradients. The stream with a steep gradient has a high velocity while the similar stream on a gentle slope travels more slowly. A very slight change in gradient can cause a significant change in velocity, which in turn can greatly affect the stream's ability to erode, transport, and deposit sediment.

Figure 10.9 shows two examples of a change in gradient along a river's course. If a river flows out of steep mountains onto a flatter plain, the river's gradient may change suddenly from steep to gentle (figure 10.9*A*). Such a change in gradient causes the river to slow down, and

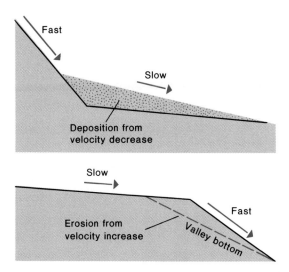

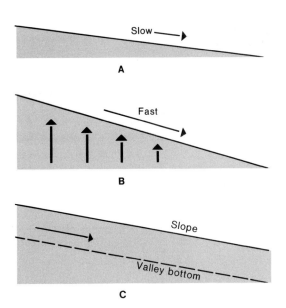

Figure 10.9 Changes in gradient can cause deposition and erosion.

Figure 10.10 Uplift can increase erosion. (*A*) Gentle gradient. (*B*) Differential uplift increases gradient. (*C*) Erosion results from increased velocity.

the sudden loss of velocity can cause sediment deposition at the base of the steep slope. If the gradient becomes steeper in a downstream direction, (figure 10.9*B*), the velocity increases on the steep slope, and the river erodes rapidly there, deepening its valley as a result.

Slow uplift of the land may steepen a stream's gradient, causing a once-sluggish stream to flow faster and cut its valley downward (figure 10.10).

A river's gradient can be steepened artificially by dredging to straighten its channel. This process, called *channelization,* is used to improve navigation on a river, or to help drain a flat-lying region, or to increase the runoff capacity of a river to help control floods. Figure 10.11 shows a once-curving river that has been straightened. The difference in elevation between points *A* and *B* is the same in the new channel as it was in the old, but the river now travels a shorter distance between the two points than it did before. The gradient is therefore steeper and the velocity increases. This can be the intent of channelization, but sometimes the resulting erosion is unanticipated.

Channel Shape and Roughness
Another factor that controls velocity is the cross-sectional *shape of the channel.* As the water travels in a stream, it drags against the stream banks and stream bed (the *wetted perimeter*), and the resulting friction tends to slow down the water. The more friction between water and channel, the more slowly the river travels. For a given cross-sectional area, different channel shapes can vary considerably in the amount of wetted perimeter. A wide,

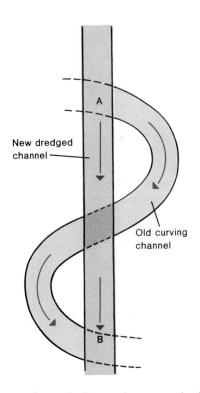

Figure 10.11 Channelization can increase a river's gradient by shortening the distance between two points.

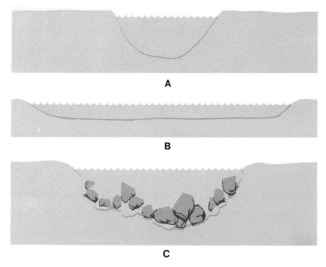

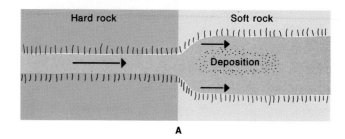

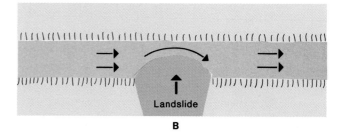

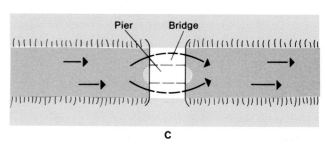

Figure 10.12 *Channel shape and roughness influence stream velocity. (A) Narrow deep channel with semicircular cross section allows stream to flow rapidly. (B) Wide shallow channel increases friction, slows river down. (C) Rough boulder-strewn channel slows river.*

shallow channel slows a river, because this channel shape has a greater wetted perimeter for the water to drag against (figure 10.12).

A stream may change its channel width as it flows across different rock types. Hard, resistant rock is difficult to erode, so a stream may have a relatively narrow channel in such rock. As a result it flows rapidly. If the stream flows onto a softer rock that is easier to erode, the channel may widen, and the river will slow down because of the increased wetted perimeter and friction. Sediment may be deposited as the velocity decreases (figure 10.13*A*).

The width of a stream may be controlled by factors external to the stream. A landslide may carry debris onto a valley floor, partially blocking a stream's channel. The constriction causes the stream to speed up as it flows past the slide, and the increased velocity may quickly erode the landslide debris, carrying it away downstream (figure 10.13*B*). Human activity can promote erosion and deposition. Construction of a culvert or bridge can partially block a channel, increasing the stream's velocity (figure 10.13*C*). If the bridge was poorly designed, it may increase velocity to the point where erosion widens the stream, perhaps even causing the bridge to collapse.

The *roughness of the channel* also controls velocity. A stream can flow rapidly over a smooth channel, but a rough, boulder-strewn channel floor creates more friction and slows the flow (figure 10.12). Coarse particles increase the roughness more than fine particles, and a rippled or wavy sand bottom is rougher than a smooth sand bottom.

Figure 10.13 *Channel width variations (map view) caused by rock type and obstructions. Length of arrow indicates velocity. (A) A channel may widen in soft rock. Deposition may result as stream velocity drops. (B) Landslide may narrow channel, increasing stream velocity. Resulting erosion usually removes landslide debris. (C) A bridge pier or other obstruction will increase velocity and sometimes erosion.*

Discharge

The **discharge** of a stream is the volume of water that flows past a given point in a unit of time. It is found by multiplying the cross-sectional area of a stream by its velocity. Discharge can be reported in cubic meters per second (m³/sec) or in cubic feet per second (cfs), which has been standard in the United States.

> Discharge (m³/sec) =
> channel width (m)
> × channel depth (m)
> × average velocity (m/sec)

A river with a channel 50 meters wide and 5 meters deep flowing at 5 kilometers an hour (1.4m/sec) would have a discharge of 350 cubic meters per second. In most streams, discharge increases downstream for two reasons: (1) water flows out of the ground into the river through the stream bed; and (2) small tributary streams flow into a larger stream along its length, adding water to the stream as it travels (figure 10.14).

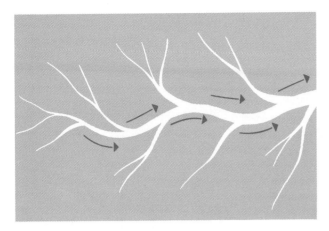

Figure 10.14 A stream generally increases in discharge and width downstream as tributaries join it.

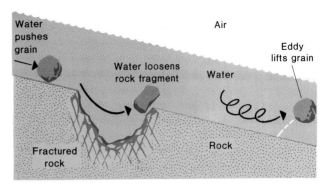

Figure 10.15 Hydraulic action.

To handle the increased discharge, streams generally increase in width and depth downstream. Some rivers also seem to increase slightly in velocity downstream, as a result of the increased discharge (the effect of discharge apparently overrides the effect of a lessening gradient).

During floods a stream's discharge and velocity increase, usually as a result of heavy rains over the stream's drainage basin. Flood discharge may be 50 to 100 times normal flow. Stream erosion and transportation generally increase enormously as a result of a flood's velocity and discharge. Flooded land may be intensely scoured, with river banks and adjacent lawns and fields washed away. As floodwaters recede, both velocity and discharge decrease, leading to the deposition of a blanket of sediment, usually mud, over the flooded area.

A river's discharge can decrease in a downstream direction in a dry climate, as river water evaporates into the air and soaks into the dry ground (or is used for irrigation). As the discharge decreases, the load of sediment is gradually deposited.

Stream Erosion

A stream usually erodes the rock and sediment over which it flows. (The removal of both rock and sediment can be called *erosion,* but some geologists prefer the term *entrainment* for the picking up of loose sediment grains.) In fact, streams are one of the most effective agents that sculpture the land. Streams cut their own valleys, deepening and widening them over long periods of time and carrying away the sediment that mass wasting delivers to valley floors. The particles of rock and sediment that a stream picks up are carried along to be deposited farther downstream. Streams erode rock and sediment in three ways— *hydraulic action, solution,* and *abrasion.*

Hydraulic action refers to the ability of the water itself to pick up and move rock and sediment (figure 10.15). The force of water swirling into a crevice in a rock may eventually crack the rock and break loose a fragment to be carried away by the stream. A loose sediment grain on the stream bed may tumble or slide along the stream bottom, pushed by the pressure of flowing water. A swirling eddy of water may exert enough force to lift a rock fragment above the stream bed into the main body of flowing water. Standing beside a swiftly flowing mountain stream, you may be able to hear pebbles and boulders tumbling along the stream bed and hitting one another. Clearly, hydraulic action is effective in moving rock and sediment.

From what you have learned about weathering (chapter 5), you know that some rocks can be dissolved by water. **Solution,** although ordinarily slow, can be an effective process of weathering and erosion (weathering because it is a response to surface chemical conditions; erosion because it removes material). A stream flowing over limestone, for example, gradually dissolves it, deepening the stream channel. The solution of calcite cement within sedimentary rocks (chapter 6) loosens sediment grains that were once tightly bound together. The loosened grains can then be picked up by hydraulic action.

The erosive process that is usually most effective on the bed rock of a stream bed is **abrasion,** the grinding away of the stream channel by the friction and impact of the sediment load. Sand grains, pebbles, and boulders tumbling along near the bottom of a stream wear away the stream bed much as moving sandpaper wears away wood. The abrasion of sediment on the stream bed is generally much more effective in wearing the rock away than hydraulic action alone. The more sediment a stream carries, the faster it is likely to wear away its bed.

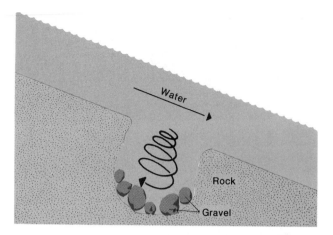

Figure 10.16 Sediment moved by swirling water can scour potholes in the rock of a stream bed.

Figure 10.17 Potholes in a stream bed (Blue Creek, Alabama). Gravel is visible in the bottom of some of the potholes.
Photo by C. Butts, U.S. Geological Survey.

The coarsest sediment is the most effective in stream erosion. Sand and gravel strike the stream bed frequently, while the finer-grained silt and clay weigh so little that they are easily suspended throughout the stream and have little impact when they hit the channel. Sand and gravel, being heavier, hit the stream bed more often and with greater force than do the finer particles.

Potholes are depressions that are eroded into the hard rock of a stream bed by the abrasive action of the sediment load. During high water when a stream is full, the swirling water can cause sand and pebbles to scour out smooth, bowl-shaped depressions in large boulders or in a stream bed that is cut into fairly hard rock (figure 10.16). Potholes tend to form in spots where the rock is a little weaker than the surrounding rock. Although potholes are fairly uncommon, you can see them on the beds of some streams at low water level. Potholes may contain sand or an assortment of beautifully rounded pebbles (figure 10.17).

Stream Transportation of Sediment

The sediment load transported by a stream can be subdivided into *bed load, suspended load,* and *dissolved load.* Most of a stream's load is carried in suspension and in solution.

The **bed load** is the large or heavy sediment particles that travel or on the stream bed. Sand and gravel, which form the usual bed load of streams, move by either *traction* or *saltation.*

The heaviest particles of sediment, such as pebbles and boulders, may never lose contact with the stream bed as they move along in the flowing water. They roll or slide along the stream bottom, eroding the stream bed and each other by abrasion. Movement by rolling, sliding, or dragging is called **traction.**

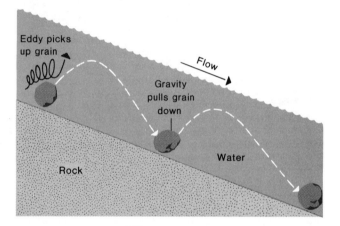

Figure 10.18 Saltation of sand grains along a stream bottom.

Sand grains also may move by traction. But if the stream is flowing with enough turbulence, sand also moves downstream by **saltation,** a series of short leaps or bounces off the bottom (figure 10.18). Saltation begins when sand grains are momentarily lifted off the bottom by turbulent water. The force of the eddying water temporarily counteracts the downward force of gravity, suspending the grains in water above the stream bed. But because the velocity of water in an eddy is not constant, the water soon slows down; then gravity can overcome the lift of the water, and the sand grain once again falls to the bed of the stream. While it is suspended, the grain moves downstream with the flowing water. After it lands on the bottom, it may be picked up again if turbulence increases, or it may be thrown up into the water by the impact of another falling sand grain. In this way sand grains saltate downstream in leaps and jumps, partly in contact with the bottom and partly suspended in the water.

Figure 10.19 Gravel bars in a river.

The **suspended load** is sediment that is light enough to remain lifted indefinitely above the bottom by water turbulence. The muddy appearance of a stream during a flood or after a heavy rain is due to a large suspended load. Silt and clay usually are suspended throughout the water, while the coarser bed load moves on or near the stream bottom. Suspended load has less effect on erosion than the less visible bed load, which causes most of the abrasion of the stream bed. Vast quantities of sediment, however, are transported in suspension.

Soluble products of chemical weathering processes can make up a substantial **dissolved load** in a stream. Most streams contain numerous ions in solution, such as sodium, calcium, potassium, bicarbonate, chloride, and sulfate. The ions may precipitate out of water as evaporite minerals if the stream dries up, or they may eventually reach the ocean. Very clear water may in fact be carrying a large load of material in solution, for the dissolved load is invisible. Only if the water begins to evaporate does the material become visible as crystals begin to form.

Stream Deposition

The sediments being transported by a stream are often deposited temporarily along the stream's course (particularly the bed-load sediments). Such sediments move sporadically downstream in repeated cycles of erosion and deposition, forming *bars* and *flood-plain deposits*. At or near the end of a stream, sediments may be deposited more permanently in a *delta* or an *alluvial fan*.

Bars

Stream deposits may take the form of a **bar,** a ridge of sediment, usually sand or gravel, in the middle or along the banks of a stream (figure 10.19). Bars may be formed by deposition when a stream's discharge or velocity decreases. During flood, a river can move all sizes of sediment, from silt and clay up to huge boulders, because the greatly increased volume of water is moving very rapidly.

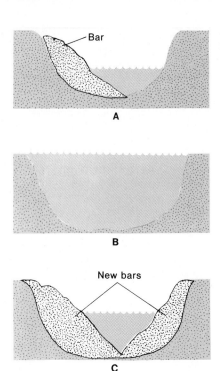

Figure 10.20 Bars in a stream can be washed away in a flood, with new bars deposited as the flood recedes. (*A*) Normal water flow with sand and gravel bar. (*B*) Increased discharge and velocity during flood moves all sediment downstream. Channel deepens and widens if banks are easily erodible. (*C*) New bars deposit as water level drops and stream slows down.

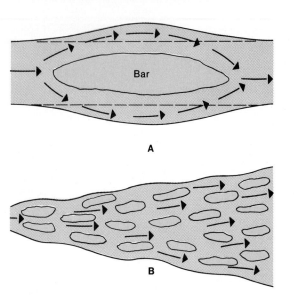

Figure 10.21 (*A*) A midchannel bar can cause a stream to divert around it, widening the stream. (*B*) Braided stream. Bars split main channel into many smaller channels, greatly widening the stream.

Figure 10.22 Braided stream in Alaska. Water flows toward bottom of photo from melting glacier in background. Large amounts of coarse bed load cause braiding.
Photo by D. A. Rahm; courtesy Rahm Memorial Collection, Western Washington University.

As the flood begins to recede, the water level in the stream falls and the velocity drops. With the stream no longer able to carry all its sediment load, the larger boulders drop down on the stream bed, slowing the water locally even more. Smaller pebbles and sand are deposited between the boulders and downstream from them. In this way, deposition builds up a sand or gravel bar that may be exposed above water level as the stream's discharge continues to decrease.

The next flood on the river may erode all the sediment in this bar and move it farther downstream. But as the flood slows, new gravel may be deposited in approximately the same place, forming a new bar (figure 10.20). After each flood, river fishermen and boat operators must relearn the size and position of the bars. Sometimes gold panners discover fresh gold in a mined-out river bar after a flood has shifted sediment downstream.

Braided Streams

Deposition of a bar in the center of a stream (a *midchannel bar*) diverts the water toward the sides, where it washes against the stream banks with greater force, eroding the banks and widening the stream. A stream heavily loaded with sediment may deposit many bars in its channel, causing the stream to widen continually as more bars are deposited. Such a stream typically goes through many stages of deposition, erosion, redeposition, and re-erosion, especially if its discharge fluctuates. The stream may lose its main channel and become a **braided stream,** flowing in a network of interconnected rivulets around numerous bars (figures 10.21 and 10.22). A braided stream characteristically has a wide, shallow channel.

Figure 10.23 River meanders on a valley floor. Crooked Creek, in Mono County, California.
Photo by W. T. Lee, U.S. Geological Survey.

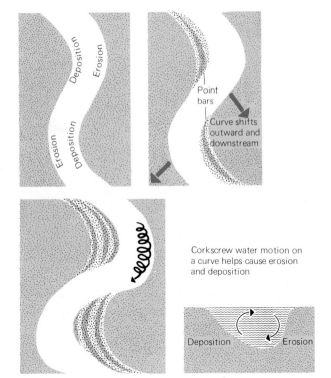

Point bars
Curve shifts outward and downstream

Erosion

Deposition

Erosion

Deposition

Erosion

Deposition

Corkscrew water motion on a curve helps cause erosion and deposition

Deposition   Erosion

Figure 10.24 Development of river meanders.

Figure 10.25 River erosion on the outside of a curve, Newaukum River, Washington. Pictures were taken in January and March 1965.
Photos by P. A. Glancy, U.S. Geological Survey.

A stream tends to become braided when it is heavily loaded with sediment (particularly bed load) and has banks that are easily eroded. The braided pattern develops in dry regions as a sediment-laden stream loses water through evaporation and through percolation into the ground. In meltwater streams flowing off glaciers, braided patterns tend to develop when the discharge from the melting glaciers is low relative to the great amount of sediment the stream has to carry. Coarse-grained bed load may favor the development of braided streams, although braiding is not confined to streams with coarse sediment. Because of their bed load, braided streams tend to have a relatively steep gradient in comparison with unbraided streams of similar discharge.

Meanders and Point Bars

Pronounced sinuous curves called **meanders** can develop along a stream's course (figure 10.23). A slight bend in a river tends to be accentuated into a large curve by erosion on the outside of the curve where the water velocity is greatest and by simultaneous deposition on the inside of the curve where the velocity is lowest (figures 10.24 and 10.25). Even after a meander is well formed, continuing erosion and deposition tend to shift the position of

Figure 10.26 River meanders, point bars, and meander scars, Laramie River, Wyoming.
Photo by J. R. Balsley, U.S. Geological Survey.

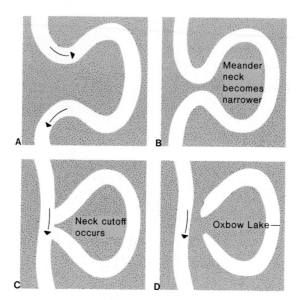

Figure 10.27 Creation of an oxbow lake by a meander neck cutoff. Old channel is separated from river by sediment deposition.

the meander across the valley floor (figure 10.26), leaving a series of bars called **point bars** on the inside of each curve.

At times, particularly during floods, a river may form a **meander cutoff,** a new, shorter channel across the narrow neck of a meander (figure 10.27). The old meander may be abandoned as sediment separates it from the new, shorter channel. The cutoff meander becomes a crescent-shaped **oxbow lake** (figure 10.28). With time, an oxbow lake may become a **meander scar,** an abandoned meander filled with sediment and vegetation (figure 10.26).

Meandering Versus Braiding

Not all rivers meander. The pattern of a river is controlled partly by *sediment type.* Rivers transporting primarily silt and clay in suspension tend to be narrow and deep and to meander in sinuous curves. Rivers transporting mostly sand and gravel as bedload tend to be wide, shallow, and straight, and they are often braided. The straightness of such a river usually means that it has a steep gradient. In general, the steeper the gradient, the straighter the river. Braided rivers, therefore, are characteristically steep as well as straight. Meanders tend to reduce a river's gradient by increasing the distance of travel (figure 10.11).

Discharge also helps control whether a river is braided or meandering, with an increase in discharge tending to favor braiding, particularly if the discharge fluctuates rapidly.

Note that two factors—sediment type and discharge —determine whether a river meanders or is braided. Either factor can override the other. Discharge usually increases downstream, but sediment usually becomes

Figure 10.28 Oxbow lakes along the White River in Arkansas.
Photo by J. R. Balsley, U.S. Geological Survey.

finer, so meandering is more common than braiding in the lower reaches of a river. If a tributary stream should deliver large quantities of gravel to a larger stream, however, the large stream may abruptly become braided where it gains the bed load.

A slow change over several centuries to a wetter climate in a drainage basin may gradually increase discharge in a river, tending to promote braiding. The increased rainfall, however, may increase the amount of vegetation and the rate of chemical weathering, which together will yield more clay and less gravel. This change in sediment type may offset the increased discharge and prevent the river from becoming braided.

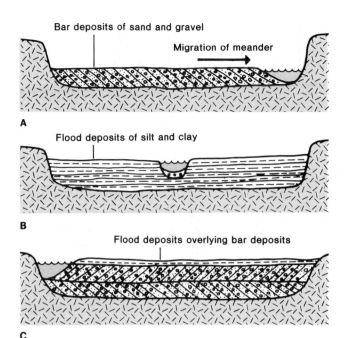

Figure 10.29 Three types of flood plain. (A) Lateral deposition of point bar deposits on the inside banks of shifting meanders. (B) Vertical deposition of flood deposits (each flood adds a new layer to top). (C) Combination of lateral deposition of bar deposits and vertical deposition of flood deposits.

Figure 10.30 Sediment deposited on a flood plain by the Trinity River in California during a 1964 flood.
Photo by A. O. Waananen, U.S. Geological Survey.

Flood Plains

A **flood plain** is a broad strip of land built up by sedimentation on either side of a stream channel, the result of lateral deposition, vertical deposition, or both (figure 10.29). As meanders shift back and forth laterally over the valley floor, point bar deposits are left on the insides of curves. Some flood plains are constructed almost entirely of such bar deposits, usually made of sand and gravel. Other flood plains owe their development to horizontal layers of fine-grained sediment deposited during flood stages when the river overflows its banks (figure 10.30). During the periodic floods that are inevitable on almost all rivers, entire flood plains may be covered with water carrying suspended load, so that fine-grained deposits are spread out over the flat lowlands. Underneath this cover, however, the bulk of the flood-plain sediment may be coarse bar deposits.

As floodwaters spread over a flood plain during high water, the velocity of the water is abruptly decreased by the increase in cross-sectional area and by friction as the water leaves the deep channel and moves in a thin sheet over the flat valley floor. The sudden decrease in velocity of the water causes the river to deposit most of its sediment near the main channel, with progressively less sediment deposited away from the channel. A series of floods may build up **natural levees**—low ridges of flood-deposited sediment that form on either side of a stream channel—and thin away from the channel (figure 10.31). The sediment

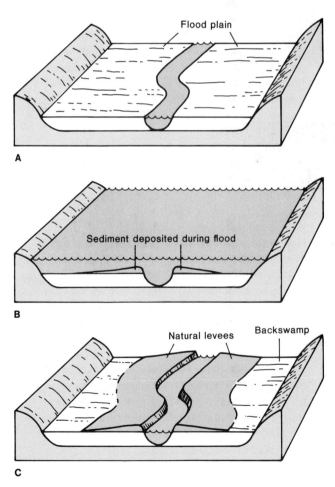

Figure 10.31 Natural levee deposition during a flood. Levees are thickest and coarsest next to the river channel, and build up from many floods, not just one. Relief of levees exaggerated. (A) Normal flow. (B) Flood. (C) After flood.

Box 10.2
River Cities

Why are many of the great and famous cities of the world built on the banks of rivers? In the United States, New York, Philadelphia, New Orleans, St. Louis, Detroit, Minneapolis, Portland (Oregon), and many others are built beside major rivers. Kansas City and Pittsburgh are built where two major rivers come together.

Transportation and trade are the obvious primary factors behind the location and growth of these cities. Some cities began when river landings developed into ports in the days when rivers were the prime means of transportation to the interior of the continent. Even today, river cities depend heavily on ships and barges to transport fuel, industrial supplies and products, and agricultural crops. Some river cities were founded near bridges and fords as road networks began to cross rivers. Others are located at major obstructions, such as rapids, that stopped boats from going upstream.

While a city may owe much of its importance to its river location, most of its inhabitants have probably had some firsthand experience in trying to cope with several of the geologic effects that occur in and near a river. Although *floods* cause little or no damage in uninhabited flood plains, high waters can be devastating to property and lives in cities built on valley floors that are subject to recurring floods. (Even though a few river cities are built on bluffs above rivers, rather than on the flood plains, which probably are too narrow, floods can still wash out railroads, highways, and other construction along the river banks.)

Although flooding is not likely to occur every year on every river, episodes of high water and overflowing banks are normal processes that must be expected (and prepared for) on all rivers. Heavy seasonal rains and rapidly melting snow in springtime are the most usual causes of high runoff and consequent flooding. The geographic paths of rainstorms, and their rate and volume of rainfall, are all highly variable, but these are the factors that control to a large extent where and whether flooding will occur.

Cities themselves, by their very existence, locally increase the height of floods. Paved areas and storm sewers increase the amount and rate of runoff, making river levels higher during storms. Bridge piers and construction on flood plains constrict the flow of floods, increasing flood height, stream velocity, and consequent erosion.

Another flood problem is *flood deposits*. Silt and clay deposited on flood plains or natural levees can be beneficial in an agricultural region, renewing the fields with topsoil from upstream. On the other hand, a meter-thick layer of mud in city streets, living rooms, and factories can destroy lawns, furniture, and machinery and take enormous amounts of time, energy, and money to clean up.

Flood-control structures can partially reduce the dangers of floodwaters and sedimentation to river cities. Upstream dams catch the water, releasing it slowly after the storm. (The dam also catches sediment, which eventually fills its reservoir.) Artificial levees are embankments built along the sides of a river channel, sometimes on top of natural levees, to contain floodwaters within the channel. Nevertheless, flood-control structures can provide only a degree of protection. Dams and levees are built with an awareness (at least on the part of planners and engineers) of the small chance that a much larger flood than anticipated will occur. The disastrous floods in Pennsylvania and New York from Hurricane Agnes in the summer of 1972 resulted from many such failures of flood control. The best procedure is to combine flood-control structures with wise land-use plans for flood plains. Wherever possible, expensive buildings should not be located in zones that might some day be inundated.

The *tendency of river channels to change position* can be a hazard to riverfront properties and bridges. River banks are eroded and buildings and piers along the banks can be undercut and destroyed by a river that is shifting sideways unless protective walls of stone (riprap) or concrete are constructed to prevent bank erosion.

Figure 10.32 The Nile Delta in Egypt as seen in a 1965 spacecraft photograph. The dark area in the center is cultivated land on the delta surface. The Nile River flows from right to left, into the Mediterranean Sea at far left. Compare with map in figure 10.33 (note north arrow).
NASA

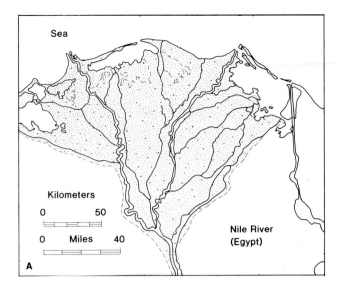

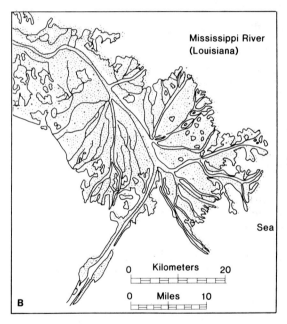

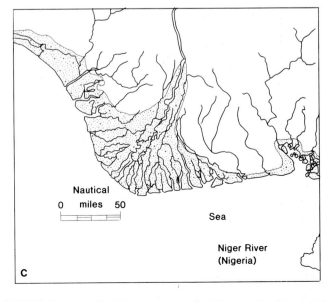

near the river is coarsest, often sand and silt, while the finer clay is carried farther from the river into the flat, lowland area (the backswamp).

Deltas

Most streams ultimately flow into the sea or into large lakes. A stream flowing into the sea or a lake usually builds a **delta,** a body of sediment deposited at the mouth of a river when the river's velocity is decreased as it flows into a standing body of water (figure 10.32).

The surface of most deltas is marked by **distributaries**—small, shifting channels that carry water away from the main river channel and distribute it over the surface of the delta. Sediment deposited at the end of a distributary tends to block the water flow, causing distributaries and their sites of sediment deposition to shift periodically.

The shape of a delta in map view depends on the balance between sediment supply from the stream and the erosive power of waves and currents in the sea or lake (figure 10.33). Some deltas, like that of the Nile River, are broadly triangular; this delta's resemblance to the Greek letter delta (Δ) is the origin of the name. Other deltas, including that of the Mississippi River, are created when very large amounts of sediment are carried into relatively quiet water. Partly because extensive dredging has kept the major distributary channels (locally called "passes") fixed in position and open to navigation for many decades, the Mississippi's distributaries have built long fingers of sediment out into the sea. The resulting shape has been termed a *birdfoot delta.* The deltas of the Amazon and the Niger Rivers are examples of what hap-

Figure 10.33 The shape of a delta depends upon the amount of sediment being carried by the river and on the vigor of waves and currents in the sea.

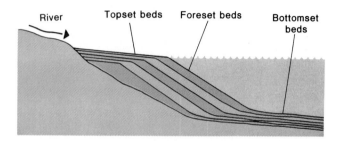

Figure 10.34 Idealized internal construction of a small delta. The steepness of the foreset beds is exaggerated. Most deltas are more complex than this.

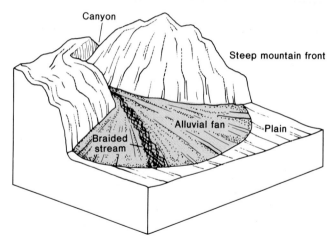

Figure 10.35 An alluvial fan at the mouth of a desert canyon.

Figure 10.36 Alluvial fans forming at the base of a mountain range in the Mojave Desert, California. The fans have joined together as they grew.
Photo by J. R. Balsley, U.S. Geological Survey.

pens when a river empties on a coast where vigorous wave and current activity sweeps much of the sediment along the shoreline. The St. Lawrence is an example of a major river that does not carry enough sediment to form a delta. This is because the St. Lawrence is the outlet for the Great Lakes, which tend to hold sediment rather than move it along.

Many deltas, particularly small ones, are built up from three types of deposits, shown in the diagram in figure 10.34. **Foreset beds** form the main body of the delta. They are deposited at an angle to the horizontal. This angle may be as great as 20–25° in a small delta where the foreset beds are sandy, or less than 5° in large deltas with fine-grained sediment. On top of the foreset beds are the **topset beds,** nearly horizontal beds of varying grain size formed by distributaries shifting across the delta surface. Out in front of the foreset beds are the **bottomset beds,** deposits of the finest silt and clay that are carried out to sea by the fresh water flow or by sediments sliding downhill on the sea floor. Many of the world's great deltas are far more complex than the simplified diagram shown in the figure. Shifting river mouths, wave energy, currents, and other factors produce many different internal structures.

Alluvial Fans

Some streams, particularly in dry climates, do not reach the sea or any other body of water. They build alluvial fans instead of deltas. An **alluvial fan** is a large, fan- or cone-shaped pile of sediment that usually forms where a stream's velocity decreases as it emerges from a narrow mountain canyon onto a flat plain (figures 10.35 and 10.36). Alluvial fans are particularly well developed and exposed in the southwestern desert of the United States and in other desert regions; but they are by no means limited to arid regions.

An alluvial fan builds up its characteristic cone shape gradually as streams shift back and forth across the fan surface and deposit sediment, usually in a braided pattern. Deposition on an alluvial fan in the desert is discontinuous

because streams typically flow for only a short time after the infrequent rainstorms. When rain does come, the amount of sediment to be moved is apt to be greater than the available water. When the rain stops, the stream ends up as a mudflow spreading out over the fan.

The sudden loss of velocity when a stream flows from steep mountains onto a plain causes the sediment deposition on an alluvial fan. The loss of velocity is due to both the decrease in gradient and the widening or branching of the channel as it leaves the mountains. The gradual loss of water as it infiltrates into the fan also promotes sediment deposition. On large fans, deposits are graded in size within the fan, with the coarsest sediment dropped nearest the mountains and the finer material deposited progressively farther away. Small fans do not usually show such grading.

Valley Development

Valleys, the most common landforms on the earth's surface, are, with a few exceptions, created by streams. By removing rock and sediment from the stream channel, a stream deepens, widens, and lengthens its own valley.

Downcutting and Base Level

The process of deepening a valley by erosion of the stream bed is called **downcutting.** If a stream removes rock from its bed, it can cut a narrow *slot canyon* down through rock. Such narrow canyons do not commonly form, because weathering, mass wasting, and sheet erosion remove rock from the valley walls and widen the valley from a narrow, vertical-walled canyon to a broader, open, V-shaped canyon (figure 10.37). Slot canyons can persist, however, in very resistant rock or in regions where downcutting is rapid and weathering is slow.

Downcutting cannot continue indefinitely because the headwaters of a stream cannot cut below the level of the stream bed at the mouth. If a river flows into the sea, the river obviously cannot cut to below sea level, or it would have to flow uphill to get to the sea. The limit of downcutting is known as **base level;** it is a theoretical limit for erosion of the earth's surface (figure 10.38). Downcutting will proceed until the stream bed reaches base level. If the stream is well above base level, downcutting can be quite rapid; but as the stream approaches base level, the rate of downcutting slows down. For streams that reach the ocean, base level is close to sea level (the ultimate base level), but since streams need some slope in order to flow toward the sea, base level slopes gently upward in an inland direction.

During the glacial ages of the Pleistocene Epoch (chapter 12), sea level rose and fell as water was removed from the sea to form the glaciers and returned when the glaciers melted. This means that base level rose and fell for streams flowing into the sea. As a result, the lower reaches of such rivers alternated between erosion (caused by low sea level) and deposition (caused by high sea level). Since the glaciers advanced and retreated several times, the cycle of erosion and deposition was repeated many times, resulting in a complex history of cutting and filling near the mouths of most rivers.

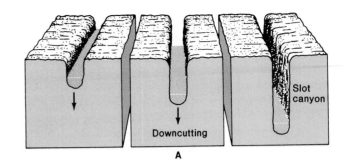

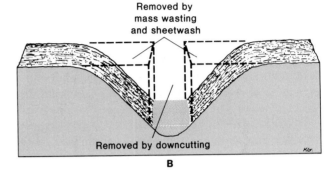

Figure 10.37 Downcutting, mass wasting, and sheetwash shape canyons and valleys. (*A*) Downcutting can create slot canyons in resistant rock, particularly where downcutting is rapid and weathering is slow. (*B*) Downslope movement of rock and soil on valley walls widens most canyons into V-shaped valleys.

Base levels for streams that do not flow into the ocean are not related to sea level. In Death Valley (figure 10.38), base level for in-flowing streams corresponds to the lowest point in the valley, nearly 90 meters *below* sea level (the valley has been dropped below sea level by tectonic movement along faults). On the other hand, base level for the part of a stream above a high reservoir or a mountain lake may be hundreds of meters above sea level. The surface of the lake or reservoir serves as base level for all the water upstream (figure 10.38). The base level of a tributary stream is governed by the level of its junction with the main stream. A ledge of resistant rock may act as a temporary base level if a stream has difficulty eroding through it.

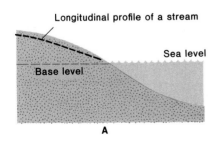

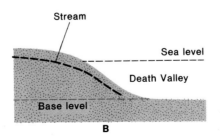

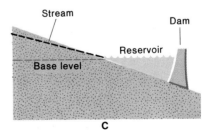

Figure 10.38 Base level is the lowest level of downcutting.

The Concept of a Graded Stream

As a stream begins downcutting into the land, its longitudinal profile is usually irregular, with rapids and waterfalls along its course (figures 10.39 and 10.40). Such a stream, termed *ungraded,* is using most of its erosional energy in downcutting to smooth out these irregularities in gradient.

As the stream smooths out its longitudinal profile to a characteristic concave-upward shape (figure 10.41), it becomes graded. A **graded stream** is one that exhibits a delicate balance between its transporting capacity and the sediment load available to it.

Earlier in the chapter you saw how changes in a stream's transporting capacity, largely caused by changes in velocity and discharge, can cause changes in sediment load. A change in gradient or channel shape, for example, can cause erosion or deposition. The relationship also works in reverse—an increase or decrease in sediment load can change a stream's characteristics.

Any change in the sediment load supplied to the stream can cause it to cut or fill the channel until a new gradient is established that once again adjusts transporting capacity to load. For example, an increased load delivered to a stream may cause the stream to deposit sediment. Deposition continues until the gradient has steepened sufficiently to increase the stream's velocity so that the flowing water can transport the additional sediment.

Similarly, a decrease in sediment load brought to a stream may bring about erosion of the channel. Because dams trap sediment in the calm reservoirs behind them, most streams are nearly sediment-free just downstream from dams. In some streams this loss of sediment has caused channel erosion below the dam.

The adjustment of the stream to a change in load need not be in the form of a gradient change; a stream can also respond by modifying channel shape or roughness.

A river's energy is used for two things—transporting sediment and overcoming resistance to flow. If the sediment load decreases, more of a river's energy becomes available. The river may use this energy to erode more

Figure 10.39 The Grand Canyon of the Yellowstone River in Yellowstone National Park shows rapids and a V-shaped cross-profile with no flood plain. The river is downcutting.
Photo by W. H. Jackson, U.S. Geological Survey.

Figure 10.40 Waterfalls represent irregularities on the longitudinal profile of a downcutting stream (Yellowstone River, Wyoming).

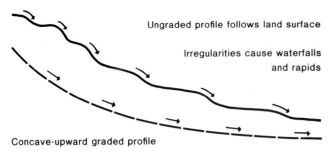

Ungraded profile follows land surface

Irregularities cause waterfalls and rapids

Concave-upward graded profile

Figure 10.41 A graded stream has smoothed out the irregularities in its longitudinal profile.

Figure 10.42 Headward erosion in California. The gully head is migrating uphill, lengthening the gully and destroying the field.
Photo by G. K. Gilbert, U.S. Geological Survey.

sediment, deepening its valley. Or it may change its channel shape, increasing resistance to flow, so the excess energy is used to overcome friction. Or the river may increase the roughness of its channel, also increasing friction. The response of a river is therefore not always predictable, and construction of a dam or channelization of a river may sometimes have unexpected, and perhaps detrimental, results.

The initial adjustment of a river to a change may not be the final adjustment. A river may respond to the construction of a dam by changing its channel shape downstream, but this change may be temporary until another change occurs, such as erosion of a deeper valley. Prediction of a river's response is made particularly difficult because changes in river characteristics are interrelated. An increase in discharge, for example, may result in a simultaneous increase in width, depth, and velocity as well as an eventual change in gradient, sediment load, and sinuosity of the channel.

Lateral Erosion

A graded stream can be deepening its channel by downcutting while part of its energy is also being used for valley widening by **lateral erosion,** the erosion and undercutting of a stream's banks as the stream swings from side to side across its valley floor. The stream channel remains the same width as it moves across the flood plain, but the valley widens by erosion, particularly on the outside of curves and meanders where they impinge against the valley walls. The valley widens as its walls are eroded by the stream and as its walls retreat by mass wasting triggered by stream undercutting. As a valley widens, the stream's flood plain increases in width also.

Headward Erosion

Building a delta or alluvial fan at its mouth is one way a river is able to extend its length. A stream can also lengthen its valley by **headward erosion,** the slow uphill growth of a valley above its original source through gullying, mass wasting, and sheet erosion (figure 10.42). This type of erosion is particularly difficult to stop. When farmland is being lost by gullies that are eroding headward into fields and pastures, farmers must divert sheet flow and fill the gully heads with brush and other debris to stop, or at least retard, the loss of topsoil.

Slope Development and Regional Erosion

How slopes develop on valley sides is a topic of considerable uncertainty among geologists. A basic unresolved question is whether the slope angle of a hillside changes with time. In other words, as the valley widens and the slopes are cut back, does the angle of the valley-side slope decrease?

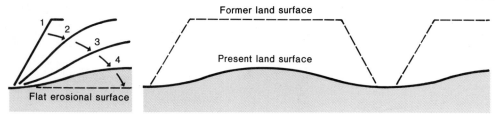

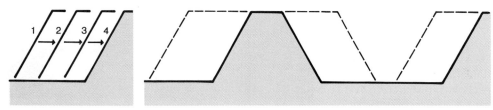

A Slopes become gentler and more rounded.

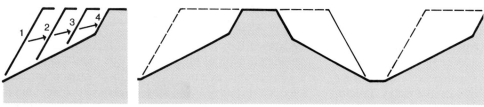

B Cliff retreats maintaining its original angle.

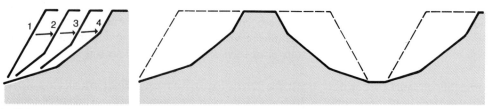

C Cliff retreats and is replaced by a lower gentler slope.

D Cliff retreats and is replaced by sequence of progressively gentler slopes.

Figure 10.43 Contrasting views of slope development. *A* can lead to a flat erosional surface. *B, C,* and *D* are varieties of parallel retreat in which a slope (or part of a slope) maintains a constant angle as it is cut back.

A concept that dominated geologic thought throughout the first half of the twentieth century was that slope angles *do* decrease with time. According to this concept, steep slopes form early in a region's erosional history and become gentler as erosion progresses (figure 10.43). As the valley sides erode back, the uplands gradually wear away, and the material is carried away by streams. The end result of such a sequence of events would be a nearly flat, erosional surface presumably produced as mass wasting, sheet erosion, and stream erosion reduced a region nearly to base level.

More recently, serious objections have been raised to the idea of decreasing slope angle. Field studies suggest that many slopes are characterized by *parallel retreat;* that is, they maintain a constant angle as they are worn away rather than becoming gentler with time (figure 10.43).

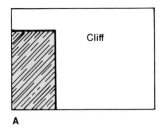
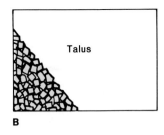
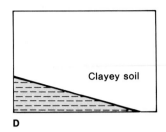

A

B

C

D

Figure 10.44 Maximum slope angles for different types of geologic materials.

Early geologists may have overemphasized the role of *time* in landscape development and largely ignored other important factors such as *climate,* geologic *processes* (which may be dependent on climate), and *rock type and structure.* Many workers today feel that slopes represent an equilibrium between process and rock type. Some geologists question now whether time has any effect at all. A slope may find its equilibrium angle and maintain it for centuries, becoming essentially independent of time.

It is clear that *rock type* influences slope angle. Figure 10.44 shows how slopes can vary on different materials. While the sequence *can* be thought of as a progression in time, becoming gentler as talus weathers to sand and then to clay, it need not be. A slope developed on shale is usually much gentler than a slope on sandstone. Figure 10.45 shows a common situation in the desert of the southwestern United States, where horizontal sandstone beds stand as resistant cliffs and shale weathers and erodes to much gentler slopes. Similar slope differences show up in wetter climates as well.

Climate may also influence the slope angle. Many geologists feel that a humid (wet) climate results in smoothly rounded topography due to a rapid rate of soil creep and other processes. An arid (dry) climate is more apt to result in sharp, angular topography, due to low precipitation, slow chemical weathering and soil creep, and sparse vegetation. (There is by no means universal agreement among geologists on these points. Some feel there is no climate influence on slope, and others feel that *humid* climates yield angular topography.)

One problem with studying hillslopes is the recent climatic fluctuations associated with the glacial ages of the Pleistocene Epoch (chapter 12). As the huge glaciers advanced and retreated, the climate for a region became alternately warmer and colder as well as wetter and drier (the exact combination is debated, and probably varied from region to region). These climatic fluctuations may mean that the present landscape of a region was formed a short time ago under a very different climate than the

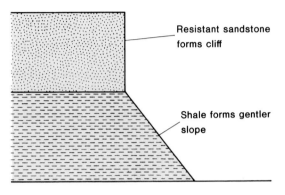

Figure 10.45 Rock type can determine slope angle.

present one. Any measurable changes in slope today may be a response to climate change, therefore, rather than an indication of a progressive change with time.

Figure 10.46 shows several examples of how *rock structure* (and rock type) contribute to slope angle and local elevation. The term *structure* refers to features such as *folds* (bends) and *faults* (breaks) in rock (see chapter 15). Horizontal sedimentary rocks of varying resistance can lead to a staircase-like topography of cliffs and slopes (figure 10.46*A*), as is well developed in the Grand Canyon. Gently folded sedimentary rocks can weather and erode as shown in figure 10.46*B*, with the result that resistant beds can form ridges with two unequal slope angles. Some types of faulting can produce mountain ranges with unequal slopes on opposite sides (figure 10.46*C*).

A series of folded sedimentary rocks of varying resistance to erosion might result in a landscape like that in figure 10.46*D*. The landscape has three different levels of land surface, one connecting the highest summits, one connecting the valley floors, and one in between. Such a landscape can form by the differential removal of resistant and nonresistant rocks. Resistant sandstones form the high ridges; nonresistant limestone, which dissolves in a humid climate, forms the valley floors. Shale, with an intermediate resistance, forms the intermediate surface.

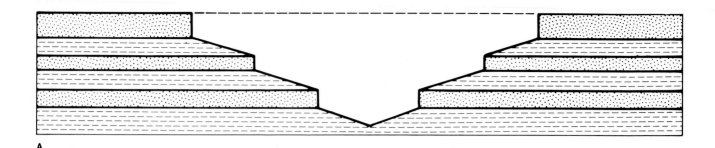

A

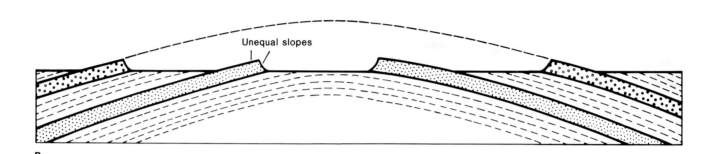

Unequal slopes

B

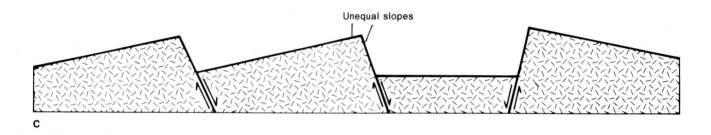

Unequal slopes

C

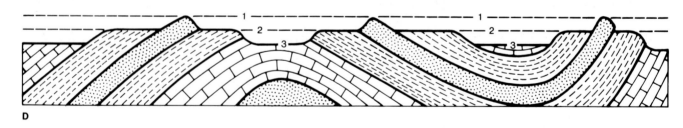

D

Figure 10.46   Rock structure and rock type greatly influence
the appearance of a landscape. (A) Horizontal sedimentary
rocks can result in cliffs and slopes. (B) Gently folded
sedimentary rocks can result in ridges with unequal slopes.
(C) Certain types of faulting can result in unequal slopes on
mountains. (D) Folded sedimentary rocks with three different
levels of land surface. See text for explanation.

Figure 10.47 Stream terraces in Montana. The man is standing on one terrace; the skyline beyond is another. Photo by H. E. Malde, U.S. Geological Survey.

Two Stream Features That Are Difficult to Interpret

Stream terraces and *incised meanders* can be difficult to interpret in terms of their origin and development. At one time most geologists thought that both features indicated regional uplift and erosion. The geologic history of a region with terraces, for example, was assumed to include uplift. Although uplift *can* cause these features, it is now clear that uplift is not *necessary* for these features to form.

Stream Terraces

Stream terraces are steplike landforms found above a stream and its flood plain (figure 10.47). Terraces may be benches cut in rock (sometimes sediment-covered), or they may be steps formed in sediment by deposition and subsequent erosion.

Paired terraces are terraces found at the same elevation on each side of a river. Figure 10.48 shows how one type of paired terrace can form as a river cuts downward into a thick sequence of its own flood-plain deposits. A stretch of river with characteristics favorable to deposition can build up a thick section of flood-plain deposits. Later the river may change from deposition to erosion and cut into its old flood plain, parts of which remain as terraces above the river.

Why might a river shift from deposition to erosion? Certainly regional uplift could cause renewed erosion. Uplift would steepen a river's gradient, causing the river to speed up and begin erosion (figure 10.10). But there are several other reasons why a river might change from deposition to erosion. An increasingly wet climate may increase discharge and cause a river to begin eroding. A drop in base level (such as lowering of sea level) can have the same effect. A situation like that shown in figure 10.48 can develop in a recently glaciated region. Thick valley fill such as glacial outwash (chapter 12) may be deposited

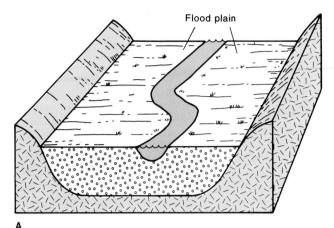

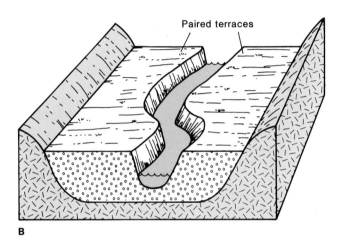

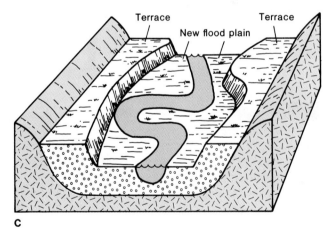

Figure 10.48 Paired terraces formed by a river cutting downward into its own flood-plain deposits. (*A*) River deposits thick, coarse flood-plain deposits. (*B*) River erodes its flood plain by downcutting. Old flood-plain surface forms paired terraces. (*C*) Lateral erosion forms new flood plain below terraces.

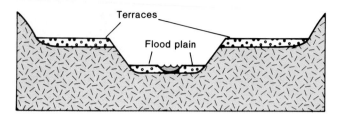

Figure 10.49   Paired terraces may be erosional benches cut in rock.

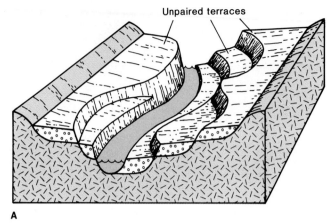

A

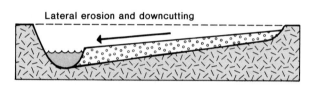

Lateral erosion and downcutting

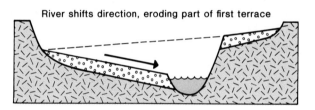

River shifts direction, eroding part of first terrace

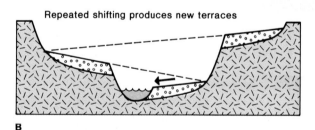

Repeated shifting produces new terraces

B

Figure 10.50   Unpaired terraces do not match across a river. They form by simultaneous downcutting and lateral erosion.

in a stream valley and later, after the glacier stops producing large amounts of sediment, be dissected into terraces by the river.

Paired terraces can also develop from erosion of a bedrock valley floor (figure 10.49). Bedrock benches are usually capped by a relatively thin veneer of flood plain deposits.

Unpaired terraces are terraces that do not have the same elevation on opposite sides of a river (figure 10.50). A river that is downcutting and laterally eroding at the same time will shift back and forth across its valley as it cuts downward. This movement can cut a series of rock benches or terraces at progressively lower levels on either side of a valley.

River terraces can develop in such a variety of ways that determining their origin requires detailed, time-consuming study that may involve an entire river system. In addition to providing clues to a region's geologic history, river terraces in many areas have considerable economic value. Many are noted for their agricultural productivity. Others may contain valuable geologic resources, such as sand and gravel used in making concrete, or placer gold (chapter 21) found with sand and gravel.

Incised Meanders

Incised meanders are meanders that retain their sinuous curves as they cut vertically downward below the level at which they originally formed. The result is a meandering *valley* with essentially no flood plain, cut into the land as a steep-sided canyon (figure 10.51).

Some incised meanders may be due to the profound effects of a change in base level. They may originally have been formed (like the meanders described earlier) by a laterally eroding river flowing over a flat flood plain, perhaps near base level. If regional uplift elevated the land high above base level, the river would begin downcutting and might be able to maintain its characteristic meander pattern while deepening its valley (figure 10.52). A drop in base level without land uplift (possibly because of lowering of sea level) could bring about the same result.

Although uplift may be a key factor in the formation of many incised meanders, it may not be *required* to produce them. Lateral erosion certainly seems to become more prominent as a river approaches base level, but some meandering can occur as soon as a river develops a graded profile. A river flowing on a flat surface high above base level may develop meanders early in its erosional history, and these meanders may become incised by subsequent downcutting. In such a case uplift would not be necessary.

It was thought at one time that the cross-profile of incised meanders could be used to distinguish the two types. A symmetrical profile, with an equal slope on each

Figure 10.51 Incised meander at Goosenecks of San Juan River, near Mexican Hat, Utah. Meandering canyon is more than 300 meters deep.

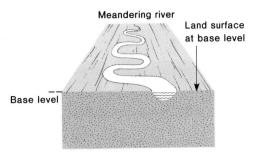

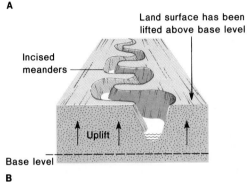

Figure 10.52 Incised meanders can form by uplift.

side of the canyon, was thought to represent inherited meanders produced as a result of uplift (*entrenched meanders*). If the profile was asymmetric, with a gentle slope on the inside of the meander curves and a steep slope on the outside of the curves, it was assumed that the meanders incised themselves by means of a combination of downcutting and lateral erosion (*ingrown meanders*), without the necessity for regional uplift or inheritance from a much older river. Recent studies of actively incising meanders, however, suggest that the distinction between the two types is not this simple. Detailed study is required in each case.

Summary

Normally stream channels are eroded and shaped by the streams that flow in them. Unconfined sheet flow can cause significant erosion.

Drainage basins are separated by *drainage divides.*

A river and its tributaries form a *drainage pattern.* A *dendritic* drainage pattern develops on uniform rock; a *rectangular* pattern on regularly jointed rock. A *radial* pattern forms on conical mountains, and a *trellis* pattern usually indicates erosion of folded sedimentary rock.

Stream *velocity* is the key factor controlling sediment erosion, transportation, and deposition. Velocity is in turn controlled by several factors.

An increase in a stream's *gradient* increases the stream's velocity. *Channel shape* and *roughness* affect velocity by increasing or lessening friction. As tributaries join a stream, the stream's *discharge* increases downstream.

Streams erode by *hydraulic action, abrasion,* and *solution.* They carry coarse sediment by *traction* and *saltation* as *bed load.* Finer-grained sediment is carried in *suspension.* A stream can also have a substantial *dissolved load.*

Streams create features by erosion and deposition. *Potholes* form by abrasion of hard rock on a stream bed. *Bars* form in the middle of streams or on stream banks, particularly on the inside of curves where velocity is low. A *braided pattern* can develop in streams with a high volume of bed load, particularly if the stream has a steep gradient.

Meanders are created when a laterally eroding stream shifts across the flood plain, sometimes creating cutoffs, oxbow lakes, and meander scars.

A *flood plain* develops by both lateral and vertical deposition. *Natural levees* are built up beside streams by flood deposition.

A *delta* forms when a stream flows into standing water. The shape and internal structure of deltas are governed by river deposition and wave and current erosion. Sediment in some deltas is deposited in *topset, foreset,* and *bottomset beds. Alluvial fans* form, particularly in dry climates, at the base of mountains as a stream's channel widens and its velocity decreases.

Rivers deepen their valleys by *downcutting* until they reach *base level,* which is either sea level or a local base level.

A *graded stream* is one with a delicate balance between its transporting capacity and its available load.

Lateral erosion widens a valley after the stream has become graded.

A valley is lengthened by both *headward erosion* and sediment deposition at the mouth.

Regional erosion may proceed as (1) slope angles decrease with time until a region is reduced to base level; or (2) slope angles remain constant during *parallel retreat* of slopes.

Stream terraces can form by erosion of rock benches or by dissection of thick valley deposits during downcutting.

Incised meanders form as (1) river meanders are cut vertically downward following uplift; or (2) lateral erosion and downcutting proceed simultaneously.

Terms To Remember

abrasion	meander cutoff
alluvial fan	meander scar
bar	mouth
base level	natural levee
bed load	oxbow lake
bottomset beds	paired terraces
braided stream	point bar
delta	potholes
dendritic pattern	radial pattern
discharge	rectangular pattern
dissolved load	saltation
distributaries	sheetwash
downcutting	solution
drainage basin	stream
drainage divide	stream channel
drainage pattern	stream gradient
flood plain	stream terrace
foreset beds	stream velocity
graded stream	suspended load
headward erosion	topset beds
headwaters	traction
hydraulic action	trellis pattern
incised meander	tributary
laminar flow	turbulent flow
lateral erosion	unpaired terraces
longitudinal profile	
meanders	

Questions for Review

1. What factors control a stream's velocity?
2. Describe how bar deposition creates a braided stream.
3. In what part of a large alluvial fan is the sediment the coarsest? Why?
4. What does a trellis drainage pattern tell about the rocks underneath it?
5. Describe one way that incised meanders form.
6. Compare and contrast an alluvial fan and a delta.
7. How does a meander neck cutoff form an oxbow lake?
8. How does a natural levee form?
9. Describe two ways in which river terraces form.
10. Describe three ways in which a river erodes its channel.
11. Name and describe the three main ways in which a stream transports sediment.
12. How does a stream widen its valley?
13. What is base level?

Questions for Thought

1. Over the last few thousand years, sea level has been rising because of the melting of large glaciers on land. What effects does such a rise in sea level have on rivers that flow into the sea?
2. Several rivers have recently been set aside as "wild rivers" on which dams cannot be built. Give at least four arguments against building dams on rivers. Give at least four arguments in favor of building dams.

Supplementary Readings

Bloom, A. L. 1978. *Geomorphology: A systematic analysis of late cenozoic landforms.* Englewood Cliffs, N.J.: Prentice-Hall.

Hoyt, W. B., and W. B. Langbein. 1955. *Floods.* Princeton, N.J.: Princeton Univ. Press.

Leopold, L. B. 1974. *Water, a primer.* San Francisco: W. H. Freeman.

Leopold, L. B., and W. B. Langbein. 1966. River meanders. *Scientific American* (June 1966). Offprint #869. San Francisco: W. H. Freeman.

Leopold, L. B., M. G. Wolman, and J. P. Miller. 1964. *Fluvial processes in geomorphology.* San Francisco: W. H. Freeman.

Morisawa, M. 1968. *Streams: Their dynamics and morphology.* New York: McGraw-Hill.

Ritter, D. F. 1978. *Process geomorphology.* Dubuque, Iowa: Wm. C. Brown Company Publishers.

Thornbury, W. D. 1969. *Principles of geomorphology.* 2nd ed. New York: John Wiley & Sons.

Tuttle, S. D. 1980. *Landforms and landscapes.* 3d ed. Dubuque, Iowa: Wm. C. Brown Company Publishers.

11

Ground Water

Purpose

Surprisingly, water underground is 30 to 40 times as plentiful as fresh water on the land surface (not including water stored as ice in glaciers). Ground water is a tremendously important resource. How it gets underground, how it is stored, how it moves while underground, how we look for it, and, perhaps most important of all, the need to protect it—these concerns are the main substance of this chapter.

Also discussed here are the relationships among springs, rivers, and ground water. Ground water forms distinctive geologic features, such as caves, sinkholes, and petrified wood. It also can appear as hot springs and geysers. Hot ground water can be used for the generation of power.

How do people get the water they need for domestic, industrial, agricultural, and recreational uses? Many communities draw surface water from rivers, lakes, or manmade reservoirs, sometimes using elaborate aqueduct or canal systems to bring water from distant sources. Another source of water, directly underneath many cities and towns, is commonly used as the principal water supply in many parts of the country. This resource is **ground water,** the water that lies beneath the ground surface, filling the cracks, crevices, and pore space of rocks.

In the dry regions of the southwestern United States, many cities and towns pump great quantities of ground water from drilled wells. After driving for hours across a barren, dusty-brown desert, you might be startled to come upon a community with green trees, flowers, lawns, and swimming pools, all supplied by water pumped up from beneath the arid land.

Cities in regions with substantial rainfall may also depend upon ground water for part of their water supply. In fact, even cities built directly on the flood plains of rivers may draw most of their supply from wells because the ground water may be more economical and safer to use, being less contaminated with pollutants than the surface water.

The Hydrologic Cycle

The movement of water and water vapor from the sea to the atmosphere, to the land, and back to the sea and atmosphere again is called the **hydrologic cycle** (figure 11.1). When rain (or snow) falls on the land surface, more than half the water is returned rather rapidly to the atmosphere by evaporation or by transpiration from plants. The remainder either flows over the land surface as runoff in streams or percolates down into the ground to become ground water. The source of nearly all ground water is, therefore, rain and snow that falls onto the land. The percentage of precipitation that soaks into the ground is influenced by climate, land slope, soil and rock type, and vegetation. In general, perhaps 15–20 percent of the total precipitation ends up as ground water, but there can be much variation locally and regionally.

Porosity and Permeability

Porosity, the percentage of a rock's volume that is taken up by openings, is a measurement of a rock's ability to hold water. Most rocks can hold some water. Some sedimentary rocks, such as sandstone, shale, and clastic limestones, tend to have a high porosity and therefore can hold a considerable amount of water. A deposit of loose sand may have a porosity of 30–40 percent, but this may be reduced to 15–20 percent by cementation and recrystallization as the sand lithifies. A sandstone in which pores are nearly filled with cement and fine-grained matrix, however, may have a relatively low porosity of 5 percent or less. Crystalline rocks, such as granite, schist, or chemical limestones, do not have pores but may hold water in joints and other openings.

Even though most rocks can hold some water, they vary a great deal in their ability to allow water to pass through them. **Permeability** refers to the capacity of a rock to transmit a fluid such as water or petroleum. In other words, permeability measures the relative ease of liquid flow and gives an indication of the interconnection of the openings in a rock. The distinction between porosity and permeability is important. A rock that holds much water is called *porous;* a rock that allows water to flow easily through it is described as *permeable.* Most sandstones and conglomerates are both porous and permeable. An *impermeable* rock is one that does not allow water to flow through it easily. Unjointed granite and schist are

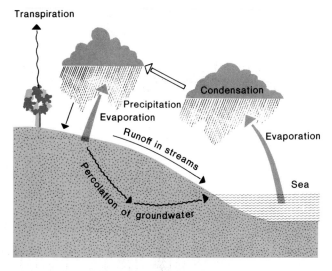

Figure 11.1   The hydrologic cycle. Water vapor evaporates from the sea and land, condenses to form clouds, and falls as precipitation. Water falling on land runs off over the surface as streams, or percolates into the ground to become ground water. It returns to the atmosphere again by evaporation and transpiration.

impermeable. Shale tends to have high porosity but is usually impermeable because its pores are too small to permit easy passage of water.

The Water Table

Responding to the pull of gravity, water percolates down into the ground through the soil and through cracks and pores in the rock. Several kilometers down in the crust percolation lessens as rock openings become smaller. Sedimentary rock, which typically lies as a relatively thin layer over the crystalline basement, usually has a higher porosity than the igneous and metamorphic crystalline rocks beneath. The amount of open space in rock decreases considerably at the boundary between sedimentary and crystalline rocks. In the sedimentary rock, pores tend to be increasingly sealed by cement the deeper the rocks are in the earth. In addition, the great weight of several kilometers of overlying rock tends to seal deep rock openings by plastic flow. Where rock openings are sealed, water stops percolating downward. This level generally lies about 5 kilometers beneath the surface, although in thick wedges of sedimentary rocks, such as those found along the Gulf Coast of the United States, percolation may continue to a depth of 10 kilometers or more.

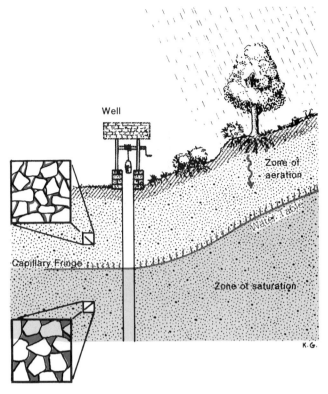

Figure 11.2 The water table marks the top of the zone of saturated rocks. Above the water table, the rock openings contain both water and air.

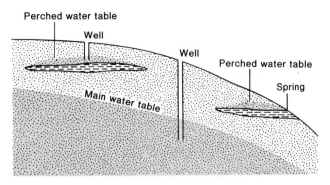

Figure 11.3 Perched water tables form above layers of impermeable rock such as shale.

The subsurface zone in which all rock openings are filled with water is called the **zone of saturation** (figure 11.2). If a well were drilled downward into this zone, ground water would fill the lower part of the well. The water level inside the well marks the upper surface of the zone of saturation; this surface is the **water table.**

Above the zone of saturation, the rock openings are filled partly with water and partly with air. This zone is termed the **zone of aeration.** The force of *surface tension* holds water droplets on the sides of rock openings. Surface tension also causes water to rise upward in small openings by *capillary action* if the openings are not completely saturated with water. (If you dip the corner of a paper towel in water, water rises up the towel by capillary action.) In rocks, capillary action causes water to rise above the zone of saturation in a **capillary fringe,** an area just above the water table creating a transitional zone a few feet thick between the saturated rocks below and the zone of aeration above. Plant roots generally obtain their water from the belt of soil moisture near the top of the zone of aeration, where fine-grained clay minerals hold water and make it available for plant growth.

A **perched water table** is the top of a body of ground water separated from the main water table beneath it by a zone that is not saturated (figure 11.3). It may be formed as ground water collects above a lens of relatively impermeable shale within a more permeable rock, such as sandstone. If the perched water table intersects the land surface, a line of springs can form along the upper contact of the shale lens.

Velocity of Ground-Water Flow

How fast ground water flows depends in part on the *permeability* of the rock or other materials through which it passes. If rock pores are small and poorly connected, water moves slowly. When openings are large and well connected, the flow of water is more rapid. One way of measuring ground-water velocity is to introduce a tracer, such as a dye, into the water and then watch for the color to appear in a well or spring some distance away. Such experiments have shown that ground water has a wide range of velocities, traveling, on the average, from several centimeters to several meters a day. Nearly impermeable rocks may allow water to move only a few centimeters a year, but highly permeable materials, such as unconsolidated gravel or cavernous limestone, may permit flow rates well over 100 meters per day.

The *slope of the water table* also strongly influences ground-water velocity. Water-table slope is controlled largely by topography—the water table roughly parallels the land surface (particularly in humid regions). Even in highly permeable rock, ground water will not move if the water table is flat. The steeper the slope of the water table the faster ground water moves. Ordinarily the water table slopes within a range of 1–10 meters per kilometer.

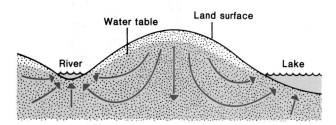

Figure 11.4 Movement of ground water beneath a sloping water table in uniformly permeable rock.

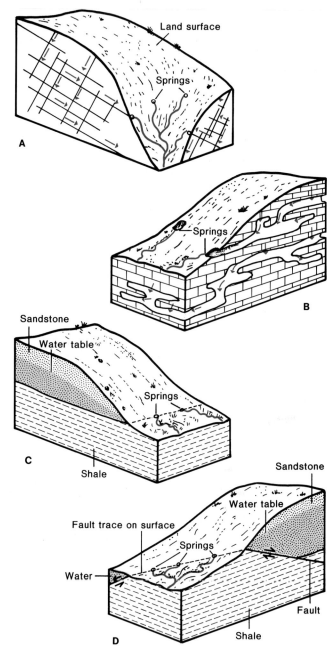

The circulation of ground water in the zone of saturation is not confined to a shallow layer beneath the water table. Ground water may move hundreds of meters vertically downward before rising again to discharge as a spring or seep into the beds of rivers and lakes at the surface (figure 11.4).

Springs and Rivers

A **spring** is a place where water flows naturally from rock onto the land surface (figure 11.5) Some springs discharge where the water table intersects the land surface, but they may also occur where water flows out from caverns or along fractures, faults, or rock contacts that come to the surface (figures 11.6 and 11.7).

Climate determines the relationship between stream flow and the water table. In rainy regions most streams are **gaining streams**; that is, they are receiving water from the zone of saturation (figure 11.8). The surface of these streams coincides with the water table. Water from the zone of saturation flows into the stream through the stream bed and banks that lie below the water table. Because of the added ground water, the discharge of these streams increases downstream. Where the water table intersects the land surface over a broad area, ponds, lakes, and swamps are found.

In drier climates rivers tend to be **losing streams**; that is, they are losing water to the zone of saturation (figure 11.8). The channels of losing streams lie above the water table. The water percolating into the ground beneath a losing stream may cause a rise in the water table below the stream, and this condition may persist even when the stream is not flowing. In a desert the nearest source of water may be a short distance under a dry stream bed.

Figure 11.5 Springs can form in many ways. (A) Water moves along fractures in crystalline rock and forms springs where fractures intersect the land surface. (B) Water enters caves along joints in limestone and forms springs at the mouths of caves. (C) Springs form at the contact between a permeable rock such as sandstone and an underlying impermeable rock such as shale. (D) Springs can form along faults when permeable rock has been moved against impermeable rock. Fault motion shown by arrows.

Figure 11.6 A small spring issuing from limestone, Butler County, Kansas.
Photo by R. B. Leonard, U.S. Geological Survey.

Figure 11.7 Large springs at Thousand Springs, near Twin Falls, Idaho. Water issues from fractured basalt flows and interflow sediment layers.
Photo by C. F. Bowen, U.S. Geological Survey.

Aquifers

An **aquifer** is a body of saturated rock or sediment through which water can move readily. A well must be drilled into an aquifer if it is to reach an adequate supply of water (figure 11.9). Aquifers are both porous and permeable. Good aquifers include sandstone, conglomerate, well-jointed limestone, bodies of sand and gravel, and some fragmental or fractured volcanic rocks such as columnar basalt. These favorable geologic materials are sought in "prospecting" for ground water or looking for good sites to drill water wells.

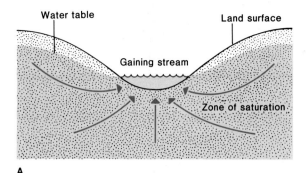

A

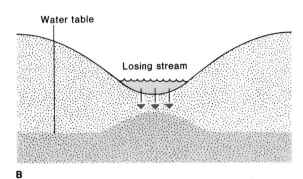

B

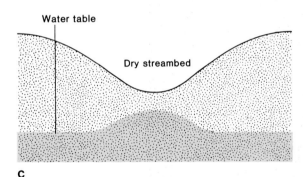

C

Figure 11.8 Gaining and losing streams. *(A)* Stream gaining water from zone of saturation. *(B)* Stream losing water through streambed to zone of saturation. *(C)* Water table can be close to land surface beneath dry streambed.

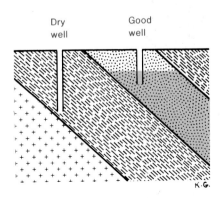

Figure 11.9 A well must hit an aquifer to obtain water.

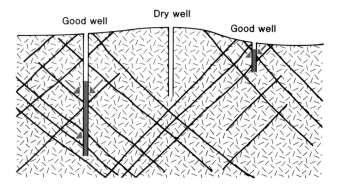

Figure 11.10 Wells can obtain some water from fractures in crystalline rock. Well must intersect fractures to obtain water.

Wells drilled in shale beds are not usually very successful because shale is highly porous but relatively impermeable. Wet mud may have a porosity of 80 to 90 percent, and even when the mud is compacted to form shale, it may still have a fairly high porosity of 30 percent or more. Yet the extremely small size of the pores, together with the electrostatic attraction that clay minerals have for water molecules (chapter 5), prevents water from moving through the shale into a well.

Because they are not very porous, crystalline rocks such as granite, gabbro, gneiss, schist, and some types of limestone are not good aquifers. The porosity of such rocks may be one percent or less. Crystalline rocks that are highly fractured, however, may be sufficiently porous and permeable to provide a dependable water supply to wells (figure 11.10).

Wells

A **well** is a deep shaft or hole, generally cylindrical, that is dug or drilled into the ground to penetrate an aquifer below the zone of saturation (figures 11.9 and 11.10). Water tapped by a well usually must be lifted or pumped to the surface. As figure 11.11 shows, a well dug in a valley usually has to go down a shorter distance to hit water than a well dug on a hilltop. During dry seasons the water table falls as water flows out of the zone of saturation into springs and rivers. Wells not deep enough to intersect the lowered water table go dry, but the rise of the water table during the next rainy season normally returns water to the dry wells.

When water is pumped from a well, the water table is usually drawn down into a depression shaped like an inverted cone known as a **cone of depression** (figure 11.12). This local lowering of the water table, called **drawdown,** tends to change the direction of flow of ground water by changing the slope of the water table. Ground water within the upper part of the zone of saturation usually flows down the slope of the water table.

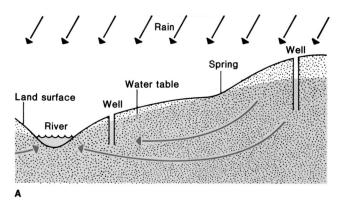

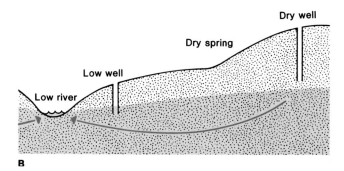

Figure 11.11 The water table rises in wet seasons and falls in dry seasons as water drains out of the zone of saturation into rivers. *(A)* Wet season: water table and rivers high, springs flow, good wells. *(B)* Dry season: water table and rivers low, some springs and wells dry up.

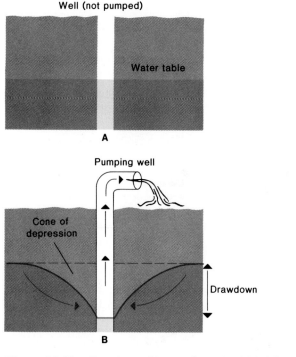

Figure 11.12 Pumping well lowers the water table into a cone of depression.

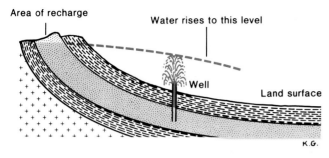

Figure 11.13 Artesian aquifer of sandstone between two shale beds. Water rises above the land surface when a well taps the artesian aquifer.

Figure 11.14 Artesian well spouts water above land surface in South Dakota, early 1900s. Heavy use of this aquifer has reduced water pressure so much that spouts do not occur today.
Photo by N. H. Darton, U.S. Geological Survey.

Artesian Aquifers and Wells

An **artesian aquifer** is an aquifer confined above, and sometimes below, by less permeable rocks. If any runoff or infiltration is to replenish such an aquifer, part of the aquifer must be exposed at (or be close to) the surface. The addition of new water to an aquifer or to the zone of saturation is called **recharge**. Figure 11.13 shows an artesian system with a sandstone bed between two shale beds.

The sandstone has been bent by tectonic action and subsequently exposed by erosion in a highland area where recharge can take place. Water from rain or snow gradually fills up the pores in the sandstone until it is completely saturated, almost up to the recharge area.

Most of the aquifer (figure 11.13) is *below* the level of recharge. Therefore the water in distant parts of the aquifer is under pressure from the weight of the water above. When a well is drilled into the aquifer, this water pressure forces water up the well. A well is known as an **artesian well** if the water in it rises above the level of the aquifer. In an artesian well, the water may rise up the well to a level above the land surface, producing a flowing well that spouts continuously into the air unless it is capped. Flowing wells used to exist in South Dakota when the extensive artesian aquifer in that state was first tapped (figure 11.14), but continued use has lowered the water pressure level below the ground surface in most parts of the state. Water still rises above the aquifer but does not reach the land surface.

Ground-Water Pollution

Ground water is a major economic resource. In some parts of the country more ground water than surface water is used to supply domestic, industrial, and agricultural needs. This is particularly true in the arid and semiarid western states. Because ground water in its natural state tends to be relatively free of contaminants, it is a better source of drinking water than surface water in many localities. Pollution of ground water can become a very serious problem.

Agricultural pesticides and herbicides applied to fields or orchards can find their way into ground water when rain or irrigation water leaches the poisons downward into the soil. Even fertilizers are of concern—nitrate, one of the most widely used agricultural fertilizers, is harmful in drinking water even in relatively small quantities.

Rain can also leach pollutants from city dumps into ground-water supplies. Consider for a moment some of the things you threw away last year. A partially empty aerosol can of ant poison? The can will rust through in the dump, releasing the poison into the ground and perhaps into the zone of saturation below. A broken thermometer? The toxic mercury may eventually find its way to the ground-water supply. A half-used can of oven cleaner? The dried-out remains of a can of lead-base paint? Heavy metals such as mercury, lead, copper, and cadmium, together with household chemicals and poisons, can all be concentrated in ground-water supplies beneath dumps.

Prospecting for Ground Water

Many wells are drilled or dug without any effort having been made to locate a promising area of ground-water flow. Many of these wells are successful (especially if only small amounts of water are needed) because most rocks hold some water, which flows into wells that intersect the water table. However, if a large and dependable supply of water is needed—as for a city water system—specialists in ground-water geology may be called in to locate a promising well site. Geologists use many methods to locate aquifers. A detailed knowledge of the local rocks is necessary, so a geologist may map the rocks and measure physical properties such as electrical resistance, temperature, or magnetism to determine the depth and type of possible aquifers. Sometimes a small-diameter test well is drilled before the larger, more expensive supply well is sunk. The geologist looks for potentially high-producing aquifers rather than searching for water directly, which would be much more difficult. In some regions, however, the presence of certain plants is sometimes a useful guide to the location of water, particularly the depth of the water table.

Some people search for water by water witching, or *dowsing,* with a divining rod (also sometimes employed to search for metals or lost objects). Usually the dowser holds a forked stick horizontally in the hands while walking over an area. The stick is supposed to deflect or twist downward of its own accord when the dowser passes over water. This method has been tried for centuries, the only modification being that a twisted metal rod, often made of a coat hanger,

now may be substituted for the stick. Carefully controlled tests conducted by workers in psychic research have shown that water witchers' "success" is equal to or less than pure chance, while geologists' results are superior to both witching and to chance. Records kept on thousands of wells in Australia in the early 1900s show that of wells that were not divined, more than 83 percent produced flows of 100 gallons per hour, and 7.4 percent were failures, finding no water at all. Of wells that were divined by water witchers, only about 70 percent produced more than 100 gallons per hour, and 14.7 percent were dry. In the early part of this century the U.S. Geological Survey concluded that any future testing of the results of water witching would be a misuse of public funds.

Despite such findings, many people believe strongly in dowsing. Water witchers themselves are devout in their belief that they can find water, and in some regions of the United States almost no wells are drilled without a witcher's advice. Dowsers are helped in locating water by the fact that most rocks hold some water, and dowsers often have a long-standing knowledge of a particular region and its potential water resources. This is not to say that dowsers are deliberate frauds. Many are convinced that they perform a valuable public service, and some do not charge for their services. Scientists see no reason for dowsing to work and are skeptical about dowsers' "success." Geologists would be nearly unanimous in urging you not to pay for a dowser's service if a fee were charged.

Liquid wastes from industry, mining, and sewage (both human and animal) are sometimes pumped into basins on the surface of the land or pumped underground for disposal. Such liquids can percolate into the zone of saturation, carrying heavy metals, toxic chemicals, and harmful bacteria.

Some contaminants can be filtered out of ground water during its passage through rock and soil. The ability

of the rock and soil to purify water depends largely on their permeability and mineral composition. In 30–40 meters of travel through a sandy loam soil (a mixture of clay minerals, sand grains, and organic humus), human sewage can (under ideal conditions) be purified through filtration, ion absorption by clay minerals and organic matter, and decomposition by soil organisms (figure 11.15). Some sandstones and shales are also capable of purifying human and even industrial sewage by filtration

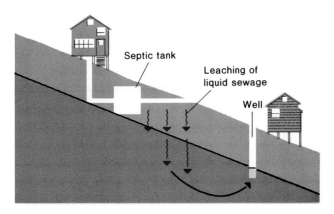

Figure 11.15 A common situation on a rural hillside. Rock type and distance will determine possible sewage contamination at the well. As little as 30 meters of movement can effectively filter human sewage in some rocks, but if the rock is fractured granite, contamination can occur many hundreds of meters away.

over short distances. Unfortunately, some pesticides and fertilizers pass unfiltered through rock and soil. Extremely permeable rock, such as highly fractured crystalline rock or cavernous limestone, has very little purifying effect on contaminated ground water. When ground water flows rapidly, it is not in contact with rock and soil long enough for purification to be accomplished. Water can flow hundreds of meters through such rocks without being cleansed of contaminants.

Pumping wells can cause or aggravate ground-water pollution (figure 11.16). Well drawdown can increase the slope of the water table locally, thus increasing the rate of ground water flow and giving the water less time to be purified underground before it is used (figure 11.16*A*). Drawdown can even reverse the original slope of the water table, perhaps contaminating wells that were pure before pumping began (figure 11.16*B*). Heavily pumped wells near a coast can be contaminated by *saltwater intrusion* (figures 11.16*C* and *D*).

Balancing Withdrawal and Recharge

A local supply of ground water will last indefinitely if it is withdrawn for use at a rate equal to or less than the rate of recharge to the aquifer. If ground water is withdrawn faster than it is being recharged, however, the supply is being reduced and will one day be gone.

Heavy use of ground water causes a regional water table to drop. In parts of western Texas and eastern New Mexico the pumping of ground water has caused the water table to drop 30 meters over the past few decades. The lowering of the water table means that wells must be deepened and more electricity must be used to pump the water to the surface. Moreover, as water is withdrawn, the ground surface may settle because the water no longer supports the rock and sediment. Mexico City has subsided

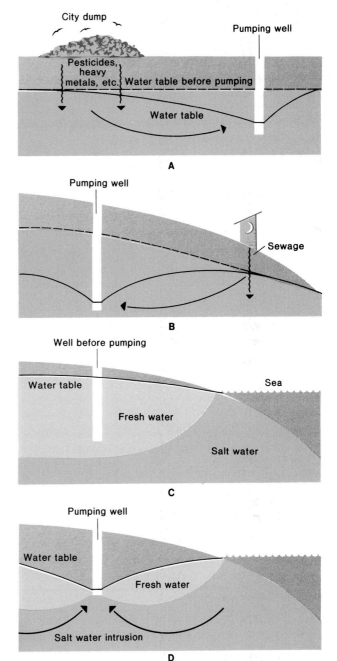

Figure 11.16 Ground-water pollution problems caused or aggravated by pumping wells. *(A)* Water table steepens near dump, increasing the velocity of ground-water flow and drawing pollutants into well. *(B)* Water-table slope is reversed by pumping, changing direction of ground-water flow and polluting well. *(C)* Well near coast before pumping. Fresh water floats on salt water. *(D)* Well in *C* begins pumping, thinning the fresh water lens and drawing salt water into the well.

more than 6 meters, and portions of California's Central Valley more than 7 meters because of extraction of ground water. Such *subsidence* can crack building foundations, roads, and pipelines.

To balance recharge with withdrawal and avoid the problems of dropping water tables and land subsidence, many communities, especially in arid and semiarid regions, practice **artificial recharge,** using engineering to increase the rate of recharge. For example, water is spread out over the surface of the land in large infiltration ponds, from which it seeps into the ground to add to the zone of saturation. Periodically floodwaters can be diverted to infiltration ponds. Reclaimed water from sewage treatment plants also can be used for artificial recharge. Water that has been used in air conditioning and for industrial cooling can be recycled. In some areas recharge water is actively pumped down wells into the zone of aeration or saturation.

Effects of Ground-Water Action

Caves, Sinkholes, and Karst Topography

Caves (or **caverns**) are naturally formed underground chambers. Most caves develop when slightly acidic ground water dissolves limestone along joints and bedding planes, opening up cavern systems as the rock components are carried away in solution (figure 11.17). Natural ground water is often slightly acidic because of the solution of carbon dioxide (CO_2) from the atmosphere or from soil gases (as discussed in chapter 5 on weathering). The equation below represents the processes of solution and deposition of calcite by ground water.

Geologists disagree as to whether limestone caves form above, below, or at the water table. Some caves probably are formed by ground water circulating below the water table, as shown in figure 11.17. If the water table drops or the land is elevated above the water table, the cave may begin to fill in again by calcite precipitation. Read the equation below from right to left for the calcite precipitation reaction.

Ground water with a high concentration of calcium (Ca^{++}) and bicarbonate (HCO_3^-) ions may drip slowly from the ceiling of an air-filled cave. As a water drop hangs on the ceiling of the cave, some of the water may

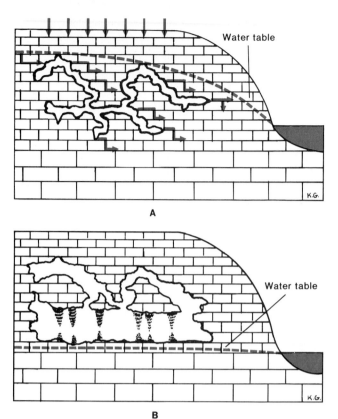

Figure 11.17 Solution of limestone to form caves. *(A)* Water moves along fractures and bedding planes in limestone, dissolving the limestone to form caves below the water table. *(B)* Falling water table allows cave system, now greatly enlarged, to fill with air. Calcite precipitation forms stalactites and stalagmites above the water table.

evaporate and some carbon dioxide (CO_2) may be lost into the cave's atmosphere. The evaporation and CO_2 loss cause a small amount of calcite (calcium carbonate) to precipitate out of the water onto the cave ceiling. When the water drop falls to the cave floor, the impact may cause more evaporation and CO_2 loss, and another small amount of calcite may precipitate on the cave floor. A falling water drop, therefore, can precipitate small amounts of calcite on both the cave ceiling and the cave floor. The next drop precipitates a bit more calcite over the first deposits, with each subsequent drop adding still more calcite.

$$
\underset{\text{(water)}}{(H_2O} + \underset{\substack{\text{(carbon}\\\text{dioxide)}}}{CO_2} \rightleftarrows \underset{\substack{\text{(carbonic}\\\text{acid)}}}{H_2CO_3} \rightleftarrows) \quad \underset{\substack{\text{(hydrogen}\\\text{ion)}}}{H^+} + \underset{\substack{\text{(bicarbonate}\\\text{ion)}}}{HCO_3^-} + \underset{\substack{\text{(calcite/}\\\text{limestone)}}}{CaCO_3} \rightleftarrows \underset{\substack{\text{(calcium}\\\text{ion)}}}{Ca^{++}} + \underset{\substack{\text{(bicarbonate}\\\text{ion)}}}{2HCO_3^-}
$$

development of caves (solution) →

← development of flowstone and dripstone (deposition)

Figure 11.18 Stalactites, stalagmites, and columns in Mammoth Cave, Kentucky. Note the alignment of stalactites along roof fractures.
Photo by W. T. Lee, U.S. Geological Survey.

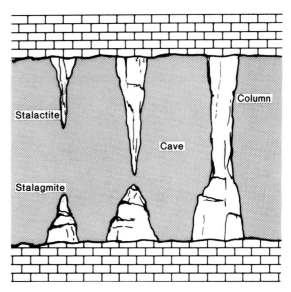

Figure 11.19 Stalactites grow downward from cave ceilings, and stalagmites build upward from cave floors. If they meet, they form a column.

Deposits of calcite (and, rarely, other minerals) built up in caves by dripping water are called **dripstone.** Figure 11.18 shows some of the intriguing features formed by dripstone. **Stalactites** are icicle-like pendants of dripstone hanging from cave ceilings. They are generally slender and often are aligned along cracks in the ceiling, which act as conduits for ground water. **Stalagmites** are cone-shaped masses of dripstone formed on cave floors, generally directly below stalactites. Splashing water precipitates calcite over a large area on the cave floor, so stalagmites are usually thicker than the stalactites above them. As a stalactite grows downward and a stalagmite grows upward, they may eventually join to form a **column** (figure 11.19).

In parts of some caves, water flows in a thin film over the cave surfaces rather than dripping from the ceiling. Sheetlike or ribbonlike **flowstone** deposits develop from calcite that is precipitated by flowing water on cave walls and floors.

The floors of most caves are covered with sediment, much of which is **residual clay,** the fine-grained particles left behind as insoluble residue when a limestone containing clay dissolves. (Some limestone contains only about 50 percent calcite.) Other sediment, including most of the coarse-grained material found on cave floors, may be carried into the cave by streams, particularly when surface water drains into a cave system from openings on the land surface.

Solution of limestone underground can sometimes produce features that are visible on the surface. Extensive cavern systems can undermine a region so that roofs collapse and form depressions in the land surface above. **Sinkholes** are closed depressions found on land surfaces underlain by limestone (figure 11.20). They form either by the collapse of a cave roof or by solution as descending water enlarges a crack in limestone. Limestone regions in Florida, Missouri, Indiana, and Kentucky are heavily dotted with sinkholes.

A

B

Figure 11.20 *(A)* A sinkhole in limestone near Cambria, Wyoming. *(B)* Collapse sinkhole 130 meters long and 45 meters deep, Shelby County, Alabama, 1972.
Photo *(A)* by N. H. Darton, 1899, U.S. Geological Survey. Photo *(B)* by U.S. Geological Survey.

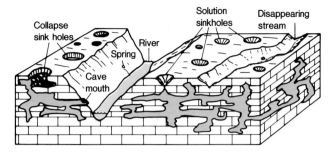

Figure 11.21 Karst topography is marked by underground caves and numerous surface sinkholes. A major river may cross the region, but small surface streams generally disappear down sinkholes.

Figure 11.22 Petrified logs in the Petrified Forest National Park, Arizona.
Photo by N. H. Darton, U.S. Geological Survey.

Figure 11.23 Concretions in sandstone, Los Angeles, California. They are more resistant to weathering than the rock around them.
Photo by R. Arnold, U.S. Geological Survey.

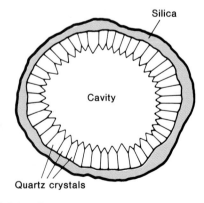

Figure 11.24 Cross section of a geode. Well-formed crystals grow toward a central cavity.

An area with many sinkholes and with cave systems beneath the land surface is said to have **karst topography** (figure 11.21). Karst areas are characterized by a lack of surface streams, although one major river may flow at a level lower than the karst area.

Streams sometimes disappear down sinkholes to flow through caves beneath the surface. In this specialized instance, a true *underground stream* exists. These are quite rare, however, as most ground water flows very slowly through pores and cracks in sediment or rock. You may hear people with wells describe the "underground stream" that their well penetrates, but this is almost never the case. Wells tap ground water in the rock pores and crevices, not underground streams. If a well did tap a true underground river in a karst region, the water would probably be too polluted to drink, especially if it had washed down from the surface into a cavern without being filtered through soil and rock.

Other Effects

Ground water is important in the preservation of fossils such as **petrified wood,** a material that forms when the organic matter of buried wood is replaced by inorganic silica carried in by ground water (figure 11.22). The result is a hard, permanent replacement for the wood, often preserving the growth lines and other details. The original material in marine shells and animal bones also can be replaced by calcite or silica carried by ground water.

Cementing material that helps in the lithification of sedimentary rock is carried into place by ground water. When a considerable amount of cementing material precipitates locally in a rock, a hard rounded mass called a **concretion** may develop, often around an organic nucleus such as a leaf, tooth, or other fossil (figure 11.23).

Geodes are partly hollow, globe-shaped bodies found in some limestones and occasionally in other rocks. The outer shell is of silica, and well-formed crystals of quartz or calcite project inward toward a central cavity (figure 11.24). The origin of geodes is not completely clear, but the crystal growth within a cavity suggests that solution and subsequent precipitation of minerals from ground water are important in their formation.

In arid and semiarid climates, **alkali soil** may develop because of the precipitation of great quantities of sodium salts by evaporating ground water. Such soil is generally unfit for plant growth. Alkali soil generally forms at the ground surface in low-lying areas. (See also chapter 5 on soils.)

Hot Water Underground

Water can gain heat in two ways while it is underground. First, and more commonly, ground water may circulate near a magma chamber or a body of cooling igneous rock. **Hot springs** are springs in which the water temperatures are warmer than human body temperature. In the United States most hot springs are found in the western states associated with relatively recent volcanism. The hot springs and pools of Yellowstone National Park in Wyoming are of this type.

Underground water also can gain heat if it circulates unusually deep in the earth, perhaps along a major fissure. The normal geothermal gradient of the earth is about 25°C/kilometer (chapter 4), so that water circulating at a depth of two or three kilometers would be warmed substantially above normal surface water temperature. The famous springs at Warm Springs, Georgia, have been warmed by deep circulation. Warm water, regardless of its origin, is lighter than cold water, and readily rises to the surface.

A **geyser** is a type of hot spring that periodically erupts hot water and steam. The water is generally near boiling (100°C). The cause of eruptions is apparently a constriction in the underground "plumbing" of a geyser, which prevents the water from rising and cooling (figure 11.25). The events that are thought to lead to a geyser eruption are illustrated in figure 11.26. Water gradually

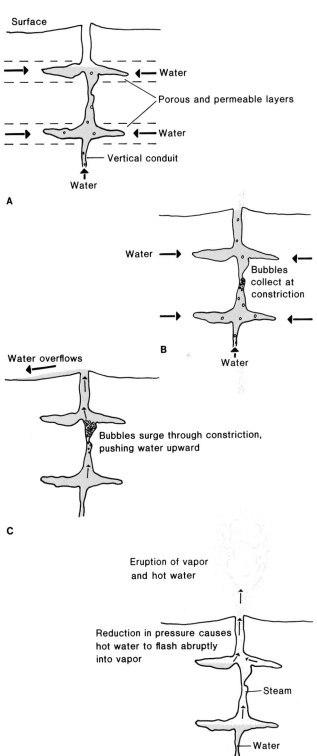

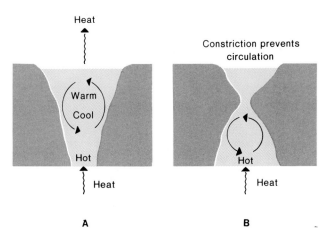

Figure 11.25 *(A)* Hot springs and *(B)* geysers. Many hot springs are funnel-shaped pools that allow water to rise and cool at the surface. Geysers have constrictions that prevent such circulation, so that the water continues to rise in temperature. Figures are simplified.

Figure 11.26 Eruption of a geyser. See text for explanation. Modified from W. R. Keefer, 1971, *U.S. Geological Survey Bulletin,* 1347.

Figure 11.27 Precipitation of calcite in the form of travertine terraces around a hot spring (Mammoth Hot Springs, Yellowstone National Park).
Photo by N. H. Darton, U.S. Geological Survey.

Figure 11.28 Geyserite deposits around vent of Castle Geyser. Yellowstone National Park.

seeps into a partially emptied geyser chamber. Heat supplied from below slowly warms the water. Bubbles of water vapor and other gases begin to form as the temperature of the water column rises. Increasing temperature forms enough bubbles to clog the constricted part of the chamber. The upward pressure of the bubbles pushes out some of the water above in a gentle surge, thus lowering the pressure on the water in the lower part of the chamber. This drop in pressure causes the chamber water, now very hot, to flash into vapor. The expanding vapor blasts upward out of the chamber, driving hot water with it and condensing into visible steam. The chamber, now nearly empty, begins to fill again and the cycle is repeated. The entire cycle may be quite regular, as it is in Yellowstone's Old Faithful Geyser, which averages about 65 minutes between eruptions (though it varies from about 30 to 95 minutes). Many geysers, however, erupt irregularly, some with weeks or months between eruptions.

As hot ground water comes to the surface and cools, it may precipitate some of its dissolved ions as minerals. **Travertine** is a porous deposit of *calcite* that often forms around hot springs (figure 11.27) while dissolved *silica* precipitates as **sinter** (called *geyserite* when deposited by a geyser, as shown in figure 11.28). The composition of the subsurface rocks generally determines which type of deposit forms, although sinter can indicate higher subsurface temperatures than travertine, because silica is

harder to dissolve than calcite. Both deposits can be stained by the pigments of algae living in the hot water. The algae can be used to estimate water temperature—they can change from green to brown to orange to yellow as the temperature rises.

Geothermal Energy
Electricity is generated in most power plants by directing a jet of steam against the curved blades of a turbine (hydroelectric plants at dams use falling water rather than steam). The steam jet causes the turbine to rotate, and the moving turbine in turn spins a generator that produces electricity. Steam to turn the turbine can be produced in many ways. Coal, petroleum, or natural gas can be burned to boil water and create steam. These fuels are expensive, however, and burning them to generate electricity adds substantially to consumers' electric bills. In addition, the burning of coal and petroleum tends to add to air pollution.

Nuclear power plants produce steam using the heat given off during nuclear reactions. Although the air pollution problems of coal and oil are eliminated, uranium is expensive and in short supply, and nuclear wastes present a disposal problem. There is also a potential danger

Figure 11.29 Geothermal power plant at The Geysers, California. Underground steam, piped from wells to the power plant, is being discharged from six large cooling towers.
Photo by U.S. Geological Survey.

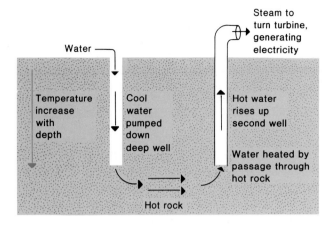

Figure 11.30 Proposed system to use earth's heat to generate power. Rock is artificially fractured between wells.

of radioactive contamination if a nuclear power plant is damaged, perhaps by an earthquake.

Geothermal energy is energy produced by harnessing naturally occurring steam and hot water in areas of anomalously high concentrations of subsurface heat. A well drilled into a geothermal system may tap steam or superheated water that can be piped to a powerhouse to run a generator. A geothermal area need not be marked by surface features such as hot springs and geysers (just as oil fields are seldom marked by surface oil and tar seeps).

The advantages of geothermal energy production are that no costly fuel in short supply need be burned to generate steam. Air pollution problems are minimal, and the radiation hazards of nuclear plants are eliminated. Geothermal energy is, therefore, a relatively clean and nonpolluting alternative to other steam-using power plants.

Tapping of geothermal power has some environmental effects. Hot water brought to the surface often contains appreciable quantities of dissolved salts, which can be detrimental to plant and fish life if allowed to enter surface streams. The salts can also corrode generating equipment. Subsidence of the land surface can occur if water is withdrawn from underground. Pumping waste water back underground can help reduce the environmental effects of generating geothermal power, however, and prolong the life of the field (geothermal fields can be depleted by pumping; they are not inexhaustible sources of energy).

At present, geothermal power is generated in relatively few locations. The largest plant in the world is at The Geysers in California (figure 11.29), 125 kilometers northeast of San Francisco. The Geysers facility is capable

of generating more than 1,000 megawatts of electricity (enough to serve a million people). The maximum potential of the area appears much larger—perhaps as much as 4,000 megawatts. The only other commercial facility currently generating geothermal power in the United States is a hot-water plant near the Salton Sea in southern California, although other geothermal areas in the west are being intensively explored. Large geothermal plants are also in operation in Italy, Mexico, El Salvador, New Zealand, Japan, the Philippines, and Iceland.

Geothermal energy's greatest potential may be in nonelectric uses such as space heating and water heating. Iceland's capital, Reykjavik, with a population of more than 100,000, is heated almost entirely by geothermal energy. Geothermal heating systems also exist in Klamath Falls, Oregon, and Boise, Idaho. Exploration of the potential for specialized uses such as heating greenhouses, manufacturing paper, processing ore, preparing food, and other industrial applications is just beginning.

Will geothermal energy ever become a major source of power generation? Areas containing substantial geothermal resources are not common, but where they do occur their power potential is great. An alternative method of geothermal energy production also may be widely used in the future in areas without hot fluids underground. Figure 11.30 shows this proposed system, called the hot dry rock system. Since deep rock in all areas is hot, cold water could be pumped down a deep well and allowed to heat through contact with deep, hot rock. The hot water could then be raised up another well to run a surface power plant. The rock usually must be fractured to allow the water to travel from one well to another, and this creates added costs and problems that are not yet solved. New technology may make geothermal energy a source of as much as 20 percent of our future energy needs, the same percentage now supplied by coal, but some estimates of geothermal potential are much more conservative.

Summary

Twenty percent or less of the water that falls on land percolates underground to become ground water. Ground water fills pores and joints in rock, creating a large reservoir of usable water in most regions.

Porous rocks can hold water. *Permeable* rocks permit water to move through them.

The *water table* lies at the top of the *zone of saturation* and is overlain by a *zone of aeration.*

Local variations in rock permeability may develop a *perched water table* above the main water table.

Ground-water velocity depends on rock permeability and the slope of the water table.

Gaining streams, springs, and lakes form where the water table intersects the land surface. *Losing streams* contribute to the ground water in dry regions.

An *aquifer* is porous and permeable and can supply water to wells. An *artesian aquifer* holds water under pressure, which can create flowing or spouting wells.

Ground water can be polluted by agriculture, industry, or human sewage disposal. Some pollutants can be filtered out by passage through moderately permeable geologic materials.

A pumped well causes a *cone of depression* that in turn can cause or aggravate ground-water pollution. Near a coast, it can cause *saltwater intrusion.*

Artificial *recharge* can help create a balance between withdrawal and recharge of ground-water supplies.

Solution of limestone by ground water causes *caves, sinkholes,* and *karst topography.* Calcite precipitating out of ground water deposits *dripstone* and *flowstone* in caves.

Precipitation of material out of solution by ground water helps form petrified wood, other fossils, sedimentary rock cement, concretions, geodes, and alkali soils.

Geysers and *hot springs* occur in regions of hot ground water. *Geothermal energy* is beginning to be utilized and may have a high potential for power generation in the future.

Terms to Remember

alkali soil
aquifer
artesian aquifer
artesian well
artificial recharge
capillary fringe
caves (caverns)
column
concretion
cone of depression
drawdown
dripstone
flowstone
gaining stream
geode
geothermal energy
geyser
ground water
hot springs
hydrologic cycle
karst topography
losing stream
perched water table
permeability
petrified wood
porosity
recharge
residual clay
sinkhole
sinter
spring
stalactite
stalagmite
travertine
water table
well
zone of aeration
zone of saturation

Questions for Review

1. What conditions are necessary for an artesian aquifer system?
2. What distinguishes a geyser from a hot spring? What conditions determine which of these will form?
3. What is karst topography? How does it form?
4. What chemical conditions are necessary for the development of caves in limestone? For the development of stalactites in a cave?
5. What causes a perched water table?
6. Describe several ways in which ground water can become polluted.
7. Discuss the difference between porosity and permeability.
8. What is the water table? Is it fixed in position?
9. Sketch four different origins for springs.
10. What controls the velocity of ground-water flow?
11. Name several geologic materials that make good aquifers. Define *aquifer*.
12. How does petrified wood form?
13. What happens to the water table near a pumped well?

Question for Thought

1. Describe any difference between the amounts of water that would percolate downward to the zone of saturation beneath a flat meadow in northern New York and beneath a rocky hillside in southern Nevada. Discuss the factors that control the amount of percolation in each case.

Supplementary Readings

Baldwin, H. L., and C. I. McGuinness. 1963. *A primer on ground water*. Washington, D.C.: U.S. Geological Survey.

Davis, S. N., and R. J. M. De Wiest. 1966. *Hydrogeology*. New York: John Wiley & Sons.

Keefer, W. R. 1971. *The geologic story of Yellowstone National Park*. U.S. Geological Survey Bulletin 1347.

Leopold, L. B., and W. B. Langbein. 1960. *A primer on water*. Washington, D.C.: U.S. Geological Survey.

Meinzer O. E., ed. 1942. *Hydrology*. New York: Dover Books.

Moore, G. W., and G. Nicholas. 1964. *Speleology: The study of caves*. Boston: D.C. Heath.

Ritter, D. F. 1978. *Process geomorphology*. Dubuque, Iowa: Wm. C. Brown Company Publishers.

Sayre, A. N. 1950. Ground water. *Scientific American* (November 1950). Offprint #818. San Francisco: W. H. Freeman.

Swenson, H. A., and H. L. Baldwin. 1965. *A primer on water quality*. Washington, D.C.: U.S. Geological Survey.

Todd, D. K. 1959. *Ground water hydrology*. New York: John Wiley & Sons.

U.S. Department of Agriculture. 1955. *Water*. U.S.D.A. Yearbook. Washington, D.C.: Government Printing Office.

Waltham, T. 1975. *Caves*. New York: Crown Publishers.

12

Glaciers and Glaciation

Purpose

In the last three chapters you have seen how the surface of the land is shaped by mass wasting, running water, and, to some extent, ground water. Running water is regarded as the erosional agent most responsible for the shaping of the earth's land surface. Where glaciers exist, however, they are far more effective agents of erosion, transportation, and deposition. Geologic features characteristic of glaciation are distinctly different from the features formed by running water. Once recognized, they lead to an appreciation of the great extent of glaciation during the recent geologic past (that age popularly known as the "Ice Age").

Immense and extensive glaciers, covering as much as a third of the earth's land surface, had a profound effect on the landscape and on our present civilization. Moreover, worldwide climatic changes during the glacial ages brought about distinctive alterations of landscapes in areas distant from the glacial boundaries. For instance, water stored as ice in glaciers lowered the levels of the world's oceans, exposing more land than is presently exposed.

These episodes of glaciation took place within only the last few million years, ending about 10,000 years ago. Preserved in the rock record, however, is evidence of extensive older glaciations. Chapter 20 shows how the record of these ancient glaciations supports the theory of plate tectonics.

To understand how glacial erosion and deposition could have created the features regarded as evidence for past glaciation, you must first appreciate how present-day glaciers erode, transport, and deposit material. In other words, you must apply the principle of uniformitarianism to your study of glaciation.

A **glacier** is a large, long-lasting mass of ice formed on the land that moves because of its own weight. It is formed as snow is compacted and recrystallized. A glacier may develop anyplace where over a period of years more snow accumulates than is melted away or otherwise lost.

Two types of *glaciated* terrain can be observed on the earth's surface. **Alpine glaciation** is found in mountainous regions, while **continental glaciation** exists where a large part of a continent (thousands of square kilometers) is covered by glacial ice. In both cases the moving masses of ice profoundly and distinctively change the landscape.

The Theory of Glacial Ages

In 1837 the Swiss naturalist Louis Agassiz proposed what seemed at the time to be an outrageous hypothesis. He had observed the characteristic erosional and depositional features of present glaciers in the Alps and had compared these with similar features found in northern Europe and the British Isles, well beyond the farthest extent of the Alpine glaciers. Based on these observations, he proposed that very large glaciers had covered most of Europe while a colder climate prevailed during the past. Agassiz later came to North America and conferred with American geologists who had found similar indications of large-scale past glaciation on this continent.

As more evidence accumulated, the hypothesis became accepted as a theory that today is seldom questioned. The **theory of glacial ages** states that at times in the past, colder climates prevailed, during which significantly more of the land surface of the earth was glaciated than at present.

Because the last episode of glaciation was at its peak only about 18,000 years ago, its record has remained largely undestroyed by subsequent erosion and so provides an abundance of evidence to support the theory. This most recent glacial episode was the last of several glacial ages that alternated with periods of warmer climate (only slightly warmer than today's climate) around the world.

The glacial ages are not just a scientific curiosity. Our lives and environment today have been profoundly influenced by their effects. For example, much of the fertile soil of the northern Great Plains of the United States developed on the loose debris transported and dumped by glaciers that moved southward from Canada. The spectacularly scenic areas in some of our national parks owe much of their beauty to glacial action. Yosemite Valley in California might have been another nondescript valley if glaciers had not carved it into its present shape (figure 12.1).

Before we can understand how a continental glacier was responsible for much of the soil of the Midwest, or how a glacier confined to a valley could carve a Yosemite, we must learn something about present-day glaciers.

Figure 12.1   Yosemite Valley, Yosemite National Park, California.

Glaciers—Where They Are, How They Form and Move

Distribution of Glaciers

Glaciers are found both in polar regions, where there is little melting during the summer, and in temperate climates that have heavy snowfall during the winter months. Certain climatic conditions are necessary for glaciation.

The coastal mountains of Washington have more glaciers than any state other than Alaska, even though the climate of Washington is considerably warmer than that of the Rocky Mountain states. Glaciers can flourish in these coastal mountains because Washington has very high precipitation during the winter months, and more snow accumulates in higher elevations than melts away during the summer. Glaciers are common even near the equator in the very high mountains of South America because of the low temperatures at high altitudes.

Glaciation is most extensive in polar regions, where little melting takes place at any time of the year. At present about one-tenth of the land surface of the earth is covered by glaciers (compared with about one-third during the peak of the glacial ages). About 85 percent of the present-day glacier ice is on the Antarctic continent, covering an area larger than the combined areas of western Europe and the United States; 10 percent is in Greenland. All the remaining glaciers of the world amount to only about 5 percent of the earth's freshwater ice. This means that Antarctica is in fact storing most of the earth's fresh water in the form of ice. Some people have suggested

Glaciers as a Water Resource

Few persons think of glaciers as frozen reservoirs supplying water for irrigation, hydroelectric power, recreation, and industrial and domestic use. In the state of Washington, however, streamflow from the approximately 800 glaciers there amounts to about 470 billion gallons of water during a summer, according to the U.S. Geological Survey. More water is stored in glacier ice in Washington than in all of the state's lakes, reservoirs, and rivers.

One important aspect of glacier-derived water is that it is available when needed most. Snow accumulates on glaciers during the wet winter months. During the winter, streams at lower elevations, where rain falls rather than snow, are full and provide plenty of water. During the summer, however, the climate in the Pacific Northwest is hotter and drier. Because of this, demand for water increases, especially for irrigation of crops. Streams that were fed by rainwater may have dried up. Yet, in the heat of summer, the period of peak demand, snow and ice on glaciers are melting, and streams draining glaciers are at their highest level.

Paradoxically, the greater the snowfall on a glacier during a winter, the smaller the amount of meltwater during the summer. A larger blanket of white snow reflects the run's radiation more effectively than the darker, bare glacier ice, which absorbs more of the heat of the sun. Experiments have shown that melting can be greatly increased by darkening the snow surface, as for instance, by sprinkling coal dust on it. Similarly, the melting of a glacier may be slowed artificially by covering it with highly reflective material. Such means of controlling glacial meltwater have been proposed to benefit power generating stations or to provide additional irrigation.

These ideas are appealing from a short-sighted point of view. However, the long-term effect of tampering with a glacier's natural regime is likely to affect adversely the overall environment. It is conceivable, for example, that we could melt a glacier out of existence. Because most of the United States' glaciers are in national parks or wilderness areas, tampering with glaciers to control the output of meltwater has not been attempted.

that ice from the Antarctic could be brought to areas of dry climate to alleviate water shortages. While nobody has suggested melting the entire Antarctic ice sheet, it is worth noting that if all that continent's ice were to melt, sea level around the world would rise about 60 meters (200 feet). This much rise would flood the world's coastal cities and significantly decrease the land surface available for humans to live on.

Types of Glaciers

A simple criterion—whether or not a glacier is restricted to a valley—is the basis for classification of glaciers by form. A **valley glacier** is one confined to a valley and which flows from a higher to a lower elevation. Like streams, small valley glaciers may be tributaries to a larger trunk system. Valley glaciers are prevalent in areas of alpine glaciation. As might be expected, most glaciers in the United States and Canada, being in mountains, are of the valley type (figure 12.2).

By contrast, an **ice sheet** is a mass of ice that is not restricted to a valley but covers a large area of land (over 50,000 square kilometers). Ice sheets are associated with continental glaciation. Only two ice sheets exist on the earth now, one in Greenland and one in Antarctica. A similar but smaller body is called an **ice cap.** Ice caps (and valley glaciers as well) are found in a few mountainous regions and on islands in the Arctic Ocean, off

Figure 12.2 Valley glacier on Mount Logan, Yukon Territory, Canada.

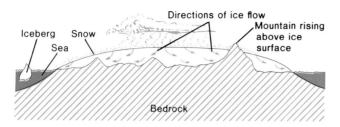

Figure 12.3 Diagrammatic cross section of an ice sheet. Vertical scale is highly exaggerated.

Canada, Russia, and Siberia. An ice cap or ice sheet flows downward and outward from a central high point as figure 12.3 shows.

Formation and Growth of Glaciers

Snow is converted to glacier ice in somewhat the same way that sediment turns into a sedimentary rock and then into metamorphic rock; figure 12.4 shows the process. A snowfall can be compared to sediment settling out of water. A new snowfall may be in the form of light "powder snow," which consists mostly of air trapped between many six-pointed snowflakes. In a short time the snowflakes settle by compaction under their own weight and much of the air between them is driven out. Meanwhile, the sharp points of the snowflakes are destroyed as flakes reconsolidate into granules—the "corn snow" of spring skiing. The compacted mass of granular snow, transitional between snow and glacier ice, is called **firn.** The granules are weakly "cemented" together by ice. Firn, then, is analogous to a sedimentary rock such as sandstone.

As fresh snow piles on top of firn, and as time passes, air is expelled, reducing the remaining pore space and forcing the granules into a tighter pattern. Individual grains, with little melting, recrystallize to fill the voids and become "welded" together, developing a mosaic-like texture similar to that of quartzite, a metamorphic rock.

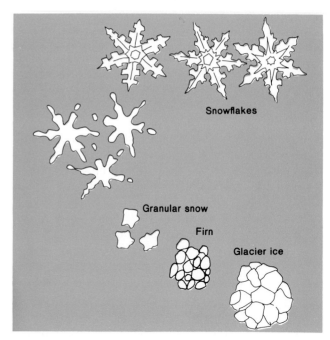

Figure 12.4 Process of conversion of snow to glacier ice.

Figure 12.5 An iceberg off the coast of Antarctica.

Under the influence of gravity, glacier ice moves downward and is eventually **wasted,** or lost. For glaciers in all but the coldest parts of the world, wastage is due mostly to melting, although some ice evaporates directly into the atmosphere. If a moving glacier reaches a body of water, blocks of ice break off (or *calve*) and float free as **icebergs** (figure 12.5). In the Antarctic wastage of the ice sheet is due largely to calving of icebergs and to direct evaporation. Only along the coast does melting take place, and there for only a few weeks of the year.

Glacial budgets   If, over a period of time, the amount of snow a glacier gains is greater than the amount of ice and water it loses, then the glacier's budget is *positive* and it expands. If the opposite occurs, then the glacier decreases in volume and is said to have a *negative budget*. Glaciers with positive budgets push outward and downward at their edges; they are called **advancing glaciers.** Those with negative budgets grow smaller and their edges melt back; they are **receding glaciers.** If the amount of

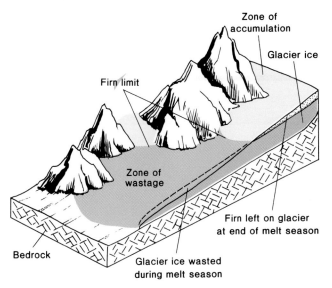

Figure 12.6 A valley glacier as it would appear at the end of a melt season. The dashed, colored line is the firn limit. Below that line glacier ice and snow have been lost during the melting season. In the zone of accumulation above that line, firn is added to the glacier from the previous winter snowfall.

Figure 12.7 Aerial photo of a glacier in Washington. If the photo were taken at the end of the melt season, the firn limit would be the dashed line. Above the line, snow covers the glacier. Small icebergs have calved into the lake in the foreground.
Photo by Austin Post, U.S. Geological Survey.

snow retained by the glacier equals the amount of ice and water lost, the glacier has a *balanced budget* and is neither advancing nor receding.

The upper part of the glacier, called the **zone of accumulation,** is the part of the glacier with a perennial snow cover (figure 12.6). The lower part is the **zone of wastage,** for there ice is lost, or wasted, by melting, evaporation, and calving.

The boundary between these two altitudinal zones of the glacier is an irregular line called the **firn limit,** which marks the highest point at which the glacier's winter snow cover is lost during a melt season (figure 12.7).

The firn limit may shift up or down from year to year, depending on whether there has been more accumulation or more wastage. Its location can therefore be used as an indicator of whether a glacier has a positive or negative budget. A firn limit migrating upglacier over a period of years is a sign of a negative budget, whereas a firn limit migrating downglacier indicates that the glacier has a positive budget. If a firn limit remains essentially in the same place year after year, the glacier has a balanced budget.

The **terminus,** the lower edge of a glacier, moves farther downvalley when a valley glacier has a positive budget. In a receding glacier the terminus melts back upvalley. Because most glaciers move slowly, migration of the terminus tends to lag several years behind a change in the budget.

An ice sheet with a positive budget increases in volume, advancing its outer margins. If the expanding ice sheet extends into the ocean, an increasing number of icebergs break off and float away in the open sea.

Advancing or receding glaciers are significant and sensitive indicators of climatic change. However, advances by a glacier are not necessarily an indication that the climate is getting colder. They may mean that the climate is getting wetter, or that more precipitation is falling during the winter months, or that the summers are cloudier. It is estimated that a worldwide decrease in the mean annual temperature of only 4° or 5°C could bring about a new ice age.

Movement of Valley Glaciers

Valley glaciers move downslope under the influence of gravity and their own weight, the rate being very variable, ranging from less than a few millimeters a day to more than 15 meters a day. The upper part of a glacier—where the volume of ice is greater and slopes tend to be steeper—generally moves faster than ice farther down or on gentler slopes. In this way ice from the higher altitudes keeps replenishing ice lost in the zone of wastage. Glaciers in temperate climates—where the temperature of the glacier is at or near the melting point for ice—tend to move faster than those in colder regions—where the ice temperature stays well below freezing.

Glaciers and Glaciation   229

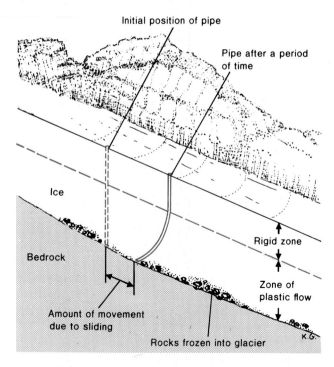

Figure 12.8   Movement of a glacier. Cross-sectional view.

Figure 12.9   Crevasses on a glacier, looking down from Mount Logan, Yukon Territory, Canada.

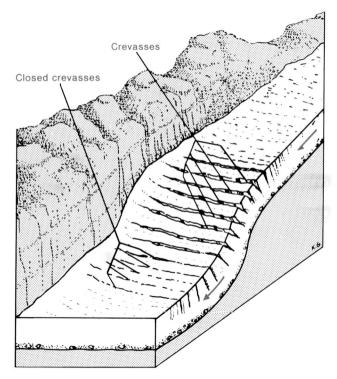

Figure 12.10   Crevasses along the course of a glacier.

Velocity also varies within the glacier itself. The central portion of a valley glacier moves faster than the sides, and the surface moves faster than the base. How ice moves within a valley glacier has been demonstrated by studies in which holes are drilled through the glacier ice and flexible pipes inserted. Changes in the shape and position of the pipes are measured periodically. The results of these studies are shown diagrammatically in figure 12.8.

Note in the diagram that the base of the pipe has moved downglacier. This indicates **basal sliding,** which is the sliding of the glacier as a single body over the underlying rock. A thin film of meltwater that develops along the base from the pressure of the overlying glacier facilitates basal sliding. Thinking of a large bar of wet soap sliding down an inclined board will help you visualize the process.

Note that the lower portion of the pipe is bent in a downglacier direction. The pipe is bent more sharply near the base of the glacier, indicating that greater pressure from the overlying ice permits greater motion within the glacier ice near the bottom. These effects are caused by **plastic flow** of ice, movement that occurs within the glacier due to the plastic or "bendable" nature of the ice itself.

In the **rigid zone,** or upper part of the glacier, the pipe has been moved downglacier; however, it has been only slightly bent. It appears that in all glaciers the ice nearer the top rides along passively on the plastically moving ice closer to the base.

Crevasses   Along its length, a valley glacier moves at different rates in response to changes in the steepness of the underlying rock. Typically a valley glacier rides over a series of rock steps. Where the glacier is passing over a steep part of the bed, movement is faster. The upper rigid zone of ice, however, cannot stretch to move as rapidly as the underlying plastic-flowing ice. Being brittle, the ice of the rigid zone is broken by the tensional forces. Open fissures, or **crevasses,** develop (figure 12.10). Theoretically, a crevasse should be no deeper than about 40 meters, the usual limit of the rigid zone.

Box 12.2
Nuclear Waste Disposal in Antarctica?

One of the serious long-range problems facing industrialized countries is what to do with the great stores of nuclear wastes that have been accumulating for years. These highly toxic radioactive wastes are byproducts of nuclear power plants and the manufacture of nuclear weapons. Rather than facing the problem, the United States has followed a policy of procrastination. Most of the country's radioactive waste is temporarily stored as liquid in tanks. Despite the fact that the waste must be isolated from humans and other organisms for many centuries before it is safe, we have not been able to store it for even a few decades without mishap. In one case, several thousand gallons of waste seeped into the ground water from a storage tank before anyone realized there was a leak.

Proposals for permanent storage sites for nuclear wastes have included (1) carving out underground vaults in granite or rock salt, (2) shooting the wastes into space, and (3) letting an oceanic plate carry the material into the mantle along a subduction zone. Another suggestion has been to use the Antarctic ice sheet as a dumping ground.

In this scheme the nuclear waste would be fused into solid blocks of glass, transported to the Antarctic, and placed on the thicker part of the ice sheet. The heat generated by radioactivity would cause a block to sink through the ice. The ice would refreeze above the descending block. Eventually the block would reach the base of the ice, where it would, in theory, remain buried beneath several kilometers of ice.

The plan has several drawbacks. Travel in Antarctica is still relatively hazardous as well as extremely expensive. It is unlikely that a failure-proof means of transporting nuclear waste to the disposal site could be guaranteed for the thousands of blocks involved. More critical are the effects the hot blocks might have on the behavior of the glacier. Holes drilled to the base of the Antarctic ice sheet have indicated that a thin film of water exists between the ice and the underlying rock. A large number of blocks could cause much more ice to melt. With more water beneath it, the ice sheet might begin to move more rapidly, perhaps carrying some of the radioactive wastes with it. A rapid reduction in the size of the ice sheet also might result in a worldwide change of climate.

Water flowing beneath the glacier might dissolve some of the nuclear waste from the blocks and carry toxic waste to the surrounding seas. The seas surrounding the Antarctic continent are the richest in the world in marine life, and pollution of these waters could have serious adverse effects on the worldwide supply of food from the ocean.

The Antarctic Treaty prohibits disposal of nuclear wastes in the Antarctic, and the countries interested in working there are very hesitant to amend the treaty in any way that might change that continent's status as the most pollution-free part of the earth. Glaciologists have urged that no nuclear disposal plan even be considered until a much more detailed understanding of the Antarctic ice sheet can be obtained.

Figure 12.11 An icefall in the Peruvian Andes.

Figure 12.12 The South Pole. Actually, the true South Pole is several kilometers from here. The moving ice sheet has carried the striped pole away from the site of the true South Pole where it was erected in 1956.

After the ice has passed over a steep portion of its course, it slows down, and compressive forces close the crevasses. If a glacier descends a long, very steep slope without slowing down, the ice splits into pinnacles and blocks forming a chaotic jumble of crevasses called an *icefall* (figure 12.11).

Movement of Ice Sheets

An ice sheet or ice cap moves like a valley glacier except that movement is downward and outward from a central high area toward the edges of the glacier (as shown in figure 12.3).

Glaciological studies in Antarctica have determined how an ice sheet grows and moves. Nearly all the Antarctic ice sheet is a zone of accumulation, because so little melting takes place and because occasional snowfalls nourish its high central part. Most of the ice sheet lies over interior lowlands, but it also completely buries several mountain ranges. At the South Pole (figure 12.12)—neither the thickest part nor the center of that vast ice sheet—the ice is 2,700 meters thick.

Some of the movement of the Antarctic ice sheet is due to sliding along its base, but most is by plastic flow. This is because the rigid zone is quite thin compared with the great thickness of most of the ice sheet.

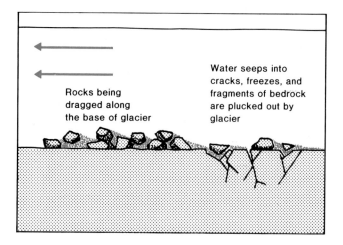

Figure 12.13 Rock fragments and bedrock being plucked out and abraded by movement of a glacier.

Glacial Erosion

Wherever basal sliding takes place, the rock beneath the glacier is abraded and modified. As meltwater works into cracks in bedrock and refreezes, pieces of the rock are broken loose and frozen into the base of the moving glacier. While being dragged along by the moving ice, the rock within the glacier grinds away at the rock beneath (figure 12.13). The thicker the glacier, the more pressure on the rocks, and the more effective the grinding and crushing.

Small pebbles and good-sized boulders that are dragged along are **faceted;** that is given a flat surface by erosion. The bedrock, as well as the ice-carried rocks, is *polished* by the grinding. Sharp corners of rock fragments

Figure 12.14 Striated and polished rock surface along the walls of Yosemite Valley.

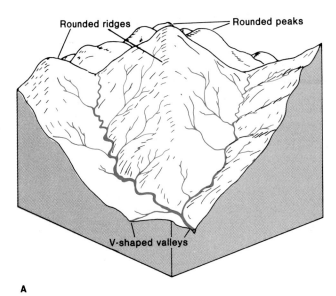

A

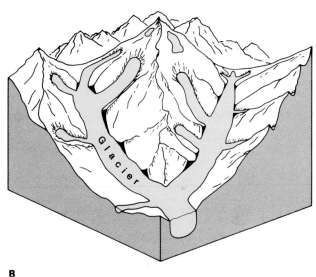

B

dragged along make grooves and **striations,** or scratches, in the rock, usually in the direction of ice movement (figure 12.14).

The grinding of rock across rock produces a powder of fine fragments called **rock flour.** Rock flour is composed largely of very fine (silt- and clay-sized) particles of unaltered minerals (pulverized from chemically unweathered bedrock). When *meltwater* washes rock flour from a glacier, the streams draining the glacier turn milky white.

Not all glacier-associated erosion is caused directly by glaciers. Frost wedging breaks up bedrock ridges and cliffs above a glacier, causing frequent rockfalls. Snow avalanches bring down loose rocks and other materials onto the glacier surface, where they ride on top of the ice. The important effects of meltwater washing out of glaciers are discussed later in this chapter.

Erosional Landscapes Associated with Alpine Glaciation

Mountain ranges and highland regions that have been subjected to alpine glaciation are noted for their rugged terrain and spectacular scenery. Figure 12.15 shows how a previously unglaciated mountainous region may have been altered by erosional effects of valley glaciers and frost wedging on exposed rock, producing some of the striking and unique features associated with mountain glaciation.

Figure 12.15 *(A)* A stream-carved mountain landscape before glaciation. *(B)* The same area during glaciation. Ridges and peaks become sharper due to frost wedging. *(C)* The same area after glaciation.

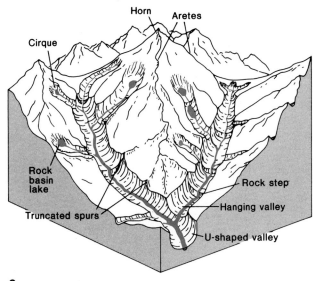

C

Figure 12.16 A hanging valley in Yosemite National Park, California.

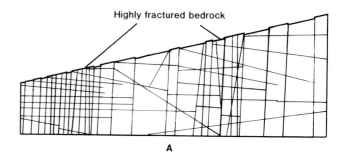

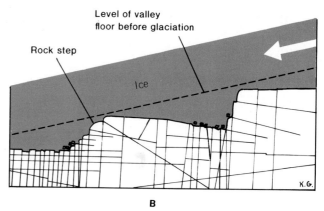

Figure 12.17 Development of rock steps. *(A)* Valley floor before glaciation. *(B)* During glaciation. *(C)* Rock steps and rock basin lakes, Washington Cascade Mountains. *A and B after F. E. Matthes, 1930, U.S. Geological Survey.*

Glacial valleys Glacially carved valleys are usually easy to recognize. A **U-shaped valley** (in cross profile) is characteristic of glacial erosion, just as a V-shaped valley is characteristic of stream erosion.

Valley glaciers, which usually occupy valleys formerly carved by streams, tend to straighten the curves formed by running water. This is because the mass of ice of a glacier is too sluggish and inflexible to move easily around the curves. In the process of carving the sides of its valley, a glacier wears away or "truncates" any ridges perpendicular to the valley. **Truncated spurs** are the lower parts of ridges which have been carved into triangular facets by glacial erosion.

The thicker a glacier is, the more erosive force it exerts on the valley floor beneath, and the more bedrock is ground away. For this reason, a large trunk glacier erodes downward more rapidly and carves a deeper valley than do the smaller tributaries that join it. After the disappearance of the glaciers, these tributaries remain as **hanging valleys** high above the main valley (figure 12.16).

Although a glacier tends to straighten and smooth the side walls of its valley, ice action often leaves the surface of the underlying bedrock carved into a series of steps. This is due to the variable resistance of bedrock to glacial erosion. Figure 12.17 shows what happens when a glacier abrades a relatively weak rock with closely spaced fractures. Water seeps into cracks in the bedrock, freezes there, and enlarges fractures or makes new ones. Rock frozen into the base of the glacier grinds and loosens more pieces. After the ice has melted back, a chain of **rock basin lakes** may occupy the depressions carved out of the weaker rock. On stronger, less fractured rock, glacial erosion works in a similar way but is less effective because of the bedrock's resistance to grinding and crushing.

Cirques, horns, and arêtes A glacial **cirque** is a steep-sided, rounded hollow carved into a mountain at the head of a glacial valley (figure 12.18). In this unique, often spectacular, topographic feature, a large percentage of the snow accumulates that eventually converts to glacier ice and spills over the threshold as the valley glacier starts its downward course.

Figure 12.18 A cirque occupied by a small glacier in the Canadian Rocky Mountains.

A

Figure 12.19 (A) A bergschrund (partially filled with snow) in the Peruvian Andes. Glacier is pulling away to the right. (B) Cutaway view of a bergschrund in a cirque.

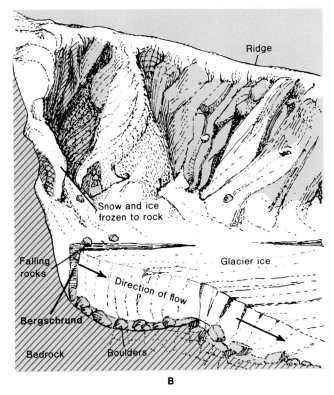

B

A cirque is not entirely carved by the glacier itself but is also shaped by the weathering and erosion of the rock walls above the surface of the ice. Frost wedging and avalanches break up the rock and steepen the slopes above the glacier. Broken rock tumbles onto the valley glacier and becomes part of its load, and some rock may fall into a crevasse, called a **bergschrund,** that develops where the glacier is pulling away from the cirque wall (figure 12.19).

The headward erosional processes that enlarge a cirque also create the sharp peaks and ridges characteristic of glaciated mountain ranges. A **horn** is the sharp peak that remains after cirques have cut back into a mountain on several sides (figure 12.20).

Frost wedging works on the rock exposed above the glacier, steepening and cutting back the side walls of the valley. Sharp ridges called **arêtes** eventually separate adjacent glacially carved valleys (figure 12.21).

Figure 12.20 The Matterhorn in Switzerland, a classic example of a horn.
Photo by UPI.

Figure 12.21   This arête in the Peruvian Andes extends downward from a horn and separates two glaciers, parts of which are visible in the lower part of the picture.

Erosional Landscapes Associated

The rock underneath an ice sheet is eroded in much the same way as the rock beneath a valley glacier. However, the weight and thickness of the ice sheet may produce more pronounced effects. Grooved and striated bedrock is common. Some grooves are actually channels several meters deep and many kilometers long. The orientation of grooves and striations gives an indication of the direction of movement of a former ice sheet.

An ice sheet may be thick enough to bury mountain ranges, rounding off the ridges and summits and perhaps streamlining them in the direction of ice movement. Much of northeastern Canada, with its rounded mountains and grooved and striated bedrock surface, shows the erosional effects of ice sheets that formerly covered that part of North America (figure 12.22).

Glacial Deposition

The rock fragments scraped and plucked from the underlying bedrock and carried along at the base of the ice make up most of the load carried by an ice sheet, but only part of a valley glacier's load. Much of a valley glacier's load comes from rocks broken from the valley walls.

Most of the rock fragments carried by glaciers are angular, as the pieces have not been tumbled around enough for the edges and corners to be rounded. The debris is unsorted, and particles ranging from clay-sized to boulder-sized are mixed together (figure 12.23). The unsorted and unlayered rock debris carried or deposited by a glacier is called **till** (figure 12.24).

Glaciers are capable of carrying virtually any size of rock fragment, even boulders as large as a house. An **erratic** is an ice-transported boulder that has not been derived from the nearby bedrock. If its bedrock source can be found, an erratic can be used to determine the direction of movement of the glacier that carried it.

Moraines

A **moraine** is a body of till either carried along on a glacier or left behind after the glacier has receded. Most of the loose material that falls from the steep cliffs along the course of a valley glacier accumulates along the edges of the ice. These ridgelike piles of till along the sides of a glacier are called **lateral moraines** (figures 12.25 and 12.26).

Where tributary glaciers come together, the adjacent lateral moraines join and are carried downglacier as a single long ridge of till known as a **medial moraine.** In a large trunk glacier that has been formed from many tributaries, the numerous medial moraines give the glacier the appearance from the air of a multilane highway (figures 12.25 and 12.27).

Figure 12.22 Air view off glacially scoured terrain in Canada. Ice moved from upper right to lower left.
National Air Photo Library of Canada.

Figure 12.23 Unsorted debris, including boulders, transported on top of and alongside a glacier in Peru. View is downglacier.

Figure 12.24 Till.
Photo by D. R. Crandell, U.S. Geological Survey.

Figure 12.25   Moraines associated with valley glaciers.

Lateral moraines   Medial moraines   End moraines

Terminus of   Recessional   Ground   Terminal
glacier   moraine   moraine   moraine

Figure 12.26   Looking downvalley in the Peruvian Andes. Lateral moraine alongside a glacier. Another high moraine to the left marks the former edge of the glacier.

Lake

Glacier

Figure 12.27   Medial moraines on valley glaciers, Yukon Territory, Canada. Ice is flowing toward viewer.

An actively flowing glacier brings debris to its terminus. If the terminus remains stationary for a few years, a distinct **end moraine,** or ridge of till, is piled up along the front edge of the ice. Valley glaciers build end moraines that are crescent-shaped or sometimes horseshoe-shaped (figures 12.25 and 12.28). The end moraine of an ice sheet takes a similar lobate form but is much larger and more irregular than that of a valley glacier.

Geologists distinguish two special kinds of end moraines. A **terminal moraine** is the end moraine marking the farthest advance of a glacier. A **recessional moraine** is an end moraine built while the terminus of a receding glacier remains temporarily stationary. A single receding glacier can build several recessional moraines (figures 12.25 and 12.28).

A

B

Figure 12.28 End moraines in the Peruvian Andes. *(A)* An end moraine in front of a valley glacier. The lake is dammed up by an earlier end moraine further downvalley. *(B)* Closely spaced recessional moraines on a valley floor, left by a glacier that has retreated upvalley. (View is upvalley.)

Figure 12.29 Drumlins in Washington.
Photo by D. A. Rahm, courtesy Rahm Memorial Collection, Western Washington University.

Figure 12.30 An esker in northeastern Washington.
Photo by D. A. Rahm, courtesy Rahm Memorial Collection, Western Washington University.

As ice melts, rock debris that has been dragged along by a glacier is deposited to form a **ground moraine,** a fairly thin, extensive layer or blanket of till (figure 12.25). Very large areas that were once covered by an ice sheet now have the gently rolling surface characteristic of ground moraine deposits.

In some areas ground moraine has been reshaped into streamlined hills of till called **drumlins** (figure 12.29). A drumlin is shaped like an inverted spoon with the long axis parallel to the direction of ice movement (they are sometimes called "whalebacks"). Drumlins are thought to have been produced by an ice sheet overriding and reshaping a deposit of till left by an earlier glacial advance.

Outwash

In the zone of wastage, large quantities of meltwater usually run over, beneath, and away from the ice. The material deposited by the debris-laden meltwater is called **outwash.** Because it has the characteristic layering and sorting of stream-deposited sediment, outwash can readily be distinguished from the unsorted and unlayered deposits of till. Because outwash is fairly well sorted and the particles generally are not chemically weathered, it is an excellent source of aggregate for building roadways and for mixing with cement to make concrete.

An outwash feature of unusual shape associated with former ice sheets and some very large valley glaciers is an **esker,** a long, sinuous ridge of water-deposited sediment (figure 12.30). Eskers may be up to 10 meters in height

Figure 12.31   A kettle (*foreground*) and outwash (*background* and *left*) from a glacier. Stagnant ice underlies much of the till. Yukon Territory, Canada.

Figure 12.32   Varves.
Photo by F. O. Jones, U.S. Geological Survey.

and are formed of cross-bedded and well-sorted sediment. Evidently eskers are deposited in tunnels within or under glaciers, where meltwater loaded with sediment flows under and out of the ice.

As meltwater builds thick deposits of outwash alongside and in front of a retreating glacier, blocks of stagnant ice may be surrounded and buried by sediment. When the ice block finally melts (sometimes years later), a depression called a **kettle** is formed (figure 12.31). Many of the small scenic lakes in the upper Middle West of the United States are kettle lakes.

The streams that drain glaciers tend to be very heavily loaded with sediment, particularly during the melt season. As they come off the glacial ice and spread out over the outwash deposits, the streams form a braided pattern (see chapter 10).

The large amount of rock flour that these streams are carrying in suspension settles out in quieter waters—in bars, mud flats, shallow lake bottoms, and the like. In dry seasons or drought, the water may dry up and the rock flour deposits be picked up by the wind and carried long distances. Some of the best agricultural soil in the United States has been formed by rock flour that has been redeposited by wind. Such fine-grained wind-blown deposits of dust are called **loess** (see chapter 13).

Glacial Lakes and Varves

Lakes often form in depressions carved by glacial erosion but can also be the result of dams built by glacial deposition. Commonly a lake forms between a retreating glacier and an earlier end moraine.

In the still water of the lake, clay and silt settle on the bottom in two thin layers, one light-colored, one dark, that are characteristic of glacial lakes. Two layers of sediment representing one year's deposition in a lake are

called a **varve** (figure 12.32). The light-colored layer consists of slightly coarser sediment (silt) deposited during the warmer part of the year when the glacier is melting and sediment is being dumped in the lake. The silt settles within a few weeks or so after being washed into the lake. The dark layer is finer sediment (clay)—material that sinks down more slowly during the winter after the supply of fresh, coarser sediment stops because of lack of meltwater. The dark color is attributed to fine organic matter mixed with the clay.

Because each varve represents a year's deposit, varves may be used like tree rings to determine how long a glacial lake was in existence.

Effects of Past Glaciation

As the glacial theory gained general acceptance during the latter part of the nineteenth century, it became clear that much of northern Europe and the northern United States as well as most of Canada had been covered by great ice sheets during the so-called Ice Age. It also became evident that even areas not covered by ice had been affected because of the changes in climate and the redistribution of large amounts of water.

We now know that the last of the great North American ice sheets melted away from Canada less than 10,000 years ago. Till from that ice sheet, however, is found in many places to overlie older tills, deposited by earlier glaciations. The older till was deeply weathered during times of warmer climate between glacial episodes and is therefore distinguishable from the newer till.

The Glacial Ages

Geologists can reconstruct with considerable accuracy the last episode of extensive glaciation, which covered large parts of North America and Europe and was at its peak about 18,000 years ago. Time has not yet permitted

Box 12.3
Causes of Glacial Ages

What caused the glacial ages? This question has been asked by scientists since the theory of glacial ages became accepted over a century ago. Only in the last few years have climatologists felt they are beginning to provide acceptable answers.

The question is of more than academic importance. Understanding climate changes could provide the key to accurate, long-range weather predictions. Even minor climate changes affect crops and the problem of feeding humanity. If we knew the causes of fluctuations between glacial and interglacial episodes, we would probably know whether another glacial age is imminent or whether we are in a cooling or warming stage in the earth's history.

A number of theories and hypotheses have been proposed to account for glacial ages. Each explains some of our observations, but none alone satisfactorily accounts for all of the data. We shall review some of the more plausible ideas.

Variations in the earth's orbit and inclination to the sun The amount of heat from solar radiation that any particular portion of the earth receives is related to the angle of the incoming sun's rays and, to a lesser degree, the distance to the sun. The dimensions of the earth's orbit around the sun change slightly over a period of thousands of years. The angle of the earth's poles relative to the plane of the earth's orbit about the sun also changes periodically. Recent analysis of data has added strong support to the theory that variations in orbital relationships and "wobble" of the earth's axis are to a large extent responsible for the glacial and interglacial episodes. Cores of deep sea sediment have provided a fairly precise record of climatic variations over the past few hundred thousand years. The cycles of warming and cooling match the times predicted from astronomical observations of orbital variations.

The orbital variation theory fails to explain the absence of glaciation over most of geologic time. One or more of the other mechanisms described below must have been a contributory cause of glacial ages.

Changes in the atmosphere A set of hypotheses seeks to explain glacial ages by changes in the ability of the atmosphere to filter solar radiation. Much of the solar energy reaching our planet is either reflected back out to space or absorbed by the atmosphere. If the composition of the atmosphere changes, the amount of the sun's heat reaching and retained by the earth's surface also changes.

One hypothesis regards carbon dioxide as responsible for major climate changes. According to this proposal, if there is an increase in the carbon dioxide content in the atmosphere, the earth may warm up. This is because of a "greenhouse effect" in which solar energy penetrates the atmosphere and heat is retained or trapped at the earth's surface. Carbon dioxide in the atmosphere reduces the amount of heat that can radiate from earth back out into space. This results in a warming trend until, for some reason, the carbon dioxide in the atmosphere decreases. High carbon dioxide content would coincide with warm episodes between glacial ages; low carbon dioxide content with periods of glaciation.

A major problem faced by the carbon dioxide hypothesis is explaining a cyclic change in the concentration of carbon dioxide in the atmosphere. One suggestion has been that when vegetation is abundant, there is less carbon dioxide in the atmosphere. The cooling that this causes results in an ice age, and much of the earth's vegetation dies, releasing carbon dioxide to the atmosphere to begin the warming trend. However, there is no evidence that profound changes of vegetation have occurred. An additional difficulty comes in explaining why the process should be effective for such a small percentage of geologic time.

Another hypothesis involves volcanoes. Worldwide temperature dropped about 2°C following the major volcanic eruption of Krakatoa in Indonesia in 1886. The dust carried by high atmospheric winds reduced solar energy penetrating the atmosphere for a few years.

Presumably a closely spaced series of large eruptions could cause a temperature drop sufficient to trigger glaciation and begin a glacial age.

Changing of the positions of continents

Another hypothesis is that when land masses move closer to polar regions, glacial ages occur. Plate tectonics provides the mechanism for motion of land masses. But the fluctuations in late Cenozoic climates are not explained by plate tectonics. All evidence for continental drift indicates that the positions of the continents have not changed significantly with respect to the poles during the late Cenozoic Era. Certainly the continents have not shuffled back and forth during the recent glacial and interglacial ages.

However, the earlier movement of continents from positions closer to the equator into more northerly latitudes might have placed the present northern continents in a position favorable to glaciation.

Changes in circulation of sea water

Our present climates are very much affected by patterns of circulation of sea water. Land masses block the worldwide free circulation of ocean water, so that some oceans are warmer than others.

According to one hypothesis, a glacial episode begins when Atlantic water circulates freely with Arctic Ocean water. At present the warmer waters of the Atlantic Ocean are not able to mix freely with water in the Arctic Ocean. For this reason the surface of the Arctic Ocean is frozen for much of the year. Continental glaciation begins, according to this hypothesis, when warmer Atlantic water flows through a shallow channel between Greenland and Canada. This would keep the Arctic Ocean from completely freezing over during the winter. The moisture picked up by winds blowing over the Arctic Ocean would precipitate heavy amounts of snow on the northern continental landmasses. Ice sheets would grow so long as ice-free seas prevailed to supply

the moisture. But as glaciation continued, sea level would drop due to the loss of water to the ice sheets. Sea level would eventually drop below the floor of the shallow channel between Greenland and Canada, shutting off the supply of warm Atlantic waters to the Arctic Ocean. Because of this, the surface of the Arctic Ocean would freeze, reducing the moist air supplied to the ice sheets. The ice sheets would recede and disappear.

Some scientists question the adequacy of this mechanism to explain large-scale glaciation. Others point out that this hypothesis cannot explain the very warm interglacial climates. Also, snow and ice reflect much solar radiation. Therefore, a frozen Arctic Ocean coupled with glacial ice covering up to one-third of the world's land mass should tend to perpetuate a glacial age by reflecting more solar radiation into space.

Sliding of the Antarctic ice sheet over the ocean

One intriguing although highly speculative hypothesis regards changes in the Antarctic ice sheet as responsible for glacial ages. It is thought that a large segment of the ice sheet, lubricated by water along its base, slides as a mass onto the ocean surface. Before the large floating slab of ice can be broken up by wave action, the ice is able to reflect a significant amount of solar heat back into space. This could result in a worldwide cooling sufficient to trigger a glacial age.

There is some evidence that parts of the Antarctic ice sheet have slid rapidly and suddenly in the past. Whether the mechanism is capable of cooling the world's climate sufficiently has yet to be demonstrated.

Summary Scientists do not fully understand what causes glacial ages and intervening warm episodes. Only recently has the theory of variations of the earth's orbit received strong scientific support. This, at least, seems to explain what controls the cycles of climatic variation. But one or more of the other postulated mechanisms must also contribute to allow a glacial age to occur.

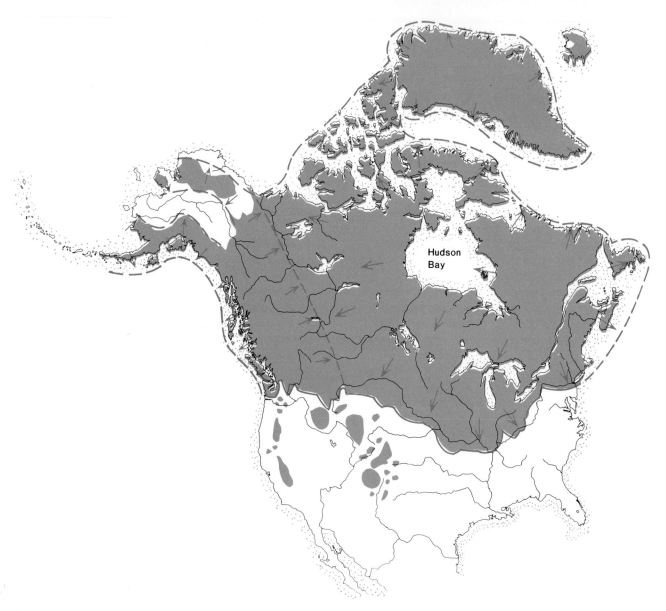

Figure 12.33 Extent of glaciation in North America during the Pleistocene. Arrows show direction of ice movement. After C. S. Denny, U.S. Geological Survey National Atlas of the United States.

weathering and erosion to alter significantly the effects of glaciation. Less evidence is preserved for each successively older glacial episode, because (1) weathering and erosion occurred during warm interglacial periods; and (2) later ice sheets and valley glaciers overrode and obliterated many of the features of earlier glaciation. However, from piecing together the evidence, geologists can see that earlier glaciers covered approximately the same region as the more recent ones.

Until a few years ago geologists regarded the Pleistocene Epoch (see chapter 8) as including all the glacial ages, but recent work indicates that worldwide climate changes necessary for continental glaciation probably began late in the Cenozoic Era, at least a million years before the Pleistocene. Antarctica has been glaciated for at least 20 million years, and continental glaciers elsewhere probably existed at least 3 million years ago.

The significance of this realization is that the earth has undergone episodic changes in climate during the last 2 to 3 million years. Actually, the climatic changes necessary for a glacial age to occur are not so great as one might imagine. During the height of a glacial age, the

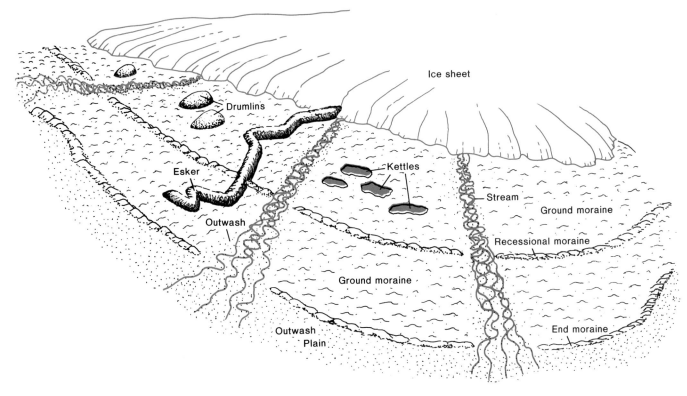

Figure 12.34 Depositional features in front of a receding ice sheet.

worldwide average of annual temperatures was probably only about 5°C cooler than at present. The intervening interglacial periods were probably a bit warmer worldwide than present-day average annual temperatures.

Direct Effects of Past Glaciation in North America

Moving ice abraded vast areas of northern and eastern Canada during the growth of the North American ice sheet (figure 12.33). Most of the soil was scraped off and bedrock was scoured. Many thousands of future lake basins were gouged out of the bedrock.

The directions of ice flow can be determined from the striations and grooves in the bedrock. The ice sheet moved outward from the general area now occupied by Hudson Bay, which is where the highest part of the North American ice sheet was located. The present generally barren surface of the Hudson Bay area contrasts markedly with the Great Plains surface of southern Canada and northern United States, where vast amounts of till were deposited. Why is this so? The ice sheet's erosive ability may have been greater in northern Canada, where it was thickest. On the other hand, the erodibility of the bedrock may have been a more significant causal factor. The scoured bedrock of northern Canada is igneous and metamorphic rock, resistant to erosion. The bedrock beneath most of the till in midwestern Canada and northern United States is easily eroded sedimentary rock.

Most of the till was deposited as ground moraine, which, along with outwash deposits, has partially weathered to give excellent soil for agriculture. In many areas along the southern boundaries of land covered by ground moraines, broad and complex end moraines extend for many kilometers, indicating that the ice margin must have been virtually stationary for a long period of time. Numerous drumlins are preserved in some areas, as in New England and upstate New York. Kettle lakes dot the landscape in large sections of Wisconsin and Minnesota.

The Great Lakes are, at least in part, a legacy of continental glaciation. Former stream valleys were widened by the ice sheet into the present lake basins. End moraines border the Great Lakes, as shown in figure 12.35. New York's Long Island was built up by morainal debris, most of it probably scoured out of New England.

Alpine glaciation was much more extensive throughout the world during the glacial ages than it is now. For example, small glaciers in the Rocky Mountains that now barely extend beyond their cirques were then valley glaciers 10, 50, or 100 kilometers in length. Yosemite Valley, which is no longer glaciated, was filled by a glacier about a kilometer thick. Its terminus was at an elevation of about 1,300 meters above sea level. Furthermore, cirques and other features typical of valley glaciers can be found in regions that at present have no glaciers, such as the

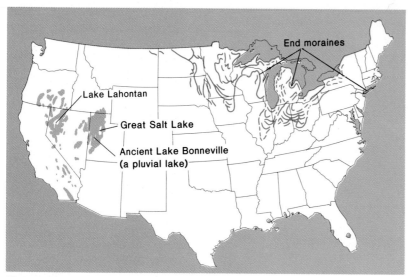

Figure 12.35 End moraines in northern United States (shown by dark lines) and pluvial lakes in the southwestern United States.
From C. S. Denny, U.S. Geological Survey and the Geological Map of North America, Geological Society of America.

northern Appalachians—notably in the White Mountains of New Hampshire. Apparently alpine glaciers were present in New England for some time after the main ice sheet retreated.

Indirect Effects of Past Glaciation

As the last continental ice sheet wasted away, what effects did the tremendous volume of meltwater have on American rivers? Rivers which now contain only a trickle of water were huge in the glacial ages. Other river courses were blocked by the ice sheet or clogged with morainal debris. Large dry stream channels have been found that are regarded as having been preglacial tributaries to the Mississippi and other river systems.

Pluvial lakes During the glacial ages the climate in North America, even beyond the glaciated parts, was more humid than it is now. Most of the presently arid regions of the western United States had moderate rainfall, as traces or remnants of numerous lakes indicate. These **pluvial lakes** (formed in a period of abundant rainfall) once existed in Nevada, Utah, and eastern California. Some may have been fed by meltwater from mountain glaciers, but most were simply the result of a wetter climate (figure 12.35).

Great Salt Lake in Utah is but a small remnant of a much larger body of fresh water called Lake Bonneville, which was, at its maximum size, nearly as large as Lake Michigan is today. (Geologists have mapped ancient beaches and wave-cut terraces that indicate Lake Bonneville's former shorelines.) As the climate became more arid, lake levels lowered, outlets were cut off, and the water became salty, eventually leaving behind the Bonneville salt flats and the present very saline Great Salt Lake.

Even Death Valley in California—now the driest place in the United States—was occupied by a deep lake during the Pleistocene. The salt flats that were left when this lake dried (see figure 6.6) include rare boron salts that were mined during the pioneering days of the American West.

Lowering of sea level All of the water for the great glaciers had to come from somewhere. It is reasonable to assume that the water was "borrowed" from the oceans and that sea level worldwide was lower than it is today—at least 130 meters lower, according to scientific estimates.

What is the evidence for this? Stream channels have been charted in the present continental shelves, the gently inclined submerged edges of the continents (described in chapter 19). These submerged channels are continuations of today's major rivers and could not have been eroded unless the continental shelf surfaces were above sea level during the glacial ages. Bones and teeth from now-extinct mammoths and mastodons have been dredged up from the Atlantic continental shelf, indicating that these relatives of elephants roamed over what must have been dry land at the time.

A **fiord** is a coastal inlet that is a drowned glacially carved valley (figure 12.36). Fiords are common along the mountainous coastlines of Alaska, British Columbia, New Zealand, and Norway. They are evidence that valleys eroded by past glaciers were later partly submerged by the rising seas.

Figure 12.36 Fiord in Alaska.
Photo by D. A. Rahm, courtesy Rahm Memorial Collection, Western Washington University.

Crustal rebound The weight of an ice sheet several thousand meters thick depresses the crust of the earth much as the weight of a person depresses a mattress. A land surface bearing the weight of a continental ice sheet may be depressed several hundred meters.

Once the glacier is gone, the land begins to rebound slowly to its previous height (see figures 17.14 and 17.15). Uplifted and tilted shorelines along lakes are an indication of this process. Rebound in the Great Lakes region is still going on as the crust slowly adjusts to the removal of the last ice sheet.

Evidence for Older Glaciation

Throughout most of geologic time, the climate has been warmer and more uniform than it is today. We think that the late Cenozoic Era is unusual because of the periodic fluctuations of climate and the widespread glaciations. However, glacial ages are not restricted to the late Cenozoic.

The evidence of older glaciation comes from rocks called tillites. A **tillite** is lithified till. Unsorted rock particles, including angular, striated, and faceted boulders, have been consolidated into a sedimentary rock. In some places, the tillite layers overlie surfaces of older rock that have been polished and striated. Tillites of late Paleozoic age and tillites representing a minor part of the late Precambrian crop out in parts of the southern continents.

Late Paleozoic tillites in the southern continents (South Africa, Australia, Antarctica, South America) have been used as evidence that these land masses were once joined (chapter 20). Directions of striations indicate that an ice sheet flowed onto South America from what

is now the South Atlantic Ocean. Because an ice sheet may build up only on land, it is reasonable to conclude that the former ice sheet was centered on the ancient supercontinent before it broke up into the present continents.

Summary

A *glacier* is a large, long-lasting mass of ice formed on land which moves by its own weight. A glacier can form wherever more snow accumulates than is lost. *Ice sheets* and *valley glaciers* are the two most important types of glaciers. Glaciers move downward from where the most snow accumulates toward where the most ice is wasted.

A glacier moves both by basal sliding and by internal flow. The upper portion of a glacier tends to stay rigid and be carried along by the ice moving beneath it.

Glaciers advance and recede in response to changes in the climate. A glacier recedes if it has a *negative budget* and advances if it has a *positive budget*. A glacier's budget for the year may be determined by noting the relative position of the *firn limit*.

Snow recrystallizes into firn, which eventually becomes converted to glacier ice. Glacier ice is lost (or wasted) by melting, by breaking off as icebergs, and by direct evaporation of the ice into the air.

A glacier erodes by the grinding action of the rock it carries. The grinding produces *rock flour* and faceted and polished rock fragments. Bedrock over which a glacier moves is generally polished and grooved.

A mountain area showing the erosional effects of alpine glaciation possesses relatively straight valleys with U-shaped cross-profiles. The floor of a glacial valley usually has a *cirque* at its head and descends as a series of rock steps. Small *rock-basin lakes* are commonly found along the steps and in cirques. *Hanging valleys* indicate that smaller tributaries joined the main glacier. A *horn* is a peak between several cirques. *Arêtes* usually separate adjacent glacial valleys.

A glacier deposits unsorted rock debris or *till*. Till contrasts sharply with the sorted and layered deposits of glacial *outwash*. Till forms various types of *moraines*.

Fine silt and clay may settle as *varves* in a lake in front of a glacier, each pair of layers representing a year's accumulation.

Multiple till deposits and other glacial features indicate several major episodes of glaciation that occurred during the late Cenozoic Era. During each of these episodes, large ice sheets covered most of northern Europe and northern North America, and glaciation in mountain areas of the world was much more extensive than at present. At the maximum extent of glaciation about a third of the earth's land surface was glaciated (in contrast to the 10 percent of the land surface presently under glaciers). Warmer climates prevailed during interglacial episodes.

The glacial ages also affected regions never covered by ice. Because of the wetter climate in the past, large lakes formed in now-arid regions of the United States. Sea level was considerably lower.

Glacial ages also occurred in the more distant geologic past. Evidence for late Paleozoic and late Precambrian glaciation is found in the southern continents.

Terms to Remember

advancing glaciers	loess
alpine glaciation	medial moraine
arête	moraine
basal sliding	outwash
bergschrund	plastic flow
cirque	pluvial lake
continental glaciation	receding glaciers
crevasse	recessional moraine
drumlin	rigid zone
end moraine	rock-basin lake
erratic	rock flour
esker	striations
faceted	terminal moraine
fiord	terminal moraine
firn	terminus
firn limit	theory of glacial ages
glacier	till
ground moraine	tillite
hanging valley	truncated spurs
horn	U-shaped valley
iceberg	valley glacier
ice cap	varve
ice sheet	wasted (or wastage)
kettle	zone of accumulation
lateral moraine	zone of wastage

Questions for Review

1. How do features caused by stream erosion differ from features caused by glacial erosion?
2. How does material deposited by glaciers differ from material deposited by streams?
3. Why is the North Pole not glaciated?
4. How would you distinguish a sample of glacial rock flour from nonglacial silt and clay deposited in a sea?
5. How do arêtes, cirques, and horns form?
6. What differences are there in the way ice moves in a valley glacier and the way it moves in an ice sheet?
7. How does the glacial budget control the migration of the firn limit?
8. How do recessional moraines differ from terminal moraines?

Questions for Thought

1. How might a warming trend result in increased glaciation?
2. How do or do not the Pleistocene glacial ages fit in with the principle of uniformitarianism?
3. Is ice within a glacier a mineral? Is a glacier a rock?
4. Could tillites be deposited by any agent other than an ice sheet?
5. What is the likelihood of a future glacial age? What effect might human activity have on causing or preventing a glacial age?

Supplementary Readings

Dyson, J. L. 1962. *The world of ice.* New York: Alfred A. Knopf.

Embleton, C., and C. A. M. King. 1975. *Glacial and periglacial geomorphology.* 2d ed., 2 vol. New York: Halsted Press.

Flint, R. F. 1971. *Glacial and quaternary geology.* New York: John Wiley & Sons.

Matsch, C. L. 1976. *North America and the great Ice Age.* New York: McGraw-Hill.

Matthes, F. E. 1930. *The geologic history of Yosemite Valley.* U.S. Geological Survey Professional Paper 160.

Post, A., and E. R. LaChappelle. 1971. *Glacier ice.* Seattle: University of Washington Press.

Ritter, D. F. 1978. *Process geomorphology.* Dubuque, Iowa: Wm. C. Brown Company Publishers.

Tuttle, S. D. 1980. *Landforms and landscapes.* 3d ed. Dubuque, Iowa: Wm. C. Brown Company Publishers.

U.S. Geological Survey. 1973. Glaciers, a water resource. U.S. Geological Survey Information Pamphlet.

Washburn, A. L. 1973. *Periglacial processes and environments.* London: Edward Arnold Ltd.

13
Deserts and Wind Action

Purpose

Deserts have their own distinctive set of landforms because an arid climate controls erosive and depositional processes and the rates at which they operate. Although most of these features are formed by running water, a dry climate gives them a special character. With water in limited supply, the role of wind becomes more significant, but the great erosive power of desert flash floods ensures that running water remains the dominant agent of land sculpture.

Mass wasting, streams, ground water, and glaciers—these agents of land sculpture have been the topics of the last four chapters. Here we discuss the fifth agent of erosion and deposition: wind. Deserts and wind are discussed together because of the wind's particular intensity in dry regions, but wind erosion and deposition can be very impressive in many other climates as well.

When you hear the word "desert," you may think of a region of shifting sand dunes. Although Hollywood filmmakers nearly always show sand dunes to represent deserts, only a small portion of most deserts is covered with dunes. Actually a **desert** is any region with low precipitation. A region is usually classified as a desert if it has an **arid climate** with less than 25 centimeters (10 inches) of rain per year. Lack of water prevents most types of plants from growing, so vegetation is generally lacking in arid regions, which therefore have a barren look. Some specialized types of plants, however, grow well in desert climates despite the dryness. These plants are generally salt-tolerant; they have extensive root systems to conserve water, so they often are widely spaced. The leaves are usually very small, minimizing water loss by transpiration, and may even drop off the plants between rainstorms. During much of the year many desert plants look like dead, dry sticks. When rain does fall on the desert, the plants may become green, and many will bloom.

Geologists disagree on the definitions of the terms *desert* and *arid climate.*

The *Glossary of Geology,* published by the American Geological Institute and considered to be *the* standard reference work by most geologists, defines a **desert** (in part) as "a region with less than 10 inches (about 25 cm) of rain per year." Similarly, an **arid climate** is characterized by less than 10 inches of rain per year, and a *semiarid climate* by 10–20 inches (25–50 cm) per year. These are the definitions used throughout this book.

Many geologists, however, including some who work in deserts, prefer a more restrictive definition and would limit the term *desert* to those regions with less than 5 inches (about 12.5 cm) of rain annually. Other workers prefer a broader definition of the term, in some cases not keyed to a specific amount of rainfall but to an excess of evaporation over precipitation.

Distribution of Deserts

The location of most deserts is related to descending air. The global pattern of air circulation is shown in simplified form in figure 13.1. The equator receives the sun's heat more directly than the rest of the earth. Air warms and rises at the equator, then moves both northward and southward to sink near 30° North latitude and 30° South latitude.

Air sinking down through the atmosphere is compressed by the weight of the air above it. As air compresses, it warms up; and as it warms, it is able to hold more water vapor. Evaporation of water from the land surface into the warm, dry air is so great under belts of sinking air that moisture seldom falls back to earth in the form of rain. The two belts at 30° North and South latitude characteristically have clear skies, much sunshine, little rain, and high evaporation.

In contrast to the belts at 30°, the equator is marked by rising air masses. The rising air expands and cools as it rises. In cooling, the air loses its moisture, causing cloudy skies and heavy precipitation. Thus a belt of high rainfall at the equator separates the two major belts of deserts, one centered at 30° North latitude and the other at 30° South latitude (figure 13.2). The largest deserts in the world lie in these belts. In other latitudes, however, there also are areas of significant size that are arid enough to be called deserts. What special conditions might cause a dry climate to prevail in regions outside the 30° belts?

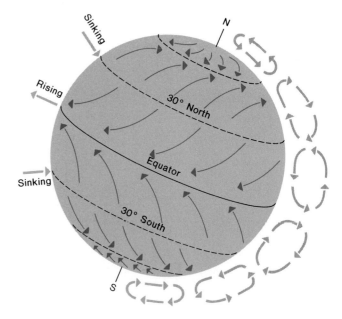

Figure 13.1 Global air circulation. Air sinks at 30° N and 30° S latitude.

The location of some of the world's deserts is the result of the **rain shadow** effect of mountain ranges (figure 13.3). As moist air is forced up to pass over a mountain range, it expands and cools, losing moisture as it rises. The dry air coming down the other side of the mountain compresses and warms, bringing high evaporation with

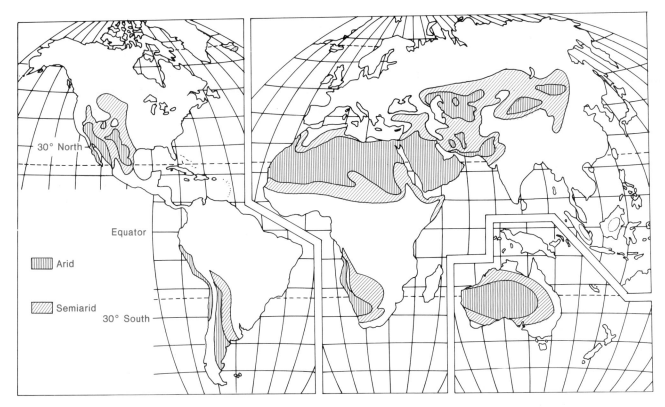

Figure 13.2 World distribution of deserts. Most deserts lie in two bands near 30° N and 30° S. From map by U.S. Department of Agriculture.

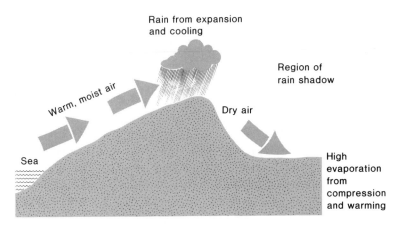

Rain from expansion and cooling

Region of rain shadow

Warm, moist air

Dry air

Sea

High evaporation from compression and warming

Figure 13.3 Rain shadow causes deserts on the downwind side of mountain ranges. Prevailing winds are from left to right.

little or no rainfall to the downwind side of the range. This dry region downwind of mountains is the *rain shadow zone.*

The parts of the southwestern U.S. desert in Nevada and northern Arizona are largely the result of the rain shadow effect of the Sierra Nevada range in eastern California.

Great distance from the ocean is another factor that can create deserts, since most rainfall comes from water evaporated from the sea. The dry climate of the large arid regions in China, well north of 30° North latitude, is due in part to their location in a continental interior. Deserts also tend to develop on tropical coasts next to *cold ocean currents.* Cold currents run along the western edges of continents, cooling the air above them. The cold marine air warms up as it moves over land, causing high evaporation and little rain on the coasts. This effect is particularly pronounced on the Pacific coast of South America and the Atlantic coast of Africa.

Some Characteristics of Deserts

Because of their low rainfall, deserts have characteristic drainage and topography, which differ from those of humid regions. Desert streams usually flow intermittently. Water runs over the surface after storms, but during most of the year stream beds are dry. As a result, most deserts *lack through-flowing streams.* The Colorado River in the southwestern United States and the Nile River in Egypt are notable exceptions. Both rise in mountainous areas where precipitation is great enough to sustain stream flow across dry regions of high evaporation and infiltration (soaking into the ground).

Many desert regions have *internal drainage;* the streams drain toward landlocked basins instead of toward the sea. The surface of an enclosed basin acts as a local base level. Because each basin is generally filled to a different level than the neighboring basins, desert erosion may be controlled by many different *local base levels.* As a basin fills with sediment, its surface rises, leading to a *rising base level,* which is a rare situation in humid regions.

The limited rainfall that does occur in deserts often comes in the form of violent thunderstorms, with a high volume of rain falling in a very short time. Such a large amount of rain cannot soak readily into the sun-baked ground, so the water runs rapidly over the land surface, particularly where vegetation is sparse. This high runoff can create sudden local floods of high discharge and short duration called **flash floods.** Flash floods are more common in arid regions than in humid regions. They can turn normally dry stream beds into raging torrents for a short time after a thunderstorm. These occasional floods can effectively erode the land surface in a desert region because soil particles are not held in place by plant roots. As a result, desert streams normally are very heavily laden with sediment. Flash floods can easily erode enough sediment to become *mudflows* (see chapter 9).

Desert stream channels are distinctive in appearance because of the great erosive power of flash floods and the intermittent nature of stream flow. Most stream channels are normally dry and covered with sand or gravel that is moved only during occasional flash floods. Rapid downcutting by sediment-laden floodwaters tends to produce narrow canyons with vertical walls and flat, gravel-strewn floors (figure 13.4).

The resistance of some rocks to weathering and erosion is partly controlled by climate. In a humid climate limestone readily dissolves, forming low places on the earth's surface. In a desert climate the lack of water

Figure 13.4   Desert stream channel showing dry, gravel-covered floor and steep, vertical sides (cut in sandstone and conglomerate) in Death Valley, California.

makes limestone resistant, so it stands up as ridges and cliffs in the desert, just as sandstone and conglomerate do. Lava flows and most igneous and metamorphic rock are also resistant. Shale is the least resistant rock in a desert, so it usually erodes deeper than other rock types and forms gentler slopes (figure 10.45).

Desert topography characteristically looks more angular than the gently rounded hills and valleys of a humid region. This may be due indirectly to the low rainfall. Shortage of water slows chemical weathering processes to the point where few minerals break down to form fine-grained clay minerals. Soils are coarse and rocky with few chemically weathered products. Plants, which help bind soil into a cohesive layer in humid climates, are rare in deserts, and so desert soils are easily eroded by wind and rainstorms. Downhill creep of thick, fine-grained soil is believed to be partly responsible for softening the appearance of topography in humid climates. With thin, rocky soil and slow rates of creep, desert topography should remain steep and angular.

As mentioned in chapter 10, not all geologists are sure that the angular topography common to many deserts was formed by the dry climate. The recent fluctuations of climate caused by the glacial ages of the Pleistocene Epoch (chapter 12) mean that most modern deserts probably had a much wetter climate a short time ago. It is possible that the angular topography formed then and is only well exposed in present deserts because the lack of vegetation allows us to see it.

As you learned in chapter 10, climate is only one of many controls on the shape and appearance of the land. Rock structure is another important control. As an example, in the next section we will look closely at two different structural regions within the desert of the southwestern United States.

Desert Features in the Southwestern United States

Much of the southwestern United States has an arid or semiarid climate, partly because of proximity to 30° North latitude and partly because of the rain shadow effect of the Sierra Nevada and other mountain ranges. Within this region of low rainfall are two areas of markedly different geologic structure. One area is the Colorado Plateau and the other is the Basin and Range province, a mountainous region centered on the state of Nevada. The boundaries of these two areas are shown in figure 13.5.

The *Colorado Plateau* centers roughly on the spot known as the Four Corners, where the states of Utah, Colorado, Arizona, and New Mexico meet at a common point. The rocks near the surface of the Colorado Plateau are mostly flat-lying beds of sedimentary rock many hundred meters above sea level. These rocks are well exposed at the Grand Canyon in Arizona.

Because the rock layers are well above sea level, they are vulnerable to erosion by the little rain that does fall in the region. Flat-lying layers of resistant rock, such as sandstone, limestone, and lava flows, form **plateaus**—broad, flat-topped areas elevated above the surrounding land and bounded, at least in part, by cliffs. As erosion removes the rock at its base, the cliff is gradually eroded back into the plateau (figure 13.6). Remnants of the resistant rock layer may be left behind, forming flat-topped mesas or narrow buttes (figure 13.7). A **mesa** is a broad, flat-topped hill bounded by cliffs and capped with a resistant rock layer. A **butte** is a narrow pinnacle of resistant rock with a flat top and very steep sides. Most buttes form

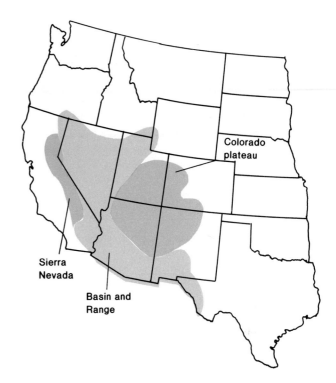

Figure 13.5 The Colorado Plateau and the Basin and Range province in the southwestern United States.

by continued erosion of mesas. (The term *butte* is also used in other parts of the country for any isolated hill.)

The *Basin and Range province* is characterized by rugged mountain ranges separated by flat valley floors (figure 13.8). The blocks of rock that form the mountain ranges and the valley floors are bounded by **faults,** cracks in the earth along which some rock movement has taken place. (Chapter 15 discusses faults in more detail.) In the Basin and Range, the rock movement on either side of the faults has lifted the mountains up and dropped the valleys down (figure 13.9). Fault-controlled topography is found throughout the Basin and Range province, which covers almost all of Nevada and portions of bordering states as well as southern Arizona and New Mexico.

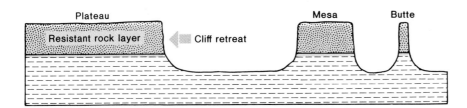

Figure 13.6 Erosional retreat of a cliff at the edge of a plateau can leave behind mesas and buttes as erosional remnants of the plateau. This is an example of parallel retreat of slopes, as discussed in chapter 10.

Figure 13.7 Mesas and buttes in Monument Valley, Arizona, an area of eroded, horizontal, sedimentary rocks.

Figure 13.8 Basin and Range topography in southeastern California. View northeastward across flat Death Valley floor, from Panamint Range in foreground to Black Mountains in distance. Faults separate valley floor from mountain ranges, particularly at base of Black Mountains.
Photo by W. B. Hamilton, U.S. Geological Survey.

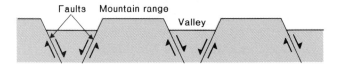

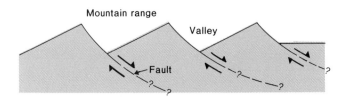

Figure 13.9 Two possible origins of the mountains and valleys of the Basin and Range province. In each case the mountains have been lifted up and the valleys dropped down. Movement along the faults is shown by arrows.

Heavy rains and storms in the mountain ranges cause rapid erosion of the steep mountain fronts and resulting deposition on the valley floors (figure 13.10). Loose rock and sediment from the mountains, picked up by flash floods and mudflows, are deposited in the form of alluvial fans at the base of the mountain ranges. Alluvial fans (described in chapter 10) build up where stream channels widen as they flow out of narrow canyons onto the open valley floors.

Although most of the sediment carried by runoff is deposited in alluvial fans, some water and very fine clay in suspension flow onto the flat valley floor. If no outlet drains the valley, the water may form a **playa lake** on the valley floor. Playa lakes are usually very shallow and temporary, lasting for only a few days after a rainstorm. After the lake evaporates, a thin layer of fine mud may be left on the valley floor. The mud dries in the sun, forming a **playa,** a very flat, dry lake bed of hard, mud-cracked clay (figure 13.11 and 13.12). If the runoff contained a large amount of dissolved salt or if seeping ground water brings salt to the surface, a playa may be covered with a bright white layer of dried salt instead of cracked mud.

Continued deposition near the base of the mountains may form a **bajada,** a broad, gently sloping depositional surface formed by the coalescing of individual alluvial fans (figure 13.10). A bajada is much more extensive than a single alluvial fan and may have a gently rolling surface resulting from the merging of the cone-shaped fans.

Erosion of the mountain can eventually form a **pediment,** which is a gently sloping surface, usually covered with a thin veneer of gravel, cut into the solid rock of the mountain (figure 13.10). A pediment develops uphill from a bajada as the mountain front retreats. It can be difficult to distinguish a pediment from the surface of the bajada downhill, since both have the same slope and gravel cover. The pediment, however, is an erosional surface, usually underlain by solid rock, while the bajada surface is depositional and may be underlain by hundreds or even thousands of meters of sediment.

An abrupt change in slope marks the upper limit of the pediment, where it meets the steep mountain front. Many geologists who have studied desert erosion believe that as this steep mountain front erodes, it retreats uphill, maintaining a relatively constant angle of slope. (This is *parallel retreat* of a slope.)

Notice that rock structure, not climate, largely controls the fact that plateaus and cliffs are found in the Colorado Plateau, while mountain ranges, broad valleys, alluvial fans, and pediments are found in the Basin and Range province.

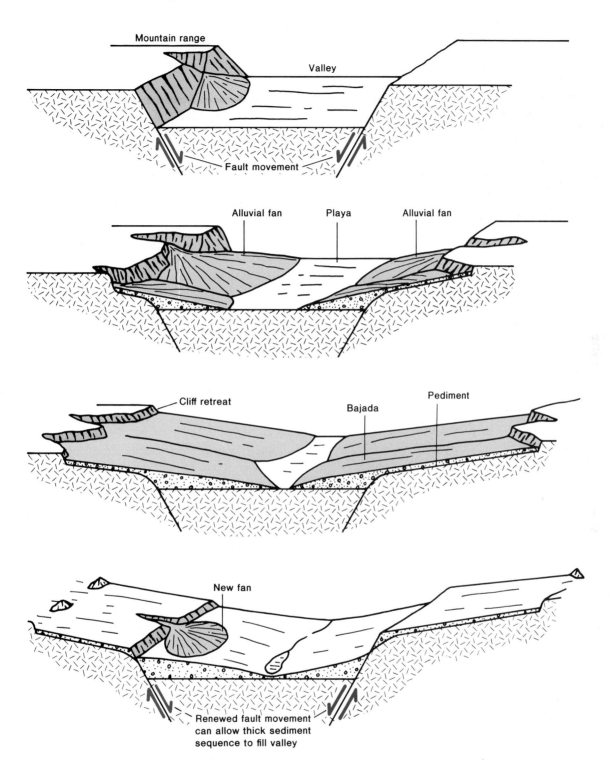

Figure 13.10 Origin of some Basin and Range topography.

Figure 13.11 Desert landforms in Death Valley, California. In the distance the Panamint Mountains rise more than three kilometers above Death Valley. Giant alluvial fans at the base of the mountains show a braided stream pattern. Fine-grained sediments and salt deposits form the playas in the foreground. Photo by H. E. Malde, U.S. Geological Survey.

Figure 13.12 Mud-cracked playa surface.

Wind Action

Wind can be an important agent of erosion and deposition in regions with different climates. Onshore winds can blow loose sand away from beaches to form sand dunes inland. Beach dunes occur on many coasts in humid regions such as New England, the Mid-Atlantic states, the Pacific Northwest, and around the Great Lakes. The "Dust Bowl" conditions in the Great Plains in the 1930s demonstrated the wind's power to erode soil particles during droughts when anchoring vegetation was absent. Volcanic ash can be picked up by winds and carried thousands of kilometers, particularly if explosive volcanic eruptions blast the ash several kilometers upward into the atmosphere, as they did at Mount St. Helens in 1980.

Wind-blown sediment may be picked up on land and carried out to sea. Particles from the Sahara Desert in Africa have been collected from the air over the islands of the West Indies after having been carried by wind across the entire Atlantic Ocean. A substantial amount of the fine-grained sediment that settles to the sea floor is land-derived sediment that the wind has deposited on the sea surface. Ships hundreds of kilometers offshore have reported dustfalls a few millimeters thick covering their decks.

Strong Winds in Deserts

One controlling factor of wind velocity is air temperature. In humid regions where rainfall is abundant, water and cloud cover moderate the temperature of the air. Much heat that could warm the air goes into evaporating water instead, so extremely high temperatures are rare in humid climates. As water freezes, it gives off heat that usually warms the air, also modifying extremely low temperatures in humid climates. Thus the presence of water helps prevent the air from becoming either very hot or very cold. A typical range of temperature on a summer day in a humid region might be from 27°C (about 80°F) in the afternoon to 16°C (about 60°F) at night.

In a desert region, there is generally not enough water (or cloud cover) to buffer the temperature in this manner, and so deserts are characterized by extreme temperature fluctuations. The maximum temperature measured in a desert in the United States is about 57°C (134°F) in Death Valley, where rainfall averages less than 5 centimeters per year. In a desert the temperature may range between 38°C (about 100°F) and 10°C (50°F) in a single day. A daily temperature range of 30°C is not unusual in a desert; ranges of more than 35°C have been measured.

Because of these temperature fluctuations, wind is generally stronger in the deserts than in humid regions. High daytime temperatures and low nighttime temperatures cause great fluctuations in the air's density; it is these changes in density that cause strong winds. Desert winds have been measured many times at speeds greater than 100 kilometers per hour. Strong winds are particularly effective in eroding the desert surface because of the general scarcity of vegetation in dry regions. Despite the effectiveness of wind erosion, however, stream erosion from the sparse rainfall remains the most important agent of erosion and deposition in most deserts. (Most desert landforms are of water, not wind, origin, and the intense erosion caused by rare desert rainstorms has been repeatedly observed.)

Erosion and Transportation of Sediment by Wind

Although wind is not confined to channels as running water is, wind and running water are in many respects similar in the ways in which they erode and transport sediment particles. As air is less dense than water, wind generally erodes and transports fewer and smaller sediment particles than streams do.

Fine-grained silt and clay, however, are easily picked up from the land surface by wind, particularly if the surface is irregular or has been disturbed by the feet of animals or by vehicle tires. In turbulent air, fine-grained particles can remain suspended for a long time. When an ample supply of silt and clay is available, strong winds may carry thick, choking clouds of dust thousands of meters upward and hundreds of kilometers horizontally. During the 1930s "Dust Bowl," wind-carried dust from cultivated fields frequently darkened the sky and sometimes caused nearly total darkness at midday (figure 13.13).

Because sand grains are heavier than silt and clay, sand moves close to the ground in the leaping pattern called *saltation* (as does some sediment in streams). High-speed winds can cause *sandstorms,* clouds of sand moving rapidly near the land surface. The impact of high-speed sand in such a storm can sandblast smooth surfaces on hard rock and scour windshields of automobiles. Because of the weight of the sand grains, however, sand rarely rises more than a meter above a flat land surface, even under extremely strong winds. Most of the sandblasting action of wind therefore occurs close to the ground (figure 13.14). Telephone poles in regions of wind-driven sand often are severely abraded near the ground. To prevent this abrasion, desert residents pile small stones around the base of the poles.

Wind-blown sand may sculpture isolated pebbles, cobbles, and boulders to form **ventifacts,** rocks with flat, polished surfaces formed by the abrasion of wind-blown sand (figure 13.15). If wind direction shifts or a pebble is turned, more than one flat face may develop on the stone (figure 13.16). However, wind seldom moves particles larger than sand grains.

Figure 13.13 Approaching dust storm, Prowers County, Colorado, late afternoon. The storm lasted almost three hours, with wind speeds of approximately 50 kilometers per hour.
Photo by U.S. Dept. Agriculture, Soil Conservation Service.

Figure 13.14 Wind erosion by sandblast near the ground on granite outcrop, Atacama, Chile.
Photo by K. Segerstrom, U.S. Geological Survey.

Figure 13.15 Large granite ventifact, Sweetwater County, Wyoming.
Photo by W. H. Bradley, U.S. Geological Survey.

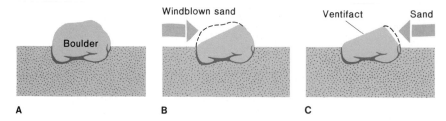

Figure 13.16 Development of a ventifact. A boulder develops a flat face from abrasion by sand carried by the wind. A second face can develop if the wind changes direction.

Deflation The removal of clay, silt, and sand particles from the land surface by wind is called **deflation.** If the sediment at the land surface is made up only of fine particles, the erosion of these particles by the wind can lower the land surface substantially. A **blowout** is a depression on the land surface caused by wind erosion (figure 13.17).

Blowouts are common in the Great Plains states (figure 13.18). Some in Wyoming are over 50 meters deep and a few kilometers long. Some enormous blowouts in Egypt exceed 100 meters in depth and extend for tens of kilometers. Deflation can continue to deepen a blowout in fine-grained sediment until it reaches the wet, cohesive sediment at the water table.

If the sediment near the land surface is made up of both fine and coarse particles, the wind removes the fine particles and leaves the coarse gravel behind. As this gravel becomes concentrated by the removal of the fine particles, it may eventually form a thin layer of closely packed gravel called a **desert pavement** (or sometimes *pebble armor*). This layer protects the underlying sediment from further deflation (figures 13.17 and 13.19).

Loess **Loess** is a deposit of wind-blown silt and clay composed of unweathered, angular grains of quartz, feldspar, and other minerals and weakly consolidated by calcareous cement. Loess has a high porosity, often near 60 percent. Deposits of loess blanket hills and valleys downwind of deserts or glacial outwash, which provide a source supply of fine sediment.

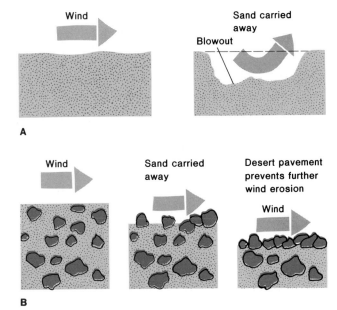

Figure 13.17 Deflation by wind erosion can cause (A) a blowout in fine-grained sediment and (B) a desert pavement in rocky sediment.

Figure 13.18 Large blowout near Harrison, Nebraska. Pillar top is the original level of land.
Photo by N. H. Darton, U.S. Geological Survey.

Figure 13.19　Desert pavement in Mojave Desert, California.

Figure 13.20　Vertical roadcuts in loess, Vicksburg, Mississippi.
Photo by E. W. Shaw, U.S. Geological Survey.

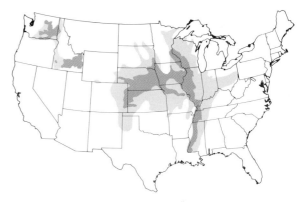

Figure 13.21　Loess deposits in the United States. Dark color shows major deposits. Light color represents thin, discontinuous deposits.
From U.S. Bureau of Reclamation, 1960, and various other sources.

China has extensive loess deposits, more than 100 meters thick in places. Wind from the Gobi Desert carried the silt and clay that formed these deposits. Loess is easy to dig into and has the peculiar ability to stand as a vertical cliff without slumping, perhaps because of its cement or perhaps because the fine, angular, sediment grains interlock with one another (figure 13.20). The Chinese have for centuries dug cavelike homes in loess cliffs. However, when a large earthquake shook China in 1920, many of these cliffs collapsed, killing about 100,000 people.

During the glacial ages of the Pleistocene Epoch (chapter 12) the rivers that drained what is now the midwestern United States transported and deposited vast amounts of glacial outwash. Later, wind eroded silt and clay (originally glacial rock flour) from the flood plains of these rivers and blanketed large areas of the Midwest with a cover of loess (figure 13.21). Soils that have developed from the loess account for much of this region's agricultural productivity. A less extensive deposit of loess in eastern Washington also supports an important food-growing economy there.

Sand Dunes

Sand dunes are mounds of loose sand grains heaped up by the wind. Dunes are most likely to develop in areas with strong winds that generally blow in the same direction. Patches of dunes are found scattered throughout the southwestern United States desert. More extensive fields of dunes occur on some of the other deserts of the world, such as the Sahara Desert of Africa, which contains vast *sand seas,* or *ergs.* Dunes are also commonly found just landward of beaches, where sand is blown inland by sea or lake breezes. Braided rivers (chapter 10) can also be sources of sand for dune fields.

The mineral composition of the sand grains in sand dunes depends on both the character of the original sand source and the intensity of chemical weathering in the region. Many dunes, particularly those near beaches in humid regions, are composed largely of quartz grains because quartz is so resistant to chemical weathering. As

Desert Varnish

Many rocks on the surface of deserts are darkened by a chemical coating known as *desert varnish*. Although the interior of the rocks may be light colored, a hard, often shiny, coating of dark manganese oxide and clay minerals can build up on the rock surface over long periods of time. Although no one is quite certain how this coating develops, it seems to be added to the rocks from the outside, for even white quartzite pebbles with no internal source of manganese or clay minerals can develop desert varnish. One current hypothesis is that the clay is windblown, perhaps sticking to rocks dampened by dew. A film of clay on a rock may draw Mn-containing solutions upward from the soil by capillary action, and the presence of the clay minerals may help deposit the dark manganese oxide that cements the clay to the rock. The longer a rock is exposed on a desert land surface, the darker it becomes.

Figure 13.22 Desert varnish has darkened the exterior of this boulder, which originally had the same color as the bedrock outcrop on which it rests.

little chemical weathering takes place in drier climates, many desert dunes are composed of grains of quartz, feldspar, ferromagnesian minerals, and rock fragments. Some dunes are formed mostly of calcite grains, particularly those near beaches that have formed of wave-abraded coral and reef debris. At White Sands, New Mexico, dunes are made of gypsum grains.

Sand grains found in dunes commonly are well sorted and well rounded because wind is very selective as it moves sediment. Fine-grained silt and clay are carried much farther than sand, and grains coarser than sand are left behind when sand moves. The result is a dune made solely of sand grains, often all very nearly the same size. The prevalence of well-rounded grains in many dunes also may be due to selective sorting by the wind. Rounded grains roll more easily than angular grains, and so the wind may take only the rounded grains away from a source to form dunes.

Most sand dunes are asymmetric in cross section, with a gentle slope facing the wind and a steeper slope on the downwind side. The steep downwind slope of a dune is called the **slip face** (figure 13.23). It forms from loose, cascading sand that generally keeps the slope at the *angle of repose*, which is about 34° for loose dry sand. Sand

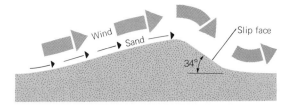

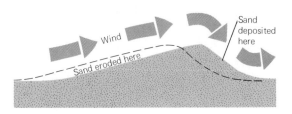

Figure 13.23 *(A)* A sand dune forms with a gentle upwind slope, a steeper slip face downwind. *(B)* Movement of sand causes the dune to move slowly downwind.

grains are blown up the gentle slope and over the top of the dune. Loose sand builds up near the top of the slip face until it becomes oversteepened and the sand grains tumble down the slip face. (The cross-bedding in sandstone formed from lithified sand dunes gives evidence of similar sand movement in the past.)

Figure 13.24 Wind ripples on a sand dune (ripples are a few centimeters apart). Prevailing wind blows from left to right.

In passing over a dune, the wind erodes sand from the gentle upwind slope and deposits the same sand on the slip face downwind. As a result, the entire dune moves slowly in a downwind direction. The rate of dune motion is much slower than the speed of the wind, of course, because only a thin layer of sand on the surface of the dune is moving at any one time. The dune may move only 10 to 20 meters per year. Over many years, however, the movement of dunes can be impressive, a fact not always appreciated by people who build homes close to moving sand dunes.

If a dune becomes overgrown with grass or other vegetation, then movement stops. The Sand Hills of northwestern Nebraska are large dunes, perhaps formed during the Pleistocene Epoch, that have become stabilized by vegetation. Grass has been planted on many beach dunes to stop their movement. Dune-buggy tires can kill the grass, however, and start the dunes moving again.

Sand moving over a dune surface often forms **wind ripples**—small, low ridges of sand produced by saltation of the grains (figure 13.24). The ripples are similar to those formed in sediment by a water current (chapter 6). Because sand moves perpendicularly to the long dimension of the ripples, a rippled sand surface can indicate the direction of sand movement.

Types of dunes As figure 13.25 shows, dunes tend to develop certain characteristic shapes, depending on (1) the wind's velocity and direction (that is, whether constant or shifting); (2) the sand supply available; and (3) how the vegetation cover, if any, is distributed.

Where the sand supply is limited, the type of dune that generally develops is a **barchan,** which is a crescent-shaped dune with the horns of the crescent pointing down-

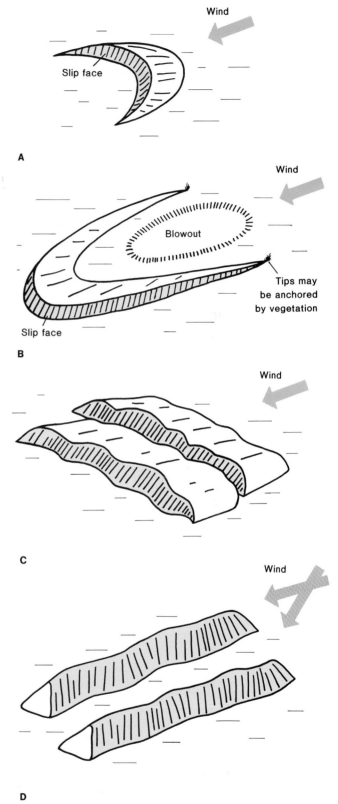

Figure 13.25 Some types of sand dune. *(A)* Barchan. *(B)* Parabolic dune. *(C)* Transverse dunes. *(D)* Longitudinal dunes (seifs).

Figure 13.26 Barchan dunes, Washington. Photo is of area several tens of meters wide.
Photo by D. A. Rahm, courtesy Rahm Memorial Collection, Western Washington University.

wind (figure 13.26). Barchans are usually separated from one another, and move across a bare rock surface. If more sand is available, the wind may develop a **transverse dune,** a relatively straight, elongate dune oriented perpendicular to the wind (figure 13.27). A **parabolic dune,** which commonly forms around a blowout, particularly near a beach, is deeply curved. The horns point upwind and are apt to be anchored by vegetation. It requires abundant sand. All three of these dune shapes develop under a steady wind direction, and all three have steep slip faces on the downwind sides.

One of the largest types of dune is the **longitudinal dune** or *seif*. It is a large, symmetrical ridge of sand parallel to the wind direction, which is often slightly variable. Longitudinal dunes in the Sahara Desert may be 200 meters high and extend more than 100 kilometers in length.

Not all dunes can be classified as to type by an easily recognizable shape. As figure 13.28 shows, many of them are quite irregular.

Summary

Deserts are located in regions where less than 25 centimeters of rain falls in a year. Such regions are found primarily in belts of descending air at 30° North and South latitude. Arid regions also may be due to *rain shadow* of a mountain range, great distance from the sea, and proximity to a cold ocean current.

Figure 13.27 Transverse dunes, Oregon. Photo is of area several hundred meters wide.
Photo by D. A. Rahm, courtesy Rahm Memorial Collection, Western Washington University.

Figure 13.28 Complex sand dunes, Nevada. Photo is of area a few hundred meters wide.
Photo by D. A. Rahm, courtesy Rahm Memorial Collection, Western Washington University.

Desert landscapes differ from those in humid regions in lacking through-flowing streams and in having internal drainage and many local, rising base levels. *Flash floods* caused by desert thunderstorms are effective agents of erosion despite the low rainfall. Limestone is resistant in deserts. Thin soil and slow rates of creep may give desert topography an angular look.

Parts of the southwestern United States are a desert, with rock structure being a major control of topography. Flat-flying sedimentary rocks of the Colorado Plateau are sculptured into cliffs, *plateaus, mesas,* and *buttes.* The fault-controlled topography of the Basin and Range province is marked by *alluvial fans, bajadas, playas,* and *pediments.*

Although wind erosion is most intense in regions of low moisture, streams are usually more effective than wind in sculpturing landscapes, regardless of climate.

Fine-grained sediment can be carried long distances by wind, even across entire continents and oceans.

Sand moves by *saltation* close to the ground, occasionally carving *ventifacts.*

Wind can *deflate* a region, creating a *blowout* in fine sediment or *desert pavement* in sediment that includes gravel.

Sand dunes move slowly downwind as sand is removed from the gentle upwind slope to be deposited on the steeper *slip face* downwind. *Wind ripples* may form on dune surfaces.

Dunes are classified as *barchans, transverse dunes, parabolic dunes,* and *longitudinal dunes,* but many dunes do not resemble these types. Dune type depends on wind strength and direction, sand supply, and vegetation.

Terms to Remember

arid climate	mesa
barchan	parabolic dune
bajada	pediment
blowout	plateau
butte	playa
deflation	playa lake
desert	rain shadow
desert pavement (pebble armor)	sand dune
fault	slip face
flash floods	transverse dune
loess	ventifact
longitudinal dune (seif)	wind ripples

Questions for Review

1. What are two reasons why parts of the southwestern United States have an arid climate?
2. Sketch a cross section of an idealized dune, labeling the slip face and indicating the wind direction. Why does the dune move?
3. Describe the geologic structure and sketch the major landforms of:
   a. the Colorado Plateau;
   b. the Basin and Range province.
4. How does a flash flood in a dry region differ from most floods in a humid region?
5. Give two reasons why wind is a more effective agent of erosion in a desert than in a humid region.
6. Describe a desert pavement and discuss its origin.
7. Name four types of sand dunes and describe the conditions under which each forms.

Questions for Thought

1. How does a pediment differ from a bajada? Discuss the differences and similarities between the two features, particularly in regard to appearance and origin.
2. Study the photos of sand dunes in the chapter. Which way does the prevailing wind blow in each case?

Supplementary Readings

Bagnold, R. A. 1941. *The physics of blown sand and desert dunes.* New York: William Morrow, 1954 (reprinted).

Blackwelder, E. 1954. Geomorphic processes in the desert. *Bulletin of California Division of Mines* 170:11–20. Sacramento: Department of Natural Resources.

Cooper, W. S. 1967. *Coastal dunes of California.* Geological Society of America Memoir 104.

Denny, C. S. 1967. Fans and pediments. *American Journal of Science* 265:81–105.

Ritter, D. F. 1978. *Process geomorphology.* Dubuque, Iowa: Wm. C. Brown Company Publishers.

Thornbury, W. D. 1969. *Principles of geomorphology.* 2d ed. New York: John Wiley & Sons.

14

Waves, Beaches, and Coasts

Purpose

Around the continents and islands of the world, and on the shores of large inland lakes, waves break against the land, building it up in some places and tearing it down in others. Water waves are another agent of erosion, transportation, and deposition of sediment. The previous five chapters have dealt with other geologic agents: mass wasting, streams, ground water, glaciers, and wind.

The energy of the waves comes from the wind. This energy is used to a large extent in eroding and transporting sediment along the shoreline. An understanding of how waves travel and move sediment can help you see how easily the balance of supply, transportation, and deposition of beach sediment can be disturbed. Such disturbances can result from natural causes, human activities, or both, and the changes that result are often harmful to coastal communities.

Beaches have been called "rivers of sand" because breaking waves, as they sort and transport sediment, tend to move sand parallel to the shoreline. In this chapter we look at how beaches are formed and also examine the influence of wave action on such coastal features as sea cliffs, barrier islands, and marine terraces.

If you spend a week at the shore during the summer, you may not notice any great change in the appearance of the beach while you are there. Even if you spend the whole summer at the seaside, it may not seem that much is happening to the beach during those months. Tides rise and fall every day and waves strike the shore, but the sand that you walk on one day looks very much like the sand that you walk on the next day. The shape of the beach does not appear to change, nor does the sand seem to move very much.

On most beaches, however, the sand is moving, in some cases quite rapidly. The beach looks the same from day to day only because new sand usually is being supplied at about the same rate that old sand is being removed.

Where is the sand going? Some sand is carried out to deep water. Some is piled up and stored high on the beach. But on most shores a greater quantity moves along parallel to the beach in relatively shallow water. Loose sand grains travel in this way several hundred meters per day along some coasts, especially those subject to strong waves.

On some beaches, sand is being removed faster than it is being replenished. When this happens, beaches become narrower and less attractive for swimming. Where erosion is severe, buildings close to the beach can be undermined and destroyed by waves as the shoreline moves inland on a disappearing beach. The sand moved from the beach may be redeposited in inconvenient places, such as across the mouth of a harbor, where it must be dredged out periodically. Because moving sand can create many problems for people in coastal towns and cities, it is important to understand something of how and why the sand moves.

Water Waves

The energy that moves sand along a beach comes from the wind-driven water waves that break upon the shore. As wind blows over the surface of an ocean or a lake, some of the wind's energy is transferred to the water surface, forming the waves that move through the water. Wave shapes can be fairly regular (long, rolling "swell") or quite variable (short, choppy storm waves). When waves break against the shore, a large portion of their energy is used to move sand along the beach.

The height of waves is the key factor in determining wave energy. **Wave height** is the vertical distance between the **crest,** which is the high point of a wave, and the

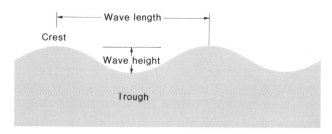

Figure 14.1 Parts of a wave

trough, which is the low point (figure 14.1). In the open ocean, normal waves have heights of 2 to 5 meters, although hurricane waves may be 15 or more meters high. The highest wave ever measured was more than 34 meters (112 feet) in height. **Wave length** is the horizontal distance between two crests (or two troughs). Most ocean waves are between 40 and 400 meters in length and move at a speed of 30 to 90 kilometers per hour in deep water.

The movement of water in a wave can be compared to the movement of wheat in a field when wind blows across it. You can see the ripple caused by wind blowing across a wheat field, but the wheat does not pile up at the end of the field. Each stalk of wheat bends over when the wind strikes it and then returns to its original position. A particle of water moves in an *orbit,* or circular path, as the wave passes; the particle, too, essentially returns to its original position after the wave has passed. In deep water, when a wave moves across the water surface, energy moves with the wave; but the water, like the wheat, does not move with the wave.

At the surface, the diameter of the orbital path of a water particle is equal to the height of the wave (figure 14.2). Below the surface the orbits decrease in size until the motion is essentially gone at a depth equal to half the wave length. This is why a submarine can cruise in deep, calm water beneath surface ships that are being tossed by the orbital motion of large waves.

Surf

As waves move from deep water to shallow water near shore, they begin to be affected by the ocean bottom. A wave first begins to "feel bottom" at the level of lowest orbital motion—that is, when the depth to the bottom equals half the wave length. For example, a wave 100 meters long will begin to be influenced by the bottom at a water depth of 50 meters.

In shallow water the presence of the bottom interferes with the circular orbits and they flatten into ovals (figure 14.3). The waves slow down and their length decreases.

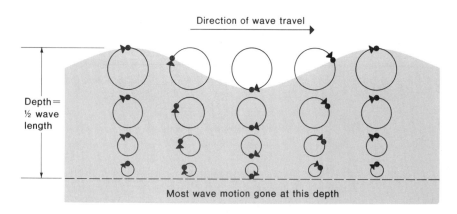

Figure 14.2 Orbital motion of water in waves dies out with depth.

Meanwhile, the sloping bottom wedges the moving water upward, increasing the wave height. Because the height is increasing while the length is decreasing, the waves become steeper and steeper until they break. A **breaker** is a wave that has become so steep that the crest of the wave topples forward, moving faster than the main body of the wave. The breaker then advances as a turbulent, often foamy, mass. Breakers collectively are called **surf.** Water in the surf zone has lost its orbital motion and moves back and forth, alternating between onshore and offshore flow.

Beaches

A **beach** is defined as a strip of sediment (usually sand, but sometimes pebbles, boulders, or mud) that extends from the low-water line inland to a cliff or zone of permanent vegetation. Waves break on beaches, and rising and falling tides may regularly change the amount of beach sediment that is exposed above water. A beach can be divided into the *foreshore* and the *backshore* (figure 14.4).

The **foreshore** of a beach is the zone that is regularly covered and uncovered by the rise and fall of tides. The steepest part of the foreshore is the **beach face,** which is the section exposed to wave action, particularly at high tide. Offshore from the beach face there is usually a **marine terrace,** a broad, gently sloping platform that may be exposed at low tide if the shore has significant tidal action. Marine terraces may be *wave-built* terraces constructed of sediment carried away from the shore by waves, or they may be *wave-cut* rock benches or platforms, perhaps thinly covered with a layer of sediment.

The upper part of the beach, landward of the high-water line, is the **backshore.** It is usually dry, being covered by waves only during severe storms. The backshore is made up of one or more **berms**—wave-deposited sediment platforms that are flat or slope slightly landward.

The sediment underlying both the beach face and the berm is usually sand, typically with a high percentage of quartz grains (because of quartz's resistance to chemical weathering). Other minerals may be present, particularly heavy minerals that lag behind as lighter minerals are carried away by waves, currents, or sea breezes. Heavy minerals are often dark in color ("black sands"). In some places waves have so concentrated heavy, metal-bearing minerals that they can be mined, as are the titanium-bearing beach sands in parts of Florida and Australia. Tropical beaches may be made largely of calcite grains from wave-eroded coral reefs. Some Hawaiian beaches are made of abraded fragments of volcanic rock. Gravel beaches are found in regions subjected to the high energy of large waves. The beach face of a gravel shoreline has a much steeper slope than the face of a sand beach. *Shingle,* a regional name for beach gravel, sometimes is re-

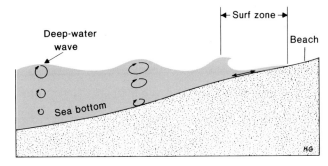

Figure 14.3 As a deep-water wave approaches shore, it begins to "feel" the sea bottom and to slow down. Circular water orbits become flattened and the wave peaks and breaks. In the foamy surf zone, water moves back and forth rather than in orbits.

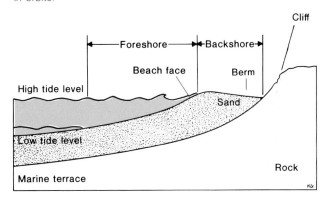

Figure 14.4 Parts of a beach

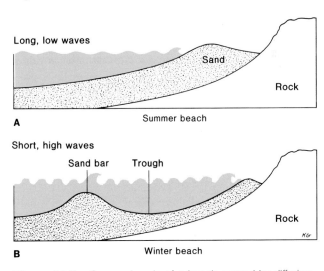

Figure 14.5 Seasonal cycle of a beach caused by differing wave types. *(A)* Summer beach. *(B)* Winter beach. Waves may break once on winter sandbar, then re-form and break again on beach face.

served for a distinctive gravel formed of coarse, flat pebbles.

In seasonal climates, beaches go through a summer-winter cycle (figure 14.5) because winter waves are usually bigger and closer together than summer waves. During summer, long, low waves wash sand from deeper water onto the beach and build out a wide berm. In winter, the short, high storm waves erode sand from the beach and narrow the berm. Offshore, in less turbulent water, the sediment settles to the bottom, building an underwater sandbar (more or less parallel to the beach) that serves as a "storage facility" for the next summer's sand supply. Each season the beach changes in shape until it comes into equilibrium with the prevailing wave type.

Some winter beaches can be dangerous because of high waves and narrowed beaches. Several beaches along the Pacific coast of the United States are nearly free of accidents in the summer, when they are heavily used, but are regularly marked by drownings in the winter as beachwalkers are swept out to sea by large storm waves.

Nearshore Circulation

Wave Refraction

If you have observed a beach, you may have noticed that long waves seldom come straight in against the shoreline. A wave crest usually arrives at an angle to the shoreline, and the wave breaks progressively along the shore. A wave breaks first at one end of the beach and then continues to break rapidly along the shoreline.

This angled approach of a wave toward shore can change the direction of wave travel. One end of the wave reaches shallow water first. This end of the wave "feels bottom" and slows down while the rest of the wave continues at its deep-water speed (figure 14.6). As more and more of the wave comes into contact with the bottom, more of the wave slows down. As the wave slows progressively along its length, the wave crest changes direction and becomes more nearly parallel to the shoreline. This process is called **wave refraction** (figure 14.6).

Longshore Currents

Although most wave crests become nearly parallel to shore as they are refracted, waves do not generally strike *exactly* parallel to shore. Even after refraction, a small angle remains between the wave crest and the shoreline. The result is that some of the water in the wave is pushed up the beach face toward land, and some of the water is pushed along parallel to shore.

Each wave that breaks at an angle to the shore pushes more water parallel to the shoreline. Eventually a moving mass of water called a **longshore current** develops parallel to the shoreline (figure 14.7). The width of the longshore current is equal to the width of the surf zone. The seaward

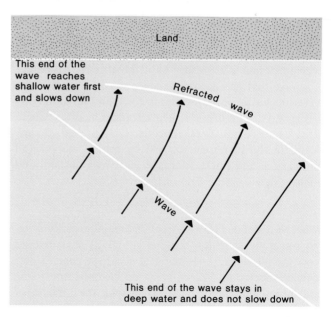

Figure 14.6 Wave refraction changes the wave direction, bending the wave so it becomes more parallel to shore.

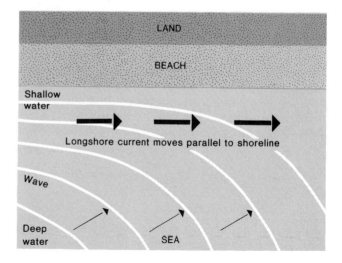

Figure 14.7 Waves approaching the shoreline at an angle are refracted, and a longshore current develops parallel to shore.

edge of the current is the outer edge of the surf zone, where waves are just beginning to break; the landward edge is the beach face. A longshore current can be very strong, particularly when the waves are large. Such a current can carry swimmers hundreds of meters parallel to shore before they are aware that they are being swept along. From a geological or engineering viewpoint, longshore currents are important because they are capable of moving great quantities of beach sediment along the shore.

Box 14.1
Rip Currents—A Common Cause of Drowning

Rip currents are narrow currents that flow straight out to sea in the surf zone, returning water seaward that breaking waves have pushed ashore. Rip currents travel at the water surface and die out with depth. They pulsate in strength, flowing most rapidly just after a set of large waves has carried a large amount of water onto shore. Rip currents can be important transporters of sediment, as they carry fine-grained sediment out of the surf zone into deep water.

Rip currents tend to develop locally in places where waves are not quite so high as the waves on either side. Rip currents that are fixed in position are apt to be found over channels or hollows on the sea floor, because depressions on the bottom reduce wave height. Complex wave interactions can also lower wave height, and rip currents that form because of wave interactions tend to shift position along the shore. Such shifting rip currents are usually spaced at regular intervals along the beach.

Rip currents are fed by water within the surf zone. They flow rapidly out through the surf zone and then die out quickly. Where waves approach parallel to a shoreline, feeder currents of equal strength develop in the surf zone on each side of a rip current (figure 14.8). However, when waves strike the shore at an angle and set up a longshore current, a rip current is fed by the longshore current, which gradually increases in strength as it nears the rip current. Rip currents are also found alongside points of land and manmade features such as jetties and piers because they can develop where an obstacle deflects longshore currents seaward.

Learning to spot rip currents at a beach is not difficult. Look for discoloration in the water where sediment is being picked up in the surf zone and moved seaward. Another sign is incoming waves breaking early within a rip current as they meet the opposing flow. The diffuse heads of rip currents outside the surf zone may be marked at the edge with foam lines. Even on very calm days rips can often be identified by subtle changes in

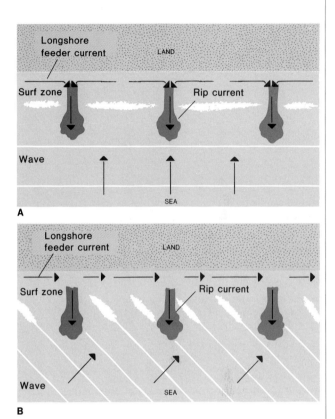

Figure 14.8 Rip currents and their feeder currents can develop regardless of the angle of approach of waves.

the water surface, such as a different pattern of water ripples or light reflection off the water.

Getting caught in a rip current and being carried out to sea can panic an inexperienced swimmer—even though the trip will stop at the outer edge of the surf zone as the rip dies out. A swimmer frightened by being carried away from land and into breaking waves can become exhausted by fighting the current to get back to shore. The thing to remember is that rip currents are narrow. Therefore, a swimmer can get out of a rip easily by swimming *parallel* to the beach instead of struggling against the current.

Surfers, on the other hand, often look for rip currents and paddle intentionally into them to get a quick ride out into the high breakers.

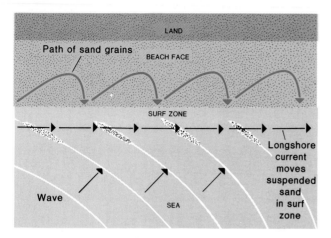

Figure 14.9 Longshore drift of sand on the beach face and by a longshore current within the surf zone.

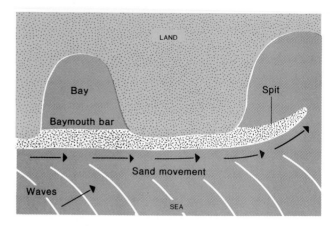

Figure 14.10 Longshore drift of sand can form spits and baymouth bars.

Longshore Drift of Sediment

Longshore drift is the movement of sediment parallel to shore when waves strike a shoreline at an angle. Figure 14.9 shows the two ways in which this movement of sediment (usually sand) occurs. Some longshore drift takes place directly on the beach face when waves wash up on land. A wave washing up on the beach at an angle tends to wash sand along at the same angle. After the wave has washed up as far as it can go, the water returns to the sea by running down the beach face by the shortest possible route; that is, straight downhill to the shoreline, not back along the oblique route it came up. (Wave run-up is known as *swash*, the return as *backwash*.) The net effect of this motion is to move the water and sand of the beach face in a series of arcs along the beach.

Much more sand is moved by longshore transport in the outer part of the surf zone, where the waves are breaking into foam. The turbulence of the breakers erodes and suspends sand from the sea bottom so that even a weak longshore current can move the sand in suspension parallel to the shoreline. The sand in the longshore currents moves in the same direction as the sand drift on the beach face.

Eventually the sand (and gravel) that has moved along the shore by these processes is deposited. Sediment may build up off a point of land to form a **spit,** a fingerlike ridge of sediment that extends out into open water (figures 14.10 and 14.11). A **baymouth bar,** a ridge of sediment that cuts a bay off from the ocean, is formed by sediment migrating across what was earlier an open bay (figures 14.10 and 14.12). Off the western coast of the United States a considerable amount of drifting sand is carried into the heads of underwater canyons, where the sediments slide down into deep, quiet water.

A striking, but rare, feature formed by longshore drift is a **tombolo,** a bar of sediment connecting a former island

Figure 14.11 Curved spit near Victoria, British Columbia.
Photo by D. A. Rahm, courtesy Rahm Memorial Collection, Western Washington University.

Figure 14.12 A baymouth bar of gravel has sealed off this bay (*left foreground*) in a lake in Glacier National Park, Montana.
Photo by E. C. Stebinger, U.S. Geological Survey.

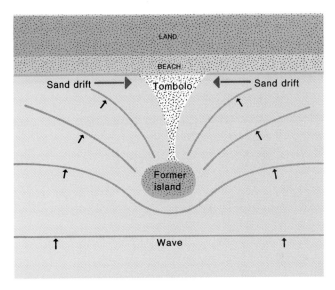

Figure 14.13 A tombolo, connecting a former island to the mainland, forms by sand drift resulting from wave refraction caused by the island. Some sand may also be supplied by erosion of the island.

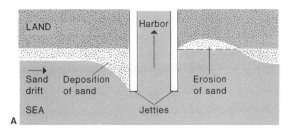

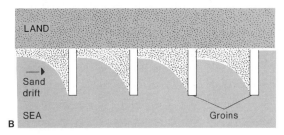

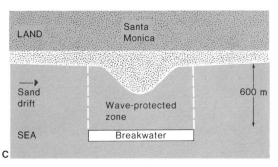

Figure 14.14 Sand piles up against obstructions and in areas deprived of wave energy.

or stack to the mainland. As shown in figure 14.13, waves are refracted around an island in such a way that they tend to converge behind the island. The waves sweep sand along the mainland (and from the island) and deposit it at this zone of convergence, forming a bar that grows outward from the mainland and eventually connects to the island or stack.

Human Interference with Sand Drift

Various types of human activities—notably the placement of structures above and below water levels—interrupt the flow of sand along a beach (figure 14.14). *Jetties,* for example, are rock walls designed to protect the entrance of a harbor from sediment deposition and storm waves. Usually built in pairs, they protrude above the surface of the water. Figure 14.14 shows how sand piles up against one jetty while the beach next to the other, deprived of a sand supply, erodes back into the shore.

Groins are sometimes built in an attempt to protect beaches that are losing sand from longshore drifting. These short walls are built perpendicular to shore to trap moving sand and widen a beach (figures 14.14 and 14.15).

Sand deposition also occurs when a stretch of shore is protected from wave action by a *breakwater,* an offshore structure built to absorb the force of large breaking waves and provide quiet water near shore. When the city of Santa Monica in California built a rock breakwater parallel to the shore to provide a protected small-boat anchorage, the lessening of wave action on the shore behind the breakwater allowed sand to build up there (figure 14.14), threatening eventually to fill in the anchorage. The city had to buy a dredge to remove the sand from the

protected area and redeposit it farther along the shore where the waves could resume moving sediment.

A beach attempts to come into equilibrium with the waves that strike it. The type and amount of sediment, the position of the sediment, and especially the movement of the sediment, adjust to the incoming wave energy. Whenever human activity interferes with one part of a beach system, particularly sand drift or wave action, the beach system responds by changing its configuration, usually through erosion or deposition in another part of the system.

Sources of Sand on Beaches

Some beach sand derives from the erosion of local rock, such as points of land or cliffs nearby. On a few beaches replenishment comes from sand stored outside the surf zone in the deeper water offshore. But the greater part of the sand on most beaches comes from river sediment brought down to the ocean. Waves pick up this sediment and move it along the beach by longshore drift.

What happens to a beach if all the rivers contributing sand to it are dammed? Although damming a river may be desirable for many reasons—flood control, power generation, water supply, recreation—nonetheless, when a

Figure 14.15 Sand deposition against groins.
Photo by Coastal Engineering Archives, U. of Florida.

river is dammed, its sediment load no longer reaches the sea. The sand that supplied the beach in the past now comes to rest in the quiet waters of the reservoir behind the dam. Longshore drift, however, continues even though little new sand is being supplied, and the result is a net loss of sand from beaches. Beaches without a sand supply eventually disappear. To prevent this, some coastal communities have set up expensive programs of draining reservoirs and trucking the trapped sand down to the beaches.

Coasts and Coastal Features

A beach is just a small part of the **coast,** which is all the land near the sea, including the beach and a strip of land inland from it. Coasts can be rocky, mountainous, and cliffed, as in northern New England and on the Pacific shore of North America; or they can be broad, gently sloping plains, as along much of the southeastern United States. Wave erosion and deposition can greatly modify coasts from their original shapes.

Classification of Coasts

Repeated attempts have been made to classify coasts in order to explain how coastal features develop, but no classification is really satisfactory. One approach divides coasts into emergent and submergent types. An *emergent coast* is one on which land formerly under water has recently become dry land, either by uplift of the land or a drop in sea level. A *submergent coast* is one on which previously dry land has been recently drowned, either by land subsidence or a rise in sea level. Many present-day

coasts are submergent as a result of the rise in sea level associated with the melting of the Pleistocene continental glaciers. Coasts also have been classified as *erosional or depositional,* or sometimes as *retreating or advancing.*

Classifications of coasts are not very helpful mainly because coasts by their nature tend to be changeable and inconsistent. A geologist, an oceanographer, or an engineer cannot classify a coast from a map or even from direct observation. To appreciate what is really happening on a coast, a scientist has to accumulate data over a period of time and, further, try to reconstruct the recent geologic history of the coastal region as a whole. In the section that follows, we discuss some coastal features and the processes that are influencing them without giving them any particular classification.

Coastal Landforms

An irregular coast with bays separated by rocky **headlands** (points of land) can be gradually straightened by wave erosion and deposition. Because wave refraction bends waves approaching such a coast until they are nearly parallel to shore, most of the waves' energy is concentrated on the headlands, while the bays receive smaller, diverging waves (figure 14.16). While rocky cliffs form on the headlands, the material eroded from them is deposited in the quieter waters of nearby bays, supplying sand (and shingle) for the broad beaches characteristic of such bays. **Coastal straightening** of an irregular shore gradually takes place through wave erosion of headlands and wave deposition in bays (figure 14.17).

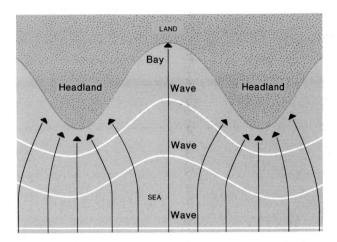

Figure 14.16 Wave refraction on an irregular coast. Shallow water slows waves off headlands while the same waves move faster through the deep bays. Arrows show energy concentrated on headlands, spread out in bays.

Wave erosion of headlands first produces **sea cliffs,** steep slopes that retreat inland by mass wasting as wave erosion undercuts them (figure 14.18). As headlands on irregular coasts are eroded landward, sea cliffs enlarge until the entire coast is marked by a retreating cliff. On some exposed coasts the rate of cliff retreat can be quite rapid, particularly if the rock is weakly consolidated. Sea-cliff erosion rates vary greatly from place to place and from year to year. Some of the sea cliffs north of San Diego, California are retreating at an average rate of nearly one meter per year. Many of these cliffs have at their very edges "ocean-view" homes, hotels, and condominiums. At Cape Cod National Seashore in Massachusetts, some sea cliffs composed of unconsolidated glacial deposits are also retreating at about one meter per year. Easily eroded cliffs on some coasts have retreated as much as 10 meters in a single severe storm. (Not all cliffs erode at these rapid rates.) At the base of sea cliffs are sometimes found **sea caves,** cavities eroded by wave action along zones of weakness in the cliff rock.

Seawalls of riprap (loose, broken stone) or concrete may be constructed along the base of retreating cliffs to prevent wave erosion. But they are difficult and expensive to build, and require considerable maintenance to prevent and repair storm wave damage.

Wave erosion produces other distinctive features in association with sea cliffs. A **wave-cut platform** (or *terrace*) is a horizontal bench of rock formed beneath the surf zone as a coast retreats by wave erosion (figure 14.19). The platform widens as the sea cliffs retreat. The depth of water above a wave-cut platform is generally 6 meters or less, coinciding with the depth at which turbulent breakers actively erode the sea bottom. **Stacks** are erosional remnants of headlands left behind as the coast retreats inland (figure 14.20). They form small, rocky

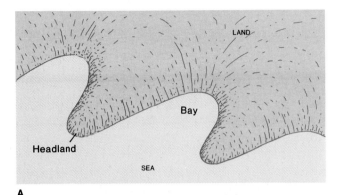

A

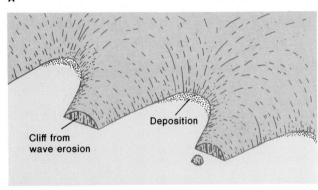

B

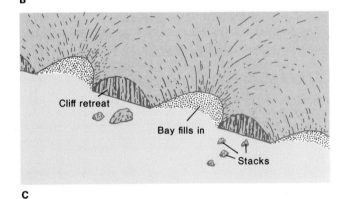

C

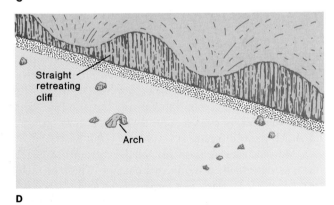

D

Figure 14.17 Coastal straightening of an irregular coastline by wave erosion of headlands and wave deposition of sediment in bays. Continued erosion produces a straight retreating cliff.

Figure 14.18 Retreating wave-cut cliff, Lake Huron, Sanilac County, Michigan.
Photo by C. H. Gordon, U.S. Geological Survey.

Figure 14.20 Stacks and an arch left behind as headlands retreated to the left. Retreating sea cliff and some bay fill are visible. Northern California.

Figure 14.19 Wave-cut platform exposed at low tide near Bolinas, California.

Figure 14.21 Arch near Pacific City, Oregon.
Photo by D. A. Rahm, courtesy Rahm Memorial Collection, Western Washington University.

islands off retreating coasts, often directly off headlands. **Arches** (or *sea arches*) are bridges of rock left above openings eroded in headlands or stacks by waves (figure 14.21). The openings are eroded through the headland in spots where the rock is weaker than normal, perhaps because of closely spaced fractures.

Marine terraces form just offshore from the beach face, as described earlier in this chapter. These terraces can be wave-cut platforms caused by erosion of rock associated with cliff retreat, or they can be wave-built terraces caused by deposition of sediment. Many coasts are geologically unstable, rising and falling in response to geologic processes deep in the earth's crust. *Uplifted marine terraces* are usually a sign of a coast that has been moved vertically upward (figure 14.22). They formed below the ocean surface and then were lifted above sea level by land movement.

Many coasts, particularly along the Atlantic Ocean and the Gulf of Mexico, are broad, gently sloping plains. Such coasts are often marked by **barrier islands**—ridges of sand that parallel the shoreline and extend above sea level (figure 14.23). These barrier islands may have been

Figure 14.22 Uplifted marine terrace, Point Reyes, California.
Photo by D. A. Rahm, courtesy Rahm Memorial Collection, Western Washington University.

Figure 14.24 High-rise condominiums built upon loose sand on a barrier island that is retreating landward, Ocean City, Maryland.
U.S. Geological Survey.

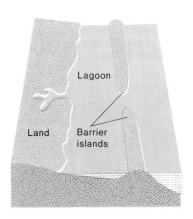

Figure 14.23 Barrier island off a gently sloping coast.

formed from sand eroded by waves from deeper water offshore, or they may be greatly elongated sand spits formed by longshore drift. The slowly rising sea level associated with the melting of the Pleistocene glaciers may have been a factor in their development. A protected lagoon separates barrier islands from the mainland. Because the lagoon is protected from waves, it provides a quiet waterway for boats. A series of such lagoons stretches almost continuously from New York to Florida, and many also exist along the Gulf Coast.

Some barrier islands along the Atlantic and Gulf coasts are densely populated. Atlantic City (New Jersey), Miami Beach (Florida), and Galveston (Texas) are examples of cities built largely on barrier islands. In some of these cities, houses, luxury hotels, and condominiums are clustered near the edge of the sea; many are built upon the loose sand of the island (figure 14.24). These developed areas are vulnerable to late-summer hurricanes that sooner or later bring huge storm waves onto these coasts, eroding the sand and undermining the building foundations at the water's edge.

During the glacial ages of the Pleistocene (chapter 12), sea level was 100 to 200 meters below its present level. The shallow sea floor near the continents was then dry land, and rivers flowed across it, downcutting valleys. As the great ice sheets melted, sea level began to rise, drowning the river valleys. These drowned river mouths, called **estuaries,** mark many coasts today (figure 14.25). As long, narrow arms of the sea, they may extend inland for many tens of kilometers. Fresh water from rivers mixes with the seawater to make most estuaries brackish. The quiet, protected environment of estuaries makes them very rich in marine life, particularly the larval forms of numerous species. Unfortunately, cities built on many estuaries are severely polluting the water and the bottom of the estuary. The poor circulation that characterizes most estuaries hinders the flushing away of this pollution.

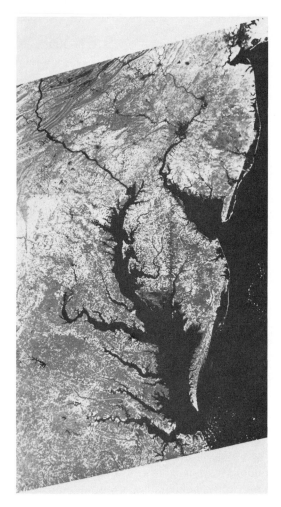

Figure 14.25 Estuaries along Atlantic coast of the United States. The large estuary is Chesapeake Bay; the smaller estuary to the north is Delaware Bay. Atlantic Ocean on far right.
NASA.

Wave refraction bends wave crests so that they tend to be parallel to shore. Few waves actually become parallel to the shore, and so *longshore currents* are set up in the surf zone.

Longshore drift of sand is caused by the waves hitting the beach face at an angle and also by longshore currents.

Deposition of sand that is drifting along the shore can form *spits* and *baymouth bars*. Drifting sand may also be deposited against jetties or groins or inside breakwaters.

Rivers supply most sand to beaches, although local erosion may also contribute sediment. If the river supply of sand is cut off by dams, the beaches gradually disappear.

Coasts are difficult to classify. They may be emergent or submergent, erosional or depositional, or advancing or retreating.

Coastal straightening by waves is caused by headland erosion and by deposition within bays.

A coast retreating under wave erosion can be marked by *sea cliffs*, a *wave-cut platform, stacks,* and *arches. Uplifted terraces* characterize emergent coasts.

Waves can form *barrier islands* off gently sloping coasts. A rise in sea level or subsidence of the land drowns river mouths and produces *estuaries*.

Terms to Remember

arch (sea arch)	longshore drift
backshore	marine terrace
barrier island	rip current
baymouth bar	sea cave
beach	sea cliff
beach face	spit
berm	stack
breaker	surf
coast	tombolo
coastal straightening	trough (of wave)
crest (of wave)	wave-cut platform
estuary	wave height
foreshore	wave length
headland	wave refraction
longshore current	

Summary

Wind blowing over the sea surface causes the formation of waves, which transfer some of the wind's energy to shorelines. Orbital water motion extends to a depth equal to half the wave length.

As a wave moves into shallow water, the influence of the bottom flattens the orbital motion and causes the wave to slow and peak up, eventually forming a *breaker* whose crest topples forward. The turbulence of *surf* is an important agent of sediment erosion and transportation.

A beach consists of a *berm, beach face,* and *marine terrace.* Summer beaches have a wide berm and a smooth offshore profile. Winter beaches are narrow, with offshore bars.

Questions for Review

1. Show in a sketch how longshore drift of sand can form a baymouth bar.
2. In a sketch, show how and why sand moves along a beach face when waves approach a beach at an angle.
3. How are summer beaches different from winter beaches? Discuss the reasons for these differences.
4. What would happen to the beaches of most coasts if all the rivers flowing to the sea were dammed? Discuss the reason for your answer.
5. What does the presence of an estuary imply about the recent geologic history of a region?
6. Describe how waves can straighten an irregular coastline.
7. Describe the transition of deep-water waves into surf.
8. Show in a sketch the refraction of waves approaching a straight coast at an angle. Explain why refraction occurs.
9. What is a longshore current? Why does it occur?

Questions for Thought

1. What might happen to a sandy beach located in a downdrift direction from a newly constructed seawall?
2. Waterfalls are uncommon where rivers enter the sea. Why?
3. Describe as many features as you can that are produced by a combination of: (a) wave action and mass wasting; (b) wave action and glaciation; (c) wave action and wind.

Supplementary Readings

Bascom, W. 1959. Ocean waves. *Scientific American* (August 1959). Offprint #828. San Francisco: W. H. Freeman.

————. 1960. Beaches. *Scientific American* (August 1960). Offprint #845. San Francisco: W. H. Freeman.

————. 1980. *Waves and beaches.* Rev. Ed. New York: Doubleday Anchor Books.

Davis, R. A., Jr., and R. L. Ethington. 1976. *Beach and nearshore sedimentation.* Tulsa: Society of Economic Paleontologists and Mineralogists Special Publication 24.

Inman, D. L., and B. M. Brush. 1973. The coastal challenge. *Science* 180 (4094): 20–32.

King, C. A. M. 1959. *Beaches and coasts.* London: Edward Arnold Ltd.

Komar, P. D. 1976. *Beach processes and sedimentation.* Englewood Cliffs, N.J.: Prentice-Hall.

Shepard, F. P. 1973. *Submarine geology.* 3d ed. New York: Harper & Row.

Shepard, F. P., and H. R. Wanless. 1971. *Our changing coastlines.* New York: McGraw-Hill.

15
Geologic Structures

Purpose

In previous chapters we have discussed how rock at the earth's surface is affected by erosional agents such as wind and water. We now shift our focus to changes in bedrock which are caused by powerful forces originating deep within the earth. In this chapter we explain how rocks respond to these tectonic forces.

The main purpose of this chapter is to help you recognize certain geologic structures, understand the forces that caused them, and thus determine the geologic history of an area.

There are some principles dealt with in chapter 8 that should aid you in interpreting the way structures in an area developed, and the sequence. The principles of original horizontality, of superposition, and of cross-cutting relationships are as important to structural geology as they are to determining relative time.

Subsequent chapters will require an understanding and knowledge of structural geology as presented in this chapter. To understand earthquakes, for instance, requires a knowledge of faults. To appreciate how major mountain belts and the continents have evolved (chapter 18) calls for a comprehension of faulting and folding. To understand plate tectonic theory as a whole (chapter 20) also presumes a knowledge of structural geology, for it was primarily to explain certain structural phenomena that plate tectonic theory was developed. Specifically, plate tectonics relates major geologic structures of the continents (chapter 18) to those of the oceanic crust (chapter 19).

Finally, an understanding of structural geology can help us appreciate more fully the problem of finding more of the earth's dwindling natural resources. Chapter 21 discusses the association of certain geologic structures with petroleum deposits and other valuable resources.

Structural geology in the broad sense can be thought of as the study of the architecture of the earth's crust, its deformational features, and their mutual relations and origins. For our purposes, **structural geology** can be de-

Figure 15.1 Folded and faulted sedimentary bedrock exposed in a roadcut near Palmdale, California.

fined as the branch of geology that is concerned with the shapes, arrangement, and interrelationships of bedrock units and the forces that cause them.

Tectonic Forces at Work

Stress and Strain

The relationship between *movements* within the earth and the resulting *deformation* of the crustal rocks is as follows. A movement of a large or small part of the crust creates **stress,** a force that acts on a body (or rock unit) and tends to change its size or shape. The adjustment of the rock unit to stress is called **strain,** the change of the rock in size (volume) or shape in response to stress.

The relationship between stress and strain may be illustrated by what happens when a car's bumper is crumpled in a collision with another moving vehicle (figure 15.2). When the two cars meet, both bumpers are stressed. The heavier the cars and the faster they are moving toward each other, the greater the stress. The result of the stress is that the bumpers crumple; in other words, they become strained.

The forces represented by the two cars moving toward each other are indicated in the figure by arrows. In this particular case the forces are said to be **compressive;** they tend to *shorten* the body (or bodies) involved. Both cars are a bit shorter because of the collision. Compressive forces are represented by a pair of arrows pointing toward one another ($\rightarrow \leftarrow$).

The opposite of compressive force is **tensional force,** which tends to *elongate,* or pull apart, a body. If you stretch a rubber band, you are applying tension to it. In our analogy with the crashed cars, the tow truck (figure 15.3) can bend or even pull off the rear bumper by exerting too much tensional stress. Tensional forces are represented by a pair of arrows pointing away from each other ($\leftarrow \rightarrow$).

Shear stress, a third type, is due to forces parallel but in opposite directions to one another. It causes strain *parallel* to the direction of the forces. If our two cars had not

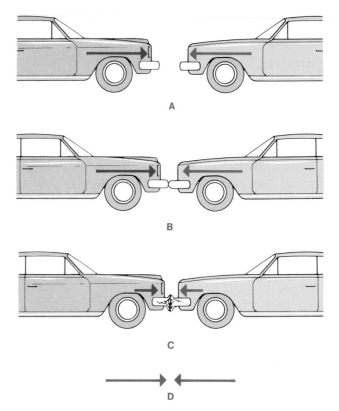

Figure 15.2 Colliding vehicles show the relationship between stress and strain. *(A)* Two cars moving toward each other. *(B)* Stress. *(C)* Strain. *(D)* Arrows used to represent compressive stress.

crashed head-on but had slid past each other, the strain would have broken door handles and outside mirrors and scraped the doors (figure 15.4). Shear stresses are represented by a pair of parallel arrows pointing in opposite directions ($\rightleftharpoons$).

In solid materials, stress can cause three types of strain or deformation: plastic, elastic, and fracture. In **plastic strain** a body is molded or bent under stress and does not return to its original shape after the stress is released. The crumpled car bumper is an example of plastic strain; so is the behavior of rocks during metamorphism or ice in glacier flow.

If a deformed body recovers its original shape after the stress is released, the strain is **elastic.** A mattress is deformed when a person is on it but recovers its original shape when the person gets out of bed. Rock is, to a certain extent, elastic. Parts of northern Europe and North America are still in the process of "bouncing back" to their former elevations after having been depressed by the weight of the last continental Pleistocene ice sheet.

In strain by **fracturing,** the body under stress cracks or breaks, as the name suggests. Brittle objects tend to fracture rather than to yield. Some rocks initially may yield elastically or plastically, but if stress is increased or maintained over a long period of time, they fracture.

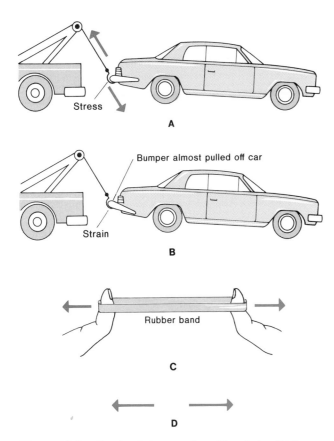

Figure 15.3   Tensional stress and resulting strain. *(A)* Tow truck with inexperienced operator attempts to pull car away by hooking tow cable onto rear bumper. *(B)* Bumper is pulled out of shape (if not pulled off) by tensional forces. *(C)* Rubber band being stretched. Tensional stress causes stretching (strain) of the rubber band. *(D)* Arrows used to represent tensional stress.

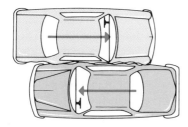

Figure 15.4   Shear stress as shown by two cars scraping past each other. The resulting strain is the deformation of the cars along their sides. Arrows indicate direction of forces.

Stress and Strain of Bedrock

Some scientists have described the crust of the earth as "mobile" or "restless" because bedrock is moving and being deformed in many parts of the world. Bedrock may be displaced suddenly during earthquakes. By contrast, much of the movement of rock within the earth's crust is continuous and very slow, at rates of less than a millimeter per year.

Figure 15.5   Displaced ditch near Hollister, California.

Compared with most geologic processes, the present-day movement of the crust in much of California is very rapid. A large slice of the coastal portion of the state is moving relentlessly northward relative to the rest of North America and has apparently been doing so for millions of years. Some of the movement is jerky and associated with earthquakes (chapter 16), but elsewhere it is essentially continuous and smooth.

Around Hollister, California, homes and buildings are being slowly torn apart because they straddle an active fault (figure 15.5). A **fault** is a fracture in bedrock along which movement has taken place. The fault that goes through Hollister (part of the San Andreas fault system) is one of several major cracks extending deep into the earth's crust that separate the northward-moving coastal portion of California from the rest of the state. Hollister residents whose homes "ride" the fault report hearing almost constant creaking, evidently due to motion along the fault. Yet the movement—about one centimeter per year (roughly the same rate at which a fingernail grows)—is slow enough so that walls can be patched with plaster as they crack.

Geologically rapid movement of the crust can be observed in young, developing mountain regions such as the California Coast Ranges, which have been forming throughout the Cenozoic Era (the last 65 million years). However, in other parts of the world the continents and sea floors are shifting very slowly up and down as well as moving laterally. Some of these motions can be detected by precise, repeated surveying.

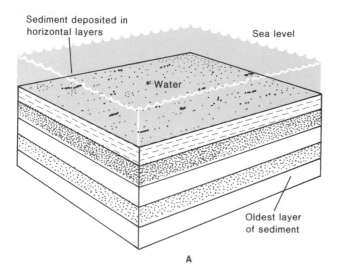

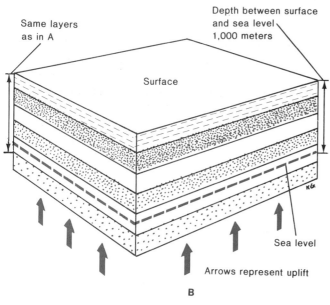

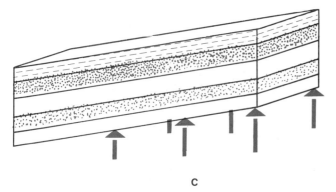

Figure 15.6 An area *(A)* during deposition of sediment below sea level and *(B)* after uplift has occurred. *(C)* Tilted layers of sedimentary rock, showing possible distributions of forces. The length of arrows indicates the relative strength of forces.

Labels in figure A:
Sediment deposited in horizontal layers
Sea level
Water
Oldest layer of sediment
A

Labels in figure B:
Same layers as in A
Depth between surface and sea level 1,000 meters
Surface
Sea level
Arrows represent uplift
B

C

Structures as a Record of the Geologic Past

Some geologic structures that give us clues to the past have been described in earlier chapters. Batholiths, stocks, dikes, and sills, for example, are keys to past igneous activity (chapter 4). In this chapter we are mainly concerned with types of structures that can provide a record of crustal deformation no longer active. Often we look for very old structures, once buried but now exposed by erosion.

The study of geologic structures is of more than academic interest. The petroleum and mining industries, for example, employ geologists to look for geologic structures associated with oil and metallic ore deposits. An understanding of geologic structures also is important in evaluating problems related to engineering decisions and environmental planning, such as the siting of dams or nuclear reactors, and even the building of houses.

Implications of Horizontal and Inclined Layers of Rock

Layered rocks generally are easier to interpret than non-layered rocks. Therefore, our descriptions are mainly of deformed sedimentary or volcanic layered rocks.

To determine what type of structure is present in an area, and to decipher the sequence of events that caused that structure, we need to find out what has happened to layered rocks since they were deposited as sediments or lava flows. According to the principle of *original horizontality,* layers of sedimentary rock (or lava flows) began as horizontal beds or strata. Where we find essentially horizontal, layered, marine sedimentary rock, such as that exposed in the walls of Grand Canyon, we conclude that the layers have been uplifted to their present position from beneath an ancient sea (figure 15.6). The uplifting has been uniform over a large area so that tilting is negligible. In this case the forces that caused the uplift can be shown with arrows of equal length, implying that the forces were equally strong throughout the area (figure 15.6*B*).

Where rock layers are observed to be inclined rather than horizontal, however, the forces responsible for the tilting must have been unequal—for example, as indicated by the arrows in figure 15.6*C*.

Geologic Maps and Field Methods

In an ideal situation, a geologist studying structures would be able to fly over an area and see the local and regional patterns of bedrock from above. Sometimes this is possible, but more often soil and vegetation conceal the bedrock. Therefore, geologists ordinarily use observations from a number of individual *outcrops* (exposures of bedrock at the surface) in determining the patterns of geologic structures. The characteristics of rock at each outcrop in an area are plotted on a map using appropriate symbols.

Figure 15.7 The sedimentary beds in the foreground are dipping to the left. View is looking in the direction of strike, which is parallel to the water line on the bedding surface exposed at the right side of the photograph.

With the data that can be collected, a geologist can make inferences regarding those parts of the area he or she cannot observe. The symbols on the field map, or rough draft, are thus converted into a **geologic map** of a given area. On such a map are plotted the distribution and nature of rock units, the occurrence of structural features (folds, faults, joints, etc.), ore deposits, and so forth. Sometimes surficial features, such as deposits by former glaciation, are included, but these may be shown separately on a different type of geologic map.

Anyone trained in the use of geologic maps can find considerable information about local geologic structures because standard symbols and terms are used on the maps and the accompanying reports. For example, the symbol ⊕ on a geologic map denotes horizontal bedding in an outcrop. Different colors or patterns on a geologic map may represent distinct rock units, such as *formations* (defined in chapter 6).

Strike and dip Where bedding has been tilted (figure 15.7), someone studying a geologic map of the area would want to know the extent and direction of tilting. By convention, this is determined by plotting the relationship between a surface of an inclined bed and an imaginary horizontal plane. You can understand the relationship by looking carefully at figure 15.8, which represents sedi-

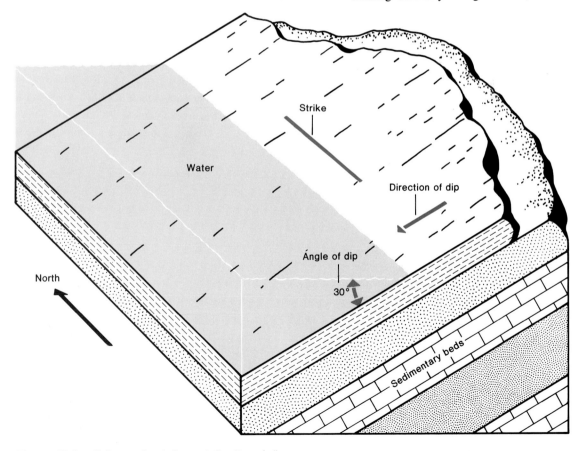

Figure 15.8 Strike, angle of dip, and direction of dip.

mentary beds cropping out alongside a lake (the lake surface provides a convenient horizontal plane for this discussion).

Strike is the compass direction of a line formed by the intersection of an inclined plane with a horizontal plane. In this example, the inclined plane is a bedding plane. You can see from figure 15.8 that the beds are striking from north to south. Customarily only the northerly direction (of the strike line) is given, so we simply say that these beds strike north.

Observe that the **angle of dip** is measured downward from the horizontal plane to the bedding plane (an inclined plane). Note that the angle of dip (30° in the figure) is measured within a vertical plane that is perpendicular to both the bedding and the horizontal planes.

The **direction of dip** is the compass direction in which the angle of dip is measured. If you could roll a ball down a bedding surface, the compass direction in which the ball rolls would be the direction of dip.

The dip angle is always measured at right angles to the strike; that is, perpendicular to the strike line as shown in figure 15.8. Because the beds could dip away from the strike line in either of two possible directions, the general direction of dip is also specified—in this example, west.

In addition to recording strike and dip measurements in a field notebook, a geologist who is mapping an area also draws strike and dip symbols on the field map, such as ⅂ or ⅃ for each outcrop with dipping or tilted beds. The long line of the symbol is aligned with the compass direction of the strike; the small tick, which is always drawn perpendicular to the strike line, is put on one side or the other, depending on which way the beds actually dip. The angle of dip is given as a number next to the appropriate symbol on the map. Thus, ³⁰⅂ indicates that the bed is dipping 30° from the horizontal. These symbols are used in figure 15.9, which is a geologic map that shows all the sedimentary layers striking northwest and dipping 30° to the southwest.

On a map the intersection of the two lines at the center of each strike and dip symbol represents the location of the outcrop where the strike and dip of the bedrock were measured. A specially designed compass, called a "Brunton" (after the inventor), is used by geologists for this purpose (figure 15.10). A Brunton compass contains a level and a device for measuring angles of inclination.

Beds with vertical dip require a unique symbol because they dip neither to the left nor the right of the direction of dip. The symbol used is ✕, which (assuming that the top of the page is north) indicates that the beds are striking northeast and that they are vertical.

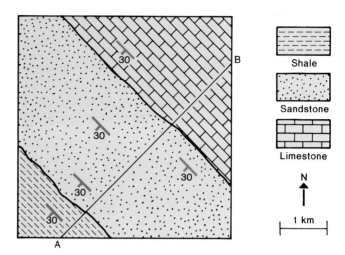

Figure 15.9 A geologic map of an area with three sedimentary formations. (Each formation may contain numerous individual sedimentary layers, as explained in chapter 6.) Beds strike northwest and dip 30° to the southwest.

Figure 15.10 Geologist determining the strike of inclined bedding using a Brunton compass. Beds dip into hillside—the left part of photograph.
Photo by J. R. Stacy, U.S. Geological Survey.

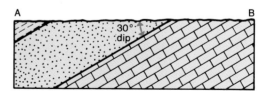

Figure 15.11 Geologic cross section for line *A–B* on the geologic map in figure 15.9.

Geologic cross sections A **geologic cross section** is a vertical representation of a portion of the earth. Geologic cross sections are very useful in aiding people to visualize geology in three dimensions. They are extensively used throughout this and many other geology books. Figure 15.11 shows a geologic cross section constructed between points *A* and *B* on the geologic map shown in figure 15.9.

Folds

Folds are bends in layered bedrock. Folded rock can be compared to several layers of rugs or blankets that have been pushed into a series of arches and troughs. Oftentimes folds in rock can be seen in roadcuts or other exposures (figure 15.12). When the arches and troughs of folds are concealed (or when they exist on a grand scale), geologists can still determine the presence of folds by noticing repeated reversals in the direction of dip taken on outcrops in the field or shown on a geologic map.

The fact that the rock is folded shows that it was strained plastically rather than elastically or by fracturing. Yet the rock exposed in outcrops is generally brittle and shatters when struck with a hammer. We can speculate that, at the time of folding, the rock layers must have been buried fairly deeply. Under such conditions of high pressure and high temperatures, the layered rock tended to yield plastically to stress and to bend rather than break. Rock also tends to bend rather than break if stress is applied very slowly. The marble slab shown in figure 15.13 sagged under its own weight during a period of over a hundred years, but rapidly applied stress, such as a hammer blow, would probably break it.

Geometry of Folds

The shapes and patterns of folds reveal much about the nature and extent of the forces of deformation that created them. Familiarity with the geometry of folds helps in understanding how to interpret them. Figure 15.14 illustrates the relationship between the arches (anticlines) and the troughs (synclines) of folds.

An **anticline** is an arched fold in which the rock layers dip away from the **axis** (or hinge line) of the fold. It can be visualized as an upfold; that is, one that opens downward. The troughlike counterpart of an anticline is a **syncline,** a fold in which the layered rock dips toward an axis. Think of it as a downfold opening upward. In the series of folds shown in figure 15.14, two anticlines are separated by a syncline. Each anticline and adjacent syncline share a **limb.** Note the axes on the crests of the two anticlines and bottom of the syncline. Similar axes would be underground at the hinge lines of contacts between any two adjacent folded layers. For each anticline and the syncline, the axes are within the shaded vertical planes. Each of these planes is an **axial plane,** a plane containing all of the axes of a fold.

Figure 15.12 Folded rock, Calico Hills, California.

Figure 15.13 Marble slab that has sagged under its own weight.
Photo by W. T. Lee, U. S. Geological Survey.

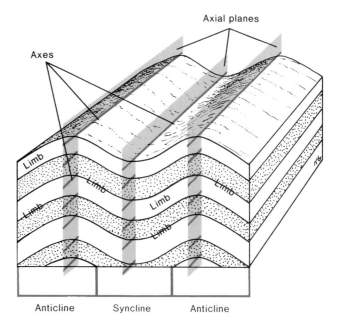

Figure 15.14 Two anticlines and a syncline.

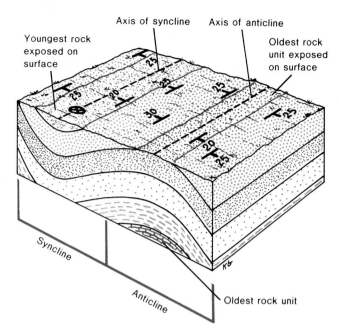

Figure 15.15 Folded rock. This view is a *block diagram*. Its top represents the land surface and its two visible sides are vertical cross sections. The surface has been eroded to a nearly horizontal plain. Side views are interpretations based on what the geologist notices on the surface.

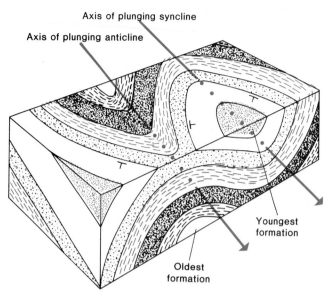

Figure 15.16 Plunging folds, anticline on left, syncline on right. The axes are at an angle to the block diagram, penetrating the surface and emerging from the front cross section.

It is important to remember that anticlines are not necessarily related to ridges nor synclines to valleys, because valleys and ridges are nearly always erosional features. In an area that has been eroded to a plain, the presence of underlying anticlines and synclines is determined by the direction of dipping beds in exposed bedrock, as shown in figure 15.15 (in the field, of course, the cross sections would not be exposed to view as they are in the diagram).

Figure 15.15 also illustrates how determining the relative ages of the rock layers, or beds, can tell us whether a structure is an anticline or a syncline. Observe that the oldest rocks are exposed along the axis of the anticline. This is because lower layers in the originally flat-lying sedimentary or volcanic rock were moved upward and are now in the core of the anticline. The youngest rocks, on the other hand, which were originally in the upper layers, were folded downward and would now crop out along the synclinal axis.

Plunging fold The examples shown so far have been of folds with horizontal axes. These are the easiest to visualize. In nature, however, anticlines and synclines are apt to be **plunging folds**—that is, folds in which the axes are not horizontal. On a surface leveled by erosion, the patterns of exposed strata (beds) resemble V's or horseshoes rather than the striped patterns of nonplunging folds (figures 15.16 and 15.17). However, plunging anticlines and synclines are distinguished from one another in the same way as are nonplunging folds—by directions of dip or by relative ages of beds.

Domes and structural basins A **dome** is a structure in which the beds dip away from a central point. In cross section, a dome resembles an anticline. In a **structural basin,** the beds dip toward a central point; in cross section, it is comparable to a syncline (figure 15.18).

Domes and basins tend to be features on a grand scale (some are more than a hundred kilometers across), formed by uplift somewhat greater (for domes) or less (for basins) than that of the rest of a region. In the central United States, Lake Superior overlies a large structural basin, and domes of similar size are found in other parts of the Middle West. Smaller domes have been located in the Rocky Mountains (figure 15.19).

A

B

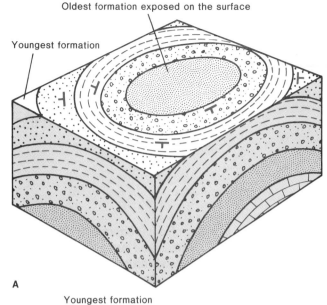

A

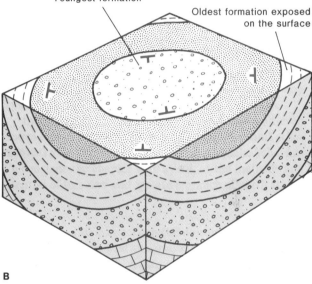

B

Figure 15.18 *(A)* Dome. *(B)* Structural basin.

Figure 15.17 Plunging folds. *(A)* Anticline in Wyoming plunging toward the upper left of the photo. The Bighorn River has cut a canyon through the anticline, exposing the cross section of the structure. *(B)* The "nose" of an anticline in Spain.
(A) from Rahm Memorial Collection, Western Washington University.

Figure 15.19 Dome near Casper, Wyoming. The ridges are sedimentary layers that are resistant to erosion. Beds dip away from the center of the dome.
Rahm Memorial Collection, Western Washington University.

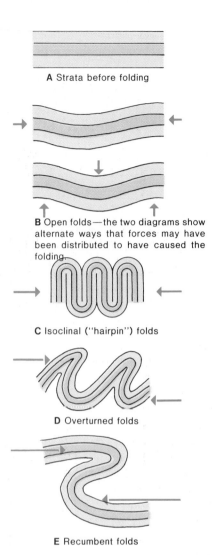

A Strata before folding

B Open folds—the two diagrams show alternate ways that forces may have been distributed to have caused the folding.

C Isoclinal ("hairpin") folds

D Overturned folds

E Recumbent folds

Figure 15.20 Cross sections of some types of folds and possible directions of stress implied by each. Intensity of forces involved is proportional to length of arrows. (A) Strata before folding. (B) Open folds—the two diagrams show alternate ways that forces may have been distributed to have caused the folding. (C) Isoclinal ("hairpin") folds. (D) Overturned folds. (E) Recumbent folds.

Interpreting Folds

Folds occur in many varieties and in any size. Some are studied under the microscope, while others may have adjacent axes tens of kilometers apart. Some folds may be a kilometer or more in height. Figure 15.20 shows several types of folds, each one revealing something about the stress that created the pattern. **Open folds** (figure 15.21*A*) have limbs that dip gently. All other factors being equal, the more open the fold, the less intense the forces that

A

B

C

Figure 15.21 Various types of folds. (A) Open fold in Death Valley, California. (B) Overturned folds in Antarctica. (C) Recumbent folds in the Canadian Rockies.

created it. By contrast, an **isoclinal fold,** one in which limbs are parallel to one another, implies intense compressive stress.

Overturned folds (figure 15.21*B*), in which limbs dip in the same direction, imply that compressive forces caused the upper part to override the lower part of the fold pattern. Looking at an outcrop in which only the

Box 15.1

Is There Oil Beneath My Property?—First Check the Geologic Structure

An "oil pool" can exist only under certain conditions. Crude oil does not fill caves underground as the term *pool* may suggest. Rather, oil simply occupies the pore spaces of certain sedimentary rocks, such as poorly cemented sandstone, in which void space exists between grains. Natural gas (being lighter) often occupies the pore spaces above the crude oil, while water (being heavier) is generally found saturating the rock below the oil pool (figure 15.22).

A *source rock,* which is always a sedimentary rock, must be present for oil to be formed. The sediment of the source rock has to include organisms buried during sedimentation. This organic matter partially decomposes into petroleum and natural gas. Once formed, the droplets of petroleum tend to migrate, following fractures and interconnecting pore spaces. Being lighter than the rock, the petroleum usually migrates upward, although horizontal migration does occur.

If it is not blocked by impermeable rock, the oil may migrate all the way to the surface, where it is dissipated and permanently lost for human

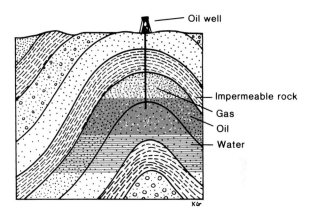

Figure 15.22   Anticlinal trap. Gas, oil, and water saturate permeable rock.

use. Natural seepage of petroleum exists both on land and offshore. Where impermeable rock blocks the oil droplets' path of migration, an oil pool may accumulate below the rock, much like helium-filled balloons might collect under a domed ceiling. For any significant amount of oil to collect, the rock below the impermeable rock must be porous as well as permeable. Such a rock, when it contains oil, is called a *reservoir rock.*

overturned limb of a fold is exposed, you would probably conclude that the youngest bed is at the top. However, the principles of *superposition* (chapter 8) cannot be applied to resolve top and bottom for overturned beds. You must either see the rest of the fold or find features within the beds that indicate the original top or upward direction.

Recumbent folds (figure 15.21C) are overturned to such an extent that the limbs are essentially horizontal. Note that the terms *syncline* and *anticline* (as used here) are not applicable to recumbent folds.

Fractured Rock

If a rock is brittle, or if the forces on it are exerted faster than it can bend to accommodate the strain, the rock fractures, commonly with some movement or displacement. If essentially no displacement occurs, a fracture or crack in bedrock is called a **joint.** If the rock on either side of a fracture moves, then the fracture is a *fault* (as defined earlier). Most rock at or near the surface is brittle, and so nearly all exposed bedrock is jointed to some extent.

Box 15.1 *Continued*

Another necessary condition is that the geologic structure must be one that favors the accumulation and retention of petroleum. An "anticlinal trap" is one of the best structures for holding oil. As oil became a major energy source and the demand for it increased, most of the newly discovered wells penetrated anticlinal traps. Geologists discovered these by looking for indications of anticlines cropping out on the earth's surface. As time went on, other types of structures were also found to be oil traps. Many of these were difficult to find because of the lack of telltale surface patterns indicating favorable underground structures. Figure 15.23 illustrates some types of traps other than anticlinal ones that might have a potential for oil production (unconformities and faults are described later in this chapter; sedimentary facies are described in chapter 6).

At present oil companies rely on detailed and sophisticated geologic studies of an area they hope may have the potential for an "oil strike." The petroleum industry also depends heavily on geophysical techniques (see chapter 17) for determining, by indirect means, the subsurface structural geology.

Even when everything indicates that conditions are excellent for oil to be present underground, there is no guarantee that oil will be found. Eventually an oil company must commit a million dollars or more to drill a deep test well, or "wildcat" well. Statistics indicate that the chance of a test well yielding commercial quantities of oil is much less than 1 in 10. As more and more of the world's supply of petroleum is used up, what is left becomes increasingly harder—and costlier—to find.

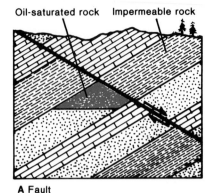

A Fault

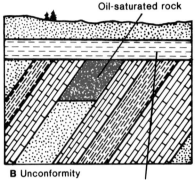

B Unconformity

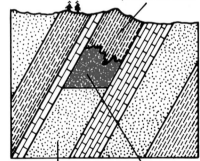

C Sedimentary facies

Figure 15.23 Other types of oil traps. *(A)* Fault. *(B)* Unconformity. *(C)* Sedimentary facies.

Joints

In discussing volcanoes (chapter 3), we described *columnar jointing,* in which hexagonal columns form as the result of contraction of a cooling, solidified lava flow. *Exfoliation* (sometimes called "sheeting"), a type of jointing caused by expansion, has been discussed along with weathering (chapter 5).

Parallel joints in bedrock can be seen in many places. Joints that are oriented in one direction, approximately parallel to one another, make up a **joint set.** More than one joint set may be present in the same outcrop. Figure

15.24 shows how compressive stress generally produces two joint sets that cut across each other and intersect the direction of stress. Tensional stress, by contrast, tends to produce a single joint set that is perpendicular to the direction of stress.

Geologists sometimes find valuable ore deposits by studying a joint system. For example, gold-bearing hydrothermal solutions may migrate upward through a set of joints and eventually cool, depositing quartz and gold in the cracks. Accurate information about joints also is important in the planning and construction of large en-

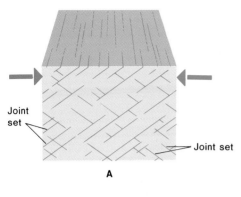

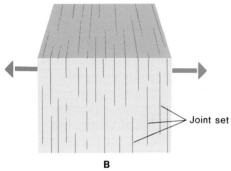

Figure 15.24 Joint sets. Arrows indicate directions of principal stress. *(A)* Two joint sets created by compressional stress. *(B)* Joint set created by tensional stress.

Figure 15.25 Jointed sedimentary rock (sandstone).

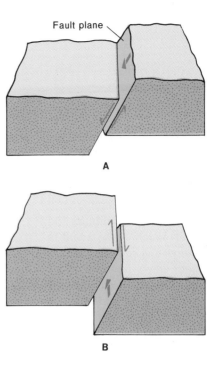

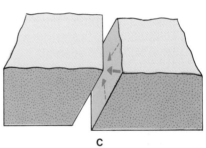

Figure 15.26 Three types of faults illustrated by displaced blocks. Heavier arrows show direction in which block to the left moved. *(A)* Dip-slip movement. *(B)* Strike-slip movement. *(C)* Oblique-slip movement. Dashed arrows show dip-slip and strike-slip components of movement.

gineering projects, particularly dams and reservoirs. If the bedrock at a proposed location is intensely jointed, the possibility of dam failure or reservoir leakage may make that site too hazardous.

Faults

Faults were defined earlier as fractures in bedrock along which movement has taken place. The displacement may be only a centimeter or may involve hundreds of kilometers. An active fault is generally regarded as one along which movement has taken place during historical time (these are the misnamed "earthquake faults"). Most faults, however, are no longer active.

The nature of past movement ordinarily can be discerned where a fault is exposed in an outcrop. The geologist looks for dislocated beds or other features of the rock that can show how much displacement has occurred and the relative direction of movement. In some faults a crack separates the two displaced sides. In others the rock has been broken or ground to a fractured or porous mass sandwiched between the displaced sides.

Geologists describe fault movement in terms of direction of slippage: dip-slip, strike-slip, or oblique-slip (figure 15.26). In a **dip-slip fault,** movement is parallel to

Box 15.2
Faults and Nuclear Power Plants

In the 1960s nuclear power was expected to provide most of the additional electrical energy needed for the rest of the century. The West Coast of the United States seemed ideal for locating future nuclear power plants for the following reasons. (1) Much of the coast is sparsely populated, so if a radiation leak were to occur, it would affect only a few people living near the power plant. (2) The urban centers requiring most of the electric power are close enough to the coast so that the costs of building power lines and transmitting electricity could be kept to a minimum. (3) The ocean water from the Pacific would provide an efficient means of cooling a nuclear reactor—a major consideration since two-thirds of the heat generated by a nuclear power plant is wasted heat that must be dispersed. Lastly, because of the mountainous coastline, power plants could be constructed out of reach of potential floods.

In spite of these advantages, problems have arisen at specific sites selected for the plants. Geologic studies of each site are always necessary to insure that there is no danger from landsliding and that the underlying material, usually bedrock, has the strength to support the structure.

Furthermore, a potential site must be carefully studied to be sure there are no active faults. The West Coast is one of the most tectonically active regions in the United States and includes many closely spaced faults, active and inactive. If a nuclear power plant were built on an active fault, even a minor amount of movement might rupture the nuclear reactor. To complicate matters further, determining whether a fault is active or inactive is seldom easy; evidence of fault motion in the recent geologic past must be found. Different government agencies define an active fault in different ways. For some, an active fault is one in which motion has occurred within the past 10,000 years; others extend the time limit to the past 100,000 years.

Most earthquakes are caused by fault movement (as explained in chapter 17). Federal regulations prohibit building a nuclear power plant within a quarter-mile of a known active fault. Moreover, before a nuclear power plant building permit will be issued, the entire earthquake history of the larger region must be carefully analyzed in order to insure that a more distant but exceptionally strong earthquake could not affect the plant.

In 1976 a nuclear power plant at Eureka, California was shut down because of concern about its safety in the event of an earthquake. The power company then spent $21 million strengthening it to comply with federal standards. In 1980 one of the strongest earthquakes in that region's history took place near the still shutdown power plant. Although the plant was undamaged, the power company dropped its plans to reactivate the nuclear reactor.

A nuclear power plant in southern California was completed and ready to be activated when new concerns about nearby active faults caused the government to withhold an operating permit. As of 1981 there was some doubt that the permit would ever be granted. The plant, which had cost over half a billion dollars to build, was being paid for by the area's electricity users despite the fact that they had not received a single watt from it.

Because of the concern about the safety of nuclear power plants, it seems likely that many nuclear plants originally projected for the West Coast will never be built.

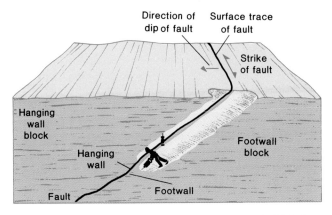

Figure 15.27 Relationship between the hanging wall block and footwall block of a fault.

the dip of the fault surface. A dip-slip fault implies *vertical* motion of the blocks of rock on either side of the fault. A **strike-slip fault** indicates *horizontal* motion, parallel to the strike of the fault surface. An **oblique-slip fault** has both strike-slip and dip-slip components.

Dip-slip faults Normal and reverse faults, the most common types of dip-slip faults, are distinguished from each other on the basis of the reative movement of the *footwall block* and the *hanging-wall block*. The **footwall** is the underlying surface of an inclined fault plane, whereas the overlying surface is the **hanging wall.** These old mining terms brought into geology are illustrated in figure 15.27. If you excavated a sloping mine shaft down dip, along the fault plane, your feet would be on the footwall as you walked down the tunnel, and you could hang lights on the hanging wall.

In a **normal fault,** (figures 15.28 and 15.29), the hanging-wall block has moved downward relative to the footwall block. The relative movement is represented on a geological cross section by a pair of arrows, because we cannot generally tell which block actually moved. As shown in figure 15.28, a normal fault may be caused by either vertical compressive stresses or horizontal tensional stress. Under the tensional stress, the downthrown hanging-wall block sags downward along the fault to compensate for the pulling apart of the rocks.

In a **reverse fault,** the hanging-wall block has moved upward relative to the footwall block. As shown in figure 15.30, horizontal compressive stress is the likely cause of a reverse fault.

A **thrust fault** is a reverse fault in which the dip of the fault plane is at a low angle to horizontal (figures

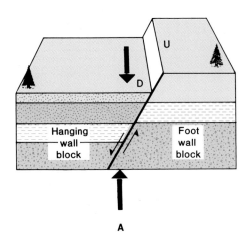

A

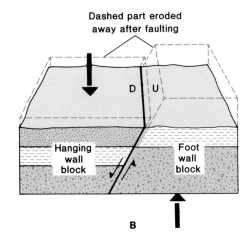

B

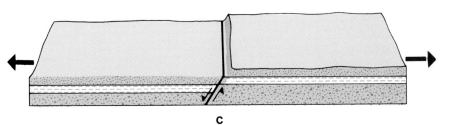

C

Figure 15.28 Normal faults. *(A)* Diagram shows the fault before erosion and the geometric relationships of the fault and how it might have been caused by vertical compressive stress. *(B)* Diagram shows the same area after erosion. *(C)* Diagram shows how tensional stress could cause a normal fault.

Figure 15.29 Normal fault.
Photo by D. E. Winchester, U.S. Geological Survey.

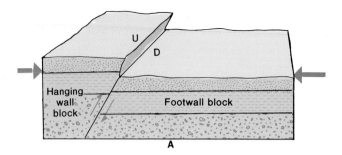

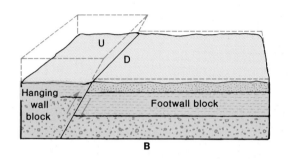

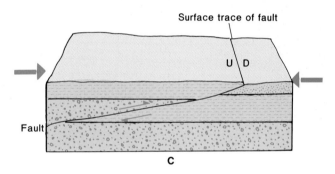

Figure 15.30 *(A)* A reverse fault. The fault is unaffected by erosion. Arrows indicate compressive stress. *(B)* Diagram shows area after erosion; dashed lines indicate portion eroded away. *(C)* Thrust fault. Note in the thrust fault that older rock layers have been placed over younger rocks due to the fault motion.

15.30C and 15.31). In some mountain regions it is not uncommon for the upper plate (or hanging-wall block) of a thrust fault to have overridden the lower plate (footwall block) for a distance of several tens of kilometers.

Strike-slip faults The displacement of strike-slip faults is either left-lateral or right-lateral; it can be determined by looking across the fault. For instance, if an active fault has displaced a trail (figure 15.32), a person walking along the trail would stop where it is truncated by the fault. If the individual looks across the fault and sees the displaced trail to the left, it is a **left-lateral fault.** A **right-lateral fault** is one in which displacement was to the right as seen from across the fault. Again, we cannot tell which side actually moved, so pairs of arrows are used to indicate relative movement.

Figure 15.31   Chief Mountain in Glacier National Park, Montana, is an erosional remnant of a major thrust fault. Precambrian rocks have been thrust over Cretaceous rocks. The trace of the fault is indicated by dashed lines where visible and dotted lines where it has been eroded away or is hidden behind a low hill.

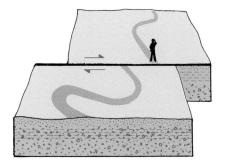

Figure 15.32   Strike-slip fault (right-lateral).

Unconformities

An **unconformity** is a surface that represents a *break in the geologic record,* with the rock unit immediately above that surface being considerably younger than the rock beneath. Most unconformities are buried erosion surfaces. Unconformities are classified into three types—disconformities, angular unconformities, and nonconformities—with each type having important implications for the geologic history of the area in which it occurs. Several types of unconformities were discussed in chapter 8 in illustrating how relative age can be determined.

Disconformities

In a **disconformity,** the surface representing missing rock strata is parallel to beds above and below it. Probably

Box 15.3
California's Greatest Fault—The San Andreas

Figure 15.33 Map showing the San Andreas fault.

The San Andreas fault in California is probably the best known geologic structure in the United States, but the geologists, seismologists, and other scientists who monitor it or who have studied it admit readily that our knowledge of its activity and its history is far from complete. Actually, the San Andreas is only the longest of a number of subparallel faults that transect western California and make up an extensive fault system. Shorter faults continue southward into Mexico, ending in the Gulf of California.

The San Andreas extends for a thousand kilometers through western California, slowly moving Los Angeles toward San Francisco (it is a right-lateral fault). Given a rate of movement now averaging about 2 centimeters per year, Los Angeles could be a western suburb of San Francisco (or San Francisco an eastern suburb of Los Angeles) in some 25 million years. Sudden movement along parts of the fault system has caused major earthquakes. During the 1906 earthquake that destroyed much of San Francisco, bedrock along the San Andreas fault was displaced as much as 5 meters. The amount of horizontal movement was determined by measuring the displacement of fences and other features that straddled the fault.

The fault itself is a zone of broken and ground-up rock, usually a hundred meters or more wide, and its presence is easily determinable throughout most of its length. Along the fault trace are long, straight valleys (formed by erosion and subsidence) that show quite different terrain on either side. Stream channels follow much of the fault zone because the weak, ground-up material along the fault is easily eroded. Locally, elongate lakes (called sag ponds) are found where the ground-up material has settled more than the surface of adjacent parts of the fault zone. The fault was named after one of these ponds, San Andreas Lake, just south of San Francisco. (figure 15.34).

Figure 15.35 Stream channel displaced by the San Andreas fault.
Photo by R. E. Wallace, U.S. Geological Survey.

One can visually follow the fault northward from San Andreas Lake into the southwestern suburbs of San Francisco (figure 15.34). There the fault zone is hidden by recently built housing tracts. Apparently the builders and residents have chosen to ignore the hazards of living on the nation's most famous fault.

Geologists have been unable to agree on the total displacement of the fault or on how long it has been active. Some believe movement began in the Mesozoic Era (over 65 million years ago); most feel that it began later, probably sometime in the Cenozoic Era. The difficulty in establishing an age for the inception of the faulting lies in finding clear evidence of displaced bedrock. What geologists would like to find, if it exists, is a rock unit that can be dated (by fossil fauna or other means) and that was formed in the fault zone (or its general area) just about the time faulting was beginning. This rock unit would have to be clearly identifiable on both sides of the fault zone as having been the same unit before displacement began.

Geologically young features that cross the fault, such as displaced stream channels (figure 15.35), are not uncommon. Similarly, ancient rocks that undoubtedly were there before faulting began are recognized as having been displaced. Many

Box 15.3 *Continued*

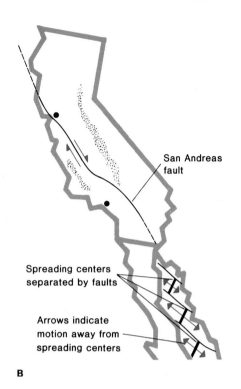

A

Figure 15.36 *(A)* Reconstruction of California and Mexico as it may have been before faulting. *(B)* Continuous opening of the Gulf of California creates motion along the San Andreas fault.
After Tanya Atwater, 1970, *Geological Society of America Bulletin.*

California geologists believe that the belt of granitic rock just west of the fault was once the southern continuation of the granitic batholiths of the Sierra Nevada (figure 15.36), which are more than 80 million years old. But these extremes tell us only that the age of the San Andreas is somewhere between approximately 80 million years and a few thousand years, when the stream channel in figure 15.35 carved its course across the fault.

The search for displaced features that would close the bracket between these two time extremes has yielded controversial results for two reasons. First, the age of displaced features may not be determinable. Second, there is a disagreement over which rock units were part of a single unit before faulting. A total displacement of about 500 kilometers seems reasonable to many geologists familiar with the geology of the fault. However, some arguments have been put forth in support of much less movement.

One hypothesis, based on plate tectonics, places the beginning of strike-slip movement for the San Andreas fault at about 30 million years ago. According to this hypothesis, the Baja California peninsula has split away from Mexico; as the Gulf of California widens, the block of crust west of the San Andreas fault is pushed continuously northward (figure 15.36).

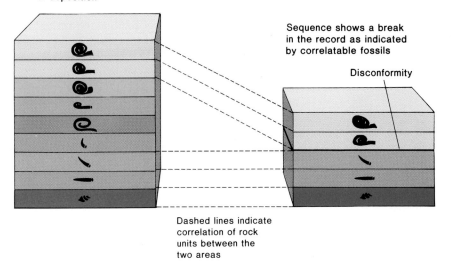

Sequence of sedimentary rock with complete record of deposition

Sequence shows a break in the record as indicated by correlatable fossils

Disconformity

Dashed lines indicate correlation of rock units between the two areas

Figure 15.37 Schematic representation of a disconformity. The disconformity is in the block on the right. Dashed lines indicate correlation of rock between the two areas.

what has happened is that older rocks were eroded away parallel to the bedding plane; renewed deposition later buried the erosion surface (figure 15.37).

Because it often appears to be just another bedding plane in a sequence of sedimentary rock, a disconformity is the hardest type of unconformity to detect in the field. Rarely, a telltale weathered zone is preserved below a disconformity. Usually the disconformity can be detected only by studying fossils from the beds in a sequence of sedimentary rocks. If certain fossil beds are absent, indicating that a portion of geologic time is missing from the sedimentary record, then it can be inferred that a disconformity is present in the sequence. Although it is most likely that some rock layers are missing, because erosion followed deposition, in some instances possibly neither erosion nor deposition took place for a certain amount of geologic time.

Angular Unconformities

An **angular unconformity** is an unconformity in which younger strata overlie an erosion surface on tilted or folded layered rock. It implies the following sequence of events, from oldest to youngest: (1) deposition and lithification of sedimentary rock (or solidification of successive lava flows if the rock is volcanic); (2) folding or tilting of the layers; (3) erosion; (4) renewed deposition on top of the erosion surface (figures 15.38 and 15.39).

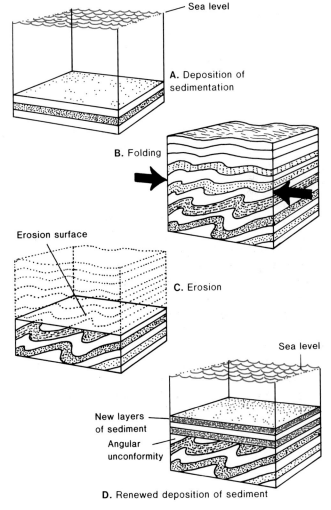

Sea level

A. Deposition of sedimentation

B. Folding

Erosion surface

C. Erosion

Sea level

New layers of sediment

Angular unconformity

D. Renewed deposition of sediment

Figure 15.38 Development of an angular unconformity. *(A)* Deposition of sediment. *(B)* Folding. *(C)* Erosion. *(D)* Renewed deposition of sediment.

Figure 15.39 An angular unconformity in Alaska.
Photo by D. J. Miller, U.S. Geological Survey.

If fossils are abundant in the rocks above and below an angular unconformity, the laws of *faunal succession* and *cross-cutting relationships* (chapter 8) can be used to determine the relative time of folding and tilting. For example, if the youngest fossils identified in the folded sequence are late Paleozoic and the fossils in the horizontal layer just over the unconformity contain middle Mesozoic fossils, then the folding must have occurred between late Paleozoic and middle Mesozoic times.

Nonconformities

A **nonconformity** is an unconformity in which an erosion surface on plutonic or metamorphic rock has been covered by younger sedimentary or volcanic rock (figure 15.40). A nonconformity generally indicates deep or long-continued erosion before subsequent burial, because metamorphic or plutonic rocks form at considerable depths in the earth's crust.

The geologic history implied by a nonconformity, shown in figure 15.41, is (1) crystallization of igneous or metamorphic rock at depth; (2) erosion of several kilometers or more of overlying rock (the great amount of erosion further implies considerable uplift of this portion of the earth's crust); (3) deposition of new sediment, which eventually becomes sedimentary rock, on the ancient erosion surface.

Figure 15.40 A nonconformity in Colorado in which Paleozoic sedimentary rocks overlie Precambrian metamorphic rocks.

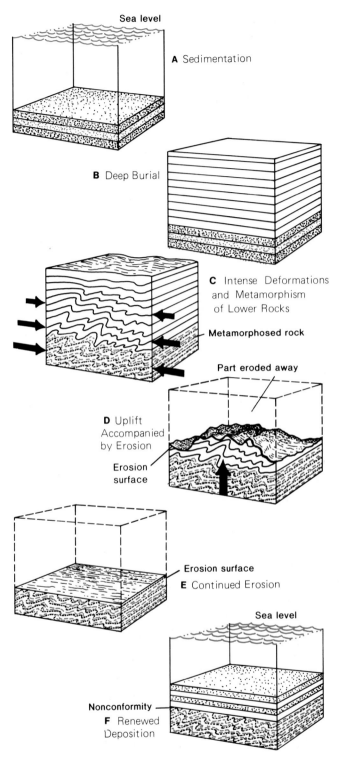

A Sedimentation

B Deep Burial

C Intense Deformations and Metamorphism of Lower Rocks

Metamorphosed rock

Part eroded away

D Uplift Accompanied by Erosion

Erosion surface

Erosion surface

E Continued Erosion

Sea level

Nonconformity

F Renewed Deposition

Figure 15.41 Sequence of events implied by a nonconformity underlain by metamorphic rock. *(A)* Sedimentation. *(B)* Deep burial. *(C)* Intense deformation and metamorphism of lower rocks. *(D)* Uplift accompanied by erosion. *(E)* Continued erosion. *(F)* Renewed deposition.

Summary

Present-day deformation of the earth's crust is studied by observing active faults. *Faults* and other geologic structures provide information about the nature and intensity of forces at work in the geologic past. Strained rock (changed in size or shape) records past stresses.

A geologic map indicates the structural characteristics of a region. *Strike* and *dip* symbols are used on geologic maps to indicate the attitudes of inclined surfaces such as bedding planes. The strike and dip of a bedding surface indicate the relationship between the inclined plane and a horizontal plane.

If rock layers bend rather than break, they become folded. Rock layers are folded into *anticlines* and *synclines* and more complex structures. If the axis of a fold is not horizontal, the fold is *plunging*. Older beds exposed in the core of a fold indicate an anticline, whereas younger beds in the center of the structure indicate a syncline. In places where folded rock has been eroded to a plain, an anticline may be distinguished from a syncline by whether the beds dip toward the center (syncline) or away from the center (anticline).

Fractures in rock are either *joints* or *faults*. A joint indicates that movement has not occurred on either side of the fracture; displaced rock along a fracture indicates a fault. In a *dip-slip* fault, bedrock is vertically displaced. In a *strike-slip* fault, which can be either left-lateral or right-lateral, horizontal movement has occurred. An *oblique-slip* fault involves both strike-slip and dip-slip motion.

Dip-slip faults are either *normal* or *reverse,* depending on the motion of the hanging-wall block relative to the footwall block. A reverse fault with a low angle of dip for the fault plane is a *thrust fault.* Reverse faults are thought to be the product of compressive horizontal forces, while normal faults are caused by vertical forces or horizontal tensional forces.

Unconformities are buried erosion surfaces that aid geologists in determining the relative sequence of events that took place in the geologic past. Beds above and below a *disconformity* are parallel, generally indicating less intense activity in the earth's crust. An *angular unconformity* implies that folding or tilting of rocks took place before or around the time of erosion. A *nonconformity* implies deep erosion because metamorphic or plutonic rocks have been exposed and subsequently buried by younger rock.

Terms to Remember

angle of dip
angular unconformity
anticline
axial plane
axis
compressive force
dip-slip fault
direction of dip
disconformity
dome
elastic strain
fault
fold
footwall
fracturing
geologic cross section
geologic map
hanging wall
isoclinal fold
joint
joint set
left-lateral fault
limb
nonconformity
normal fault
oblique-slip fault
open folds
overturned folds
plastic strain
plunging fold
recumbent folds
reverse fault
right-lateral fault
shear stress
strain
stress
strike
strike-slip fault
structural basin
structural geology
syncline
tensional force
thrust fault
unconformity

Questions for Review

1. On a geologic map, if no cross sections were available, how could you distinguish an anticline from a syncline?
2. If you locate a dip-slip fault while doing field work, what kind of evidence would you look for in order to determine whether the fault is normal or reverse?
3. What is the difference between stress and strain?
4. Name several geologic structures described in earlier chapters.
5. What is the difference between strike, direction of dip, and angle of dip?
6. Draw a simple geologic map, using strike and dip symbols for a syncline plunging to the west.
7. What sequence of events in the geologic past is implied by each of the three types of unconformities?
8. How does a dome differ from a plunging anticline?

Questions for Thought

1. What criteria would you use to distinguish a nonconformity from an intrusive contact of a stock?
2. Can a fault always be distinguished from an unconformity?
3. In what parts of North America would you expect to find the most intensely folded rock?
4. A subduction zone could be regarded as a very large example of what type of fault?
5. Why do some horizontal compressive forces cause thrust faults while others cause strike-slip faults?
6. What features in sedimentary or volcanic rock layers would you look for to tell you that the rock was part of the overturned limb of a fold?
7. Can you identify and name the various geologic structures shown in the figures in chapter 8 on geologic time?

Supplementary Readings

Anderson, D. L. 1971. The San Andreas fault. *Scientific American* (Nov. 1971). Offprint #896. San Francisco: W. H. Freeman.

Billings, M. P. 1972. *Structural geology*. Englewood Cliffs, N.J.: Prentice-Hall.

Iacopi, Robert. 1971. *Earthquake country*. Menlo Park, Calif: Lane Press.

Sumner, J. S. 1969. *Geophysics, geologic structures, and tectonics*. Dubuque, Iowa: Wm. C. Brown Company Publishers.

16
Earthquakes

Purpose

To provide background and help you gain a better understanding of the nature, origin, and causes of earthquakes, we discuss kinds of seismic waves; how earthquakes are measured and located; and some effects of earthquakes, such as ground motion and displacement, damage to buildings, and quake-caused fires, landslides, and tsunamis (huge ocean waves).

Earthquake activity is largely confined to a few narrow belts on earth. This distribution could not be accounted for adequately before the development of plate tectonics theory. How the concept of moving plates can explain this fundamental fact is examined here also.

Intriguing possibilities for the prediction—and even control—of earthquakes increase as geologists and other scientists gain new knowledge about earthquake behavior. We conclude the chapter with a look at the methods and potential of this new and tentative branch of earth study.

On April 18, 1906, at 5:12 in the morning, part of California slid abruptly past the rest of the state and caused a great earthquake. A visible scar 450 kilometers long was left where the earth was torn. Horizontal displacement of the land was as much as 5 meters. The quake, located on the San Andreas fault near San Francisco, shook the ground for one full minute.

Buildings toppled in San Francisco, and broken gas mains fed fires that raged for three days. Broken water mains hampered fire-fighting. The fires were finally extinguished when buildings were dynamited to create a firebreak. Terrified and homeless people moved to refugee camps set up in city parks. Looters were shot on sight. As the city gradually recovered from the shock of the devastation, it was found that 700 people had died, and $400 million (in 1906 dollars) of damage had been done. Perhaps 90 percent of the destruction was caused by the fires.

At 5:30 p.m. on March 27, 1964, southern Alaska was rocked by an earthquake that lasted for three minutes. Although the force of this earthquake was twice as strong as the 1906 San Francisco earthquake, loss of life and

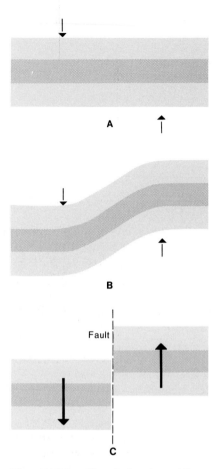

Figure 16.1 The elastic rebound theory of the cause of earthquakes. The view can be either horizontal or vertical. (A) Rock with stress acting on it. (B) Stress has caused strain in the rock. Strain builds up over a long period of time. (C) Rock breaks suddenly, releasing energy, with rock movement along a fault.

Causes of Earthquakes

What causes earthquakes? An **earthquake** is a trembling or shaking of the ground that is caused by the sudden release of energy stored in the rocks beneath the earth's surface. As described in chapter 15, great forces acting deep in the earth may put a *stress* on the rock, which may twist and bend or change in volume (*strain*). If you bend a stick of wood, your hands put a stress (the force) on the stick; its bending (a change in shape) is the strain.

Like a bending stick, rock can deform only so far and then it breaks. When a rock breaks, waves of energy are sent out through the earth. These are **seismic waves,** the waves of energy produced by an earthquake. It is the seismic waves which cause the ground to tremble and shake during an earthquake.

The sudden release of energy when rock breaks may cause one huge mass of rock to slide past another mass of rock into a different relative position. As you know from chapter 15, the crack between the two rock masses is a *fault*. This explanation of why earthquakes take place is called the **elastic rebound theory** (figure 16.1). It involves the sudden release of progressively stored strain in rocks, causing movement along a fault.

In the elastic rebound theory, earthquakes are associated with movement on a fault, and most earthquakes probably occur in this manner. Some, however, are not connected with faults or elastic rebound. Volcanic activity can cause earthquakes as magma forcibly fills underground chambers. Explosive eruptions can also cause earthquakes. The brittle behavior of rock assumed in the elastic rebound theory is characteristic only of rocks near the earth's surface. Rocks at depth are subject to increased temperature and pressure, which tend to reduce brittleness. Thus it is possible that deep earthquakes are caused by some as yet unknown process, different from elastic rebound.

Seismic Waves

The point within the earth where seismic waves originate is called the **focus** of the earthquake (figure 16.2). This is the center of the earthquake, generally at or near the greatest amount of movement on a fault. The point on the earth's surface directly above the focus is the **epicenter.**

Two types of seismic waves radiate outward from the earthquake focus. **Body waves** are seismic waves that travel through the earth's interior, spreading outward from the focus in all directions, like sound waves moving through air. **Surface waves** are seismic waves that travel on the earth's surface away from the epicenter, like water waves spreading out from a pebble thrown into a pond. Rock movement associated with seismic surface waves dies out with depth into the earth, just as water movement in waves on the ocean dies out with depth.

property was relatively low because of Alaska's small population—15 people died as a direct result of the shaking, and damage amounted to slightly over $300 million (in 1964 dollars). The tremor was felt over an area of more than a million square kilometers, and major damage occurred over an area greater than 100,000 square kilometers. A section of the earth's surface 50 kilometers across and 200 kilometers long was raised as much as 13 meters, and a similar block of land sank 1 to 2 meters. Horizontal movement was slight. In Anchorage, 150 kilometers from the center of the earthquake, landslides wrecked parts of the city. The greatest loss of life was caused by large sea waves generated by land movement associated with the earthquake—almost 100 people drowned in Alaska, and a few people as far away as Oregon and northern California.

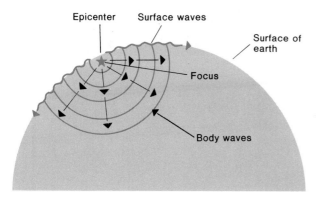

Figure 16.2 Earthquake focus, epicenter, and seismic waves.

A. P wave

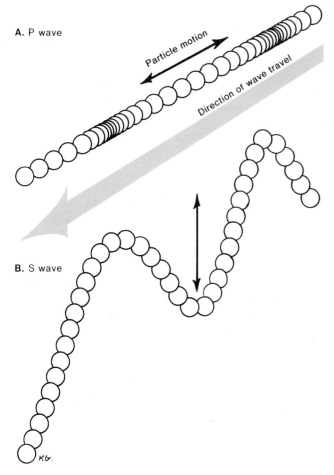

B. S wave

Figure 16.3 Particle motion in (*A*) a P wave and (*B*) an *S* wave.

There are two main types of body waves, both shown in figure 16.3. A *P* **wave** is a compressional (or longitudinal) wave in which rock vibrates *parallel* to the direction of wave propagation; that is, in the same direction as the waves are moving. Because it is a very fast wave (traveling through surface rocks at speeds of 4 to 7 kilometers per second), a *P* wave is the first (or *primary*) wave to arrive

at a recording station following an earthquake. The second type of body wave is called an *S* **wave** (*secondary*) and is a slower, transverse wave that travels at 2–5 kilometers per second. An *S* wave is propagated by a shearing motion much like that in a stretched, shaken rope. The rock vibrates *perpendicular* to the direction of wave propagation; that is, crosswise to the direction the waves are moving. Both *P* waves and *S* waves pass easily through solid rock. A *P* wave can also pass through a fluid (gas or liquid), but an *S* wave cannot. (We will return to this important fact in discussing the earth's interior in chapter 17.)

Surface waves, the slowest waves set off by quakes, are known as *L* **waves** (*long*). Surface waves in general cause more property damage than do body waves because the large *L* waves produce more ground movement and travel more slowly, so they take longer to pass.

Locating and Measuring Earthquakes

Seismographs and Seismograms

The invention of instruments that could accurately record seismic waves was an important scientific advance. This breakthrough enabled those studying earthquake phenomena to measure objectively the amount of ground motion and, eventually, to pinpoint the location of the disturbance.

Fundamental to this study is the **seismometer,** an instrument designed to detect seismic waves. The principle of the seismometer involves keeping a heavy suspended mass as motionless as possible—suspending it by springs or hanging it as a pendulum from the frame of the instrument (figure 16.4). When the ground moves, the frame of the instrument moves with it. However, the inertia of the heavy mass suspended inside keeps the mass motionless so that it acts as a point of reference to determine the amount of ground motion.

A seismometer by itself cannot record the motion that it measures. A **seismograph** is a seismometer with a recording device that produces a permanent record of earth motion, usually in the form of a wiggly line drawn on a moving strip of paper (figure 16.5). The paper record of earth vibration is called a **seismogram.**

A network of seismograph stations is maintained all over the world to record and study earthquakes (and nuclear bomb explosions). Within minutes after an earthquake occurs, distant seismographs begin to pick up seismic waves. A large earthquake can be detected by seismographs all over the world.

Because the different types of seismic waves travel at different speeds, they arrive at a seismograph station in a definite order, first the *P* waves, then the *S* waves, and finally the *L* waves. (Not all seismograph stations receive all three waves, as you will see in chapter 17.) These three different waves can be distinguished on the paper seis-

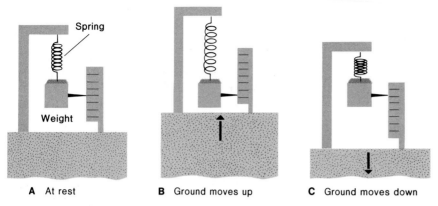

Spring

Weight

A At rest **B** Ground moves up **C** Ground moves down

Figure 16.4 A simple seismometer. The indicator needle moves on the scale as ground motion stretches and compresses a spring. Frame and scale move with the ground. Inertia of the weight keeps it relatively motionless.

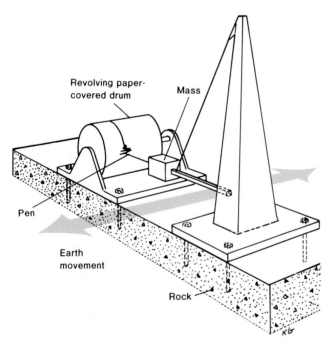

Revolving paper-covered drum

Mass

Pen

Earth movement

Rock

Figure 16.5 Modern seismographs record earth motion on moving strips of paper.

mograms. By analyzing these seismograms, geologists can learn a great deal about an earthquake, including its location and size.

Determining the Location of an Earthquake

P, S, and *L* waves all start out from an earthquake at essentially the same time. As they travel away from the quake, the three types of waves gradually become separated because they are traveling at different speeds. On a seismogram from a station close to the earthquake, the first arrival of the *P* wave is separated from the first arrival of the *S* wave by a short distance on the paper record; the

first *S* wave, similarly, is separated a short distance from the first *L* wave (figure 16.6). At a recording station far from the earthquake, however, the first arrivals of these waves will be recorded much farther apart on the seismogram. The greater the distance the seismic waves travel, the more they are separated on the seismograms, and the longer the time intervals between the arrivals of *P* and *S* waves and of *S* and *L* waves.

Because the time intervals between the first arrivals of *P, S,* and *L* waves increase with distance from the focus of an earthquake, these intervals can be used to determine the distance from the seismograph station to a quake. The increase in time intervals is regular with increasing distance for several thousand kilometers and so can be graphed in a **travel-time curve,** which plots seismic-wave arrival time against distance (figure 16.7).

In practice, a station records the three waves from a quake, then matches the intervals between the waves to a standard travel-time curve. By reading directly from the graph, a station may determine, for example, that an earthquake had occurred 5,500 kilometers away. This determination can often be made very rapidly, even while the ground is still trembling from the quake.

A single station can determine only the distance to a quake, not the direction. A circle can be drawn on a globe with the center of the circle being the station and its radius the distance to the quake (figure 16.8). The scientists at the station would then know that the quake must have occurred somewhere on that circle, but from the information they have recorded, they would not be able to tell exactly where. With information from other stations, however, they can pinpoint the location of the quake. If three or more stations have determined the distance to a single quake, then a circle can be drawn for each station. If this is done on a global map, the intersection of the circles locates the quake.

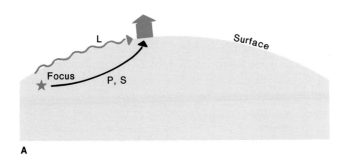

A

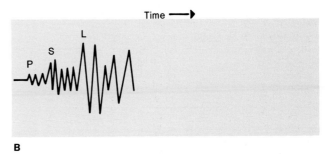

B

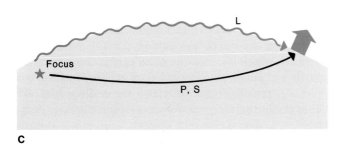

C

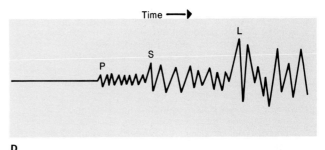

D

Figure 16.6 Intervals between *P*, *S*, and *L* waves increase with distance from the focus. (*A*) Station near focus. (*B*) Seismogram. (*C*) Station far from focus. (*D*) Seismogram.

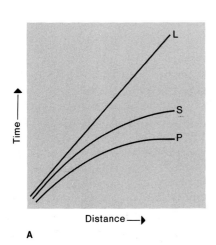

A

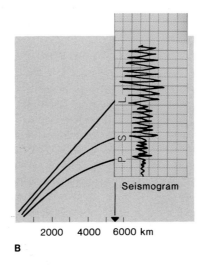

B

Figure 16.7 (*A*) A travel-time curve. (*B*) Matching a seismogram to a travel-time curve. This earthquake occurred 5,500 kilometers away.

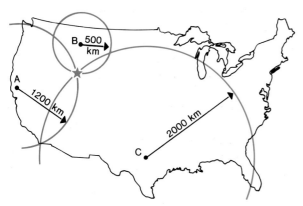

Figure 16.8 Locating an earthquake. The distance from each of three stations (*A*, *B*, *C*) is determined from seismograms and travel-time curves. Each distance is used for the radius of a circle about the station. The star shows the location of the earthquake, where the three circles intersect.

Table 16.1

Percentage of Total Quake Energy

Shallow focus	0–70 km deep	85
Intermediate focus	70–350 km	12
Deep focus	350–700 km	3

Table 16.2

Modified Mercalli Intensity Scale of 1931 (Abridged)

I. Not felt except by a very few under especially favorable circumstances.

II. Felt only by a few persons at rest, especially on upper floors of buildings. Delicately suspended objects may swing.

III. Felt quite noticeably indoors, especially on upper floors of buildings, but many people do not recognize it as an earthquake. Standing motor cars may rock slightly. Vibration like passing of truck. Duration estimated.

IV. During the day felt indoors by many, outdoors by few. At night some awakened. Dishes, windows, doors disturbed; walls made cracking sound. Sensation like heavy truck striking building. Standing motor cars rocked noticeably.

V. Felt by nearly everyone; many awakened. Some dishes, windows, etc., broken; a few instances of cracked plaster; unstable objects overturned. Disturbance of trees, poles and other tall objects sometimes noticed. Pendulum clocks may stop.

VI. Felt by all; many frightened and run outdoors. Some heavy furniture moved; a few instances of fallen plaster or damaged chimneys. Damage slight.

VII. Everybody runs outdoors. Damage *negligible* in buildings of good design and construction; *slight* to moderate in well-built ordinary structures; *considerable* in poorly built or badly designed structures; some chimneys broken. Noticed by persons driving motor cars.

VIII. Damage *slight* in specially designed structures; *considerable* in ordinary substantial buildings with partial collapse; *great* in poorly built structures. Panel walls thrown out of frame structures. Fall of chimneys, factory stacks, columns, monuments, walls. Heavy furniture overturned. Sand and mud ejected in small amounts. Changes in well water. Persons driving motor cars disturbed.

IX. Damage *considerable* in specially designed structures; well designed frame structures thrown out of plumb; *great* in substantial buildings, with partial collapse. Buildings shifted off foundations. Ground cracked conspicuously. Underground pipes broken.

X. Some well-built wooden structures destroyed; most masonry and frame structures destroyed with foundations; ground badly cracked. Rails bent. Landslides considerable from river banks and steep slopes. Shifted sand and mud. Water splashed (slopped) over banks.

XI. Few, if any, (masonry) structures remain standing. Bridges destroyed. Broad fissures in ground. Underground pipe lines completely out of service. Earth slumps and land slips in soft ground. Rails bent greatly.

XII. Damage total. Waves seen on ground surface. Lines of sight and level distorted. Objects thrown upward into the air.

Analyses of seismograms can also indicate at what depth beneath the surface the quake occurred. Most earthquakes occur relatively close to the earth's surface, although a few occur much deeper. The maximum **depth of focus**—the distance between focus and epicenter—for earthquakes seems to be 700 kilometers. Quakes are classified into three groups according to their depth of focus, as shown in table 16.1. Note that intermediate- and deep-focus earthquakes combined account for only 15 percent of the total quake energy released.

Earthquake Strength

The strength (or size) of earthquakes is measured in two ways. One method is to find out how much and what kind of damage the quake has caused. This determines the **intensity,** which is a measure of an earthquake's effect on people and buildings. Intensities are expressed as Roman numerals ranging from I to XII on the **modified Mercalli scale** (table 16.2); higher numbers indicate greater damage.

Using intensity as a measure of earthquake strength has a number of drawbacks, although intensities are widely reported at earthquake locations throughout the world. Because damage generally lessens with distance from a quake's epicenter, different locations report different intensities for the same earthquake. Moreover, damage to buildings and other structures depends greatly on the type of geologic material on which a structure was built as well as the type of construction. Houses built on solid rock are normally damaged far less than houses built upon loose sediment, such as delta mud or bay fill. Intensity maps can be drawn for a single earthquake to show the approximate damage over a wide region (figure 16.9). But such maps cannot be drawn for uninhabited areas (the central ocean, for instance), and so not all quakes can be assigned intensities. The one big advantage of intensity ratings is that no instruments are required for making the determinations.

The second method of measuring the strength of a quake is to calculate the amount of energy released at the earthquake's focus. In practice this is done by measuring the height (amplitude) of one of the wiggles on a seismogram. This method is commonly used in the United States. The larger an earthquake, the more the ground vibrates. After measuring a specific wave on a seismogram, and correcting for the type of seismograph and distance from the quake, scientists can assign a number called the **magnitude.** It is a measure of the energy released during the earthquake. The **Richter scale** (table

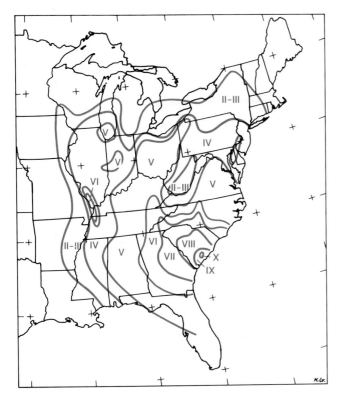

Figure 16.9 Zones of different intensity from the 1886 Charleston, South Carolina earthquake.
U.S. Geological Survey.

Table 16.3
Richter Scale magnitudes.

Magnitude		Number Per Year (World)
2	Just Felt	more than 100,000
4.5	Damage Begins	a few 1,000
7	"Major"	16 to 18
8	"Great"	1 or 2
8.6	Maximum Recorded	

Some Representative Magnitudes			Revised magnitudes (Kanamori, 1977)
1906	San Francisco	8.25	7.9
1960	Chile	8.5	9.5
1964	Alaska	8.6	9.2
1970	Peru	7.75	7.9
1971	San Fernando Valley, Cal.	6.4	
1972	Nicaragua	6.2	
1976	Guatemala	7.9	
1976	China	7.6	7.5
1977	Romania	7.2	

16.3) is a numerical scale of magnitudes from 0 to 8.6, with higher numbers indicating larger earthquakes. The largest quake measured so far is 8.6, but because larger quakes might be measured in the future, 8.6 is not the upper limit of the Richter scale. It seems probable, however, that values near 9 represent a limit of elastic strength beyond which rocks will break; earthquakes larger than magnitude 9 are therefore unlikely.

In 1977 a geophysicist named Kanamori revised the Richter magnitudes for very large earthquakes, using such factors as fault length and displacement to calculate energy released. Some of Kanamori's magnitudes, shown in table 16.3, exceed 9.0. We use Richter magnitudes throughout the book, not the revised magnitudes of Kanamori.

Because the Richter scale is logarithmic, the difference between two consecutive whole numbers on the scale means an increase of 10 times in the amplitude of the earth's vibrations. It has been estimated that a tenfold increase in the size of the earth vibrations is caused by an increase of about 31.5 times in terms of energy. A quake of magnitude 5, for example, releases 31.5 times more energy than one of magnitude 4. A magnitude 6 quake is almost 1,000 times (31.5×31.5) more powerful in terms of energy released than a magnitude 4 quake.

Although a seismograph is required to measure magnitude, this measure has many advantages over intensity as an indicator of earthquake strength. A worldwide network of standard seismograph stations now makes determination of magnitude a routine matter; and the press reports Richter-scale numbers for all earthquakes of interest to the United States. A single magnitude number can be assigned to a single earthquake, whereas intensity varies for a single earthquake, depending on local damage. Magnitudes can be reported for all quakes, even those in distant uninhabited areas where no property is harmed.

Earthquakes in the United States

Figure 16.10*A* shows the locations of all moderate-to-large earthquakes that occurred in the United States through 1970 (small quakes, which are very common, have been omitted). Note that only a few localities are relatively earthquake-free. Nearly all parts of the United States are subject to earthquakes, although the quakes in some regions are seldom destructive.

Figure 16.10*B* leaves out moderate earthquakes and shows only large, destructive quakes in the United States through 1970. Note that most of the large quakes occur in the western states, generally along well-known faults.

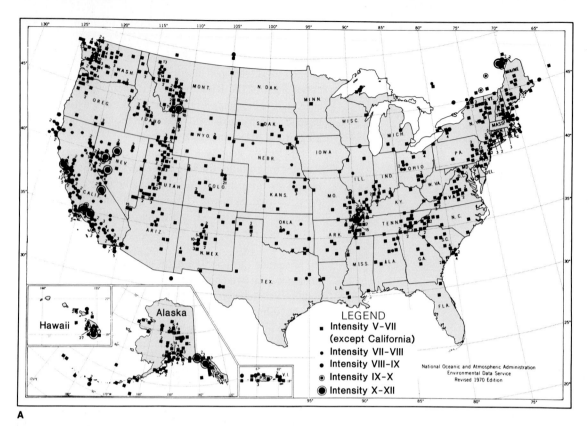

A

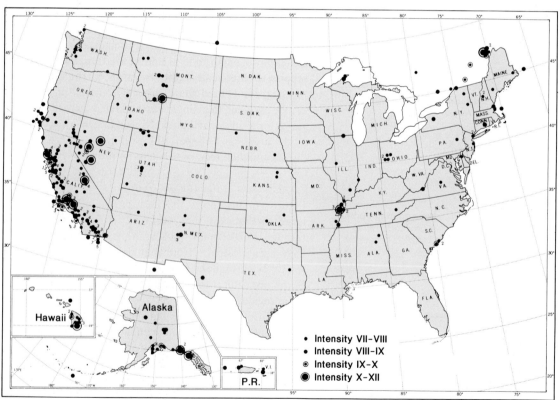

B

Figure 16.10 (*A*) Locations of earthquakes (intensity V and above) in the United States and southern Canada through 1970.
(*B*) Locations of destructive earthquakes (intensity VII and above) in the United States and southern Canada through 1970.
National Oceanic and Atmospheric Administration.

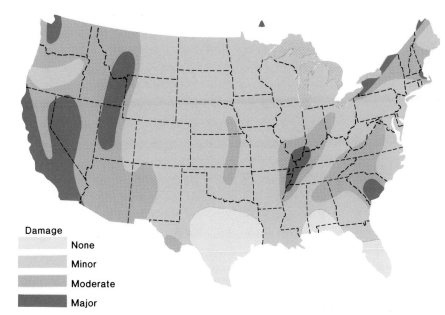

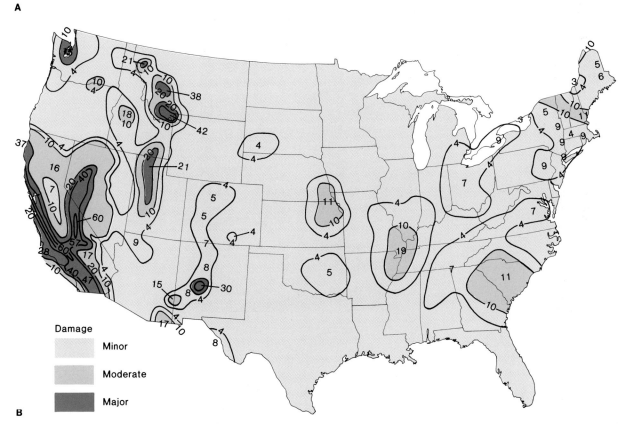

Figure 16.11 (A) A 1969 map of seismic risk in the United States, showing the expected effect of future earthquakes based on the location and intensity of earthquakes in the past and on known geologic structure. (B) A 1976 map of seismic risk, more useful to builders and planners than the 1969 map. The risk is shown as the expected maximum horizontal acceleration of the ground during an earthquake, shown as a percent of gravity. Damage usually begins at 10 percent of gravity. Acceleration shown has only a 1-in-10 chance of being exceeded in a 50-year period. Maximum acceleration (in California) is 80 percent of gravity.
Map *A*; National Oceanic and Atmospheric Administration. Map *B*; U.S. Geological Survey.

Geologists have mapped regions of seismic risk in the United States (figure 16.11) primarily on the assumption that large earthquakes will occur in the future in places where they have occurred in the past.

Effects of Earthquakes

Ground motion is the trembling and shaking of the land that can cause buildings to vibrate. During small quakes windows and walls may crack from such vibration. In a very large quake the ground motion may be visible. It can be strong enough to topple large structures such as bridges and office buildings (figure 16.12). Most people injured or killed in an earthquake are hit by falling debris from buildings. Because proper building construction can greatly reduce the dangers of injury and death, building codes need to be strict in earthquake-prone areas.

A

B

C

Figure 16.12 Earthquake damage to man-made structures.
(*A*) Fallen statue at Stanford University, San Francisco
earthquake, 1906. (*B*) Wreckage of San Francisco City Hall,
1906. (*C*) Collapse of freeway overpasses, San Fernando
Valley, California, 1971.
Photo *A* by W. C. Mendenhall, U.S. Geological Survey. Photo *B* by
W. C. Mendenhall, U.S. Geological Survey. Photo C from U.S.
Geological Survey.

Fire is a particularly serious problem just after an
earthquake because of broken gas and water mains and
fallen electrical wires. Although fire was the cause of most
of the damage to San Francisco in 1906 (figure 16.13),

changes in building construction and improved fire-fighting methods have considerably reduced (but not eliminated) the fire danger to modern cities.

Landslides (chapter 9) can be triggered by the shaking of the ground (figure 16.14). The 1959 Madison Canyon landslide in Montana was triggered by a nearby quake
of magnitude 7.2. Landslides and subsidence caused extensive damage in downtown and suburban Anchorage
during the 1964 Alaskan quake (magnitude 8.6). The

1970 Peruvian earthquake (magnitude 7.75) set off thousands of landslides in the steep Andes Mountains, burying more than 17,000 people. In 1920 in China over 100,000 people living in hollowed-out caves in cliffs of loess (chapter 13) were killed when a quake collapsed the cliffs.

Permanent displacement of the land surface may be the result of rock movement along a fault (chapter 15).

Figure 16.13 Damage caused by earthquake-triggered fire, San Francisco, 1906.
Photo by W. C. Mendenhall, U.S. Geological Survey.

Rocks may move vertically, those on one side of a fault rising while those on the other side drop. Rocks can also move horizontally, those on one side of a fault sliding past those on the other side. Both vertical and horizontal movement can occur during a single quake. Such movement can affect huge areas, although the displacement in a single earthquake seldom exceeds 7 or 8 meters in any direction and almost never exceeds 15 meters. The trace of a fault on the earth's surface may appear as a low cliff, called a *scarp,* or as a closed tear in the ground (figure 16.15). In rare instances small open cracks form during a quake (but not to the extent that Hollywood films often portray). Ground displacement during quakes can tear apart buildings, roads, and pipelines that cross faults. Sudden subsidence of land near the sea can cause flooding and drownings.

Aftershocks are small earthquakes that follow the main shock. In the months after the Alaskan earthquake of 1964 there were several thousand aftershocks, gradually tapering off in frequency. Although aftershocks are smaller than the main quake, they can cause considerable damage, particularly to structures previously weakened by the powerful main shock. A long period of aftershocks can be extremely unsettling to people who have lived through the main shock.

Figure 16.14 Landslides caused by the Alaskan earthquake in 1964.
Photo by U.S. Geological Survey.

A

B

C

D

Figure 16.15 Varieties of ground displacement caused by earthquakes. (*A*) Scarp formed by vertical ground motion, Gallatin County, Montana, 1959. (*B*) Tearing of the ground near Olema, California, 1906. (*C*) Fence offset nearly three meters near Woodville, California, 1906. (*D*) Fence compressed by ground movement, Gallatin County, Montana, 1959.
Photo A by I. J. Witkind, U.S. Geological Survey. Photo B by G. K. Gilbert, U.S. Geological Survey. Photo C by G. K. Gilbert, U.S. Geological Survey. Photo D by J. R. Stacy, U.S. Geological Survey.

Tsunamis

The sudden movement of the sea floor upward or downward during a submarine earthquake can generate very large sea waves, popularly called "tidal waves." Because the ocean tides have nothing to do with generating these huge waves, the Japanese term **tsunami** is the preferred designation. Tsunamis are also called **seismic sea waves.**

They usually are caused by earthquakes that disturb the sea floor, but they also result from submarine landslides or volcanic explosions. When a large section of sea floor suddenly rises or falls during a quake (figure 16.16), all the water over the moving area is lifted or dropped for an instant. As the water returns to sea level, it sets up a long, low wave that spreads very rapidly over the ocean (figure 16.17).

Figure 16.16 Uplift of the sea floor caused by the Alaskan earthquake, 1964. The trace of the Hanning Bay fault runs vertically through the photograph. The block of rock on the left has been displaced upward four to five meters. The large, light-colored area left of the fault is bleached reef rock that was once sea floor, but is now above sea level.
Photo by G. Plafker, U.S. Geological Survey.

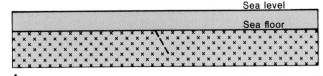

A

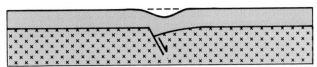

B Sudden displacement of sea floor causes sea level to drop momentarily

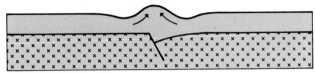

C Water rushes into depression and overcorrects, raising sea level slightly

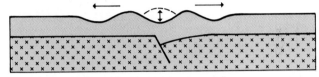

D Sea level oscillates before coming to rest; long, low waves (tsunami) are sent out over sea surface

Figure 16.17 Generation of a tsunami by a submarine earthquake (rock and water displacements are not drawn to scale). (A) Before earthquake. (B) Sudden displacement of sea floor causes sea level to drop momentarily. (C) Water rushes into depression and overcorrects, raising sea level slightly. (D) Sea level oscillates before coming to rest; long, low waves (tsunami) are sent out over sea surface.

Tsunamis are unlike ordinary water waves on the sea surface. A large wind-generated wave may have a wave-length of 400 meters and be moving in deep water at a speed of 90 kilometers per hour (about 55 miles per hour). The wave height when it breaks on shore may be only 3–5 meters. (In the middle of hurricanes, wind waves can reach heights of 15–20 meters.) A tsunami, however, may have a wave length of 150 *kilometers* and be moving at a speed of 750 kilometers per hour (about 450 miles per hour). In deep water the wave height may be only 1–3 meters, but near shore a tsunami may peak up to heights of 15–30 meters. Although the speed of the wave slows drastically as it moves through shallow water, a tsunami still hits shore as a very large, very fast wave. Because of its extremely long wave length, a tsunami does not withdraw quickly as normal waves do. The water keeps on rising for 5–10 minutes, causing great flooding before the wave withdraws. A tsunami's long duration and great height can bring widespread destruction to the entire shore zone (figure 16.18).

A tsunami that formed after the 1960 Chilean quake crossed the Pacific Ocean and did extensive damage in Japan. One of the most destructive tsunamis of modern times was generated April 1, 1946 by an earthquake off-shore from Alaska. It devastated the city of Hilo, Hawaii, causing 159 deaths. The tsunami following the 1964 Alaskan quake drowned 12 people in Crescent City, California, a small coastal town near the Oregon border. Wave damage near an epicenter can be awesome. The 1946 Alaska tsunami destroyed the Scotch Cap lighthouse on nearby Unimak Island, sweeping it off its concrete base, which was 10 meters above sea level, and killing its 5 occupants. The wave height at this location must have exceeded 33 meters.

Figure 16.18 Tsunami damage in Alaskan earthquake, 1964. (*A*) Fishing boat carried inland in Resurrection Bay. (*B*) Two-foot-thick spruce trees broken by a wave at an elevation of one hundred feet above sea level. Photos by U.S. Geological Survey.

Distribution of Earthquakes

Most earthquakes are concentrated in narrow geographic belts (figure 16.19), although *some* earthquakes have occurred in most regions on earth. The most important concentration of earthquakes by far is in the **circum-Pacific belt,** which encircles the rim of the Pacific Ocean. Within this belt occur approximately 80 percent of the world's shallow-focus quakes, 90 percent of the intermediate-focus quakes, and essentially 100 percent of the deep-focus quakes (figure 16.19*B*).

Another major concentration of earthquakes is in the **Mediterranean-Himalayan belt,** which runs through the Mediterranean Sea, crosses the Mideast and the Himalayas, and passes through the East Indies to meet the circum-Pacific belt north of Australia.

A number of shallow-focus earthquakes occur in two other significant locations on earth. One is along the summit or crest of the *mid-oceanic ridge,* a huge underwater mountain range that runs through all the world's oceans (chapter 19). A few earthquakes have also been recorded in isolated spots usually associated with basaltic volcanoes, such as those of Hawaii.

In most parts of the circum-Pacific belt, earthquakes, andesitic volcanoes, and *oceanic trenches* (chapter 19) appear to be closely associated. Careful determination of the locations and depths of focus of earthquakes has revealed the existence of distinct *earthquake zones* that begin at oceanic trenches and slope landward and downward into the earth at an angle of about 30–60° (figure 16.20). Such zones are called **Benioff zones** after the man who first recognized them.

All Benioff zones seem to slope under a continent or a curved line of islands called an **island arc** (figure 16.21). Andesitic volcanoes occur landward of the oceanic trench. The volcanoes may form the volcanic islands of the island arc, or they may be found near the edge of a continent.

Most of the circum-Pacific belt is made up of Benioff zones associated in this manner with oceanic trenches and andesitic volcanoes. Parts of the Mediterranean-Himalayan belt represent Benioff zones, too, notably in the eastern Mediterranean Sea and in the East Indies. Essentially all the world's intermediate- and deep-focus earthquakes occur in Benioff zones.

First-Motion Studies of Earthquakes

By a study of seismograms of an earthquake on a distant fault, geologists are able to tell which way rocks moved along that fault. Rock motion is determined by examining seismograms from many locations surrounding a quake. Each seismograph station can determine whether the first

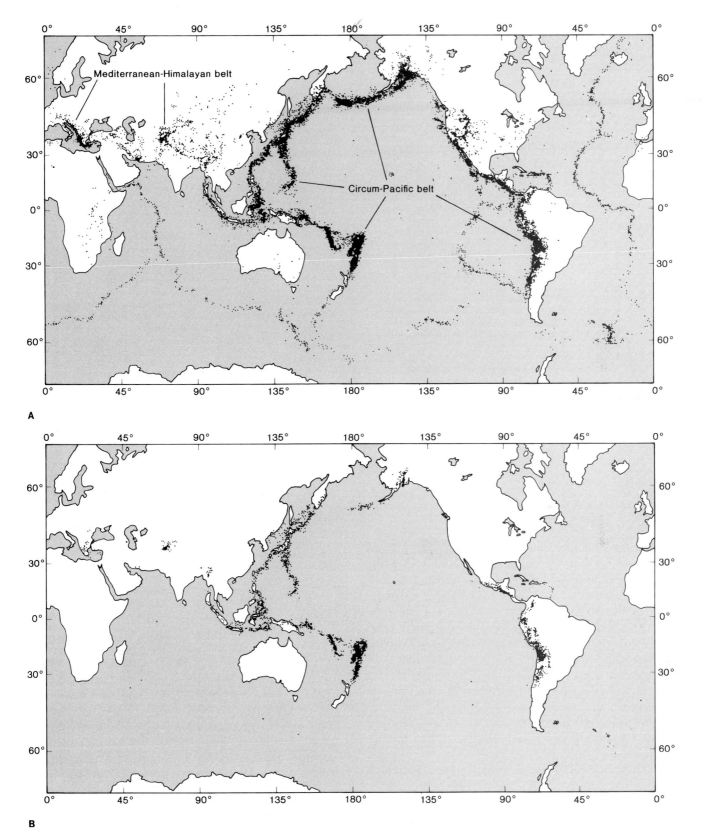

Figure 16.19 World distribution of earthquakes from 1961 to 1967. (*A*) Epicenters of quakes with depth of focus between 0 and 700 kilometers. (*B*) Epicenters of quakes with depth of focus between 100 and 700 kilometers.

From Barazangi and Dorman, *Bulletin of Seismological Society of America,* 1969.

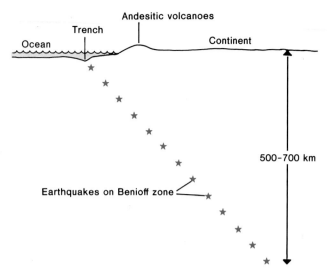

Figure 16.20 A Benioff zone of earthquakes begins at an oceanic trench and dips under a continent (such as South America). Andesitic volcanoes form near the edge of the continent. Horizontal scale is the same as vertical scale.

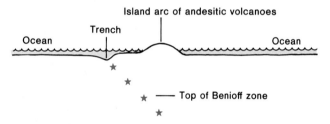

Figure 16.21 A Benioff zone can begin at a trench and dip under an island arc (such as the Aleutian Islands). Only the upper part of the Benioff zone is shown.

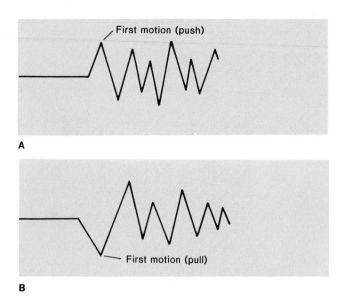

Figure 16.22 Seismograms showing how first horizontal motions of rocks along a fault are determined. (*A*) If the first motion is a push (from the epicenter to the seismograph station), the seismogram trace is deflected upward. (*B*) If it is a pull (away from the station), the deflection is downward.

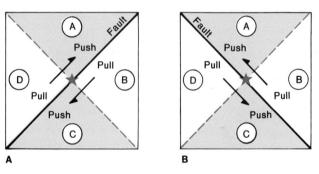

Figure 16.23 Map view of two possible solutions for the same pattern of first motion. Each solution has a different fault orientation. If the fault orientation is known, the correct solution can be chosen. The star marks the epicenter, and rock motion is shown by the arrows.

rock motion recorded there was a push or a pull (figure 16.22). If the rock moved toward the station (a push), then the pen drawing the seismogram is deflected up. If the first motion is away from the station (a pull), then the pen is deflected down.

If an earthquake occurs on a fault as shown in figure 16.23*A*, then there will be large areas around the fault that receive a push as first motion, and different areas that receive a pull. Any station within the area marked *A* will receive a push, for the rock is moving from the epicenter toward those stations, as shown by the arrows in the figure. All stations in area *C* will also receive a push, but areas *B* and *D* will record a pull as the first motion.

In figure 16.23*B* you can see the same pattern of pushes and pulls, but in this case the pattern is caused by a fault with a different orientation. Either fault can cause the same pattern, if the rock moves in the direction shown by the arrows. In other words, there are two possible solutions to any pattern of first motions.

If the orientation of the fault trace on the earth's surface is known, as it is for most faults on land (and for a few on the ocean floor), then the correct choice of the two solutions can be made. But if the orientation of the fault is not known—as is the usual case for earthquakes at sea or at great depth—then the choice between the two possible solutions can be difficult. One solution may be more *likely* to be true, based on the study of topography, other faults, or similar factors. But such a solution is by no means *proven* if the fault orientation is not known. As you read about first-motion studies, keep in mind that there are always two solutions to any pattern.

Figure 16.24 shows a different pattern of first motion, and the two possible solutions for that pattern.

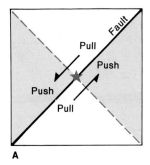

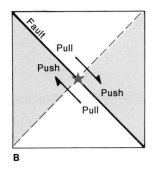

A   **B**

Figure 16.24   Two possible solutions for a different pattern of first motion.

Figure 16.25   The major plates of the world in the theory of plate tectonics. Compare locations of plate boundaries with earthquake locations shown in figure 16.19. Double lines show diverging plate boundaries, single lines show transform boundaries. Heavy lines with triangles show converging boundaries; triangles point down subduction zone.
Modified from Hamilton, U.S. Geological Survey.

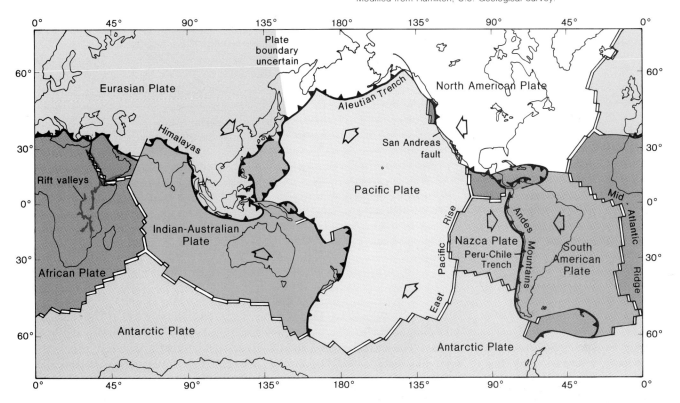

Earthquakes and Plate Tectonics

One of the great attractions of the concept of plate tectonics is its ability to explain the distribution of earthquakes and the rock motion associated with them.

As described briefly in chapter 1, the concept of plate tectonics is that the earth's surface is divided into a few giant *plates*. Plates are rigid slabs of rock, thousands of kilometers wide and perhaps 100 kilometers thick, that move across the earth's surface. Because the plates carry continents and sea floors on their upper surface, the plate tectonics concept really means that the continents and sea floors are moving. The plates change not only position, but also size and shape (as we will discuss in more detail in chapter 20).

Earthquakes occur commonly at the edges of plates, but only occasionally in the middle of a plate. The close correspondence between plate edges and earthquake belts can be seen by comparing the map of earthquake distribution in figure 16.19 with the plate map in figure 16.25.

To a considerable degree, plates are identified and defined by earthquakes, for according to plate tectonics, most earthquakes are caused by interactions between plates along plate boundaries. Narrow bands of earthquakes therefore outline plates. This can be clearly seen in the east Pacific Ocean off South America, where the Nazca plate (figure 16.25) is almost completely outlined by earthquake epicenters (figure 16.19).

The earthquakes on the western border of the Nazca plate are shallow-focus quakes, and they occur in a narrow belt along the crest of the mid-oceanic ridge here, locally called the East Pacific Rise. The quakes along the eastern boundary occupy a broader belt that lies mostly within South America. This belt includes shallow-, intermediate-, and deep-focus earthquakes in a Benioff zone which

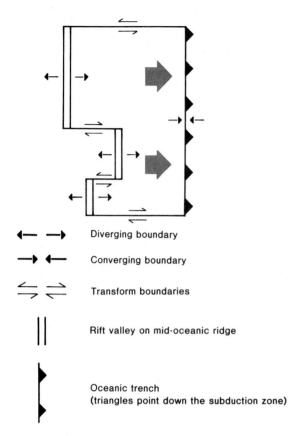

Diverging boundary

Converging boundary

Transform boundaries

Rift valley on mid-oceanic ridge

Oceanic trench
(triangles point down the subduction zone)

Figure 16.26 Relation of three types of plate boundaries to one another. Plate moves to right (as shown by the large arrows), away from rift valley at diverging boundary, and toward oceanic trench at converging boundary.

begins at the Peru-Chile Trench just offshore and slopes steeply down under South America to the east. The Nazca plate moves eastward, away from the spreading center on the crest of the mid-oceanic ridge and toward the subduction zone at the trench, where the plate plunges down into the mantle. The plate's western boundary is located at the crest of the East Pacific Rise, and its eastern boundary is at the bottom of the Peru-Chile Trench.

Earthquakes at Plate Boundaries

As you have learned, there are three types of plate boundaries, *diverging boundaries* where plates move away from each other, *transform boundaries* where plates move horizontally past each other, and *converging boundaries* where plates move toward each other. Each type of boundary has a characteristic pattern of earthquake distribution and rock motion.

One example of the relation of the three types of boundaries to each other is shown in figure 16.26. Note how the motion at each boundary (shown by the pairs of small arrows) agrees with the motion of the plate (shown by the large arrows).

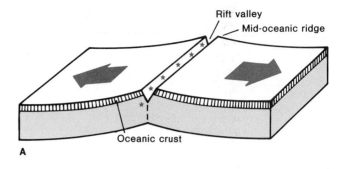

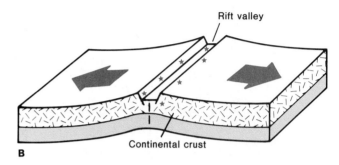

Figure 16.27 Diverging plate boundaries. (A) On the ocean floor. (B) On a continent. Each is marked by a rift valley and shallow-focus earthquakes (shown as stars).

Diverging boundaries At a spreading center, where plates move away from each other, earthquakes are shallow and restricted to a narrow band. A diverging boundary on the sea floor is marked by the crest of the mid-oceanic ridge and the *rift valley* that is often (but not always) found on the ridge crest (figure 16.27A). The earthquakes are located along the sides of the rift valley and beneath its floor. The rock motion that is deduced from first-motion studies shows that the faults here are normal faults, parallel to the rift valley. (This is the most likely solution of the first-motion studies. Keep in mind as you read this section that there are always two solutions for first motion; we give only one—the more likely solution.) If this interpretation of the first motions is correct, it implies that the ridge crest is being subjected to horizontal tension, which is apparently tearing the sea floor open here, creating the rift valley and causing the earthquakes.

A diverging boundary within a continent is usually also marked by a rift valley, shallow-focus quakes, and normal faults (figure 16.27B). The African Rift Valleys in eastern Africa (figure 16.25) seem to be such a boundary. Horizontal tension here may be tearing eastern Africa slowly apart, creating the rift valleys, some of which contain lakes.

Transform boundaries Where two plates move past each other along a transform boundary, the earthquakes are shallow. First-motion studies indicate strike-slip mo-

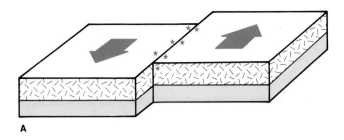

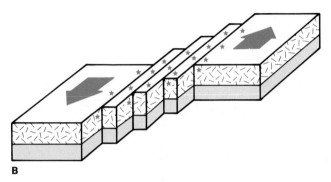

Figure 16.28 Transform boundaries. (*A*) Narrow band of shallow-focus earthquakes along single fault. (*B*) Broad band of earthquakes along a system of parallel faults.

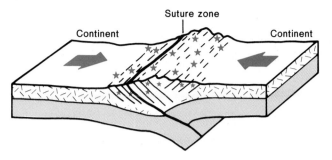

Figure 16.29 A converging boundary marked by the collision of two continents. A very broad zone of shallow-focus earthquakes occurs along a complex system of faults.

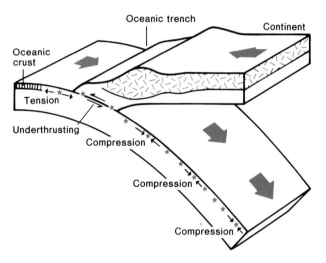

Figure 16.30 A converging boundary with ocean floor subducting under a continent. Earthquakes occur near the top of the subducting plate due to tension, underthrusting, and compression.

tion on faults parallel to the boundary. The earthquakes may be aligned in a narrow band along one fault (figure 16.28*A*), or they may form a broader zone if plate motion is taken up by movement along a system of parallel faults (figure 16.28*B*). The San Andreas fault in California (figure 16.25) may be an example of a single fault forming a plate boundary, but many geologists believe that the broad zone of seismicity in the western United States (figure 16.10*A*) shows that a system of faults parallel to the San Andreas forms (in part) the plate boundary here.

Converging boundaries Converging boundaries are of two general types, one marked by the *collision* of two continents (figure 16.29), the other marked by *subduction* of the ocean floor under a continent (figure 16.30) or another piece of sea floor. Each type has a characteristic pattern of earthquakes.

Collision boundaries are characterized by broad zones of shallow earthquakes on a complex system of faults (figure 16.29). Some of the faults are parallel to the dip of the suture zone that marks the line of collision; some are not. One continent usually overrides the other slightly (continents are not dense enough to be subducted), creating thick crust and a mountain range. The Himalaya Mountains are thought to represent such a boundary (figure 16.25). The seismic zone is so broad and complex at such boundaries that other criteria, such as detailed geologic maps, must be used to identify the position of the suture zone at the plate boundary.

During *subduction,* earthquakes occur for several different reasons (figure 16.30). As a dense oceanic plate bends to go down at a trench, it stretches slightly, and normal faults occur as a result of *tension*. This gives a block-faulted character to the outer (seaward) wall of a trench. For some distance below the trench, the subducting plate is in contact with the overlying plate. First-motion studies of earthquakes at these shallow depths show that the quakes are caused by shallow-angle thrust-faulting. This is the motion expected as one plate slides beneath another, a process commonly called *underthrusting.*

At greater depths, where the descending plate is out of contact with the overlying plate, earthquakes are common, but the reasons for them are not obvious. The quakes are confined to a thin zone, only 20–30 kilometers thick, within the lithosphere of the descending plate, which is about 100 kilometers thick (figure 16.30). This zone is thought to be near the top of the lithosphere, where the rock is colder and more brittle, but there is little real evidence for this. It is clear, however, that these deep earthquakes cannot be located at the upper *surface* of the

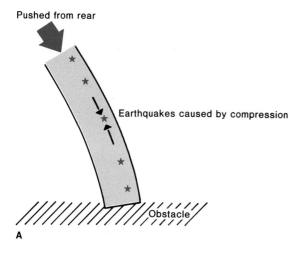

Pushed from rear

Earthquakes caused by compression

Obstacle

A

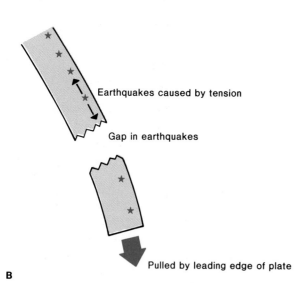

Earthquakes caused by tension

Gap in earthquakes

Pulled by leading edge of plate

B

Figure 16.31 Cross-section views of subducting plates. (*A*) Quakes caused by compression, perhaps resulting from the plate being pushed from the rear (or hitting an obstacle). (*B*) Quakes caused by tension, perhaps resulting from the plate being pulled downward.

Figure 16.32 Various angles of subduction, which may become steeper or gentler with depth.

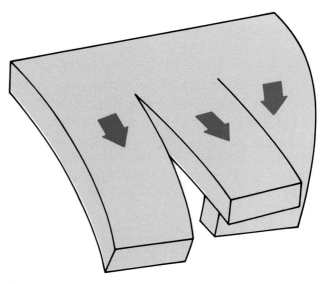

Figure 16.33 A descending plate may tear into segments, each of which may have different subduction angles.

plate, for there is very little friction between the cold, descending lithosphere and the hot plastic asthenosphere above it. The deep quakes must be located completely *within* the descending lithosphere.

First motions of these quakes imply that along many subduction zones the quakes are caused by *compression* parallel to the dip of the plate (figure 16.30). This could mean that the plates are being pushed from the rear, or that they are running into some obstacle at depth, or both (figure 16.31*A*).

Earthquake first motion on other subduction zones, however, implies *tension* parallel to the dip of the descend-

ing plates (figure 16.31*B*). This might mean that the plates are being pulled along by their leading edges. Descending lithosphere is slightly denser than the surrounding asthenosphere (because it is colder and because low-density minerals within a descending plate may either "distill" off the plate by partial melting or be converted to denser minerals by pressure). This inference of tension is supported by evidence that some plates break apart as they sink, resulting in gaps in the earthquake pattern along some subduction zones (figure 16.31*B*).

Subduction Angle

The distribution of earthquakes can be used to determine the angle of subduction of a down-going plate. Subduction angles vary considerably from trench to trench, and in some cases become steeper or gentler with depth (figure 16.32).

The reasons for these variations are not clear. The angle may depend on a complex interaction between spreading rate, cooling rate, plate density, duration of subduction, and other factors.

Descending plates may tear or break into segments or they may become folded, usually below a depth of 200 kilometers. Individual segments may descend at different angles (figure 16.33), which can be determined from the distribution of earthquakes. The segmentation or folding may be required geometrically to allow subduction of curved rigid plates to successively greater depths. The plate forms with a radius of curvature equal to that of the earth's surface, and during subduction it sinks to regions of a progressively smaller radius.

In summary, earthquakes are very closely related to plate tectonics. In many cases the plate boundaries themselves are defined by the distribution of earthquakes, and plate motion can be deduced by the first motions of the quakes. Analysis of first motions can also help determine the type and orientation of forces that act on plates, such as tension and compression. Quake distribution with depth indicates the angles of subduction, and has shown that some plates change subduction angle and even break up as they descend. A few quakes, such as those that occur in the center of plates, cannot easily be related to plate motion.

Earthquake Prediction

Although people who live in earthquake-prone regions are plagued by unscientific predictions of impending earthquakes by popular writers and self-proclaimed prophets, several techniques are being developed for scientifically forecasting a coming earthquake. Most of these methods involve monitoring slight changes that occur in rock next to a fault before the rock breaks and moves.

Just as a bent stick may crackle and pop before it breaks with a loud snap, so does rock give warning signals that it is about to break. Before a large quake, small cracks may open within the rock, causing small tremors, or *microseisms,* to increase. The *properties of the rock* next to the fault may be changed by the opening of such cracks. If these changes are monitored, they may give some warning of an imminent quake, especially if the electrical resistivity of the rock or the speed of seismic waves is observed to be changing. Rock magnetism and porosity are other properties that may be altered by cracks and stresses in advance of a quake. In some areas the *surface of the earth tilts and changes elevation* slightly before an earthquake occurs. Through the use of highly sensitive instruments that measure increasing strain in rocks, scientists are sometimes able to make quake predictions with considerable accuracy.

Patterns of earthquakes in space and time are being recognized along some faults, particularly on the faults along some plate boundaries. If one plate is sliding diagonally under another plate, a series of earthquakes may occur in a regular way along the plate boundary (figure

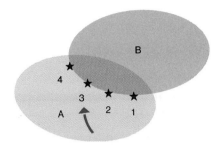

Figure 16.34 As plate *A* slides under plate *B*, earthquakes occur in a regular series from one to four. The entire sequence may repeat.

16.34). If such a pattern is known to repeat itself in the same area over several centuries, it becomes possible to predict where the next large quake might occur. Along some long active faults, there are short inactive segments called *seismic gaps* where earthquakes have not occurred for a long time. These gaps are widely thought to be the most likely sites for future earthquakes, so many of them are being carefully studied.

Several other methods are used to try to predict quakes. One interesting method—though very local in application—is to time the *intervals between eruptions* of Old Faithful geyser in Yellowstone National Park. Long-term records of the time between eruptions have shown that this interval changes in a regular way before a large local earthquake, probably because of porosity changes within the surrounding rock. Another prediction method based on porosity changes is the monitoring of *water levels in wells,* which often changes before earthquakes. Chinese scientists claim successful predictions by watching *animal behavior*—horses become skittish and snakes leave their holes shortly before a quake. United States scientists have done little work along these lines, and many are skeptical of the Chinese claims.

Japanese and Russian geologists were the first to predict earthquakes successfully, and Chinese geologists have recently made some very accurate predictions (along with some embarrassingly inaccurate and missed predictions). Geologists in the United States are now becoming increasingly confident of their ability to predict earthquakes along some segments of some faults. Since the techniques are new and in some cases only partly understood, some errors will undoubtedly be made. Many faults are not monitored at all because of lack of money and personnel, and so we will never have a warning of impending quakes in some regions. For large urban areas near active faults, however, earthquake prediction techniques are rapidly lessening the danger of an earthquake's occurring without warning.

Box 16.1

Earthquakes in the Eastern United States—Rare but Occasionally Strong

Although most earthquakes in the western United States are clearly related to known faults, earthquakes that occur east of the Rocky Mountains are more difficult to relate to faulting. Earthquakes in the eastern United States are uncommon, generally small, and deeper than western U.S. quakes; they are not associated with surface displacement of the ground or known faults. (They may lie along the landward extensions of oceanic fracture zones—see chapter 19.)

Although large quakes are extremely rare in the central and eastern United States (figure 16.10B), when they do occur, they can be very destructive and widely felt. The Saint Lawrence River Valley along the Canadian border has had several intensity IX and X earthquakes, most recently in 1944. Plymouth, Massachusetts had an intensity IX quake in 1638, and a quake of intensity VIII occurred near Cambridge, Massachusetts in 1755. In 1929 in Attica, New York an earthquake of intensity IX knocked over 250 chimneys. A series of quakes (intensity XI) that occurred near New Madrid, Missouri in the winter of 1811–1812 may have been the largest recorded earthquakes ever to occur in North America. The quakes knocked over chimneys as far away as Richmond, Virginia. The 1886 quake in Charleston, South Carolina (intensity X) was felt throughout almost half the United States (figure 16.9), and killed 60 people.

Because the origin of these quakes is not clear, and because they are not associated with surface faults that can be monitored, future quake prediction in the eastern United States will be much more difficult than in the western states.

Earthquake Control

Even though earthquakes probably cannot be stopped entirely, it would be desirable to control when and where they occur.

The potential for future damage to some cities is so great that some control measures may one day be attempted along some major faults. Portions of the San Andreas fault in California seem to be slipping regularly. Great strain does not build up along these segments, probably because of the straightness of the fault and the type of rock found there. But two segments of the San Andreas fault appear to be locked, and perhaps great strain is building up there that will be released in a giant earthquake. One such locked segment is the section of the fault near San Francisco, which last moved in 1906. The other segment is the part nearest Los Angeles, which last broke in a very large quake in 1857. Although geologists disagree about the amount of damage that a quake would do in these cities, and the amount of strain being stored in the locked segments, most feel that the fault does pose substantial danger to both cities. The amount of death and destruction *could* be vast in either city, depending upon the earthquake's magnitude and what time of day it occurs. The 1971 San Fernando Valley earthquake, with a magnitude of 6.4, caused about 60 deaths and $500 million worth of damage to the greater Los Angeles area. If a quake the size of the 1906 San Francisco tremor should occur again near either city, the devastation would be much greater. The 1906 quake, at magnitude 8.25, was about 500 times as powerful as the 1971 San Fernando quake.

One method of earthquake control seems to hold some promise. It has been discovered, partly by accident, that pumping water down into the ground under high pressure near a fault may release the strain that has accumulated in the rocks near the fault. The pressure of the water may force the rock walls of the fault apart and lubricate them so that the rocks move, causing small quakes. Such earthquakes have occurred around a disposal well near Denver and in an oil field in Colorado where water was forced underground. Without water, more strain would build up until a much larger quake occurred. With the water reducing the friction, strain can be released in smaller, timed quakes. Could such a method of quake release be used on the locked portions of the San Andreas fault? Perhaps, but only after extensive testing, and then only as a trial in a relatively uninhabited section of the fault. The enormous expense of such a program might prove to be prohibitive. Still, it is exciting to consider the possibility that in the future the danger of quakes along some faults can be greatly lessened by controlled release of strain.

It is important to realize that such experiments release strain that is already there. The advantage is in timing the release of the strain. The water does not *cause* the quake; it allows a quake that would occur sometime anyway to be *controlled*.

Summary

Earthquakes usually occur when rocks break and move along a fault to release strain that has gradually built up in the rock. Volcanic activity can also cause earthquakes.

Seismic waves move out from the earthquake's *focus*. *Body waves* (*P* waves and *S* waves) move through the earth's interior, and *surface waves* (*L* waves) move on the earth's surface.

Seismographs record seismic waves on *seismograms*, which can be used to determine an earthquake's strength, location, and depth of focus. Most earthquakes are shallow-focus quakes, but some occur as deep as 700 kilometers below the earth's surface.

The time intervals between first arrivals of *P, S,* and *L* waves are used to determine the distance between a seismograph and an *epicenter*. Three or more stations are needed to determine the location of earthquakes.

Earthquake *intensity* is determined by measuring damage and is measured on the *modified Mercalli scale*.

Earthquake *magnitude* is determined by the amplitude of seismic waves on a seismogram and is measured on the *Richter scale*.

The most noticeable effects of earthquakes are ground motion and displacement (which may cause building destruction and thereby kill or injure people), fire, landslides, and *tsunamis*. *Aftershocks* can continue to cause damage months after the main shock.

Earthquakes are generally distributed in belts. The *circum-Pacific belt* contains most of the world's earthquakes. Earthquakes also occur on the Mediterranean-Himalayan belt, the crest of the mid-oceanic ridge, and in association with basaltic volcanoes.

Benioff zones of shallow-, intermediate-, and deep-focus earthquakes are associated with andesitic volcanoes, oceanic trenches, and the edges of continents or island arcs.

The concept of plate tectonics explains most earthquakes as being caused by interactions between two plates at their boundaries. Plate boundaries are generally defined by bands of earthquakes.

Diverging plate boundaries are marked by a narrow zone of shallow earthquakes along normal faults. Transform boundaries are marked by shallow quakes caused by strike-slip motion along one or more faults.

Converging boundaries where continents collide are marked by a very broad zone of shallow quakes. Converging boundaries involving deep subduction are marked by Benioff zones of quakes caused by tension, underthrusting, and compression.

The distribution of quakes indicates subduction angles and shows that some plates break up as they descend.

The potential for successful earthquake prediction is rapidly increasing, largely through the measurement of rock properties near faults and the recognition of patterns of quakes at plate boundaries.

The timing of the release of accumulating rock strain may be controlled in the future by pumping water underground to trigger limited earthquakes.

Terms to Remember

aftershocks
Benioff zone
body waves
circum-Pacific belt
depth of focus
earthquake
elastic rebound theory
epicenter
focus
intensity
island arc
L wave
magnitude
Mediterranean-Himalayan belt
modified Mercalli scale
P wave
Richter scale
seismic waves
seismogram
seismograph
seismometer
surface waves
S waves
travel-time curve
tsunami (seismic sea wave)

Questions for Review

1. Describe in detail how earthquake epicenters are located by seismograph stations.
2. What causes earthquakes?
3. Compare and contrast the concepts of intensity and magnitude of earthquakes.
4. Name and describe the various types of seismic waves.
5. Discuss the distribution of earthquakes with regard to location and depth of focus.
6. Show with a sketch how the concept of plate tectonics can explain the distribution of earthquakes in a Benioff zone and on the crest of the mid-oceanic ridge.
7. Describe several ways that scientists are working on earthquake prediction.
8. How may earthquakes someday be controlled as to time of energy release?
9. Describe several ways that earthquakes cause damage.
10. How do earthquakes cause tsunamis?
11. What are aftershocks?

Questions for Thought

1. What are some arguments in favor of and against predicting earthquakes? What would happen in your community if a prediction were made today that within a month a large earthquake would occur nearby?
2. Stone, brick, and adobe buildings often collapse completely during an earthquake while wood-frame houses sustain little damage. Two-story buildings are damaged more than single-story buildings. Why?

Supplementary Readings

Anderson, D. L. 1971. The San Andreas fault. *Scientific American* (Nov. 1971). Offprint #896. San Francisco: W. H. Freeman.

Bolt, B. A. 1978. *Earthquakes: A Primer.* San Francisco: W. H. Freeman.

Hodgson, J. H. 1964. *Earthquakes and earth structure.* Englewood Cliffs, N.J.: Prentice-Hall.

Iacopi, R. 1964. *Earthquake country.* Menlo Park, Cal.: Lane Press.

Press, F. 1975. Earthquake prediction. *Scientific American* (May 1975). Offprint #917. San Francisco: W. H. Freeman.

Richter, C. F. 1958. *Elementary seismology.* San Francisco: W. H. Freeman.

U.S. Geological Survey, 1965–70. *The Alaska earthquake.* Professional Papers 541–546.

U.S. Geological Survey, 1971. *The San Fernando, California, earthquake of February 9, 1971.* Professional Paper 733.

Yanev, P., 1974. *Peace of mind in earthquake country.* Chronicle Books.

17

The Earth's Interior

Purpose

The only rocks that geologists can study directly in place are those of the crust; and the earth's crust is but a thin skin of rock, making up less than one percent of the earth's total volume. To learn about the inside of the earth, geologists must study it *indirectly,* largely by using the tools of geophysics—that is, seismic waves and the measurement of gravity, heat flow, and earth magnetism.

Such indirect evidence has shown that the earth is a zoned planet, the crust being the outer shell, the core being at the center, and the mantle in between. Further subdivisions of the earth's interior include differences between the continental crust and oceanic crust, the relatively brittle lithosphere and the plastic asthenosphere, the existence of a concentric-shell structure in the mantle, and the differentiation of the earth's core into a liquid outer core and a solid inner core.

You will discover in this chapter how gravity measurements can indicate where certain regions of the crust and upper mantle are being held up or held down out of their natural position of equilibrium. We will also discuss the earth's magnetic field and its history of reversals. We will show how magnetic anomalies can indicate hidden ore and structures. We close with a discussion of the distribution and loss of the earth's heat.

Geologists who have considerable exposure to the public (such as in government offices and universities) occasionally encounter people who are convinced that geologists are misled about the interior of the earth. These people have strongly held convictions about what is deep inside the earth. For example, some feel that the earth is hollow and the supposed cavity is a storage place for water or, possibly, flying saucers.

What *do* geologists know about the earth's interior? How do they obtain information about the parts of the earth beneath the surface? Is there even a slight chance that geologists are wrong; that the earth really is hollow?

Geologists, in fact, are not able to sample rocks very far below the earth's surface. Some deep mines penetrate three kilometers into the earth, and a deep oil well may go as much as eight kilometers beneath the surface. Rock samples can be brought up from a mine or a well so that geologists can study them. But the earth has a radius of about 6,370 kilometers, so it is obvious that geologists can only scratch the surface when they try to study *directly* the rocks beneath their feet.

Deep parts of the earth are studied *indirectly,* however, largely through the branch of geology called **geophysics,** which is the application of physical laws and principles to a study of the earth. Geophysics involves, for example, studying how seismic waves move through the earth and investigating the earth's magnetic field, gravity, and heat. All these things tell us something about the nature of the deep part of the earth. Together they give a convincing picture of what makes up the earth's interior.

Evidence from Seismic Waves

Seismic waves from a large earthquake may pass entirely through the earth. A nuclear bomb explosion also generates seismic waves. Geologists obtain new information about the earth's interior after every large earthquake and bomb test.

One important way of learning about the earth's interior is the study of **seismic reflection,** the return of some of the energy of seismic waves to the earth's surface after the waves bounce off a rock boundary. If two rock layers of differing densities are separated by a fairly sharp boundary, seismic waves can reflect off that boundary just as light reflects off a mirror. These reflected waves can be recorded on a seismogram, which can show the amount of time the waves took to travel down to the boundary, reflect off it, and return to the surface. From the amount of time necessary for the round trip, geologists calculate the depth of the boundary (figure 17.1).

Another method used to locate rock boundaries is the study of **seismic refraction,** the bending of seismic waves as they pass from one material to another, which is similar to the way that light waves bend when they pass through the lenses of eyeglasses. As a seismic wave strikes a rock boundary, much of the energy of the wave passes across the boundary. As the wave crosses from one rock layer to another, it changes direction (figure 17.2). This change of direction, or refraction, occurs only if the velocity of seismic waves is different in each layer (which is generally true if the rock layers differ in density or strength).

The boundaries between such rock layers are usually distinct enough to be located by seismic refraction techniques, as shown in figure 17.3. Seismograph station 1 is receiving seismic waves that pass directly through the upper layer *A.* Stations farther from the epicenter, such as station 2, receive seismic waves from two pathways:

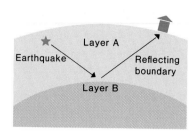

Figure 17.1 Seismic reflection indicates a rock boundary deep within the earth.

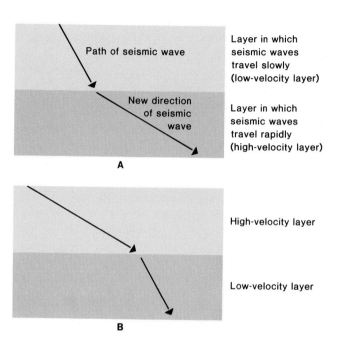

Figure 17.2 Seismic refraction occurs when seismic waves bend as they cross rock boundaries. (*A*) Low-velocity layer above high-velocity layer. (*B*) High-velocity layer above low-velocity layer.

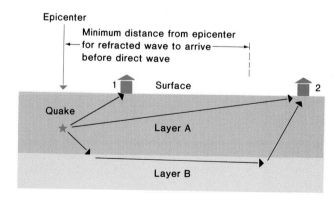

Figure 17.3 Seismic refraction can be used to detect boundaries between rock layers. See text for explanation.

(1) a direct path straight through layer *A*, and (2) a refracted path through layer *A* to a higher-velocity layer *B* and back to layer *A*. Station 2, therefore, is receiving the same wave twice.

Seismograph stations close to station 1 receive only the direct wave or receive two waves, with the direct (upper) wave arriving before the refracted (lower) wave. Stations near station 2 receive both the direct and the refracted waves. Somewhere between station 1 and station 2 is the point where there is a transformation from receiving the direct wave first to receiving the *refracted* wave first. Even though the refracted wave travels farther, it can arrive at a station first, because most of its path is in the high-velocity layer *B*.

The distance between this point of transformation and the epicenter of the earthquake is a function of the depth to the rock boundary between layers *A* and *B*. A series of portable seismographs can be set up to find this distance, and the depth to the boundary can then be calculated. The velocities of seismic waves within the layers can also be found.

Figure 17.2 shows how waves bend as they travel downward into higher velocity layers. But why do waves return to the surface, as shown in figure 17.3? The answer is that advancing waves give off energy in all directions. Much of this energy continues to travel horizontally within layer *B* (figure 17.3). This energy passes beneath station 2 and out of the figure toward the right. A small part of the energy "leaks" upward into layer *A*, and it is this pathway that is shown in the figure. Many other pathways exist for this wave's energy, but they are not shown here.

A sharp rock boundary is not necessary for the refraction of seismic waves. Even in a thick layer of uniform rock, the increasing pressure with depth tends to increase the velocity of the waves. They follow curved paths through such a layer, as shown in figure 17.4. The reason for the curving path can be understood by visualizing the thick rock layer as a stack of very thin layers, each with a slightly higher velocity than the one above. The curved path results from many small changes in direction as the wave passes through the many layers.

The Earth's Internal Layers

It was the study of seismic refraction and seismic reflection that enabled scientists to plot the three main zones of the earth's interior (figure 17.5). The **crust** is the outer layer of rock, which forms a thin skin on the earth's surface. Below the crust lies the **mantle,** a thick shell of rock that separates the crust above from the core below. The **core** is the central zone of the earth. It is probably metallic and is where the earth's magnetic field is thought to be generated.

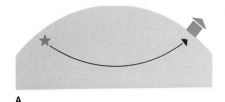

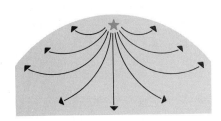

Figure 17.4 Curved paths of seismic waves caused by uniform rock with increasing seismic velocity with depth. (*A*) Path between earthquake and recording station. (*B*) Waves spreading out in all directions from earthquake focus.

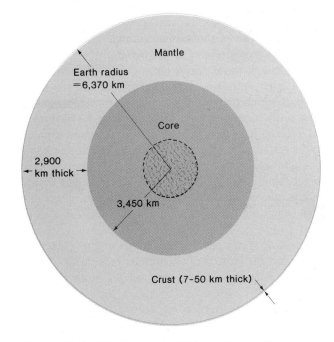

Figure 17.5 The three main divisions of the earth as determined from a study of seismic waves.

The Earth's Crust

Studies of seismic waves have shown (1) that the earth's crust is thinner beneath the oceans than beneath the continents (figure 17.6); and (2) that seismic waves travel faster in oceanic crust than in continental crust. Because of this velocity difference, it is assumed that the two types of crust are made up of different kinds of rock.

Seismic *P* waves travel through oceanic crust at about 7 kilometers per second, which is also the speed at which they travel through basalt. This seismic evidence suggests

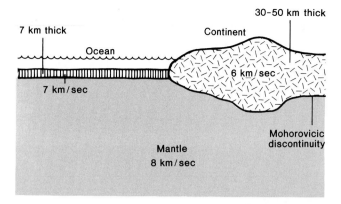

Figure 17.6 Thin crust with a *P*-wave velocity of 7 kilometers per second underlies the ocean. Thick crust with lower velocity makes up continents. Detailed study of continental crust shows many layers with velocities increasing from 6 to 7 kilometers per second with depth (not shown above—two such layers can be seen in figure 17.7). Mantle velocities are about 8 kilometers per second.

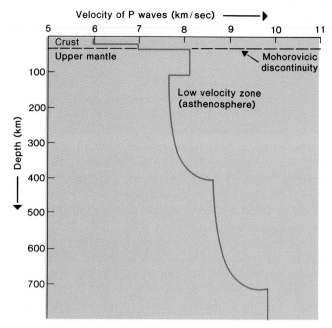

Figure 17.7 The velocity of *P* waves generally increases with depth except in the low-velocity zone.

that oceanic crust is made of basalt. Samples of rocks taken from the sea floor by oceanographic ships verify this suggestion. Most of the sea-floor samples are basalt, although other rock types also are found.

Seismic *P* waves travel more slowly through continental crust—about 6 kilometers per second, the same speed at which they travel through granite. Continental crust is often referred to as being "granite." The term is put in quotation marks because most of the rocks exposed on the surface of continents are not granite. Since a single rock term cannot accurately describe crust that varies in composition, many geologists use the terms **sial** (rocks high in *si*licon and *al*uminum) for continental crust and **sima** (rocks high in *si*licon and *ma*gnesium) for oceanic crust.

Seismic waves passing beneath mountain ranges indicate that the crust is thickest under mountains. A protruding *mountain root* of crust bulges down into the mantle.

The boundary that separates the crust from the mantle beneath it is called the **Mohorovičić discontinuity** ("Moho" for short). Note from figure 17.6 that the mantle lies closer to the earth's surface beneath the ocean than it does beneath continents. The idea behind an ambitious program called Project Mohole (begun during the early 1960s) was to use specially equipped ships to drill through the oceanic crust and obtain samples from the mantle. Although the project was abandoned because of high costs, much ocean-floor drilling has taken place since then, but not to the great depth necessary to sample the mantle. Perhaps as drilling at sea becomes more routine, the original concept of drilling to the mantle through oceanic crust will be revived. (Ocean drilling is discussed in more detail in chapters 19 and 20.)

The Mantle

Because of the way seismic waves pass through the mantle, geologists believe that it, like the crust, is made of solid rock. (Localized magma chambers may occur as isolated pockets of liquid in both the crust and the upper mantle.) Because *P* waves travel at about 8 kilometers per second in the upper mantle, it seems apparent that the mantle is a different type of rock from either oceanic crust or continental crust. The best hypothesis that geologists can make about the composition of the mantle is that it consists of *ultramafic rock* such as peridotite. Ultramafic rock is heavy igneous rock made up chiefly of ferromagnesian minerals such as olivine and pyroxene. Some ultramafic rocks contain garnet, and all of them lack feldspar. Outcrops of peridotite (often serpentinized by metamorphism) found at the earth's surface reinforce the hypothesis that the mantle is ultramafic rock. The outcrops may be mantle rock that has somehow been brought to the surface.

About 100 kilometers beneath the earth's surface is a curious mantle layer where seismic waves slow down. Generally seismic waves increase in velocity with depth into the earth as increasing pressure alters the properties of the rock. At the 100-kilometer depth, however, seismic waves travel more slowly than they do in shallower layers, and so this zone is often called the **low-velocity zone** (figure 17.7). This zone, beginning at a depth of 100 kilometers and extending to a depth of perhaps 250 kilometers, is also called, in plate tectonic theory, the **asthenosphere.** In this zone the rocks may be closer to their melting point than the rocks above or below the zone. (The rocks are probably not *hotter* than the rocks below,

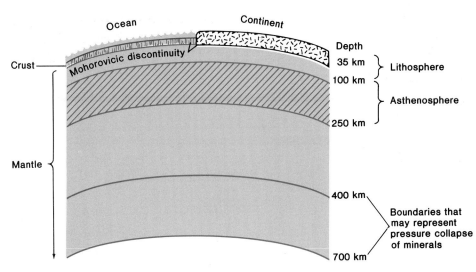

Figure 17.8 Concentric shell structure of the upper mantle. The lithosphere varies in thickness, but these variations are not shown.

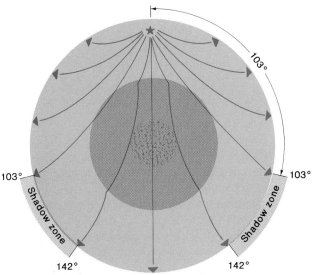

Figure 17.9 The *P*-wave shadow zone.

however, inasmuch as melting point is a function of both temperature and pressure.) If this is so, then the asthenosphere may represent (1) a zone where magma is likely to be generated, and (2) a zone where rocks are weaker than the rocks above and below.

Above the asthenosphere lies the **lithosphere** (figure 17.8). This is the outer shell of the earth, about 100 kilometers thick (it is thicker beneath continents than beneath oceans). It includes the crust and the upper part of the mantle that lies above the seismic low-velocity zone. The lithosphere is strong and relatively brittle and makes up the plates of plate tectonic theory. In the asthenosphere the mantle rocks are weaker than they are in the overlying lithosphere, so they deform easily by plastic flow. Plates of brittle lithosphere are thought to move readily over the asthenosphere, which may act as a lubricating layer below.

Data from seismic reflection and refraction indicate several concentric layers in the mantle (figure 17.8). It is doubtful that the layering is due to the presence of several different kinds of rock. Most geologists feel that the chemical composition of the mantle rock is about the same throughout the mantle. Because pressure increases with depth into the earth, the boundaries between mantle layers possibly represent depths at which pressure collapses the internal structure of certain minerals into denser forms (figure 17.8). For example, at a pressure equivalent to a depth of about 400 kilometers, the mineral *olivine* should collapse into a denser mineral called *spinel,* which has the same composition although it is more compact. If the concentric layers within the mantle represent pressure-caused transformations of minerals, then the entire mantle may have the same *chemical* composition throughout, although not the same *mineral* composition.

The Core
Seismic-wave data provide the primary evidence for the existence of the core of the earth. Seismic waves do not reach certain areas on the opposite side of the earth from a large earthquake. Figure 17.9 shows how *P* waves spread out from a quake until, at 103° of arc (11,500 km) from the epicenter, they suddenly disappear from seismograms. At more than 142° (15,500 km) from the epicenter, *P* waves reappear on seismograms. The region between 103° and 142°, which lacks *P* waves, is called the **P-wave shadow zone.**

The *P*-wave shadow zone can be explained by the refraction of *P* waves when they encounter the core boundary deep within the earth's interior. The size and shape of the core also can be determined because the paths of *P* waves can be accurately calculated. In figure 17.9, notice that the earth's core deflects the *P* waves and, in effect, "casts a shadow" where their energy does not reach the surface. In other words, *P* waves are missing within

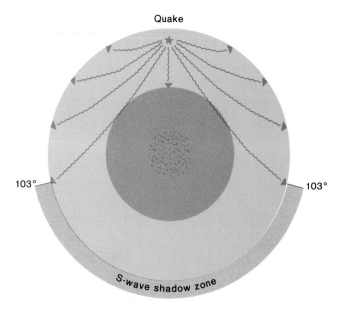

Figure 17.10 The S-wave shadow zone. Because no S waves pass through the core, it is suggested that the core acts like a liquid.

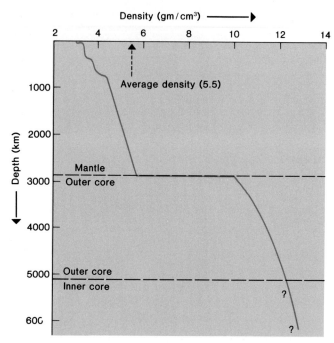

Figure 17.11 Density variations with depth into the earth. Note the great increase in density at the core-mantle boundary.

the shadow zone because they have been bent (refracted) by the core.

Chapter 16 explained that while *P* waves can travel through solids and fluids, *S* waves can travel only through solids. As figure 17.10 shows, an **S-wave shadow zone** also exists, larger than the *P*-wave shadow zone. *S* waves are not recorded in the entire region more than 103° away from the epicenter. The *S*-wave shadow zone seems to indicate that *S* waves do not travel through the core at all. If this is true, it implies that the core of the earth is a liquid, or at least acts like a liquid.

The way in which *P* waves are refracted within the earth's core (as shown by careful analysis of seismograms) suggests that the core is differentiated into two parts, a *liquid outer core* and a *solid inner core*.

Composition of the core When evidence from astronomy and seismic-wave studies is combined with knowledge about the properties of materials, it appears that the earth's core is made of metal—not rock—and that this metal is probably iron (along with a minor amount of sulfur or nickel). How did geologists arrive at this conclusion?

The overall density of the earth is 5.5 gm/cm³, according to astronomers who calculate the speed of the earth's revolution about the sun and the speed of its rotation on its own axis. The crustal rocks are relatively light in weight, from 2.7 gm/cm³ for granite to 3.0 gm/cm³ for basalt. The ultramafic rock thought to make up the mantle probably has a density of 3.3 gm/cm³ in the upper mantle, although rock pressure should raise this

value to about 5.5 gm/cm³ at the base of the mantle (figure 17.11).

If the crust and the mantle, which have approximately 85 percent of the earth's volume, are at or below the average density of the earth, then the core must be very heavy to bring the average up to 5.5 gm/cm³.

Calculations show that the core has to have a density of about 10 gm/cm³ at the core-mantle boundary, increasing to 12 or 13 gm/cm³ at the center of the earth (figure 17.11). This great density would be enough to give the earth an average density of 5.5 gm/cm³.

Under the great pressures existing in the core, iron would have a density slightly greater than that required in the core. Iron mixed with a small amount of a lighter element, such as sulfur, would have the required density. Therefore, many geologists feel that such a mixture makes up the core.

But a study of density by itself is hardly convincing evidence that the core is mostly iron, for many other heavy substances could be there instead. The choice of iron as the major component of the core comes from looking at meteorites that have fallen to earth. Meteorites are thought by some scientists to be remnants of the basic material that created our own solar system. An estimated 10 percent of meteorites are composed of iron mixed with small amounts of nickel. Material similar to these meteorites may have helped create the earth, perhaps settling to the center of the earth because of its high density. The composition of these meteorites, then, may tell us what is in the earth's core. Nickel is heavier than iron, however, so a mixture of just iron and nickel would have a density greater than that required in the core. (The other 90 percent of meteorites are mostly ultramafic rock and perhaps represent material that formed the earth's mantle.)

Curiously, some core material may be exposed at the earth's surface in Josephine County, Oregon. Pebbles composed of iron and nickel are found in stream gravels there. Some think that this iron-nickel mixture, called *josephinite,* represents core material that somehow rose through the earth's mantle and crust to the earth's surface. This hypothesis is difficult to prove, of course, and the origin of josephinite is controversial.

Seismic and density data, together with assumptions based on meteorite compositions, point to a core that is largely iron, with at least the outer part being liquid. The existence of the earth's magnetic field, which is discussed later in this chapter, also suggests a metallic core. Of course, no geologist has seen the core, nor is anyone likely to in the foreseeable future. But since so many lines of indirect evidence point to a liquid metal core, most geologists and scientists in other fields accept this theory as the best conclusion that can be made about the core's composition. Geologists could be wrong about the earth's interior, but the current model of a solid rock mantle and a liquid metallic core with a solid inner core is widely accepted because it is consistent with all available knowledge.

Isostasy

Isostasy is a balance or *equilibrium* between adjacent blocks of brittle crust "floating" on the plastic upper mantle. Since crustal rocks weigh less than mantle rocks, the crust can be considered to float on the denser mantle much as wood floats on water (figure 17.12).

Blocks of wood floating on water rise or sink until they displace an amount of water equal to their own weight. The weight of the displaced water buoys up the wood blocks, allowing them to float. The higher a wood block appears above the water surface, the deeper the block goes under water. Thus a tall block has a deep "root."

In a greatly simplified way, crustal rocks can be thought of as tending to rise or sink gradually until they are balanced by the weight of displaced mantle rocks. This concept of vertical movement to reach equilibrium is called **isostatic adjustment.** Just as with the blocks of wood, once crustal blocks have come into isostatic balance, a tall block (a mountain range) extends deep into the mantle (a *mountain root,* as shown in figure 17.12).

Figure 17.12 shows both the blocks of wood and the blocks of crustal rock in isostatic balance. The weight of the wood is equal to the weight of the displaced water.

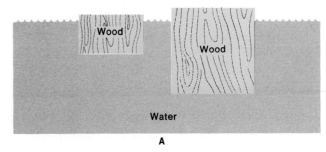

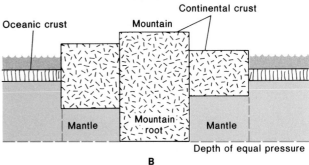

Figure 17.12 Isostatic balance. (*A*) Wood blocks float in water with most of their bulk submerged. (*B*) Crustal blocks "float" on mantle in approximately the same way. The thicker the block, the deeper it floats.

Similarly, the weight of the crustal blocks is equal to the weight of the displaced mantle. As a result, the rocks (and overlying seawater) in figure 17.12 can be thought of as separated into vertical columns, each with the same pressure at its base. At some *depth of equal pressure,* each column is in balance with the other columns, for each column has the same weight. A column of thick continental crust (a mountain and its root) has exactly the same weight as a column containing thin continental crust and some of the upper mantle. A column containing seawater, thin oceanic crust, and a thick section of heavy mantle weighs the same as the other two columns.

Visualizing the crust as isolated blocks moving vertically past each other does not really give a good picture of crustal structure. Generally vertical faults do not separate the crust into discrete blocks. It is more accurate to think of the crust as bending in broad warps and flexures without vertical faults.

Let us look at some examples of isostatic balance (equilibrium) in crustal rocks. Suppose that two sections of crust of unequal thickness are next to each other as in figure 17.13. Sediment from the higher part, which is subject to more rapid erosion, is deposited on the lower part. The decrease in weight from the high part causes it to rise, while the increasing weight on the low part causes it to sink. These vertical movements (isostatic adjustment) do actually take place whenever large volumes of material are eroded from or deposited on parts of the crust.

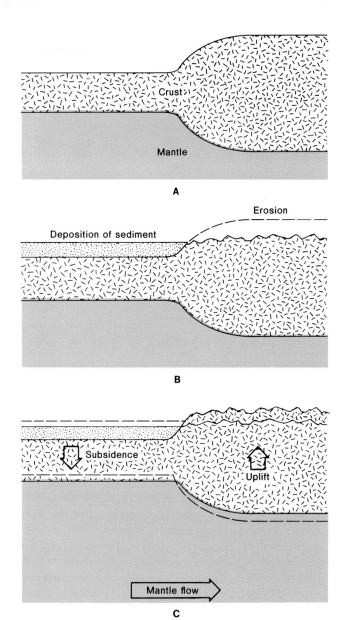

Figure 17.13 Isostatic adjustment due to erosion and deposition of sediment. Rock within the mantle must flow to accommodate vertical motion of crustal blocks. Mantle flow occurs in asthenosphere, deeper than shown in *C*.

Rise or fall of the crust, of course, requires plastic flow of the mantle to accommodate the motion. By measuring the rate of rise or fall, the viscosity of the mantle can be calculated. It is likely that the plastic flow of the mantle takes place within the asthenosphere in the upper mantle.

The upward movement of large areas of the crust that has been going on since the glacial ages provides another

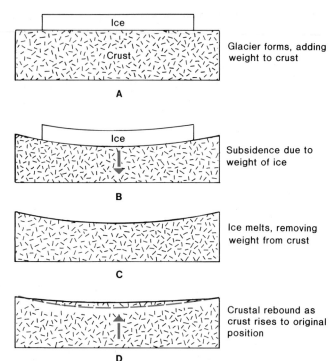

Figure 17.14 The weight of glaciers depresses the crust, and the crust rebounds when the ice melts.

example of isostatic adjustment. The weight of the thick continental ice sheets during the Pleistocene Epoch depressed the crust underneath the ice (figure 17.14). After the melting of the ice, the crust rose back upward, a process that is still going on in some areas (figure 17.15). This rise of the crust after the removal of the ice is known as **crustal rebound.**

Another example of isostatic adjustment may occur at subduction zones. As you have seen in chapters 3 and 4, a subducting plate may generate molten magma, which sometimes rises all the way to the surface to erupt as lava. Some geologists feel, however, that in certain cases the magma may stop at the base of an overlying continent (or perhaps within the continent near its base). This accumulation of magma can locally thicken the continent when the magma cools (figure 17.16*A*). The thickening of continents from below (which is not accepted by all geologists) causes the crust to be out of isostatic equilibrium, so it rises, reestablishing equilibrium and forming a mountain range (figure 17.16*B*).

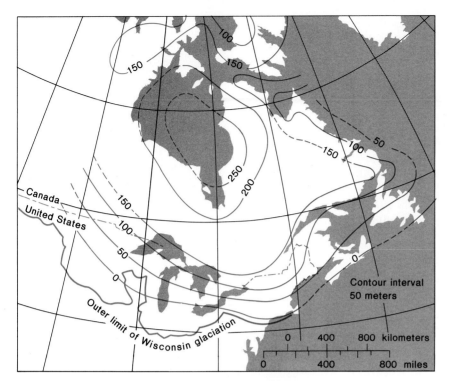

Figure 17.15 Uplift of land surface caused by crustal rebound after glaciers melted. Lines show the amount of uplift in meters since the ice disappeared.
From Phillip B. King, "Tectonics of Quaternary Time in Middle North America," in *The Quaternary of the United States,* H. C. Wright, Jr. and David G. Frey, eds., fig. 4A, p. 836. Reprinted by permission of Princeton University Press.

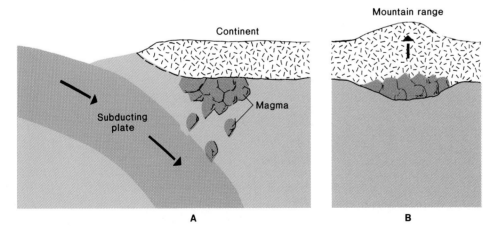

Figure 17.16 Isostatic uplift as a result of crustal thickening from below. (*A*) Rising blobs of magma accumulate at the base of a continent, thickening the crust (base of lithosphere below continent not shown). (*B*) Uplift produces a mountain range.

Gravity Measurements

The force of gravity between two objects varies with the masses of the objects and the distance between them (figure 17.17):

Force of gravity between A and B $= \text{constant} \left(\dfrac{\text{mass}_A \times \text{mass}_B}{\text{distance}^2} \right).$

The force increases with an increase in either mass. The gravitational attraction between the earth and the moon, for example, is vastly greater then the extremely small attraction that exists between two bowling balls. The equation also shows that force decreases with the square of the distance between the two objects. The gravitational attraction between the earth and the sun is less than the earth-moon attraction because the sun is so much farther away than the moon (the increased distance overrides the fact that the sun has a greater mass than the moon).

A useful tool for studying the crust and upper mantle is the **gravity meter,** which measures the gravitational attraction between the earth and a mass within the instrument. One use of the gravity meter is to explore for local variations in rock density (mass = density × volume). Dense rock such as metal ores and ultramafic rock will pull strongly on the mass inside the meter (figure 17.18*A*). The strong pull stretches a spring, and the amount of stretching can be very precisely determined. A gravity meter can, therefore, be used to explore for metallic ore deposits. A cavity or a body of low-density material such as sediment causes a much weaker pull on the meter's mass (figure 17.18*B*).

One of the most important uses of a gravity meter is to discover whether regions are in isostatic equilibrium. If a region is in isostatic balance, as in figure 17.19, then each column of rock has the same mass. If a gravity meter were carried across the rock columns, it would register the same amount of gravitational attraction for each column.

Some regions, however, are held up out of isostatic equilibrium by deep tectonic forces. Figure 17.20 shows a region with uniformly thick crust. Tectonic forces are holding the center of the region up. This uplift creates a mountain range without a mountain root. There is a thicker section of heavy mantle rock under the mountain range than there is on either side of the mountain range. The central "column" therefore has more mass than the neighboring columns, and a gravity meter shows that the gravitational attraction is correspondingly greater over the central than over the side columns.

A gravity reading higher than the normal regional gravity is called a **positive gravity anomaly** (figure 17.20). It can indicate that tectonic forces are holding a region up out of isostatic equilibrium, as shown in figure 17.20.

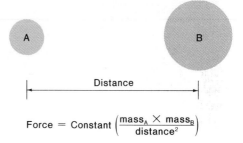

Force = Constant $\left(\dfrac{\text{mass}_A \times \text{mass}_B}{\text{distance}^2} \right)$

Figure 17.17 The force of gravitational attraction between two objects is a function of the masses of the objects and the distance between them (see text).

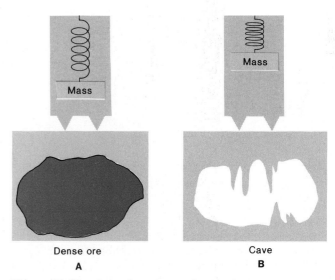

Figure 17.18 A gravity meter reading is affected by the density of the rocks beneath it. (*A*) Dense ore pulls strongly on the mass within the meter. (*B*) A cave causes a weak pull on the mass.

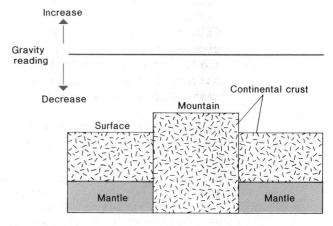

Figure 17.19 A region in isostatic balance gives a uniform gravity reading (no gravity anomalies).

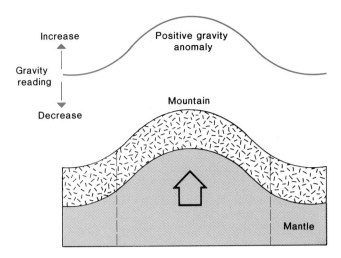

Figure 17.20 A region being held up out of isostatic equilibrium gives a positive gravity anomaly.

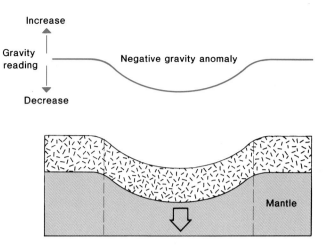

Figure 17.21 A region being held down out of isostatic equilibrium gives a negative gravity anomaly.

When the forces stop acting, the land surface sinks until it reestablishes isostatic balance. The gravity anomaly then disappears. For the region shown in figure 17.20, equilibrium would be established when the land surface became level.

Another cause of positive gravity anomalies, particularly small ones, is local concentrations of dense rock such as metal ore. The gravity meter in figure 17.18*A* is registering a positive gravity anomaly over ore (the spring inside the meter is stretched). Since there can be more than one cause for a positive gravity anomaly, geologists may disagree about the interpretation of anomalies. Drilling into a region with a gravity anomaly can usually disclose the reason for the anomaly.

A region can be held down, out of isostatic equilibrium, as shown in figure 17.21. The mass deficiency in such a region produces a **negative gravity anomaly**—a gravity reading lower than the normal regional gravity. Negative gravity anomalies can indicate either that a region is being held down (figure 17.21) or that local mass deficiencies exist for other reasons (figure 17.18*B*).

The greatest negative gravity anomalies in the world are found over oceanic trenches (chapters 19 and 20). These negative anomalies are interpreted to mean that trenches are actively being held down and are out of isostatic balance.

The Earth's Magnetic Field

A region of magnetic force, or **magnetic field,** surrounds the earth. The invisible lines of magnetic force surrounding the earth deflect magnetized objects, such as compass needles, that are free to move. The field has north and south **magnetic poles,** one near the geographic North Pole,

the other near the geographic South Pole. (Because it has two poles, the earth's field is called *dipolar*.) The strength of the magnetic field is greatest at the magnetic poles where magnetic lines of force appear to leave and enter the earth vertically (figure 17.22).

Because of the importance of the compass in navigation, scientific observations of the earth's magnetism have been made for centuries. It has long been known that the magnetic poles are displaced about 11½° from the geographic poles (about which the earth rotates). Furthermore, changes in position of the magnetic poles have been well documented, especially since the time of the great explorations of the globe. The magnetic poles appear to be slowly moving around the geographic poles. The separation between the two types of poles has probably never been much greater than it is today.

More recently, geophysical studies have been directed toward the *source* of the earth's magnetism. The rapid rate of the poles' changes in position together with the strength of the magnetic field strongly suggest that the magnetic field is generated within the liquid metal of the outer core rather than within the solid rock of the crust or the mantle.

How is earth's magnetic field generated? A number of hypotheses have been put forth to account for earth magnetism. One widely accepted hypothesis suggests that the magnetic field is created by electric currents within the slowly circulating liquid part of the core. The core is, in other words, an electrical conductor. Metals are good conductors of electricity, whereas rock is generally a poor electrical conductor. Indirectly, this is further evidence that the core is metallic.

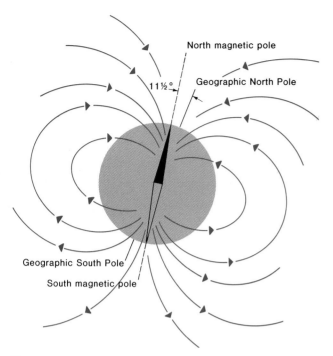

Figure 17.22   The earth's magnetic field.

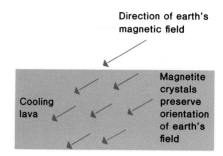

Figure 17.23   Some rocks preserve a record of the earth's magnetic field.

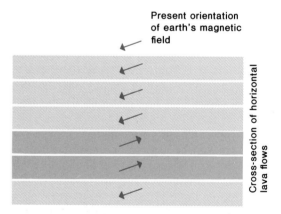

Normal   Reverse

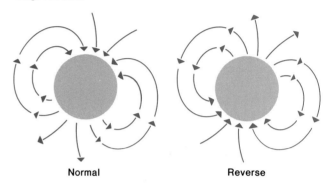

Figure 17.24   Stacked lava flows show evidence of magnetic reversals.

Magnetic Reversals

In the 1950s evidence began to accumulate that the earth's magnetic field had reversed its polarity periodically in the past. Such a change in the polarity of the earth's magnetic field is a **magnetic reversal.** During a time of *normal polarity,* magnetic lines of force leave the earth near the geographic South Pole and reenter the earth near the geographic North Pole (figure 17.22). During a time of *reversed polarity,* the magnetic lines of force run the other way, leaving the earth near the North Pole and entering the earth near the South Pole. In other words, during a magnetic reversal, the north magnetic pole and the south magnetic pole exchange positions.

Many rocks contain a record of the strength and direction of the earth's magnetic field *at the time the rocks formed.* When the mineral magnetite, for example, is crystallizing in a cooling lava flow, the atoms within the crystals respond to the earth's magnetic field and form magnetic alignments that "point" toward the north magnetic pole. As the rocks solidify, this magnetic record is permanently trapped in the rock (figure 17.23). Unless the rock is heated again, this magnetic record is retained and can be studied to determine what the direction of the earth's magnetic field was at the time the lava cooled. Other rock types, including sedimentary rocks stained red by iron compounds, also record former magnetic field directions. The study of ancient magnetic fields is called **paleomagnetism.**

Most of the evidence for magnetic reversals comes from lava flows on the continents. Paleomagnetic studies of a series of stacked lava flows often show that some of the lava flows indicate a magnetic orientation directly opposite to the earth's present orientation (figure 17.24). That is, at the time these lava flows cooled, the magnetic poles had exchanged positions. During this time of magnetic reversal, a compass needle would have pointed south rather than north. Many periods of normal and reverse magnetization are recorded in continental lava flows. They are worldwide events. Since lava flows can be dated radioactively, the actual time of these reversals in the earth's past can be determined. The times of normal and reversed magnetization are shown for the past 4.5 million years in figure 17.25.

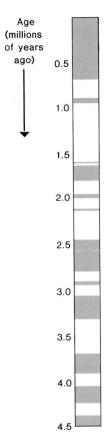

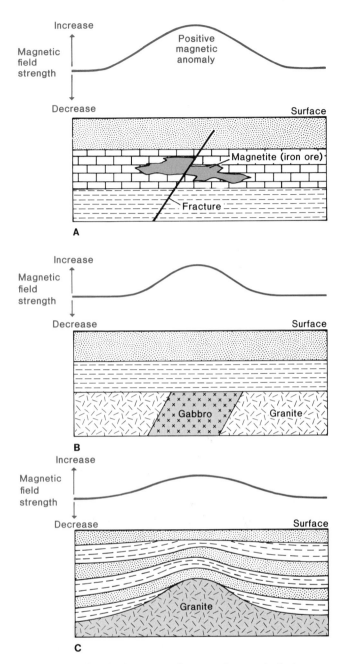

Figure 17.25 Magnetic reversals during the past 4.5 million years. Color represents normal magnetism; white represents reverse magnetism.

From A. Cox, 1969, *Science*, vol. 163, p. 240, copyright 1969 by the American Association for the Advancement of Science.

Magnetic Anomalies

A **magnetometer** is an instrument used to measure the strength of the earth's magnetic field. A magnetometer can be carried over the land surface or it can be flown over land or sea. At sea, magnetometers can also be towed behind ships.

The strength of the earth's magnetic field varies from place to place. As with gravity, a deviation from average readings is called an *anomaly*. Very broad regional magnetic anomalies may be due to *circulation patterns in the liquid outer core* or to other deep-seated causes. Smaller anomalies generally reflect *variations in rock type,* for the magnetism of near-surface rocks adds to the main magnetic field generated in the core. Rocks differ in their magnetism, depending upon their content of iron-containing minerals.

A **positive magnetic anomaly** is a reading of magnetic field strength that is higher than the regional average. Figure 17.26 shows three geologic situations that can cause positive magnetic anomalies. In figure 17.26*A*, a

Figure 17.26 Positive magnetic anomalies can indicate hidden ore and geologic structures.

body of magnetite ore (a highly magnetic ore of the metal iron) has been emplaced in a bed of limestone by hot solutions rising along a fracture. The magnetism of the iron ore adds to the magnetic field of the earth, giving a stronger magnetic field measurement at the surface (a positive anomaly). In figure 17.26*B* a large dike of gabbro has intruded into granitic basement rock. Because gabbro contains more ferromagnesian minerals than granite, gabbro is more magnetic than is granite and causes a positive magnetic anomaly. Figure 17.26*C* shows a granitic basement high (perhaps originally a hill) that has influenced

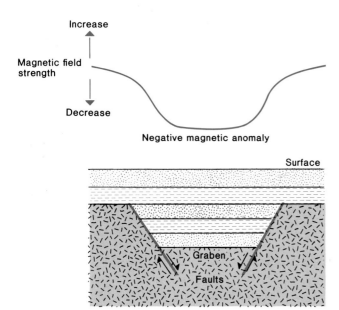

Figure 17.27 A graben filled with sediment can give a negative gravity anomaly.

later sediment deposits, causing a draping of the layers as the sediments on the hilltop compacted less than the thicker sediments to the sides. Such a structure can form an *oil trap* (see chapter 21). The granite in the hill contains some iron in its ferromagnesian minerals, so a small positive magnetic anomaly occurs where the rock is closer to the surface, increasing the magnetic field strength. Note how each example shows horizontal sedimentary rocks at the surface, with no surface hint of the subsurface geology. The magnetometer can thus help find hidden ores and geologic structures.

A **negative magnetic anomaly** is a reading of magnetic field strength that is lower than the regional average. Figure 17.27 shows how a negative anomaly can be produced by a downdropped fault block (a *graben*) in igneous rock. The thick sedimentary fill above the graben is less magnetic than is the igneous rock, so a weaker field (a negative magnetic anomaly) develops over the thick sediment.

Not all local magnetic anomalies are caused by variations in rock type. The linear magnetic anomalies found at sea are apparently caused by a *variation in the direction of magnetism,* as you will see in chapter 19.

Heat Within the Earth

Geothermal Gradient

The temperature increase with depth into the earth is called the **geothermal gradient.** The geothermal gradient can be measured on land in abandoned wells or on the sea floor by dropping specially designed probes into the mud. The average temperature increase is 25°C per kilometer (about 75°F per mile) of depth. Some regions have a

much higher gradient, indicating concentrations of heat at shallow depths. Such regions have a potential for the generation of *geothermal energy* (chapter 11).

The temperature increase creates a problem in deep mines, such as in a three-kilometer-deep gold mine in South Africa, where the temperature is close to the boiling point of water. Deep mines must be cooled by air-conditioning so that the miners can survive. High temperatures at depth also complicate the drilling of deep oil wells. A well drilled to a depth of seven or eight kilometers must pass through rock with a temperature of 200°C. At such high temperatures, a tough steel drilling pipe will become soft and flexible unless it is cooled with a special mud solution pumped down the hole.

Geologists believe that the geothermal gradient must taper off sharply a short distance into the earth. The high values of 25°C/kilometer recorded near the earth's surface could not continue very far into the earth. If they did, the temperature would be 2,500°C at the shallow depth of 100 kilometers. This temperature is above the melting point of all rocks at that depth—even though the increased pressure with depth into the earth increases the melting point of rocks. Seismic evidence seems to show a solid, not molten, mantle, so the geothermal gradient must drop to as low as 1°C/kilometer within the mantle (figure 17.28*A*).

At the boundary between the inner core and the outer core, there would be some constraints on possible temperatures if the core is molten metal above the boundary and solid metal below. The weight of the thick rock layer of the mantle and the liquid metal of the outer core raises the pressure at this boundary (figure 17.28*B*) to about 3 million atmospheres. (An *atmosphere* of pressure is force per unit area caused by the weight of the air in the atmosphere. It is equal to 14.7 pounds per square inch.) Calculations show that a temperature of 3,700°C (±500°C) at this pressure would melt the metal of the outer core. The inner core would remain solid because of the greater pressure upon it. Geologists feel reasonably certain, therefore, that the temperature at the boundary between the inner core and the outer core is about 3,700°C and probably rises to about 4,000°C at the center of the core (figure 17.28*A*). These values, of course, are only estimates, but they fit well with the picture of the earth's interior that geologists accept today.

Heat Flow

A small but measurable amount of heat from the earth's interior is being lost gradually through the earth's surface. This gradual loss of heat through the earth's surface is called the **heat flow.** No one is sure of the origin of the heat. It could be "original" heat from the time that the earth formed; that is, *if* the earth formed as a hot mass

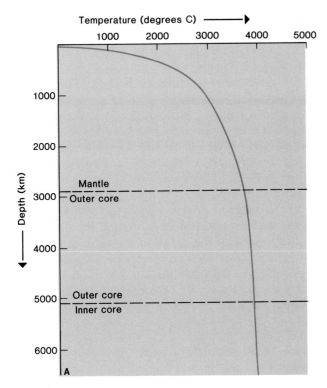

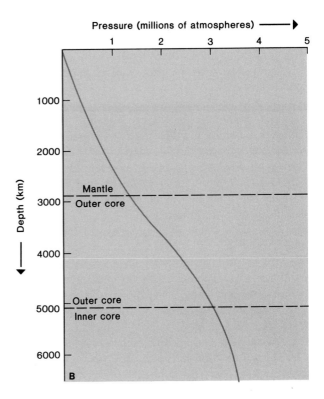

Figure 17.28 Distribution of (*A*) temperature and (*B*) pressure with depth into the earth.

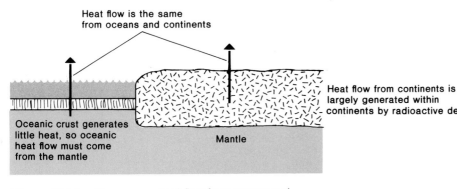

Figure 17.29 The average heat flow from oceans and continents is the same, but the origin of the heat differs from the ocean to continents.

that is now cooling down. Or the heat could be a by-product of the decay of radioactive isotopes inside the earth. Radioactive decay *may* actually be warming up the earth. Geologists are not sure whether the earth formed as a hot or cold mass, or whether the earth is now cooling off or warming up. Changes in the earth's temperature are extremely slow, and trying to work out its thermal history is a slow, often frustrating, job.

The average heat flow from continents is the same as the average heat flow from the sea floor, a surprising fact if you consider the greater concentration of radioactive material in continental rock (figure 17.29). The unexpectedly high average heat flow under the ocean may be due to hot mantle rock rising slowly by convection under parts of the ocean (chapter 1). Regional patterns of high heat flow and low heat flow on the sea floor may also be explained by convection of mantle rock (chapter 19).

Summary

The interior of the earth is studied indirectly by *geophysics*—a study of seismic waves, gravity, earth magnetism, and earth heat.

Seismic reflection and *seismic refraction* can indicate the presence of boundaries between rock layers.

The earth is divided into three major units—the *crust,* the *mantle,* and the *core.*

The earth's crust beneath oceans is seven kilometers thick and made of basalt (*sima*). Continental crust is 30–50 kilometers thick and made of rock that has the same seismic velocity as granite (*sial*).

The *Mohorovicic discontinuity* separates the crust from the mantle.

The mantle is a layer of solid rock 2,900 kilometers thick, and probably composed of an ultramafic rock such as peridotite. Seismic waves show the mantle to have a structure of concentric shells, perhaps caused by pressure transformations of minerals.

The *low-velocity zone* (asthenosphere) occurs at a depth of about 100 kilometers and may represent rock close to its melting point. It is probably the region of most magma generation and isostatic adjustment.

The *lithosphere,* which forms plates, is made up of brittle crust and upper mantle. It is about 100 kilometers thick. Plastic *asthenosphere* underlies the lithosphere.

Seismic-wave shadow zones show the core to have a radius of 3,450 kilometers and to be divided into a liquid outer core and a solid inner core. A core composition of iron mixed with sulfur (and perhaps nickel) is suggested by the earth's density, the composition of meteorites, and existence of the earth's magnetic field.

Isostasy is an equilibrium between crustal columns floating on plastic mantle. *Isostatic adjustment* occurs when weight is added to or subtracted from a column of rock. *Crustal rebound* is isostatic adjustment that is occurring after the melting of glacial ice.

A *gravity meter* can be used to study variations in rock density or to find regions that are out of isostatic equilibrium.

A *positive gravity anomaly* forms over dense rock or over regions being held up out of isostatic balance. A *negative gravity anomaly* indicates low-density rock or a region being held down.

The earth's *magnetic field* has two *magnetic poles,* probably generated by slow circulation and electric currents in the earth's outer core.

Some rocks can record the earth's magnetism at the time they formed. *Paleomagnetism* is the study of ancient magnetic fields.

Magnetic reversals of polarity occurred in the past, with the north magnetic pole and south magnetic pole exchanging positions. Radioactive dating of rocks can show the age of the reversals.

A *magnetometer* measures the strength of the earth's magnetic field.

A *positive magnetic anomaly* develops over rock that is more magnetic than neighboring rock. A *negative magnetic anomaly* indicates rock with low magnetism.

Magnetic anomalies can also be caused by circulation patterns in the earth's core and by variations in the direction of rock magnetism.

The *geothermal gradient* is about 25°C/kilometer near the earth's surface, but decreases rapidly with depth. The temperature at the center of the earth is probably near 4,000°C. *Heat flow* measurements show that heat loss per unit area from continents and oceans is about the same, perhaps because of convection of hot mantle rock beneath the oceans.

Terms to Remember

asthenosphere
core
crust
crustal rebound
geophysics
geothermal gradient
gravity meter
heat flow
isostasy
isostatic adjustment
lithosphere
low-velocity zone
magnetic field
magnetic poles
magnetic reversal
magnetometer
mantle
Mohorovicic discontinuity
negative gravity anomaly
negative magnetic anomaly
paleomagnetism
positive gravity anomaly
positive magnetic anomaly
P-wave shadow zone
seismic reflection
seismic refraction
sial
sima
S-wave shadow zone

Questions for Review

1. Describe how seismic reflection and seismic refraction show the presence of layers within the earth.
2. Sketch a cross section through the entire earth showing the main subdivisions of the earth's interior and indicating the name, thickness, and probable composition of each.
3. What facts point to a probable iron composition for the earth's core?
4. Describe the differences between continental crust and oceanic crust.
5. What is a gravity anomaly, and what does it generally indicate about the rocks in the region where it is found?
6. Discuss seismic-wave shadow zones and what they indicate about the earth's interior.
7. Describe the earth's magnetic field. Where is it generated?
8. What is the temperature distribution with depth into the earth?
9. Heat flow has been found to be about equal through continents and the sea floor. Why was this unexpected? What might cause this equality?
10. What is the Mohorovicic discontinuity?
11. What is the low-velocity zone? Why is it important?
12. How does the lithosphere differ from the asthenosphere?
13. What is a magnetic reversal? What is the evidence for magnetic reversals?
14. What is a magnetic anomaly? How are magnetic anomalies measured at sea?

Questions for Thought

1. If the earth were hollow, what evidence would we have from seismic-wave shadow zones? Could a hollow earth have an average density of 5.5 gm/cm^3? Could a hollow earth have a magnetic field?
2. What isostatic adjustment of the sea floor takes place as huge amounts of sediment are deposited on it? Would this adjustment have any effect on sea level? Would the addition of the sediment to the sea have any other effect on sea level? (What effect does a boulder have if it is dropped into a brimful bathtub?)
3. Subsidence of the earth's surface sometimes occurs as reservoirs fill behind newly built dams. Why?

Supplementary Readings

Anderson, D. L. 1962. The plastic layer of the earth's mantle. *Scientific American* (July 1962). Offprint #855. San Francisco: W. H. Freeman.

Bolt, B. A. 1973. The fine structure of the earth's interior. *Scientific American* (March 1973). Offprint #906. San Francisco: W. H. Freeman.

Bullen, K. E. 1955. The interior of the earth. *Scientific American* (September 1955). Offprint #804. San Francisco: W. H. Freeman.

Clark, S. P. 1971. *Structure of the earth.* Englewood Cliffs, N.J.: Prentice-Hall.

Oliver, J. 1959. Long earthquake waves. *Scientific American* (March 1959). Offprint #827. San Francisco: W. H. Freeman.

Sumner, J. S. 1969. *Geophysics, geologic structures, and tectonics.* Dubuque, Iowa: Wm. C. Brown Company Publishers.

Wyllie, P. J. 1975. The earth's mantle. *Scientific American* (March 1975). Offprint #915. San Francisco: W. H. Freeman.

18

Mountain Belts and the Continental Crust

Purpose

As you begin to look at the major features of the earth's crust, in this chapter and the next, you are ready to bring together various specific aspects of physical geology and appreciate how they are interrelated. In this chapter we summarize what geologists have learned from a varied approach to the study of major mountain belts and continental crust; in the next chapter we show how geologic concepts have been used to interpret the nature of the sea floor and the oceanic crust.

Mountain belts evolve from marine-deposited rocks to towering peaks over hundreds of millions of years. Ultimately the peaks are eroded to plains and become part of the stable interior of a continent. To appreciate the long and complex process of mountain building, you need to know much of the material covered in previous chapters. For instance, you must understand structural geology in order to appreciate what a particular pattern of folds and faults can tell us about the history of mountain building in a particular region. To understand how the rocks formed during the various stages of a mountain belt's history means that you already know about volcanism, plutonism, sedimentation, and metamorphism. Your earlier study of weathering and erosion helps you understand how mountains are worn away.

Mountains, as everyone knows, are large terrain features that rise more or less abruptly from surrounding levels. Several kinds of mountains are of geologic interest but are not related to the topic of this chapter—for example, erosional remnants of plateaus (mesas). We are concerned here with the earth's **major mountain belts,** chains thousands of kilometers long composed of numerous mountain ranges. A **mountain range** is a group of closely spaced mountains or parallel ridges (figure 18.1). These ranges have been produced by intense deformation of part of the earth's crust or by extensive igneous activity.

Figure 18.1 View of glaciated peaks in one of the mountain ranges in the Andes mountain belt. A parallel but much lower range is visible at the extreme right skyline of the picture.

The map in figure 18.2 shows that most of the world's mountains are in long chains that extend for thousands of kilometers. The Himalaya, the Andes, the Alps, and the Appalachians are examples of major mountain belts, each comprising numerous mountain ranges. Although it is natural to compare mountains in terms of their height and shape, these aspects reflect mainly the extent to which uplift and erosion have progressed. They may be of little value in helping us understand the complex earlier history of a mountain range.

Geologists' knowledge about the evolution of mountain belts has been gained from many decades of study of the geologic structures and the rocks exposed in the mountains themselves. There the rocks that were once below the earth's surface can be seen and studied. Our knowledge of plutonism and metamorphism has been derived largely from the contributions of geologists working in mountainous regions. The general picture of how mountain belts were formed is the result of putting together the work of many individuals who did field work in many parts of the world.

Geologists find working in mountains difficult but challenging. Sometimes mountain ranges exhibit very complex interrelationships between rock units. Geologic structures that are necessary to an understanding of the events that took place may have been eroded away or may be buried underneath soil or glaciers. Mountaineering techniques may sometimes be the only way to reach rock exposures (figure 18.3).

Despite the complexities of individual ranges, the major characteristics of large mountain belts are surprisingly similar. We shall point out these general characteristics before presenting a sequence of events for the evolution of a "typical" mountain belt.

Characteristics of Major Mountain Belts

Size and Alignment

Major mountain belts are very long compared to how wide they are. For instance, the mountain belt that forms the western part of North America (the *North American Cordillera*) starts as the Aleutian Island arc in southwestern Alaska. The trend of the Aleutians is continuous with the trend of the mountain ranges that make up much of the Alaskan mainland (figure 18.4). Through Alaska the ranges trend more or less east-west, but in northern Canada they curve into a more north-south trend. The north-south ranges include the many individual ranges of western Canada and western United States. The belt is widest in the United States where it extends from the Coast Ranges of California and Oregon eastward to the Rocky Mountains of Montana, Wyoming, and Colorado. The belt narrows as the north-south trend continues through Mexico.

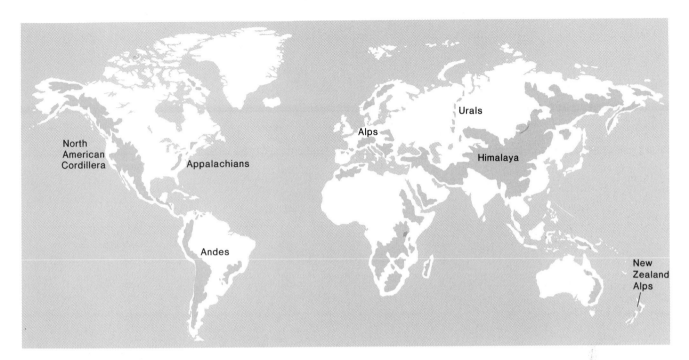

Figure 18.2 Map of the world showing major mountain belts.

Figure 18.3 Technical ciimbing is sometimes required for a geologist to work in mountains. Teton Range, Wyoming.

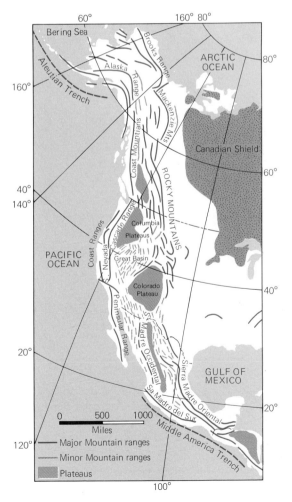

Figure 18.4 The mountain belts of Western North America. Some of the major ranges in the Cordillera are shown.

**Mountain Belts and
the Continental Crust** 347

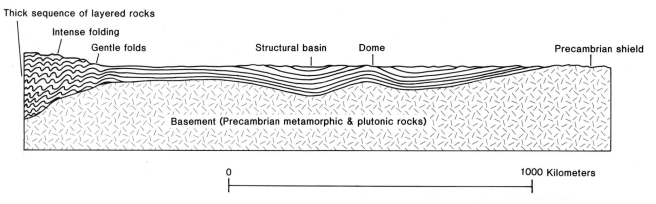

Figure 18.5   Schematic cross section through part of a mountain belt (*left*) and part of a continental interior (craton). Vertical scale is exaggerated.

Ages of Mountain Belts and Continents

The major mountain belts of the world that have higher mountain ranges tend to be geologically younger than those where mountains are lower. However, this is not always true. Most mountain regions show evidence that they were once high above sea level, were eroded to hills or low plains, and then rose again in a later episode of uplift. Such episodes of uplift and erosion may occur a number of times during the long history of a mountain range. Thus a newer range which is in a temporary erosional state may be low, or, by contrast, an old range in a temporary state of uplift may be high. Ultimately mountain ranges seem to stabilize and be eroded to plains.

On the North American continent, the Appalachian Mountains extend from eastern Canada southward through the eastern United States into Alabama. Fossils and radioactively determined ages of rocks in the Appalachians indicate that these mountains began to evolve earlier than did the mountain belt along the western coast of North America. The interior plains between the Appalachians and the Rockies are considered to have evolved from mountain belts in the very distant geologic past (early Precambrian). The once deep-seated roots of the former Precambrian mountain belts are the *basement* rock for the now stable central part of the continent. Layers of Paleozoic and younger sedimentary rock cover most of that basement. The great age of the mountain building episodes that preceded the Paleozoic sedimentation is confirmed by radioactively determined dates of over one billion years taken from the rocks in the few scattered locations where the basement is exposed. (These are the Grand Canyon in Arizona, the Ozark dome in Missouri,

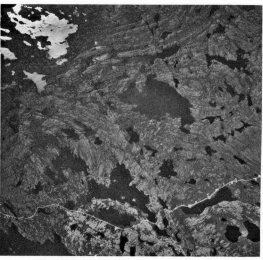

Figure 18.6   Aerial photograph of a portion of Precambrian shield (the Canadian shield) showing the pattern of foliation of intensely metamorphosed rock. The white line in the lower part of the picture is a road. Dark patches are small lakes.
National Air Photo Library of Canada.

the Black Hills of South Dakota, and the Adirondacks in New York). Continental interiors that have been structurally stable for a prolonged period of time are called **cratons** (figure 18.5).

Most of the central United States has a very thin layer—only 1,000–2,000 meters—of sedimentary rocks overlying its basement. However, in much of eastern Canada no sedimentary rocks whatsoever cover the eroded remnants of old mountain ranges (figure 18.6). Rather, this region is a **Precambrian shield;** that is, a complex of Precambrian metamorphic and plutonic rocks exposed over a large area. Such shields and basement complexes of cratons represent the roots of mountain ranges that completed the deformation process more than a billion years ago.

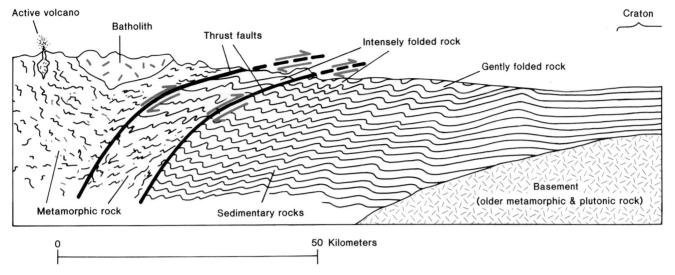

Active volcano

Batholith

Thrust faults

Intensely folded rock

Craton

Gently folded rock

Basement
(older metamorphic & plutonic rock)

Metamorphic rock

Sedimentary rocks

0   50 Kilometers

Figure 18.7 Schematic cross section of part of a mountain belt showing progressively more intense deformation from right to left of diagram. Vertical scale is expanded.

Thickness of Rock Layers

The relatively thin cover of sedimentary rock overlying the basement in the craton contrasts sharply with the thick sedimentary sequence of a mountain belt. In mountain belts, layered sedimentary rock commonly is more than 10 kilometers thick. The sedimentary rock in cratons may show no deformation or it may have been gently warped into basins and domes above the basement (figure 18.5). By contrast, mountain belts are characterized by tightly folded and faulted structures indicating intense deformation.

Most of the sedimentary rock in mountains is of marine origin, indicating that today's highlands must have been part of the sea floor in the geologic past. Commonly the part of a mountain belt closest to a present-day ocean contains much volcanically derived rock—volcanic ash, sediments from eroded volcanic rock, and great thicknesses of lava flows. This contrasts with the part of the belt commonly adjacent to the craton, which tends to consist mostly of rocks that are similar to those on the craton—limestones, shales, and sandstones, with only minor (if any) amounts of volcanic rock.

Patterns of Folding and Faulting

Reconstructing the original position and determining the thickness of layers of sedimentary and volcanic rock in mountain belts is complicated because in most instances the layered rocks have been folded and faulted at some time after they were deposited. Folding and faulting are generally more intense as one progresses from the stable interior of the continent further into the mountain belt

(figure 18.7). Folds near the craton are generally open (figure 18.8), becoming progressively tighter toward the center of the mountain belt. Large overturned and recumbent folds (figure 18.9) may be exposed in the interior portion of a mountain belt. Reverse faults and large thrust faults, some indicating several tens of kilometers of movement, are commonly found along with the tight folds. These folds and faults indicate tremendous compressive stress. The sedimentary rocks of the Alps, for instance, are estimated to have covered an area of ocean floor about 500 kilometers wide when they were deposited. They were later compressed into the present width of the Alps, which is less than 200 kilometers.

Metamorphism and Plutonism

A complex of regional metamorphic and plutonic rock is generally found in the mountain ranges of the most intensely deformed portions of major mountain belts (figure 18.7). Most of the metamorphic rocks were originally sedimentary and volcanic rocks that had been deeply buried and subjected to intense stress and high temperature. Where found, *migmatites* (interlayered granitic and metamorphic rocks) may represent those parts of the mountain belts that were once at even deeper levels in the crust, where higher temperatures caused partial melting of the rocks (as described in chapter 4). Granite batholiths indicate that large volumes of magma may have accumulated from partial melting of the lower crust (or upper mantle) and then welled upward, eventually to solidify.

Figure 18.8 Part of that portion of the Appalachian Mountains characterized by large, open folds. The ridges are sedimentary beds resistant to erosion and are part of the Cove Mountain syncline. The river is the Susquehanna. The area shown is near Harrisburg, Pennsylvania.
Photo by John S. Shelton.

Figure 18.9 Recumbent folds exposed on a mountainside in the Andes. Trace of a bedding plane is shown in color.

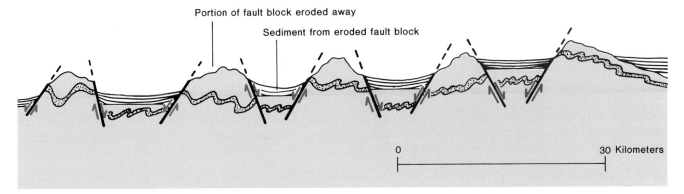

Figure 18.10 Fault block mountains with uplift along normal faults. Only one layer of previously folded rock is shown in order to highlight the pattern of offset due to normal faulting.

Episode of Normal Faulting
Older portions of some major mountain belts have undergone normal faulting (figure 18.10). Cross-cutting relationships show that the normal faulting occurred after the intense deformation that resulted in tight folding, thrust faulting, and metamorphism and after most batholiths had formed. The later stage of normal faulting is a result of vertical uplift or tensional stress. Either of these forces contrasts sharply with the compressive stress that caused the folding, thrust faulting, and metamorphism of the original marine rocks.

Thickness and Density of Rocks
Geophysical investigations yield additional information about mountains and the continental crust. As was discussed in chapter 17, gravity measurements indicate that the rocks of the continental crust and mountains are lighter (less dense) than those of the oceanic crust, and seismic velocities indicate a composition approximating that of granite. Furthermore, evidence from seismic studies supports the view that this lighter crust is much thicker beneath mountain belts than under the craton and that the crust is thicker under younger mountain belts than under older ones. The height of each mountain range within a belt tends to reflect the degree of isostatic compensation of lighter continental crust "floating" on heavier mantle material.

Features of Active Mountain Ranges
Frequent earthquakes are characteristic of portions of mountain belts that are geologically young and considered still "active." Also, deep ocean trenches are found parallel to many young mountain belts (the Andes, for example). Similar trenches lie off the coasts of island arcs, which are in many respects similar to very young mountain ranges. Isolated active volcanoes perched on top of older rock in a mountain range suggest that melting is still taking place at depth.

The Evolution of a Mountain Belt
Although each mountain belt differs in details, plate tectonics has given us a general picture of how mountain belts evolve. The evolution begins when sediment is deposited; it ends hundreds of millions of years later when the former mountain belt has become part of a craton. For discussion, three stages in the history of a mountain belt are described: (1) the accretion, (2) the orogenic, and (3) the uplift and block faulting stages.

The following paragraphs present an account of the first two stages from the perspective of plate tectonic theory. Specifically, they describe how a variety of mountain building processes are controlled by either plate divergence or plate convergence.

The Accretion Stage
As we noted earlier, mountain belts typically contain thick sequences of sedimentary and volcanic rocks. The accumulation of these great thicknesses (several kilometers) of sedimentary or volcanic rocks takes place in the **accretion stage** of mountain building. Most of the sedimentary rocks and much of the volcanic material accumulates in a marine environment. The source for the sediment deposited in the water must be a nearby landmass, belonging to either an adjoining continent or part of a volcanic island arc.

Accretion in an opening ocean basin   At present, sediment is eroding off the eastern portion of North America and is accumulating in the Atlantic Ocean basin adjoining the continent (as described in detail in chapter 19). Sedimentation has been going on here for tens of millions of years, and a great thickness of layered sedimentary rock has accumulated offshore. According to plate tectonics (described in more detail in chapter 20), accretion of sediment off the Atlantic coast began when North America and Europe split apart (which was during

Box 18.1
Ultramafic Rocks in Mountain Belts— From the Mantle to Talcum Powder

Ultramafic rocks (described in chapter 4) occur commonly in the portions of mountain belts occupied by metamorphic and plutonic rocks. Ultramafic rocks tend to crop out along long, narrow zones that parallel the trend of a mountain belt. Most geologists believe the bodies of ultramafic rocks represent mantle material that was faulted into the crust during the mountain-building process. Some of the ultramafic bodies are found associated with marine-deposited volcanic and sedimentary rocks, in a so-called *ophiolite sequence* (described more fully in chapter 19). This may represent a segment of a former oceanic floor together with its underlying mantle.

Ultramafic rocks in mountain belts commonly show the effects of the metamorphism that has altered adjacent rock units. Two of the foliated metamorphic products of ultramafic rocks are of special interest. One is *serpentinite,* a rock composed of the mineral serpentine. Another is a rock composed mostly of the mineral talc, commonly known as *soapstone.*

Serpentinite is a shiny, mottled, dark green and black rock that looks rather like a snake's skin. It splits apart easily along irregular, slippery, foliation surfaces. Hillsides or slopes with serpentinite as bedrock are sparsely vegetated because constant sliding prevents soil and vegetation from building up. Houses built out of ignorance on serpentinite hillsides also slide downslope. Serpentinite is the official state rock of California—a state in which a large number of homes have been destroyed because they were built on sliding hillsides. (Serpentinite, however, is not always to blame.)

Most asbestos is a fibrous variety of serpentine. Because it does not ignite or melt in fire, asbestos is valuable for a number of industrial applications. Woven into cloth, it is used to make suits for firefighters. It is also used as a fireproof insulation for homes and other buildings.

But serpentine causes cancer. People who work with asbestos and occasionally breathe fibers into their lungs have a high incidence of cancer. Similarly, individuals working with talc have a high incidence of cancer because soapstone usually has some serpentine fibers along with the talc.

In 1978 it was noted that a federal recreation area in California had concentrations of asbestos dust in the air that exceeded permissible levels for industry. The area is underlain by serpentinite. The surface is being eroded at a rapid rate because of heavy use by dune buggies and motorcycles and the dust raised by vehicles and by wind is approximately ninety percent asbestos fiber. Officials considered closing the area to recreation but decided instead to warn users to avoid repeated or long-term visits.

Soapstone, which is less common than serpentinite, is valuable mainly because of talc's softness (no. 1 on Mohs' scale). Many sculptures (most notably Eskimo carvings) are made from soapstone because of the ease with which it may be cut. The best-known product of talc, however, is talcum powder.

Talc's perfect cleavage has gained it a unique application in reflecting highway signs and center road stripes. Finely crushed talc is mixed with paint. The many fine, parallel cleavage flakes reflect light in a specific direction depending on how the mixture is brushed on the sign. For the signs showing different daytime and nighttime speed limits, the daytime speed limit is painted with ordinary black paint, and the nighttime limit is painted with talc mixed into the white paint. At night the light from a car's headlights reflects back to the car from the cleavage surfaces of many tiny flakes of talc.

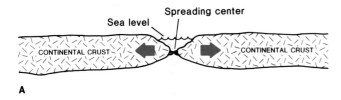

A

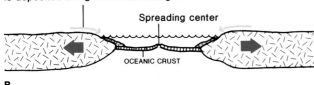

B

C

Figure 18.11 Sedimentation in an opening ocean basin. Not drawn to scale. (A) Beginning of continental breakup. (B) As spreading progresses, sediment is deposited on ocean floor along the continental margins. (C) The longer spreading continues, the greater the buildup of sediment.

the Jurassic Period, around the middle part of the Mesozoic Era). The two continents moved progressively further apart from a spreading center, the Mid-Atlantic Ridge. As the Atlantic Ocean basin opened, a progressively bigger mass of land-derived sediment built outward from the land at either side of the ocean (figure 18.11).

Sedimentary rock layers that accumulate under conditions such as we just described are shales, sandstones, and limestones. Volcanic rocks are rare or absent. Where we presently find thick sequences of shale, sandstone, and limestone cropping out in a mountain range, it is reasonable to assume that these rocks were originally deposited under conditions similar to those along the present continental margin of eastern North America.

Accretion along a converging boundary A large variety of rock types are created near a converging plate boundary. Volcanic rocks—most characteristically andesites—accumulate near the boundary either as pyroclastic layers or as flows. Sedimentary rocks, moreover, may accumulate in equal or greater amounts than volcanic rocks. Limestone, however, is usually absent or present in minor proportions. Shales and sandstones are the predominant sedimentary rock types. Typically, the sandstone contains grains of incompletely weathered igneous rock, indicating that it was derived from a nearby landmass containing

volcanic or plutonic rocks. (This contrasts with the sandstone deposited off the east coast of North America, which typically is composed mostly of grains of quartz.)

The source of this sedimentary as well as volcanic material is a **magmatic arc,** a chain of volcanoes or batholiths along a line (usually curved as seen from above). The magmatic arc has accumulated on and intruded the older igneous and metamorphic rocks of the continental crust (figure 18.12). The source of the magma is the underlying subduction zone.

Sediment eroded from the magmatic arc, as well as newly erupted pyroclastic debris, is transported to and deposited in the basins on either side of the arc. Typically, the basin to the seaward side will be underwater, at least initially, and in time will fill with sediment. Once the basin has filled, sediment may be transported beyond it and accumulate outward onto the deep ocean floor. However, as layers accumulate on the edge of the oceanic crust, they are pulled at least partially down the subduction zone, along with the underlying oceanic crust.

The Orogenic Stage
Intense deformation follows or is contemporanous with the accretion stage. An **orogeny** is an episode of intense deformation of the rocks in a region; the deformation is usually accompanied by metamorphism and igneous activity. During an orogeny, layered sedimentary and volcanic rocks are compressed into folds and broken by reverse and thrust faults. The more deeply buried rocks, subjected to regional metamorphism, are converted to schists and gneisses. Magma generated from very deep crustal rocks (or perhaps even from the upper mantle) may work its way upward to erupt in volcanoes or form large batholiths.

Orogenies and ocean-continent convergence The relationships among magmatism, metamorphism, and subduction were described in chapters 3, 4, and 7. Plate convergence also accounts for the folded and reverse-faulted layered rocks found in mountain belts. Newly formed layers of sedimentary and volcanic rock are caught between the oceanic plate and the craton and are compressed into folds and faults (for instance, the "younger folds and reverse faults" on the continental side of the magmatic arc in figure 18.13). As would be expected, rock that is pulled down the subduction zone is especially intensely deformed (for instance, the "deformed sedimentary rock" overlying oceanic crust in figure 18.13).

It is important to note that where there are converging boundaries, accumulation and deformation are occurring simultaneously. In other words, the accretion stage and the orogenic stage are taking place at the same time. This was not evident to early geologists, who did not have the

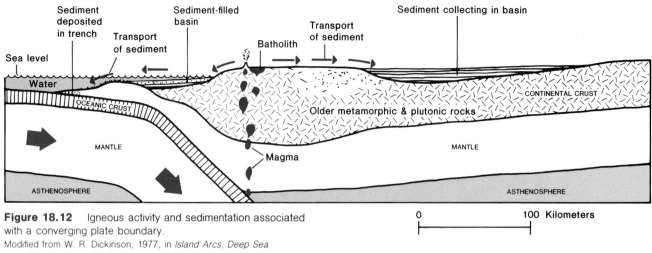

Figure 18.12 Igneous activity and sedimentation associated with a converging plate boundary.
Modified from W. R. Dickinson, 1977, in *Island Arcs, Deep Sea Trenches and Back-Arc Basins* (pp. 33–40), copyrighted by American Geophysical Union.

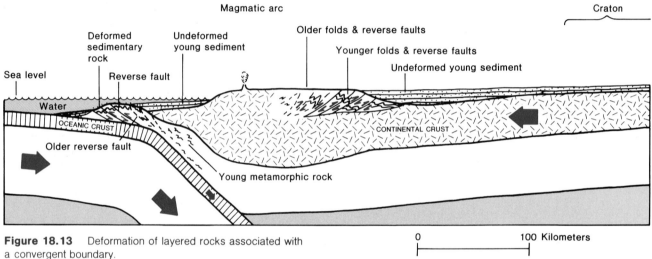

Figure 18.13 Deformation of layered rocks associated with a convergent boundary.
Modified from W. R. Dickinson, 1977, in *Island Arcs, Deep Sea Trenches and Back-Arc Basins* (pp. 33–40), copyrighted by American Geophysical Union.

perspective of plate tectonic theory for understanding mountain building (see box 18.2). They generally assumed that the accretion stage would end before the orogenic stage would begin.

Orogenies and continent-continent convergence

The North Atlantic Ocean continues to widen due to spreading along the Mid-Atlantic Ridge. North America as well as the western Atlantic Ocean floor are propelled westward from the spreading center while the eastern Atlantic Ocean floor and Europe move eastward. Accretion continues on both sides of the Atlantic. An orogeny is not taking place because there is no subduction. But suppose spreading ceased along the present diverging boundary and the Atlantic Ocean began to close (figure 18.14). A new subduction zone would develop at one or

Figure 18.14 A mountain belt due to continental-continental collision. (*A*) Accumulation of sediment along the margins of two continents that are moving away from each other. (*B*) Spreading ceases and ocean basin begins closing. A subduction zone develops at one continental margin. Sedimentary rock that had formed at the edge of the continent becomes folded and faulted. (*C*) The ocean continues to close. (*D*) As ocean basin becomes completely closed, colliding sedimentary rocks are folded and faulted. Subduction stops when the more buoyant continental crust is partially subducted.
Modified from W. R. Dickinson, 1977, in *Island Arcs, Deep Sea Trenches and Back-Arc Basins* (pp. 33–40), copyrighted by American Geophysical Union.

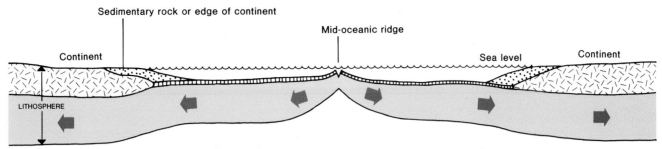

A Accumulation of sediment along the margins of two continents that are moving away from each other.

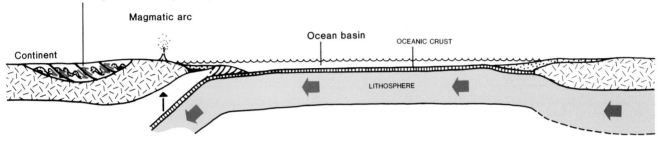

B Spreading ceases and ocean basin begins closing. A subduction zone develops at the continental margin. Sedimentary rock that had formed at the edge of the continent becomes folded and faulted.

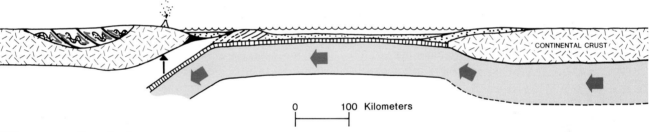

C The ocean continues to close.

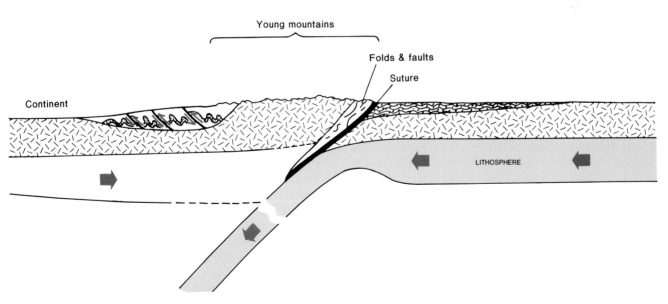

D As ocean basin becomes completely closed, colliding sedimentary rocks are folded and faulted. Subduction stops when the more buoyant continental crust is partially subducted.

Box 18.2
Geosynclines and Geoclines

In 1859 James Hall, an early American geologist with the New York Geological Survey, introduced the concept of a *geosyncline* (the name, however, came later). A geosyncline, as conceived by Hall, is a great, elongate downwarp of the earth's crust, about the length and width of a mountain belt, which accumulates thicknesses of thousands of meters of sedimentary and volcanic rock. Geosynclines were postulated to account for the great thicknesses of sedimentary and volcanic rock layers observed in mountain belts. For approximately a hundred years geologists accepted the idea that a geosyncline was a necessary predecessor of a mountain belt.

Geosynclines were regarded as bordering continents along one edge of the subsiding trough and bounded by a line of volcanic islands at the seaward side of the trough. In 1940 the volcanic portion of the geosyncline was named the *eugeosyncline* and the nonvolcanic portion nearer the continent was called the *miogeosyncline.*

With the advent of plate tectonic theory, geologists realized that thick submarine accumulation need not be in a subsiding trough but could take place under a variety of conditions, as explained in this chapter. The term *geocline* was proposed to replace the older term (since the *syn* in *geosyncline* implied a trough shape). Similarly, *miogeocline* and *eugeocline* were coined to replace *miogeosyncline* and *eugeosyncline,* respectively. Many geologists now use these new terms for the rocks that build up during the accretion stage of mountain building. For instance, the miogeocline would be the sedimentary rocks that accumulate on the continental margin of an opening oceanic basin, and the eugeocline would be the sequence of rocks that form during oceanic-continental convergence.

Some geologists prefer to completely discard the geosynclinal-geoclinal terminology while others feel that the original geosynclinal terms should be retained even though what they represent has been modified by plate tectonic theory.

The rise and fall of geosynclinal theory is a good example of how science works. For about a hundred years the geosynclinal concept was accepted by geologists because the available data tended to support it. However, when new data led to the formulation of plate tectonic theory, geologists were able to recognize that the new theory explained the data better than the old theory.

---

the other continental margin. As the subduction progresses, a magmatic arc would develop, probably near the seaward edge of the thick sequence of sediment that had accumulated while the ocean basin was opening. If the subduction zone were to develop beneath the east coast of North America, we would expect a chain of volcanoes to form near the eastern Atlantic coastline.

In time the thick accumulations of sediment from both sides of the closing ocean would collide. During the continental collision the thick layers of sedimentary rocks would be compressed into folds and faults. Probably the continental crust would begin to follow the oceanic crust down the subduction zone. However, since the continental crust is not as dense as oceanic crust, it would only reach the depth where its own buoyancy prevented further downward movement. At this point subduction would stop and the two continents would be *sutured* together into a single continent.

A mountain belt that is entirely within a continent (rather than on the edge of a continent) is considered to be a product of a continent-continent convergence. The Himalayan belt is believed to have formed in just this way. In this case the collision was between Asia and India (India moved northward from the southern hemisphere).

Could the present Atlantic Ocean close and a new mountain belt develop between the two former continents of Europe and North America? Apparently that is just what happened in the past. During early Paleozoic time a thick sequence of sediment built outward from what was then the eastern edge of North America. Later in the Paleozoic the predecessor of the North Atlantic Ocean

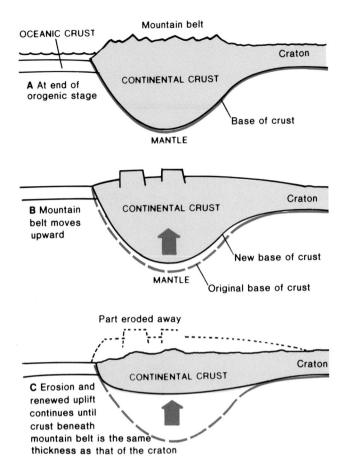

Figure 18.15 Isostasy in a mountain belt. Thickness of the continental crust is exaggerated. (*A*) At end of orogenic stage. (*B*) Mountain belt moves upward. (*C*) Erosion and renewed uplift continues until crust beneath mountain belt is the same thickness as that of the craton.

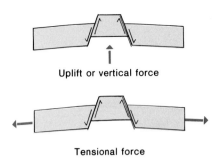

Figure 18.16 Normal faults bounding fault-block mountain ranges. Two ways in which forces might be distributed.

Uplift and Block-faulting Stage

After the compressive stress of the orogeny ceases, there is a long period of uplift accompanied by erosion. During this stage, which lasts many millions of years, large regions in the mountain belt move vertically upward. Erosion may keep pace with uplift and the area may remain low. Alternatively, uplift may temporarily outpace erosion, which results in plateaus or mountain ranges. Eventually erosion triumphs, and a mountain belt slowly evolves into a part of the craton.

The most likely explanation for this stage is that after an orogeny, the newly thickened continental crust adjusts isostatically (as explained in chapter 17 and as shown in figure 18.15).

Along with the general uplift, greater uplift may occur along normal faults (or, less commonly, vertical faults) and create **fault-block mountain ranges.** Normal faults imply either vertical forces or horizontal tensional forces (figure 18.16). The fault-block mountain ranges are therefore caused either by tensional forces pulling apart the uplifting crust or by unequal vertical movement of parts of the crust.

Block faulting is taking place in much of the western United States—the Basin and Range province of Nevada (also called the Great Basin, as shown in figure 18.4) and parts of Utah, Arizona, New Mexico, Idaho, and California (figure 18.17). Hundreds of small, block-faulted mountain ranges are in evidence. They are separated by valleys which are filling with debris eroded from the mountains.

Although most fault-block mountain ranges are bounded by normal faults on either side of the range, some are tilted fault-blocks in which the uplift has been much greater along one side of the range while the other side of the range has pivoted as if it were hinged (figure 18.18). The Sierra Nevada (California) and Grand Teton (Wyoming) Ranges are tilted fault-block mountains (figure 18.19).

basin closed (the closing took millions of years). Volcanic and other rock types associated with a converging boundary were added to the eastern boundary adjacent to the previously accumulated sediments. The ocean closed completely and Europe was sutured onto North America. As the Paleozoic Era was ending, the supercontinent once again split, roughly parallel to the old suture zone. The two present continents moved (and continue to move) farther and farther away from their present diverging boundary, the Mid-Atlantic Ridge.

What happened to the Appalachians would seem too implausible even for a science fiction plot. Yet, if one accepts the principles of plate tectonic theory, and examines the rocks and structures in the Appalachians (and their counterparts in Europe), the argument for this sequence of events is not only plausible, but convincing.

Figure 18.17 The Basin and Range province of the United States.

Basin and
Range

Figure 18.18 Development of fault-block mountain ranges. (*A*) Before block faulting. Folding and intrusion of a pluton during an orogeny has been followed by a period of erosion. (B) The same area after block-faulting. Tilted fault-block mountain range on *left*. Range to right is bounded by normal faults.

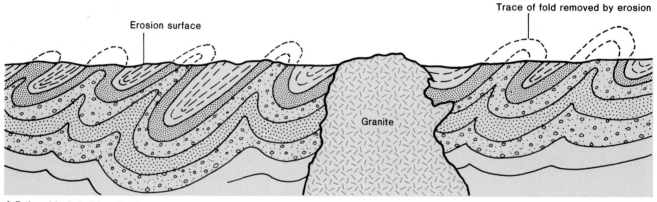

Trace of fold removed by erosion

Erosion surface

Granite

A Before block faulting. Folding and intrusion of a pluton during an orogeny has been followed by a period of erosion.

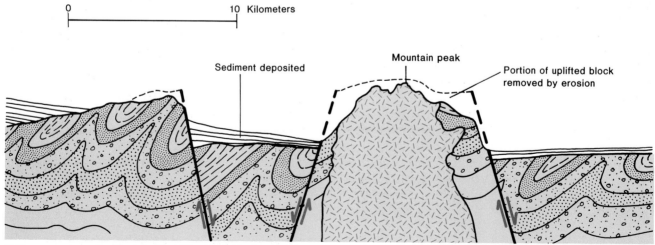

0   10 Kilometers

Sediment deposited

Mountain peak

Portion of uplifted block removed by erosion

B The same area after block-faulting. Tilted fault-block mountain range on left. Range to right is bounded by normal faults.

Figure 18.19 The Teton Range in Wyoming, a tilted fault-block range. The rocks exposed in the range are mostly Precambrian metamorphic and igneous rocks that moved upward. The flat area in the foreground moved downward and is covered by recent sediments derived from erosion of the mountains.
Photo by Leigh N. Ortenburger.

Isolated volcanic activity may be associated with this stage of a mountain belt's evolution. Eruptions occur along faults extending deep into the crust or the upper mantle.

Uplift is neither rapid nor continuous. A mountain range may suddenly move upward a few centimeters (or, more rarely, a few meters) and then not move again for hundreds of years. Erosion works relentlessly on newly uplifted mountains, carving the block into peaks during the long, spasmodic rise. Over the lengthy time period involved, the later episodes of renewed faulting and uplift involve successively less and less vertical movement.

According to the concept of isostasy (chapter 17), lighter, less dense continental crust "floats" higher on the mantle than does the denser oceanic crust. The stable interior of the continent has achieved an equilibrium and is floating at the proper level for its thickness. Mountains, being thicker continental crust, "float" higher than the stable continent. As material is removed from mountains by erosion, the range floats upward to regain its isostatic balance.

Not all geologists agree that fault-block mountain ranges are due to isostasy. Some feel that the general uplift is due to a hot mantle plume beneath a portion of a continent. Others think that since the pattern of normal faults may be caused by regional tensional stress, places like the Basin and Range province have a spreading center developing beneath them.

The evolution of a mountain belt can be considered complete when the belt becomes part of the craton, the stable continental interior. The forces of erosion and of uplift have been brought into balance. The surface is a low-lying plain. The crust shows little tendency toward uplift and may be considered isostatically balanced with respect to the underlying mantle (that is, it is "floating" at its proper level). The rocks exposed at the surface (or buried under a cover of sedimentary rock) are plutonic rocks and highly metamorphosed rocks—the same rocks that were very deeply buried during the accretion and orogenic stages.

Summary

Major mountain belts are made up of a number of *mountain ranges*. Mountain belts are generally several thousand kilometers long but only a few hundred kilometers wide.

Mountain belts generally evolve as follows: (1) Accumulation of a thick sequence of sedimentary and volcanic rock takes place (the *accretion stage*). (2) The accretion stage is either accompanied or followed by an *orogenic stage*, which involves intense compression of the layered rocks into folds and reverse (including thrust) faults, along with metamorphism, and igneous activity. (3) The area is then subjected to a long period of uplift, perhaps block-faulting, and erosion. Eventually the mountain belt is eroded down to a plain and incorporated into the *craton*, or stable interior of the continent.

According to the theory of plate tectonics, mountains on the edge of continents are formed by continent-oceanic convergence, and mountains in the interior of continents are formed by continent-continent collisions.

The uplift of a region following termination of an orogeny is generally attributed to isostatic adjustment of continental crust.

Terms to Remember

accretion stage
craton
fault-block mountain range
magmatic arc
major mountain belt
mountain range
orogeny
Precambrian shield

Questions for Review

1. Describe what takes place during an orogeny.
2. How are orogenies detected and dated?
3. What is the difference between the forces that could explain fault-block mountains and the forces that could account for an orogenic stage?
4. Explain how erosion and isostasy eventually produce stable, relatively thin, continental crust.
5. How do the sequences of sedimentary rocks in cratons differ from those in mountain belts?
6. What sequence of events accounts for a mountain belt that is bounded on either side by cratons?

Questions for Thought

1. What has the seismic study of the earth's interior contributed to our concepts of how mountain belts form?
2. How do basalt and ultramafic rocks from the oceanic lithosphere become part of mountain belts?
3. Why is a craton locally warped into basins and domes?
4. Where in a mountain belt would you expect to find contact metamorphic rocks?
5. What causes an orogeny to end?

Supplementary Readings

Dickinson, W. R. 1981. Plate tectonics and the continental margin of California. In *The geotectonic development of California,* ed. W. G. Ernst. Englewood Cliffs, N.J.: Prentice-Hall.

Dietz, R. S. 1972. Geosynclines, mountains and continent-building. *Scientific American* (March 1972). San Francisco: W. H. Freeman (off print).

Kay, Marshall, 1955. The origin of continents. *Scientific American* (Sept. 1955). San Francisco: W. H. Freeman (off print).

King, P. B. 1977. *The evolution of North America.* Princeton, N.J.: Princeton University Press.

Wyllie, P. J. 1976. *The way the earth works.* New York: John Wiley & Sons.

19

The Sea Floor and Sea-Floor Spreading

Purpose

Because the rocks and topography of the sea floor are so different from those on land, in the first part of this chapter we describe sea-floor features, such as continental margins, the mid-oceanic ridge, oceanic trenches, and fracture zones, and we comment on their distribution. In the last part of the chapter we show how many of these features can be explained by a theory called *sea-floor spreading.* This theory gained great acceptance by geologists in the 1960s because it offers an explanation for the origin of most of the features on the sea floor.

We also discuss two successful tests of the sea-floor spreading concept, one involving marine magnetic anomalies and the other the seismicity of fracture zones.

In the next chapter you will see how sea-floor spreading has been incorporated into the broader concept of plate tectonics, which explains not only sea-floor features, but many continental features as well.

Oceans cover more than 70 percent of the earth's surface. Even though the rocks of the sea floor are widespread, they are difficult to study. Geologists have to rely on small samples of rock taken from the sea floor and brought to the surface, or they must study the rocks indirectly by means of instruments on board ships. Despite the difficulties, however, a great deal has been learned about the sea floor in the past few decades. Much of the information that led to the concept of plate tectonics was obtained by geologists working at sea.

Methods of Studying the Sea Floor

Samples of rock and sediments can be taken from the sea floor in several ways (figure 19.1), the choice of equipment being governed to some degree by water depth and bottom conditions. Rocks can be broken from the sea floor by a *rock dredge,* which is an open steel container dragged over the ocean bottom at the end of a cable. Sediments can be sampled with a *corer,* a weighted steel pipe dropped vertically into the mud and sand of the ocean floor.

B

Figure 19.1 Bottom sampling devices. (*A*) Rock dredge for sampling hard rock. (*B*) Corer for sampling sea-floor sediment. Sediment is caught inside the pipe when the corer is dropped to the sea floor.
A from Scripps Institution of Oceanography, University of California, San Diego.

Figure 19.2 *Glomar Challenger.*
Deep Sea Drilling Project, Scripps Institution of Oceanography.

Both rock and sediments can be sampled by means of *sea-floor drilling.* The Deep Sea Drilling Project is an ambitious sea-floor sampling program funded cooperatively by the governments of the United States and several other countries. Holes are drilled in the sea floor from the *Glomar Challenger,* a ship constructed with a drilling derrick on its deck (figure 19.2). The drill is capable of cutting long, rodlike rock cores from the sea floor. The *Glomar Challenger* has drilled hundreds of holes in the

sea floor, and the rock and sediment cores recovered from these holes have greatly expanded scientific knowledge of sea-floor features and history.

A basic tool for indirectly studying the sea floor is the *echo sounder,* which draws profiles of submarine topography (figure 19.3). A sound sent downward from a ship bounces off the sea floor and returns to the ship. The water depth is determined from the time it takes the sound to make the round trip. A *seismic profiler* works on essentially the same principles as the echo sounder but uses a louder noise at lower frequency. This sound penetrates the bottom of the sea and reflects from layers within the rock and sediment. The seismic profiler gives more information than the echo sounder. It records water depth and reveals the internal structure of the rocks and sediments of the sea floor, such as bedding planes, folds and faults, and unconformities (figure 19.4). *Magnetic, gravity,* and *seismic refraction* surveys also can be made at sea. *Deep-sea cameras* can be lowered to the bottom to photograph the rock and sediment (figure 19.5).

Features of the Sea Floor

Figure 19.6, a simplified profile of the sea floor, shows that continents have two types of margins. An *Atlantic-type continental margin* includes a continental shelf, continental slope, and continental rise. An abyssal plain usually forms a remarkably flat ocean floor beyond the continental rise. A *Pacific-type continental margin* has a continental shelf and slope, but the slope extends much

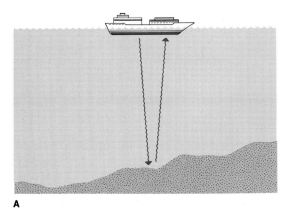

A

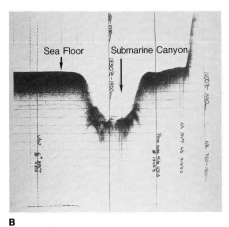

B

Figure 19.3 Echo-sounding. (*A*) A sound bounces off the sea floor and returns to a ship. (*B*) An echo-sounder record of a submarine canyon, Northern Pacific.
Geological Data Center, Scripps Institution of Oceanography, University of California, San Diego.

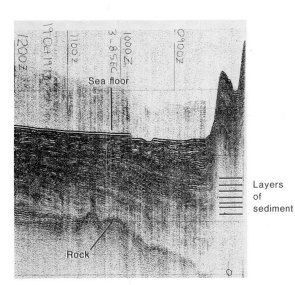

Figure 19.4 Seismic profiler record of sediment layers that have buried an irregular rock surface in the Indian Ocean.
Geological Data Center, Scripps Institution of Oceanography, University of California, San Diego.

A

B

Figure 19.5 Photographs of the sea floor. Field of view for each is approximately 5 by 7 feet. (*A*) Manganese nodules on an abyssal plain in the South Pacific, depth 5,300 meters. (*B*) Rippled sediment between rocks indicates current movement of sea-floor sediment on the side of a South Pacific island, depth 1,000 meters.
Lamont-Doherty Geological Observatory.

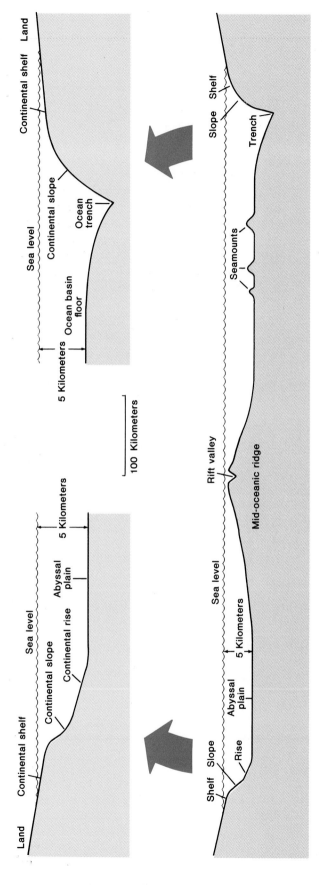

Figure 19.6 Profiles of sea-floor topography. The vertical scales differ from the horizontal scales.

Many figures illustrating sea-floor topography show angles of slope to be much steeper than they are in nature. Figure 19.7 is an example. The continental slope, averaging 4°–5° of slope, is drawn at an angle of approximately 60°. This steepening of natural slope angles is called *vertical exaggeration.* It results from using two different scales in such drawings. Note that the bar representing the vertical scale in the figure is only 2 kilometers long while a bar of the same length represents 50 kilometers on the horizontal scale. The drawing has a vertical exaggeration of 25 times (written "25X"). In other words, the scale of vertical representation is stretched out 25 times compared to the horizontal. A true-scale (unexaggerated) profile drawing of the sea floor would show little contrast or detail. When you look at illustrations with differing scales, keep in mind that slopes that appear steep are actually gentle. They are drawn in this exaggerated way to make subtle changes in topography more apparent.

Although we have used different vertical and horizontal scales in some previous figures in the book, vertical exaggeration has usually been slight. The extreme vertical exaggeration of sea-floor profiles, however, is common in geologic literature and can be misleading to an unwary reader.

deeper to form one wall of an *oceanic trench.* Abyssal plains are seldom found off Pacific-type margins. The deep ocean floor seaward of trenches is hilly and irregular, lacking the extreme flatness of abyssal plains. Encircling the globe is a *mid-oceanic ridge,* usually (but not always) near the center of an ocean. Conical *seamounts* stick up from the sea floor in some regions. As we define and describe these features, you will be referring back to figure 19.6. However, some important submarine features do not show in a profile view—in particular, fracture zones, submarine canyons, and aseismic ridges.

Continental Shelves and Continental Slopes

Almost all continental edges are marked by a shallow continental shelf and a steeper continental slope that leads down to the deep ocean floor (figure 19.7).

A **continental shelf,** a shallow submarine platform at the edge of a continent, inclines very gently seaward, generally at an angle of less than 1°. Continental shelves vary in width. On the Pacific coast of North America the shelf is only a few kilometers wide, but off Newfoundland in

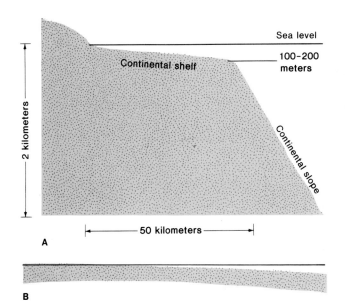

Figure 19.7 Continental shelf and continental slope. (*A*) Vertical exaggeration 25 X. (*B*) Same profile with no vertical exaggeration.

the Atlantic Ocean it is about 500 kilometers wide. Portions of the shelves in the Arctic Ocean off Siberia and northern Europe are even wider. Water depth over a continental shelf tends to increase regularly away from land, with the outer edge of the shelf being about 100–200 meters below sea level.

Continental shelves are *topographic features,* defined by their depth, flatness, and gentle seaward tilt. Their *geologic origin* varies from place to place and will be discussed further in the next chapter. Some generalities about shelves, however, are worth noting here.

The continental shelves of the world are usually covered with relatively young sediment, in most cases derived from land. The sediment is usually sand near shore, where the bottom is shallow and influenced by wave action. Fine-grained mud is deposited farther offshore in deeper, quieter water. On narrow shelves this mud may blanket the outer shelf and extend over the shelf edge onto the continental slope (figure 19.8A). On wide shelves the modern sediment may not cover the entire shelf (figure 19.8B). The outer part of a wide shelf is often covered with coarse sediment that was deposited near shore during a time of lower sea level. The advance and retreat of continental glaciers during the Pleistocene Epoch caused sea level to rise and fall several times by 100–200 meters. This resulted in a complex history of sedimentation for continental shelves as they were alternately covered with sea water and exposed as dry land.

Marine seismic surveys and drilling at sea have shown that the young sediments on many continental shelves are underlain by thick sequences of sandstone, shale, and, in tropical climates, limestone. These sedimentary rocks were deposited during the Tertiary Period (or sometimes before) and appear to have been deposited in much the same way as the modern shelf sediments. Beneath these rocks is the thick continental (sialic) crust. Therefore the continental shelves are truly part of the continents, even though the shelves are covered by sea water.

A **continental slope** is a relatively steep slope that extends from a depth of 100–200 meters at the edge of the continental shelf down to oceanic depths. The average angle of slope for a continental slope is 4°–5°, although some parts are much steeper.

Because the continental slopes are more difficult to study than the continental shelves, less is known about them. The greater depths of water and locally steep inclines on the continental slopes hinder dredging and drilling and make the results of seismic refraction and reflection harder to interpret. This is unfortunate, for the rocks that underlie the slopes are of particular interest to marine geologists who believe that in this area the thick

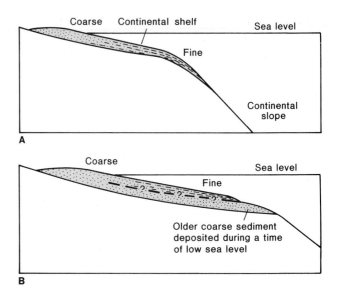

Figure 19.8 Modern sediment on continental shelves. (A) Modern sediment on narrow shelves may extend onto continental slope. (B) Modern sediment may not completely cover wide shelves, leaving older sediment exposed on outer shelf.

continental crust (beneath the land and the continental shelves) grades into thin oceanic crust (underneath the deep ocean floor).

Although relatively little is known about continental slopes, it is clear that their character and origin vary greatly from place to place. Because these variations can be best described within the context of plate tectonics, we will postpone discussion of them until the next chapter.

Submarine Canyons

Submarine canyons are V-shaped valleys that run across continental shelves and down continental slopes (figure 19.9). On narrow continental shelves, such as those off the Pacific coast of the United States, the heads of submarine canyons may be close to shore. On wide shelves, such as those off the Atlantic coast of the United States, canyon heads usually begin near the outer edge of the continental shelf, perhaps tens of kilometers from shore. Great fan-shaped deposits of sediment called **abyssal fans** are found at the base of many submarine canyons (figure 19.9). Abyssal fans appear to be made up of land-derived sediment that has moved down the submarine canyons. Along continental margins that are cut by submarine canyons, many coalescing abyssal fans may build up at the base of the continental slope.

Submarine canyons are erosional features, but how sediment is removed from these steep-walled undersea valleys is a controversial question. It is likely that erosional agents vary in relative importance from canyon to

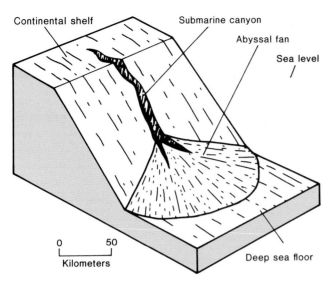

Figure 19.9   Submarine canyon and abyssal fan.

canyon. Divers have filmed *down-canyon movement of sand* in slow, glacierlike flow and in more rapid sand falls (figure 19.10). This sand movement, which has been observed to cause erosion, is particularly common in Pacific coast canyons, which collect great quantities of sand from longshore drift. *Bottom currents* have been measured moving up and down the canyons in a pattern of regularly alternating flow. The origin of these currents is uncertain, but they often move fast enough to erode and transport sediment. *River erosion* may have helped to cut canyons when the drop in sea level during the Pleistocene glaciations left canyon heads above the water. Many (but not all) submarine canyons are found off land canyons or rivers, which tends to support the view that river erosion helped shape them. It is unlikely, however, that the deeper parts of submarine canyons were ever exposed as dry land.

Turbidity Currents

Considerable difference of opinion exists about the role of *turbidity currents* in canyon origin. At one time geologists felt that turbidity currents cut submarine canyons, but in recent years their importance has been deemphasized.

Turbidity currents are great masses of sediment-laden water that are pulled downhill by gravity. The sediment-laden water is heavier than clear water, so the turbidity current flows beneath the clear water along a sloping sea floor. Although large turbidity currents have not been directly observed in the sea, small turbidity currents can be made and studied in the laboratory. Much indirect evidence also indicates that turbidity currents occur in the sea.

Figure 19.10   A 10-meter-high sand fall in a submarine canyon near the southern tip of Baja California, Mexico. The sand is beach sand, fed into the nearshore canyon head by longshore currents.
Scripps Institution of Oceanography, University of California, San Diego.

The best evidence comes from the breaking of submarine cables that carry telephone and telegraph messages across the ocean floor. Figure 19.11 shows a downhill sequence of cable breaks that followed a 1929 earthquake in the Grand Banks region of the northwest Atlantic. This sequence of cable breaks has been interpreted to be the result of an earthquake-caused turbidity current flowing rapidly down the continental slope.

If cable breaks are caused by turbidity currents, they give good evidence of the currents' dramatic size, speed, and energy. Breaks in transoceanic cables in the Grand Banks region continued for more than 13 hours after the 1929 earthquake, the last of the series occurring more than 700 kilometers from the epicenter. The velocity of the flow that caused the breaks has been calculated to be from 15 to 60 kilometers per hour. Sections of cable more than 100 kilometers long were broken off and carried away, both ends of a missing section being broken simultaneously. Attempts to find broken cable sections were fruitless, and it is assumed that they were buried by sediment.

The Grand Banks 1929 cable breaks were not unique. Cables crossing submarine canyons are broken frequently, particularly after river floods and earthquakes. In the submarine canyons off the Congo River of Africa and off the Magdalena River in Colombia, for example, cables break every few years.

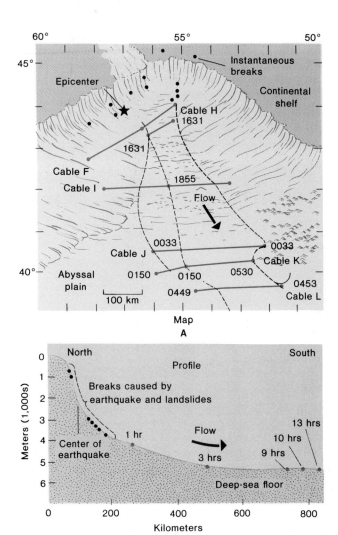

Figure 19.11 Submarine cable breaks following the Grand Banks earthquake of 1929. (*A*) Map view of the cable breaks. Black dots near the epicenter show locations of cable breaks that were simultaneous with the earthquake (cables not shown for these breaks). Colored dots show cable breaks that followed the earthquake, with the time of each break shown (on the 24-hour clock). Segments of cable more than 100 kilometers long were broken simultaneously at both ends and then carried away. Dashes show sea-floor channels that probably concentrated the flow of a turbidity current, increasing its velocity. (*B*) Profile showing the time elapsed between the quake and each cable break.

A from H. W. Menard, 1964, *Marine Geology of the Pacific,* copyright McGraw-Hill, Inc. B from B. C. Heezen and M. Ewing, 1952, *American Journal of Science.*

Additional indirect evidence for the existence of turbidity currents comes from the character of the sediments that make up the continental rise and the abyssal plains of the Atlantic-type continental margins described in the next section.

Atlantic-type Continental Margins

An **Atlantic-type continental margin** includes a continental shelf, continental slope, and continental rise and generally extends down to an abyssal plain at a depth of about 5 kilometers (figure 19.6).

Atlantic-type margins are found on the edges of most land masses bordering the Atlantic Ocean as well as in most parts of the Indian and Arctic Oceans and a few parts of the Pacific Ocean. Because this type of margin tends to develop on geologically quiet coasts, it is sometimes called a *passive margin.* Earthquakes, active volcanism, and young mountain ranges are seldom associated with Atlantic-type margins.

The Continental Rise

Along the base of many parts of the continental slope lies the **continental rise,** a wedge of sediment that extends from the lower part of the continental slope to the deep sea floor. The continental rise, which slopes more gently than the continental slope, typically ends in a flat abyssal plain at a depth of about 5 kilometers. The rise rests upon oceanic crust.

Types of deposition   Sediments appear to be deposited on the continental rise in two ways—by turbidity currents flowing *down* the continental slope and by *contour currents* flowing *along* the continental slope.

Cores of sediment recovered from some parts of the continental rise show layers of fine sand or coarse silt interbedded with layers of fine-grained mud. The composition of the mineral grains and the fossil content of the coarser layers indicate that the sand and silt came from the shallow continental shelf. Some transporting agent must have carried these sediments from shallow water to deep water. The coarse layers also exhibit graded bedding, which indicates that they settled out of suspension; therefore, the transporting agent for these sediments was most likely turbidity currents. The continental rise in these locations probably formed largely from turbidity current deposition, perhaps as abyssal fans coalesced at the base of a continental slope.

Sediments in other parts of the continental rise, however, are uniformly fine-grained and show no graded bedding. This sediment appears to have been deposited by the regular ocean currents that flow along the sea bottom, rather than by the intermittent turbidity currents that occasionally flow downslope.

A **contour current** is a bottom current that flows parallel to the slopes of the continental margin (*along* the contour rather than *down* the slope). Such a current runs south along the continental margin of North America in

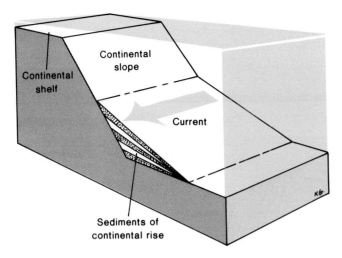

Figure 19.12 A contour current flowing along the continental margin shapes the continental rise.

the Atlantic Ocean (figure 19.12). Flowing at the relatively slow speed of a few centimeters per second, this current carries a small amount of fine sediment from north to south. The current is thickest along the continental slope and gets progressively thinner seaward. The thick landward part of the current carries and deposits the most sediment. The thinner seaward edge of the current deposits less sediment. As a result, the deposit of sediment beneath the current is wedge shaped, becoming thinner away from land. Similar contour currents apparently shape parts of the continental rise off other continents as well.

Abyssal Plains

Abyssal plains are very flat regions that usually are found at the base of the continental rise. Seismic profiling has shown that abyssal plains are formed of horizontal layers of sediment. The gradual deposition of sediment buried an older, more rugged topography that can be seen on seismic profiler records as a rock basement beneath the sediment layers (figure 19.4). Samples of abyssal plain sediment show that it is derived from land. Graded bedding within sediment layers suggests deposition by turbidity currents.

Abyssal plains are the flattest features on earth. They generally have slopes less than 1:1000 (less than one meter of vertical drop for every 1000 meters of horizontal distance) and some have slopes of only 1:10,000.

Not all parts of the deep ocean basin floor consist of abyssal plains. The deep floor is normally quite rugged, broken by faults into hills and depressions and dotted with volcanic seamounts. Abyssal plains form only where turbidity currents can carry in enough sediment to bury and obscure this rugged relief. If the sediment is not available,

or if the bottom-hugging turbidity currents are stopped by a barrier such as an oceanic trench, then abyssal plains cannot develop.

Pacific-type Continental Margins

A **Pacific-type continental margin** consists of a continental shelf, a continental slope, and an oceanic trench. Generally there is neither a continental rise nor an abyssal plain. (Refer again to figure 19.6 to compare the two types of continental margins.)

Pacific-type margins are found on the edges of most of the land masses in the Pacific Ocean, as well as a few other places in the Atlantic and Indian Oceans. A notable exception in the Pacific Ocean is much of the coast of North America, although most geologists believe that a Pacific-type margin used to exist there. Land-derived sediment is currently building large abyssal fans off the coasts of California, Oregon, and Washington, forming a typical Atlantic-type continental rise.

Oceanic Trenches

An **oceanic trench** is a narrow, deep trough parallel to the edge of a continent or an island arc (a curved line of islands like the Aleutians), as shown in figure 19.13. The continental slope on a Pacific-type margin forms the landward wall of the trench, its steepness often increasing with depth. The slope typically is 4°–5° on the upper part, steepening to 10°–15° or even more near the bottom of the trench. The elongate oceanic trenches, often 8–10 kilometers deep, far exceed the average depth of abyssal plains on Atlantic-type margins. The deepest spots on earth, almost 12 kilometers below sea level, are in oceanic trenches.

Geologic Activity

Intense geologic activity such as earthquakes and volcanism is characteristic of Pacific-type margins. Hence they are also called *active margins*. Associated with oceanic trenches are the earthquakes of the Benioff seismic zones (chapter 16), which begin at a trench and dip landward under continents or island arcs (figure 19.14). Volcanoes are found above the upper part of the Benioff zones and typically are arranged in long belts parallel to oceanic trenches. These belts of volcanoes form island arcs or erupt within young mountain ranges on the edges of continents. The rock produced by these volcanoes is usually andesite, a type of extrusive rock intermediate in composition between basaltic oceanic crust and "granitic" continental crust.

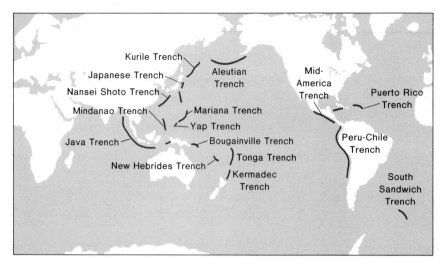

Kurile Trench
Japanese Trench
Nansei Shoto Trench
Mindanao Trench
Java Trench
Aleutian Trench
Mariana Trench
Yap Trench
Bougainville Trench
New Hebrides Trench
Tonga Trench
Kermadec Trench
Mid-America Trench
Puerto Rico Trench
Peru-Chile Trench
South Sandwich Trench

Figure 19.13 The distribution of oceanic trenches.

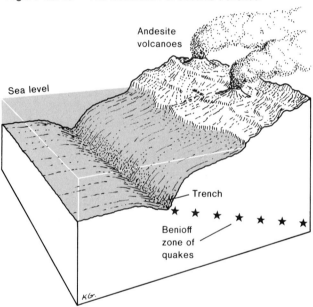

Andesite volcanoes

Sea level

Trench

Benioff zone of quakes

KG.

Figure 19.14 Pacific-type margin with an oceanic trench, Benioff zone, and volcanic chain. The size of the features above sea level, such as the volcanoes, has been greatly exaggerated.

The Mid-Oceanic Ridge

The **mid-oceanic ridge** is a giant undersea mountain range that extends around the world like the seams on a baseball (figure 19.15). The ridge, which is made up mostly of basalt, is more than 80,000 kilometers long, and 1,500–2,500 kilometers wide. It rises 2–3 kilometers above the ocean floor.

Except in the Pacific Ocean, a **rift valley**—a large crack, apparently of tensional origin—runs down the crest of the ridge (figure 19.6). The rift valley is 1–2 kilometers deep and several kilometers wide—about the dimensions of Grand Canyon in Arizona. The rift valley on the crest of the mid-oceanic ridge is a unique feature—no mountain range on land has such a valley running along its crest.

Geologic Activity on the Ridge

Associated with the rift valley at the crest of the mid-oceanic ridge, and also with the riftless crest of the ridge in the Pacific Ocean, are *shallow-focus earthquakes* (chapter 16).

Careful measurements of the heat loss from the earth's interior through the crust have shown a very *high heat flow* on the crest of the mid-oceanic ridge. The heat loss at the ridge crest is many times the normal value found elsewhere in the ocean.

Basalt eruptions occur in and near the rift valley on the ridge crest. Sometimes these eruptions build up volcanoes that protrude above sea level as oceanic islands. The large island of Iceland, which is mostly basaltic, appears to be a section of the mid-oceanic ridge elevated above sea level. Many geologists have studied the active volcanoes, high heat flow, and central rift valley of Iceland in an attempt to learn about the mid-oceanic ridge. As Iceland is above sea level, however, it may not be a typical portion of the ridge.

In the summer of 1974 geologists were able to get a firsthand view of part of the submerged ridge and rift valley. A series of more than 40 dives by small research submarines carried French and American marine geologists directly into the rift valley in the North Atlantic Ocean. The project (called FAMOUS for *French-American Mid-Ocean Undersea Study*) allowed the ridge rock to be seen, photographed, and sampled directly, rather than indirectly from surface ships.

The geologists on the FAMOUS project saw clear evidence of tensional cracks within the rift valley. These run parallel to the axis of the rift valley and range in width from hairline cracks to gaping fissures wide enough to allow the submarines to dive into them. Fresh pillow basalts occur in a narrow band along the bottom of the rift valley, suggesting very recent volcanic activity there.

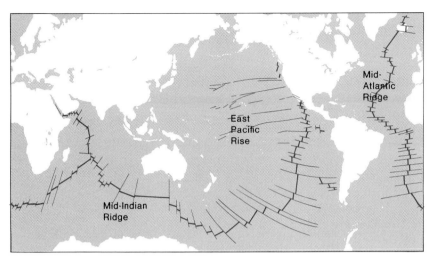

Figure 19.15 The mid-oceanic ridge, offset by fracture zones. Darker lines indicate the ridge crest; lighter lines show the fracture zones.

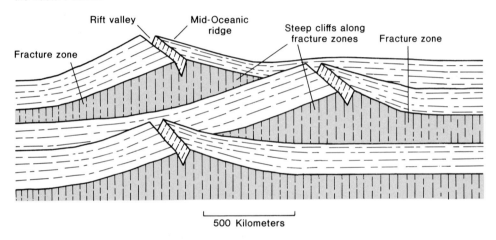

Figure 19.16 Fracture zones, which run perpendicular to the ridge crest and offset the ridge into segments, are often marked by steep cliffs. Cliffs may be up to 3 or 4 kilometers high.

No active eruptions were observed. It appeared to the geologists that tensional cracking of the rift was continuous, with volcanic activity occurring sporadically as a result of the rifting.

Fracture Zones

Fracture zones are major lines of weakness in the earth's crust that cross the mid-oceanic ridge at approximate right angles (figure 19.15). The rift valley of the mid-oceanic ridge is offset in many places across fracture zones (figure 19.16), and the sea floor on one side of a fracture zone is often at a different elevation than the sea floor on the other side. Shallow-focus earthquakes occur on fracture zones but are confined to those portions of the fracture zones between segments of the rift valley (figure 19.17). Fracture zones extend for thousands of kilometers

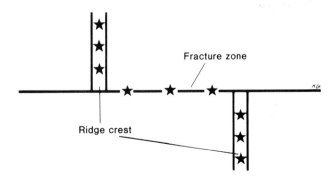

Figure 19.17 Shallow-focus earthquakes (shown by stars) occur on the ridge crest and on the segment of the fracture zone that offsets the ridge crest (map view).

across the ocean floor, generally heading straight for continental margins. Although fracture zones are difficult to trace, particularly where they are buried by the sediments of the abyssal plain and the continental rise, a number of geologists feel that they can trace the extensions of fracture zones onto continents. Some earthquake epicenters and some major structural trends on continents appear to lie along the hypothetical extension of fracture zones onto the continents.

Seamounts, Guyots, and Aseismic Ridges

Conical undersea mountains that rise 1,000 meters or more above the sea floor are called **seamounts** (figure 19.18*A*). They sometimes rise above sea level to form islands. They are scattered on the flanks of the mid-oceanic ridge and on other parts of the sea floor, including abyssal plains. One area of the sea floor with a particularly high concentration of seamounts—one estimate is 10,000—is the southwestern Pacific. Rocks dredged from seamounts are nearly always basalt, so it is thought that most seamounts are extinct volcanoes. Of the thousands of seamounts on the sea floor, only a few are active volcanoes. Most of these are on the crest of the mid-oceanic ridge. A few others, such as the two active volcanoes on the island of Hawaii, are found at locations not associated with the ridge.

Guyots are flat-topped seamounts (figure 19.18*B*) found mostly in the western Pacific Ocean. Most geologists feel that the flat summits of guyots were cut by wave action. These flat tops are now many hundreds of meters below sea level, well below the level of wave erosion. If the guyot tops were cut by waves, the guyots must have subsided after erosion took place. Evidence of such subsidence comes from the dredging of dead reef corals from guyot tops. Since such corals grow only in shallow water, they must have been carried to their present depths as the guyots sank.

Many of the guyots and seamounts on the sea floor are aligned in chains. Such volcanic chains, together with some other ridges on the sea floor, are given the name **aseismic ridges** (figure 19.19); that is, they are submarine ridges that are not associated with earthquakes. The name *aseismic* is used to distinguish these features from the much larger mid-oceanic ridge, where earthquakes occur along the rift valley.

Sediments of the Sea Floor

The basaltic crust of the sea floor is covered in many places with layers of sediment. This sediment is either *terrigenous,* derived from land, or *pelagic,* settling slowly through sea water.

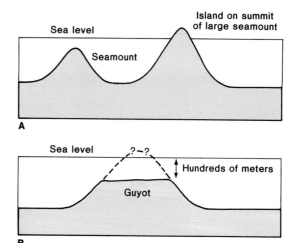

Figure 19.18 (*A*) Seamounts are conical mountains on the sea floor, occasionally rising above sea level to form islands. (*B*) The flat summit of a guyot was probably eroded by waves when the top of a seamount was above sea level. The present depth of a guyot is due to subsidence.

Terrigenous sediment is land-derived sediment that has found its way to the sea floor. The sediment that makes up the continental rise and the abyssal plains is mostly terrigenous and apparently has been deposited by turbidity currents or similar processes. Once terrigenous sediment has found its way down the continental slope, it may be distributed along the continental rise by contour currents. On Pacific-type continental margins, oceanic trenches may act as traps for terrigenous sediment and prevent it from spreading out onto the deep sea floor beyond the trenches.

Pelagic sediment is sediment that settles slowly through the ocean water. It is made up of fine-grained clay and the skeletons of microscopic organisms. Fine-grained pelagic clay is found almost everywhere on the sea floor, although in some places it is masked by other types of sediments that accumulate rapidly. The clay is mostly derived from land; part of it may be volcanic ash. This sediment is carried out to sea primarily by wind, although rivers and ocean currents also help to distribute it.

Microscopic shells and skeletons of plants and animals also settle slowly to the sea floor when marine organisms of the surface waters die. In some parts of the sea, such as the polar and equatorial regions, great concentrations of these shells have built unusually thick pelagic deposits.

The constant slow rain of pelagic clay and shells occurs in all parts of the sea. Although the rate of accumulation varies from place to place, pelagic sediment should be expected on all parts of the sea floor.

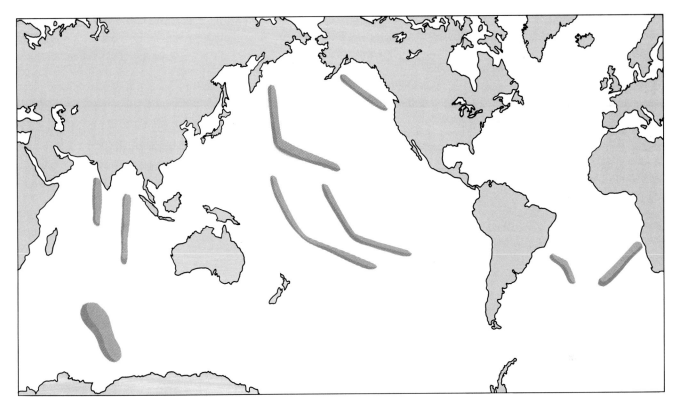

Figure 19.19 The distribution of the major aseismic ridges on the sea floor.
From W. Jason Morgan, 1972, *Geological Society of America Memoir 132*, and other sources.

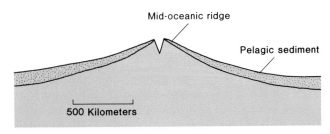

Figure 19.20 Pelagic sediment is thin or absent on the crest of the mid-oceanic ridge and becomes progressively thicker away from the ridge crest (distribution of sediment highly simplified).

Surprisingly, however, pelagic sediment is almost completely absent on the crest of the mid-oceanic ridge. Pelagic sediment is found on the flanks of the mid-oceanic ridge, often thickening away from the ridge crest (figure 19.20). But its absence on the ridge crest was an unexpected discovery about sea-floor sediment distribution.

Oceanic Crust and Ophiolites
Seismic reflection and seismic refraction surveys at sea have shown the oceanic crust to be about 7 kilometers thick and divided into three layers (figure 19.21).

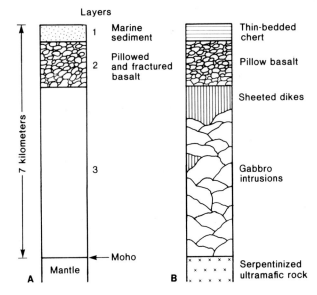

Figure 19.21 A comparison of oceanic crust and an ophiolite sequence. (*A*) Structure of oceanic crust, determined from seismic studies and drilling. Layer 3 is blank because it has not yet been drilled. (*B*) Typical ophiolite sequence found in mountain ranges on land. Thickness approximate—sequence is usually highly faulted.

The top layer (Layer 1), of variable thickness and character, is marine sediment. In an abyssal fan or on the continental rise, Layer 1 may consist of several kilometers of terrigenous sediment. On the upper flanks of the mid-oceanic ridge, there may be less than 100 meters of pelagic sediment. An average thickness for Layer 1 might be 0.5 kilometer.

Beneath the sediment is Layer 2, about 1.5 kilometers thick, that has been drilled extensively by the *Glomar Challenger*. The layer is mostly basalt, highly fractured and containing pillows that form when hot lava erupts into cold water. Widely sampled by dredging, Layer 2 has also been observed directly by the geologists in the FAMOUS expedition to the rift valley of the mid-oceanic ridge in the Atlantic Ocean.

The lowest layer in the crust is Layer 3. It is 5 kilometers thick and is thought to consist of parallel vertical dikes ("sheeted dikes") in its upper part and sill-like gabbro bodies in its lower part. The evidence for this interpretation is scanty. A few gabbro samples have been dredged from steep submarine scarps where this layer may be exposed by faulting, and seismic velocities are consistent with these rock choices. The interpretation of this layer, however, is primarily based upon the study of *ophiolites* on land.

Ophiolites are distinctive rock sequences found in many mountain ranges on continents (figure 19.21). The top thin layer in an ophiolite sequence consists of marine sedimentary rock, often including thin-bedded chert. Below the sedimentary rock lies a zone of pillow basalt. The similarity between the upper two layers of an ophiolite and Layers 1 and 2 in oceanic crust is obvious.

Beneath the pillow basalt in a continental ophiolite sequence lies a zone of closely spaced dikes that are interpreted to be the feeder dikes for the pillowed lava flows above. Below this "sheeted-dike" complex is a zone of podlike intrusive bodies of gabbro, perhaps fat sills. The dikes and gabbro together may represent oceanic Layer 3, for their total thickness in a complete ophiolite is about 5 kilometers, and their seismic velocities are about 7 kilometers per second, which is the required velocity for oceanic crust (chapter 17).

Beneath the gabbro in an ophiolite lies ultramafic rock such as peridotite (chapter 17). The ultramafic rock has usually been extensively serpentinized by metamorphism, so its original character is not always clear. If the upper part of an ophiolite represents Layers 1, 2, and 3 of oceanic crust, then the serpentinized ultramafic rock may be part of the upper mantle. The contact between the ultramafic rock and the overlying gabbro would then be the Mohorovičić discontinuity.

How could oceanic crust and upper mantle rocks find their way into mountain ranges on land? It is possible that slivers of sea floor were caught between converging plates and wedged upward onto continents. The next chapter deals with plate motions and describes how plate collisions occur.

The Age of the Sea Floor

As marine geologists began to determine the age of sea-floor rocks (by radioactive dating) and sediments (by fossils), an astonishing fact was discovered. All the rocks and sediments of the sea floor proved to be younger than 200 million years old. This was true only for rocks and sediments from the *deep* sea floor, not those from the continental margins. The rocks and sediments presently found on the deep sea floor formed during the Mesozoic and Cenozoic Eras, but not earlier.

By contrast, as you have learned in studying geologic time (chapter 8), the earth is estimated to be 4.5 billion years old. Every continent contains some rocks formed during the Paleozoic Era and the Precambrian. Some of the Precambrian rocks on continents are more than 3 billion years old, and a few are almost 4 billion years old. Continents, therefore, preserve rocks from most of the earth's history. In sharp contrast to the continents is the deep sea floor, which covers more than half of the earth's surface but preserves less than one-twentieth of earth's history in its rocks and sediment.

Sea-Floor Spreading

Many hypotheses have been put forth to explain the age or some of the features of the deep sea floor. Several hypotheses, for example, explain the existence of the mid-oceanic ridge, while several different ones attempt to account for the oceanic trenches. Most of these hypotheses have now been discarded, and we cannot discuss them all. One hypothesis, however, put forth in the early 1960s by Harry Hess, a geologist at Princeton University, is the only one that accounts for most of the sea floor's major features as well as the very young age of the rocks. His hypothesis of **sea-floor spreading** (parts of which existed decades earlier) suggests that the ocean floor is moving away from the mid-oceanic ridge as a result of mantle convection.

According to the concept of sea-floor spreading, the sea floor is moving like a conveyor belt away from the crest of the mid-oceanic ridge, down the flanks of the ridge, and across the deep ocean basin, to disappear finally

Box 19.2
Geologic Riches in the Sea

Many resources are currently being extracted from the sea floor and from sea water, and in some instances the potential for increased future extraction is very great.

Offshore oil and gas are perhaps the most widely known resources now being taken from the sea. Approximately one-fifth of the United States' oil production comes from drilling platforms set up on the continental shelf. Offshore oil will continue to supply a significant fraction of the world's total oil needs and probably will become increasingly important. Although there is considerable debate about how much oil and gas are available from the rocks beneath the continental shelf, these fuels are undoubtedly the most valuable geologic resources found in the sea. Evidence of oil and gas within deeper parts of the sea floor, such as the continental slope and continental rise, has recently been discovered. Production of oil from these deeper regions will be much more costly than present production and will require new technological advances. Oil spills from wells in very deep water would be especially hard to control.

Other important resources are dredged from the sea floor. *Phosphorite* can be recovered from shallow shelves and banks and used for fertilizers. *Gold, diamonds,* and heavy *black sands* (which are black because they contain metal-bearing minerals) are being separated from the surface sands and gravels of some continental shelves by specially designed ships.

Manganese nodules (figure 19.5) cover many parts of the deep sea floor, notably in the central Pacific. These black, potato-sized lumps contain approximately 25 percent manganese, 15 percent iron, up to 2 percent nickel and 2 percent copper, along with smaller amounts of cobalt. Although the nodules are difficult to recover, and there are international legal problems as to who owns them, larger industrial countries such as the United States are beginning to mine them. The

Figure 19.22 Offshore oil drilling platform. As many as fifty different wells can be drilled from a single platform. UPI.

concentration of copper and nickel in the richer nodules provides the initial reason for mining them. The high concentration of manganese is particularly attractive to the United States, for manganese is critical to producing steel, and the United States currently imports more than 95 percent of its manganese.

Metallic brines and sediments, associated with some sections of the rift valley on the mid-oceanic ridge, are another potential source for metals of economic value, most notably in a few localities in the Red Sea. These brines and sediments are the result of hydrothermal processes active at the ridge crest. The Red Sea sediments contain more than 1 percent copper and more than 3 percent zinc, together with impressive amounts of silver, gold, and lead. Because of their great value, the sediments will probably be mined even though they are at great depth. Deposits similar to those of the Red Sea— although not of such great economic potential— have been found on some other parts of the ridge.

A few substances can be extracted from the salts dissolved in sea water. Approximately two-thirds of the world's production of *magnesium* and *bromine* is obtained from sea water, and in many regions *sodium chloride* (table salt) is obtained by solar evaporation of sea water.

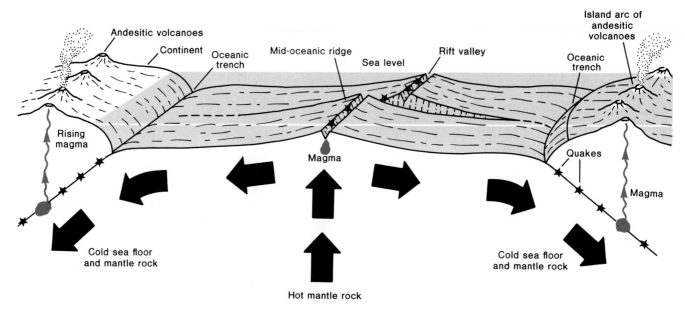

Figure 19.23 Sea-floor spreading. Hot mantle rock rising beneath the mid-oceanic ridge (a spreading center) causes basaltic volcanism and high heat flow. Divergence of sea floor splits open the rift valley and causes shallow-focus earthquakes (stars on ridge). Sinking of cold rock causes subduction of older sea floor at trenches, producing Benioff zones and andesitic magma.

by plunging beneath a continent or island arc (figure 19.23). The ridge crest, with sea floor moving away from it on either side, is called a **spreading center.** The sliding of the sea floor beneath a continent or island arc is termed **subduction.** The sea floor is generally moving at a rate of 1–6 centimeters per year. Although this may seem to be quite slow, it is rapid compared to most geologic processes.

The Driving Force

Why does the sea floor move? The explanation offered in the 1960s at the time of the original hypothesis was that sea-floor spreading is driven by deep mantle convection. **Convection** in the mantle was discussed in chapter 1. Let's assume for the moment that a slow convective circulation *does* occur in the mantle because of temperature differences within the mantle rock (this was the assumption made by Hess in the 1960s, but it is not widely accepted today, as you will see in chapter 20). Such convection could cause sea-floor spreading, which in turn can explain many ocean features.

Explanations and Predictions

The mid-oceanic ridge If convection drives sea-floor spreading, then hot mantle rock must be rising under the mid-oceanic ridge (figure 19.23). The *existence of the ridge* itself can be explained by convection in two possible ways: (1) the ridge may be pushed up from below by the

rising mantle rock; or (2) the expansion of the hot mantle rock may cause the bulge of the ridge to form as a result of the increased volume of the mantle rock.

The *high heat flow* associated with the ridge crest is plausible if hot mantle rock is rising beneath it. The *active volcanism* of the ridge crest also can be explained. Very hot but still solid mantle rock rises upward beneath the mid-oceanic ridge, moving from a region of high pressure to a region of low pressure. The drop in pressure lowers the melting point of the mantle rock, so that some of the hot mantle rock melts without the addition of any new heat. The melted mantle rock creates magma near the ridge crest (figure 19.23), and the magma erupts as basaltic lava.

The *rift valley* of the mid-oceanic ridge crest is formed when the rising mantle rock splits and diverges sideways. Sea floor moving in opposite directions on either side of the ridge crest pulls on the rock at the ridge crest, creating the rift valley as a large tensional crack. *Shallow-focus earthquakes* occur as the tensional crack opens. This tensional crack does not grow indefinitely wider, for the basaltic lavas erupted at the ridge crest tend to fill in the rift valley and create new oceanic crust. Those areas of the ridge without a rift valley may have such a high rate of lava extrusion that the rift never opens.

The *lack of pelagic sediments* at the ridge crest can also be explained by sea-floor spreading (figure 19.24). New sea floor forms constantly at the ridge crest, splits,

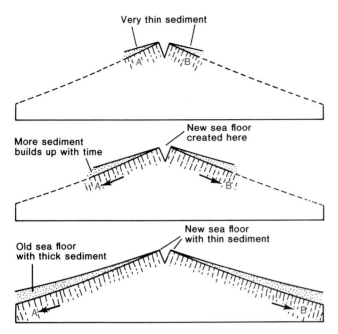

Figure 19.24 New sea floor formed at the rift valley has very little pelagic sediment, but as it moves away from the ridge crest, it collects a progressively thicker layer of sediment.

and moves sideways. The youngest sea floor, therefore, should be at the ridge crest, and the sea floor should become progressively older with increasing distance from the rift valley. The oldest rocks on the deep sea floor should be those on the ocean side of an oceanic trench, just before they disappear by subduction down into the trench. (This progressive increase in age away from a ridge crest was not known at the time the hypothesis of sea-floor spreading was developed but was an important prediction based on that hypothesis.)

If the sea floor forms at the ridge crest and then moves down the ridge flank, then the new floor at the crest is too young to have received a blanket of pelagic sediment. Older sea floor on the flanks, however, has been moving under a constant rain of pelagic sediment, building up a progressively thicker layer as it goes.

Oceanic trenches and subduction   Subduction of the sea floor beneath continents or island arcs can explain several features associated with oceanic trenches (figure 19.23). The rocks of the sea floor are denser than the rocks of continents, and so the sea floor always slides under continents when the two come together. The *existence of the oceanic trenches* can be explained by the downward plunge of the sea floor as it is subducted back into the mantle. This downward plunge may be due to cooling of the plastic mantle rock, which becomes denser and sinks. Relatively *low heat-flow values* found in

oceanic trenches may indicate that the rock beneath the trenches is cooler than normal.

Very large *negative gravity anomalies* associated with trenches seem to indicate that some force is holding the trenches down out of isostatic equilibrium (chapter 17). In the sea-floor spreading hypothesis, this force is the subduction of sea floor caused by cooling and sinking of mantle rock.

The *Benioff zones* of earthquakes associated with oceanic trenches could be caused by several mechanisms associated with moving sea floor, such as bending of the sea floor and friction between the subducting sea floor and the continent above it (chapter 16). Localized melting during subduction may create the *andesitic volcanoes* found above the Benioff zones. Partial melting of the basaltic oceanic crust or of the mantle, followed by magmatic differentiation, could create a more silica-rich andesitic magma (chapter 3).

The *young age* of the sea floor is also explained by sea-floor spreading—all the old sea floor has been subducted back into the mantle by convection.

Aseismic ridges   *Aseismic ridges* may be caused when the sea floor moves over a center of eruption. In the Hawaiian Island group, for example, the only two active volcanoes are found in the extreme southeastern corner (figure 19.25). If the Pacific Ocean floor moved slowly over an eruptive center (sometimes called a *hot spot* or *melting spot*), a line of volcanoes would be formed (figure 19.26). The volcanoes would gradually be carried away from the eruptive center, sinking as they go because of cooling. The result would be a line of extinct volcanoes increasing in age away from an active volcano above the eruptive center. Most aseismic ridges on the sea floor appear to have active volcanoes at one end. The three large aseismic ridges in the Pacific Ocean change direction abruptly (figure 19.19), suggesting that the direction of sea-floor spreading in the Pacific has changed in the past.

Two Tests of Sea-Floor Spreading

Marine Magnetic Anomalies

In the mid-1960s, magnetometer surveys at sea disclosed some intriguing characteristics of marine magnetic anomalies. Most magnetic anomalies at sea are arranged in bands that lie parallel to the rift valley of the mid-oceanic ridge. Alternating positive and negative anomalies (chapter 17) form a stripelike pattern parallel to the ridge crest (figure 19.27).

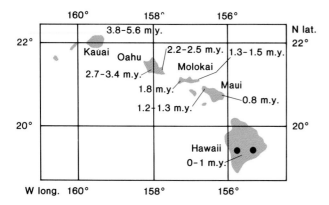

Figure 19.25 Ages of volcanic rock of the Hawaiian island group. Ages increase to northwest. Two active volcanoes on Hawaii shown by black dots.
From I. McDougall, 1964, *Geological Society of America Bulletin.*

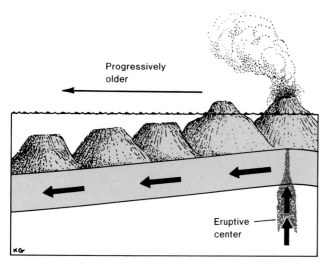

Figure 19.26 Sea floor moving over an eruptive center forms an aseismic ridge as a chain of volcanoes and guyots.

The Vine-Matthews Hypothesis Two British geologists, Fred Vine and Drummond Matthews, made several important observations about these anomalies. They recognized that the pattern of magnetic anomalies was symmetrical about the ridge crest. That is, the pattern of magnetic anomalies on one side of the mid-oceanic ridge was a mirror image of the pattern on the other side (figure 19.28). Vine and Matthews also noticed that the same pattern of magnetic anomalies exists over different parts of the mid-oceanic ridge. The pattern of anomalies over the ridge in the northern Atlantic Ocean is the same as the pattern over the ridge in the southern Pacific Ocean.

The most important observation that Vine and Matthews made was that the pattern of magnetic *anomalies* at sea matches the pattern of magnetic *reversals* already known from studies of lava flows on the continents (figure 17.25). This correlation can be seen by comparing the

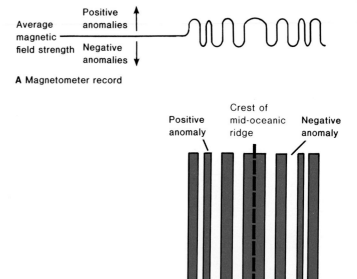

A Magnetometer record

B Map of anomalies

Figure 19.27 Magnetic anomalies: (*A*) as recorded on a magnetometer; (*B*) in parallel bands as mapped on the sea floor.

pattern of colored bands in figure 17.25 (reversals) with the pattern in figure 19.28 (anomalies).

Putting these observations together with Hess's concept of sea-floor spreading, which had just been published, Vine and Matthews proposed an explanation for magnetic anomalies. They suggested that there is continual tensional opening of the rift valley on the mid-oceanic ridge crest, together with intrusion of dike-forming basaltic magma into the tensional cracks on the ridge crest. Cooling magma in the dikes records the earth's magnetism at the time the magnetic minerals crystallize. The process is shown in figure 19.29.

When the earth's magnetic field has a *normal polarity* (the present orientation), cooling dikes are normally magnetized. Dikes that cool when the earth's field is reversed (figure 19.29), are reversely magnetized. So each dike preserves a record of the polarity that prevailed during the time when the magma cooled. Tension produced by the moving sea floor then cracks a dike in two, and the two halves are carried away by sea-floor spreading in opposite directions down the flanks of the ridge. New magma eventually intrudes the newly opened fracture. It cools, is magnetized, and forms a new dike, which in turn is split by continued tension. In this way a system of reversely magnetized and normally magnetized dikes forms parallel to the rift valley. These dikes, in the Vine-Matthews hypothesis, are the cause of the anomalies.

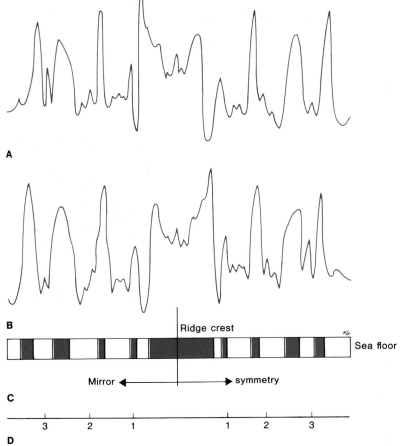

A

B

Ridge crest

Sea floor

Mirror ←———————→ symmetry

C

3 2 1 1 2 3

D

Figure 19.28 Correlation of magnetic anomalies and magnetic reversals for the mid-oceanic ridge in the East Pacific. (*A*) The original record of magnetic field strength, made by a magnetometer at sea. Peaks are positive anomalies and valleys are negative anomalies. (*B*) The same profile as *A*, reversed by rotating it about the ridge axis (i.e., the left end of this profile is the right end of profile *A*). Reversing the profile helps show its mirror symmetry about the ridge crest. (*C*) Pattern of magnetic *reversals* from figure 17.25. Colored bands represent normal magnetism; white bands represent reverse magnetism. Note how the *reversal* pattern here matches the *anomaly* pattern in the profile above. (*D*) Age of reversals in millions of years ago from figure 17.25.

Modified from F. J. Vine, 1966, *Science* vol. 154, p. 1409. Copyright 1966 by the American Association for the Advancement of Science.

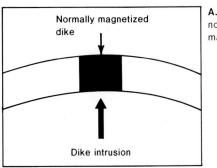

A. Time of normal magnetism

Normally magnetized dike

Dike intrusion

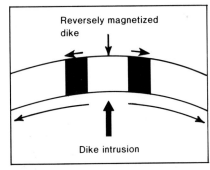

B. Time of reverse magnetism

Reversely magnetized dike

Dike intrusion

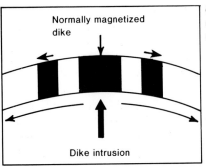

C. Time of normal magnetism

Normally magnetized dike

Dike intrusion

Figure 19.29 Origin of magnetic anomalies. Dikes intrude the ridge crest, become magnetized, and then split, moving sideways away from the crest. (*A*) Time of normal magnetism. (*B*) Time of reverse magnetism. (*C*) Time of normal magnetism.

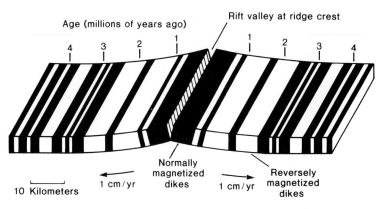

Age (millions of years ago)

Rift valley at ridge crest

4 3 2 1   1 2 3 4

10 Kilometers

← 1 cm/yr   Normally magnetized dikes   1 cm/yr →   Reversely magnetized dikes

Figure 19.30 Correlation of magnetic anomalies with magnetic reversals allows anomalies to be dated. Magnetic anomalies can therefore be used to predict the age of the sea floor and to measure the rate of sea-floor spreading.

The magnetism of normally magnetized dikes adds to the earth's magnetism, and so a magnetometer carried over such dikes registers a stronger magnetism than average—a *positive* magnetic anomaly. Dikes that are reversely magnetized subtract from the present magnetic field of the earth, and so a magnetometer towed over such dikes measures a weaker magnetic field—a *negative* magnetic anomaly. Since sea-floor spreading separates these dikes into halves, the patterns on either side of the ridge are mirror images.

Measuring the rate of spreading   Two significant points are to be noted about the Vine-Matthews hypothesis of magnetic anomaly origin. The first involves the *rate of sea-floor spreading*. Because magnetic reversals have already been dated from lava flows on land, the anomalies caused by these reversals also are dated and can be used to discover how fast the sea floor has moved (figure 19.30). For instance, a piece of the sea floor representing the reversal that occurred 4.5 million years ago may be found 45 kilometers away from the rift valley of the ridge crest. The piece of sea floor, then, has traveled 45 kilometers since it formed 4.5 million years ago. Dividing the distance the sea floor has moved by its age gives 10 km/million years, or 1 cm/year for the rate of sea-floor spreading here. In other words, on each side of the ridge, the sea floor is moving away from the ridge crest at a rate of 1 centimeter per year. Such measured rates generally range from 1–6 centimeters per year.

Predicting sea-floor age   The other important point of the Vine-Matthews hypothesis is that it *predicts the age of the sea floor* (figure 19.30). Magnetic reversals are known to have occurred through the entire Cenozoic Era and back into the Mesozoic Era (perhaps even into the Paleozoic Era). Sea floor that formed at the ridge crest and spread during the Mesozoic Era and the early part of the Cenozoic Era is characterized by parallel bands of magnetic anomalies just as is sea floor that formed during the last 4.5 million years.

The ages of magnetic anomalies (and the reversals that caused them) have been carefully worked out (figure 19.31). The distinctive pattern of these anomalies through time allows them to be identified as to age.

Now, even before they sample the sea floor, marine geologists can predict the age of the igneous rock of the sea floor by measuring the magnetic anomalies at the sea surface. Most sections of the sea floor have magnetic anomalies. By matching the measured anomaly pattern with the known pattern (figure 19.31), the age of the sea floor in the region can be predicted, as shown on the map in figure 19.32.

This is a very powerful test of the sea-floor spreading hypothesis. Suppose, for example, that the sea floor in a particular spot is predicted to be 70 million years old from a study of its magnetic anomalies. If the hypothesis of sea-floor spreading and the Vine-Matthews hypothesis of magnetic anomaly origin are correct, a sample of igneous

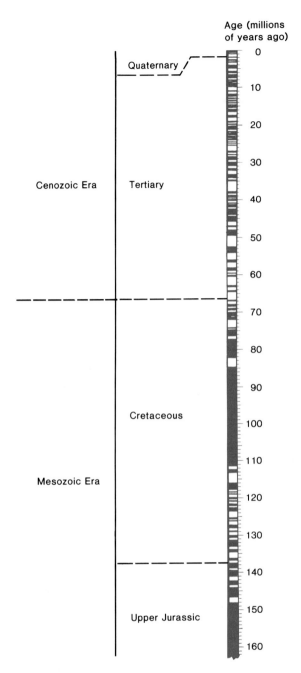

Figure 19.31 Magnetic anomaly (and reversal) pattern during the Cenozoic and Mesozoic Eras.
From R. L. Larson and W. C. Pitman, III, 1972, *Geological Society of America Bulletin.*

rock from that spot must be 70 million years old. If the rock proves to be 10 million years old or 200 million years old or 1.2 billion years old, or any other age except 70 million years, then both these hypotheses are wrong. But if the rock proves to be 70 million years old, as predicted, the hypotheses have been successfully tested.

Hundreds of rock and sediment cores recovered from holes drilled in the sea floor by the ship *Glomar Challenger* have provided a means of testing these hypotheses. Close correspondence has generally been found between the predicted age and the measured age of the sea floor. (The sea-floor age is usually measured by fossil dating of sediment in the cores rather than by radioactive dating of igneous rock.) This evidence from deep-sea drilling has been widely accepted by geologists as verification of the hypotheses of sea-floor spreading and magnetic anomaly origin. Most geologists now feel that these concepts need no longer be called hypotheses but can now be called *theories.* (A theory, as discussed in chapter 1 in connection with the scientific method, is a concept with a much higher degree of certainty than a hypothesis.)

Another Test: Fracture Zones and Transform Faults
Deep-sea drilling tested the sea-floor spreading hypothesis by allowing comparison of the actual age of the sea floor with its age as predicted from magnetic anomalies. Another rigorous test of the sea-floor spreading hypothesis has been made by studying the seismicity of fracture zones.

The mid-oceanic ridge is offset along fracture zones, which have the appearance of strike-slip faults (figure 19.15). Conceivably the mid-oceanic ridge was once continuous across a fracture zone but has been offset by strike-slip motion along the fracture zone (figure 19.33*A*). If such motion is occurring along a fracture zone, we would expect to find two things: (1) earthquakes should be distributed along the entire length of the fracture zone; and (2) the motion of the rocks on either side of the fracture zone should be in the direction shown by the arrows in figure 19.33*A*.

In fact, these things are not true about fracture zones. Earthquakes do occur along fracture zones, but only in those segments between offset sections of ridge crest. In addition, first-motion studies of earthquakes (chapter 16) along fracture zones show that the motion of the rocks on either side of the fracture zone during an earthquake is

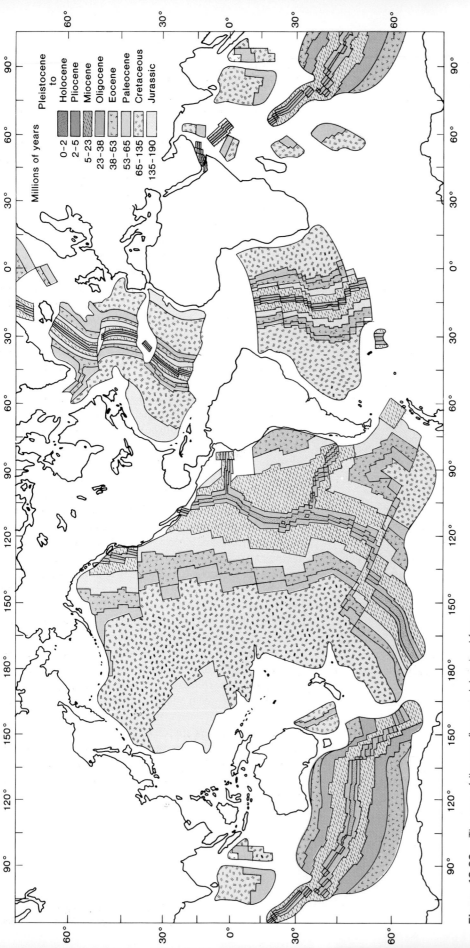

Figure 19.32 The age of the sea floor as determined from magnetic anomalies.
From a map by W. C. Pitman, III, R. L. Larson, and E. M. Herron, 1974, Geological Society of America.

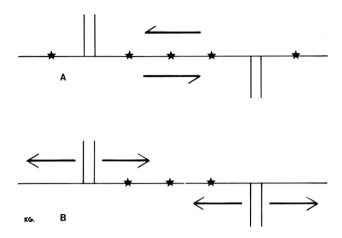

Figure 19.33 Two possible origins for a fracture zone: (A) as a strike-slip fault; (B) as a transform fault.

exactly opposite to the motion that would be expected if the fracture zone were a strike-slip fault. The actual motion of the rocks as determined from first-motion studies is shown in figure 19.33B. The portion of a fracture zone between two offset portions of ridge crest is called a **transform fault.**

The motion of the rocks on either side of a transform fault was predicted by the hypothesis of sea-floor spreading. As sea floor spreads away from the ridge crest, blocks of rock move in opposite directions only on that section of the fracture zone between the two segments of ridge crest. Earthquakes, therefore, occur only on this section of the fracture zone, the transform fault. The direction of motion of rock on either side of the fracture zone is exactly predicted by the assumption that rock is spreading away from the ridge crests. Verification by first-motion studies of this predicted motion along fracture zones was another successful test of the sea-floor spreading hypothesis.

The Unifying Concept of Plate Tectonics
The concept of sea-floor spreading explains many features of the sea floor, as well as the surprisingly young age of the sea floor. As any valid hypothesis should, it made several predictions—such as the increase in age of the sea floor away from the ridge crest—which have been and are now being tested.

In the late 1960s a new concept arose combining most of the hypothesis of sea-floor spreading with the much older concept of *continental drift.* This unifying concept, which took into account the movements of both the sea floor and the continents, is *plate tectonics.* This concept has been mentioned throughout this book in relation to many aspects of the earth, and it is discussed in detail in the next chapter.

Summary
The *continental shelf* and the steeper *continental slope* lie under water along the edges of continents. They are separated by a change in slope angle at a depth of about 100 meters.

Submarine canyons are cut into the continental slope and outer continental shelf by a combination of turbidity currents, sand flow and fall, bottom currents, and river erosion during times of lower sea level.

Abyssal fans form as sediment collects at the base of submarine canyons.

An *Atlantic-type continental margin* occurs off passive coasts and is marked by a continental rise and abyssal plains at the base of the continental slope.

The *continental rise* and *abyssal plains* may form from sediment deposited by turbidity currents. Graded bedding and cable breaks suggest the existence of turbidity currents in the ocean.

The continental rise may also form from deposition of sediment by *contour currents* at the base of the continental slope.

A *Pacific-type continental margin* occurs on active coasts, and is marked by an *oceanic trench* at the base of the continental slope; the continental rise and abyssal plains are absent.

Oceanic trenches are twice as deep as abyssal plains, which generally lie at a depth of 5 kilometers. Associated with trenches are *Benioff zones* of earthquakes and andesitic volcanism, forming either an island arc or a chain of volcanoes near the edge of a continent.

The *mid-oceanic ridge* is a globe-circling mountain range of basalt, located mainly in the middle of ocean basins. The crest of the ridge is marked by a *rift valley,* shallow-focus earthquakes, high heat flow, and active basaltic volcanism.

Fracture zones are lines of weakness that apparently offset the mid-oceanic ridge.

Seamounts are conical, submarine volcanoes, now mostly extinct. *Guyots* are flat-topped seamounts, probably leveled by wave erosion before subsiding.

Chains of seamounts and guyots form *aseismic ridges.*

Terrigenous sediment is composed of land-derived sediment deposited near land by turbidity currents and other processes. *Pelagic sediment* is made up of windblown dust and microscopic skeletons that settle slowly to the sea floor.

The crest of the mid-oceanic ridge lacks pelagic sediment.

Ophiolites in continental mountain ranges probably represent slivers of oceanic crust somehow emplaced on land.

The oldest rocks on the deep sea floor are 200 million years old. The continents, in contrast, contain some rock that is 3 to 4 billion years old.

Hess's hypothesis of *sea-floor spreading* suggests that the sea floor moves away from the ridge crest and toward trenches as a result of mantle convection.

According to the concept of sea-floor spreading, the high heat flow and volcanism of the ridge crest are caused by hot mantle rock rising beneath the ridge. Diverging convection currents in the mantle cause the rift valley and earthquakes on the ridge crest, which is a *spreading center*. New sea floor near the rift valley has not yet accumulated pelagic sediment.

Sea-floor spreading explains trenches as sites of sea-floor *subduction,* which causes low heat flow and negative gravity anomalies. Benioff zones and andesitic volcanism are caused by interaction between the subducting sea floor and the rocks above.

Sea-floor spreading also explains the young age of the rock of the sea floor as due to the loss of old sea floor through subduction into the mantle.

Aseismic ridges may form as sea floor spreads over an eruptive center.

An apparent confirmation of Hess's sea-floor spreading came in the early 1960s with the correlation of marine *magnetic anomalies* to *magnetic reversals* by Vine and Matthews. The origin of magnetic anomalies at sea apparently is due to the recording of normal and reverse magnetization by dikes that intrude the crest of the mid-oceanic ridge, then split and move sideways to give anomaly patterns a mirror symmetry.

The Vine-Matthews hypothesis gives the rate of sea-floor spreading (generally 1–6 centimeters/year) and can predict the age of the sea floor before it is sampled.

Deep-sea drilling has apparently verified both the motions involved in sea-floor spreading and the age predictions made from magnetic anomalies.

Earthquake distribution and first-motion studies on *transform faults* on fracture zones also verify the spreading of the sea floor.

Terms to Remember
abyssal fan
abyssal plain
aseismic ridge
Atlantic-type continental margin
continental rise
continental shelf
continental slope
contour current
convection
fracture zone
guyot
mid-oceanic ridge
oceanic trench
ophiolite
Pacific-type continental margin
pelagic sediment
rift valley
sea-floor spreading
seamount
spreading center
subduction
submarine canyon
terrigenous sediment
transform fault
turbidity current

Questions for Review
1. What is a submarine canyon? How do submarine canyons form?
2. Discuss the appearance, structure, and origin of abyssal plains.
3. Sketch a cross profile of the mid-oceanic ridge, showing the rift valley. Label your horizontal and vertical scales.
4. Sketch an Atlantic-type continental margin and a Pacific-type continental margin, labeling all their parts. Show approximate depths.
5. What is a fracture zone? Sketch the relation between fracture zones and the mid-oceanic ridge.
6. In a sketch show the association between an oceanic trench, a Benioff zone of earthquakes, and volcanoes on the edge of a continent.
7. Describe two different origins for the continental rise.
8. What is a turbidity current? What is the evidence that turbidity currents occur on the sea floor?

9. Describe the appearance and origin of seamounts and guyots.
10. Describe the two main types of sea-floor sediment.
11. How does the age of the sea-floor rocks compare with the age of continental rocks? Be specific.
12. In a single cross-sectional sketch, show the concept of sea-floor spreading and how it relates to the mid-oceanic ridge and oceanic trenches.
13. Explain how sea-floor spreading can account for the existence of the mid-oceanic ridge and its associated rift valley, earthquakes, high heat flow, and basaltic volcanism.
14. Explain how sea-floor spreading can account for the existence of oceanic trenches as well as their low heat flow, their negative gravity anomalies, the associated Benioff zones of earthquakes, and andesitic volcanism.
15. How does sea-floor spreading account for the age of the sea floor?
16. Explain how an aseismic ridge could be caused by sea-floor spreading.
17. What is the origin of marine magnetic anomalies according to Vine and Matthews?
18. Why does the pattern of magnetic anomalies at sea match the pattern of magnetic reversals (recorded in lava flows on land)?
19. How has deep-sea drilling tested the concept of a spreading sea floor?
20. How has the study of fracture zones tested the concept of a spreading sea floor?

Questions for Thought

1. Why are there essentially no trenches in the Atlantic Ocean, which has a mid-oceanic ridge and presumably is undergoing sea-floor spreading?
2. If mantle convection is strong enough to drag the sea floor along like a conveyor belt, what might convection be doing to continents?

Supplementary Readings

Dietz, R. S. 1964. Origin of continental slopes. *American Scientist* 52:50–69.

Heezen, B. C., and C. D. Hollister. 1971. *The face of the deep.* New York: Oxford University Press.

Keen, M. J. 1968. *An introduction to marine geology.* New York: Pergamon Press.

Menard, H. W. 1964. *Marine geology of the Pacific.* New York: McGraw-Hill.

Menard, H. W. ed. 1977. *Ocean science—Readings from Scientific American.* San Francisco: W. H. Freeman.

Moore, J. R. ed. 1971. *Oceanography—Readings from Scientific American.* San Francisco: W. H. Freeman.

Shepard, F. P. 1973. *Submarine geology.* 3rd ed. New York: Harper and Row.

Turekian, K. K. 1976. *Oceans.* 2d ed. Englewood Cliffs, N.J.: Prentice-Hall.

(See also the list of readings for chapter 20.)

20
Plate Tectonics

Purpose

In studying such topics as volcanoes, igneous and metamorphic rock, earthquakes, mountain ranges, and sea-floor features, you have become aware of how all these geologic phenomena are related to the unifying concept of plate tectonics. In this chapter we review many of these topics and describe more specifically (1) the plates themselves; (2) plate motion and its possible driving forces; (3) plate boundaries; and (4) how plates change in size. How the theory of plate tectonics developed is also discussed—from Alfred Wegener's idea of continental drift to the continuing modifications and refinements of the concept in its present form.

A summary of earth features that can be explained by plate tectonic activity is also included in the chapter. We close with a discussion of mantle plumes and aulacogens.

Because it can explain in a general way so many different features found on earth, plate tectonics has come to dominate geological thought today. Why is this theory so attractive to geologists?

The basic idea of **plate tectonics** is that the earth's surface is divided into a few large, thick plates that are slowly moving and are changing in size. Intense geologic activity occurs at *plate boundaries* where plates move away from one another, past one another, or toward one another. The eight large plates shown in figure 20.1, plus a few dozen smaller plates, make up the outer shell of the earth (the crust and upper part of the mantle).

Among the hypotheses suggested to explain the evolution of mountain belts was the idea of *continental drift*, the movement of continents over the earth's surface (chapter 1). Another hypothesis, *sea-floor spreading* (chapter 19), postulated that the ocean floor is developing at the mid-oceanic ridge and spreading away from it. In the late 1960s these hypotheses became part of the overall

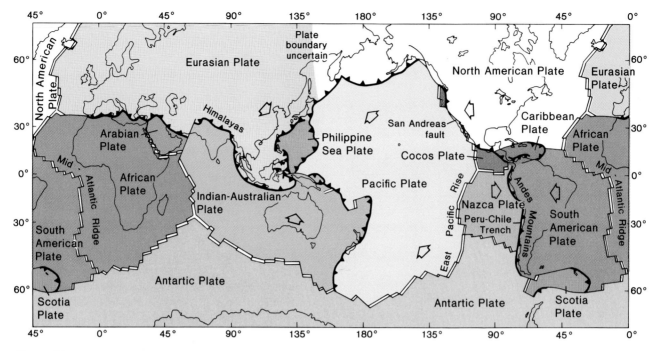

Figure 20.1 The major plates of the world. The western edge of the map repeats the eastern edge so that all plates can be shown unbroken. Double lines indicate spreading centers on diverging plate boundaries. Single lines show transform boundaries. Heavy lines with triangles show converging boundaries, with triangles pointing down subduction zones.
Modified from W. Hamilton, U.S. Geological Survey.

theory of plate tectonics, which encompasses both ideas— that is, a spreading sea floor and moving continents. Before we look closely at plates and plate boundaries, we will examine the history of the idea of continental drift.

The Early Case for Continental Drift

The idea of moving continents is not new. The similarities in shape of the Atlantic coastlines of South America and Africa were noticed by Francis Bacon in 1620. In 1858 Antonio Snider showed on maps how these continents might once have been joined but then split apart and moved away from one another to form the Atlantic Ocean. The coastlines of other continents also can be made to fit together in "jigsaw puzzle" fashion. For example, the Atlantic coast of the United States fits fairly well against the Atlantic coast of northwestern Africa. Similarities in shoreline shape, of course, do not *prove* that the continents were ever together.

The Ideas of Alfred Wegener

In the early 1900s Alfred Wegener, a German meteorologist, carefully studied the fit of continents and assembled other evidence to make the strongest case he could for continental drift. He showed that the continents could fit together to form a giant supercontinent, which he called *Pangaea* (figure 20.2).

Fossils and paleoclimates Wegener showed that fossils of plants of late Paleozoic age found on several different continents were quite similar. In particular, the plant fossil *Glossopteris* was found in rocks in South America, Africa, India, and Australia (figure 20.3). Although these localities are now widely separated from one another, in Wegener's reconstruction of Pangaea they fit closely together. If *Glossopteris* had developed while the continents were joined, the similarity of the fossils would be explained.

Rocks with some significant similarities also are found in India, Africa, South America, Australia, and Antarctica. At all five localities are found sequences in which late Paleozoic tillites (lithified glacial till) are overlain by thick continental sedimentary rocks containing coal beds and *Glossopteris* fossils. Early Mesozoic lava flows overlie the sedimentary layers (figure 20.4). The five sequences of rocks are strikingly similar, even though today the localities are widely separated. More-

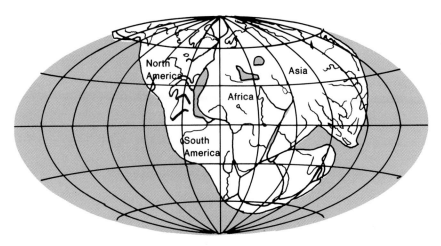

Figure 20.2 Pangaea.
From A. Wegener, 1928, *The Origin of Continents and Oceans*, reprinted and copyrighted, 1968, Dover Publications.

Figure 20.3 A leaf of *Glossopteris*.

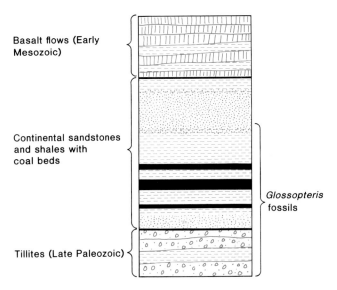

Basalt flows (Early Mesozoic)

Continental sandstones and shales with coal beds

Tillites (Late Paleozoic)

Glossopteris fossils

Figure 20.4 Rock sequences similar to this are found in India, Africa, South America, Australia, and Antarctica.

over, the younger rocks in the five localities are very dissimilar. Wegener interpreted this to mean that the rock sequences formed together as a single unit while the continents were joined as Pangaea. Beginning in early Mesozoic time, the continents split apart and began to migrate away from each other, splitting the rocks apart. The continents retained the outline of the original pieces that broke away from Pangaea.

Wegener also believed that the evidence for late Paleozoic glaciation on the continents of the southern hemisphere supported his idea of Pangaea (figure 20.5). If South America, Africa, India, and Australia were spread over the earth in Paleozoic time as they are today, a climate cold enough to produce extensive glaciation would have had to prevail over almost the whole world. Yet evidence has not been found of widespread Paleozoic gla-

ciation in the northern hemisphere. In fact, the late Paleozoic coal beds of North America and Europe were being laid down at that time in swampy, probably warm, environments. If the continents are arranged according to Wegener's Pangaea reconstruction, then glaciation in the southern hemisphere is confined to a much smaller area (figure 20.5), and the absence of widespread glaciation in the northern hemisphere becomes easier to explain.

Wegener also worked with evidence from sedimentary rocks in an attempt to reconstruct old climate zones. (The study of ancient climates is called *paleoclimatology*.) The earth today has distinct climate zones—for instance, cold polar regions and warmer tropical regions. Deserts are found largely in two belts, one at 30° North latitude and

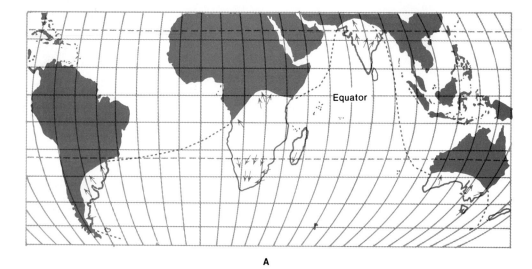

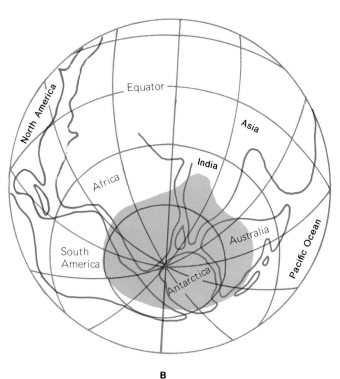

Figure 20.5 Distribution of Late Paleozoic glaciations; arrows show direction of ice flow. (*A*) Continents in present positions show wide distribution of glaciation (white land areas with flow arrows). (*B*) Continents reassembled into Pangaea. Glaciated region (shaded area) becomes much smaller.
From Arthur Holmes, 1965, *Principles of Physical Geology*, 2d ed., Ronald Press.

the other at 30° South latitude (chapter 13). Coral reefs are confined to warm water near the equator (figure 20.6).

Wegener cataloged paleoclimatic evidence from the sedimentary rocks of each geologic period to see if he could find evidence of old climate zones. For example, glacial till and striations would indicate a past cold climate and perhaps proximity to the position of the geographic North or South Pole in the past. Fossil coral reefs might indicate an earlier position near the equator. Cross-bedded sandstones from old sand dunes might locate past desert belts.

Polar wandering From such paleoclimatic evidence, Wegener found that many ancient climate belts were in different positions from the present belts (figure 20.7). One way of explaining this shift in climate belts through geologic time is the apparent movement of the earth's geographic North and South Poles, a process that is called **polar wandering** (figure 20.7*A*). Polar wandering, however, is a deceptive term. The process can actually be explained in two different ways:

1. The continents remained motionless and the poles actually *did* move or wander (figure 20.7*A*).

2. The poles stood still and the continents moved (figure 20.7*B*).

Wegener plotted curves of apparent polar wandering (figure 20.8). Since one interpretation of polar wandering data was that the continents moved, Wegener felt that this supported his concept of continental drift. (Notice that in only one interpretation of *polar wandering* do the poles actually move. You should keep in mind that when

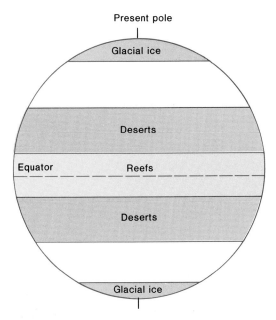

Figure 20.6 Generalized climate zones today produce belts of geologic features such as glaciers, deserts, and reefs.

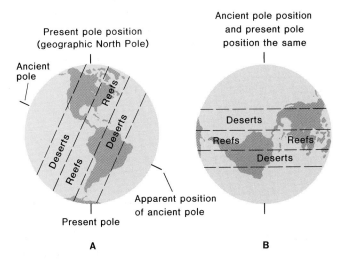

Figure 20.7 Two ways of interpreting the distribution of ancient climate belts. (A) Continents fixed, poles wander. (B) Poles fixed, continents drift. For simplicity, the continents in B are shown as having moved as a unit, without changing positions relative to each other. If continents move, they should change relative positions, complicating the pattern shown.

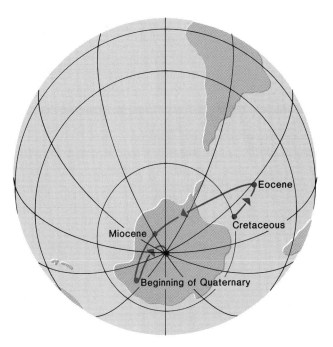

Figure 20.8 Wandering of the South Pole since the Cretaceous Period as determined by Wegener from paleoclimate evidence. Wegener, of course, believed that *continents* rather than poles moved.
From A. Wegener, 1928, *The Origins of Continents and Oceans*, reprinted and copyrighted, 1968, Dover Publications.

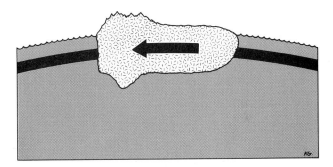

Figure 20.9 Wegener's concept of continental drift implied that continents drifted *through* oceanic crust, crumpling up mountain ranges on their leading edges as they pushed against oceanic crust.

geologists use the term "polar wandering" they are referring to an *apparent* motion of the poles, which may or may not have actually occurred.)

Skepticism about Continental Drift

Although Wegener presented the best case possible in the early 1900s for continental drift, much of his evidence was not clear-cut. Fossil plants, for example, could have been spread from one continent to another by winds or ocean currents. Distribution over more than one continent need not signify that the continents were all joined as one, Pangaea. In addition, polar wandering might have been caused by moving poles rather than by moving continents. Because his evidence was not conclusive, Wegener's ideas were not widely accepted. This was particularly true in the United States, largely because of the mechanism Wegener proposed for continental drift.

Wegener proposed that continents plowed through the oceanic crust (figure 20.9), perhaps crumpling up mountain ranges on the leading edges of the continents where they pushed against the sea floor. Most geologists in the United States felt that this idea violated what was known about the strength of rocks at the time. In addition, it was difficult for geologists to conceive of a driving force that could move continents. So Wegener's ideas received little support in the United States or much of the northern hemisphere in the first half of the twentieth century. In the southern hemisphere, however, where Wegener's matches of fossils and rocks between continents were more evident, geologists were more impressed with the concept of continental drift.

Paleomagnetism and the Revival of Continental Drift

Much work in the 1940s and 1950s set the stage for the revival of the idea of continental drift and its later incorporation, along with sea-floor spreading, into the new concept of plate tectonics. The new investigations were in two areas: (1) study of the sea floor (chapter 19), and (2) geophysical research, especially in relation to rock magnetism.

Convincing new evidence regarding the nature of polar wandering came out of the study of the magnetism of rocks. Because the rotation of the earth is probably related to the generation of the earth's magnetic field, we can assume that the *geographic* poles of rotation have been continuously near the north and south *magnetic* poles (chapter 17)—that is, the two sets of poles would have "wandered" together in approximately the same relative positions. As we discuss magnetic evidence for polar wandering, we are referring to an apparent motion of the magnetic poles. Because the magnetic and geographic poles are close together, our discussion will refer to apparent motion of the geographic poles as well.

As we discussed in chapter 17, many rocks record the strength and direction of the earth's magnetic field at the time the rocks formed. Small magnetite crystals in a cooling lava flow act like tiny compass needles, preserving a record of the earth's magnetic field when the lava solidifies (figure 20.10). Iron-stained sedimentary rocks such as red sandstone can also record earth magnetism. The magnetism of old rocks can be measured to determine the direction and strength of the earth's magnetic field in the past. The study of ancient magnetic fields is called *paleomagnetism.*

For instance, paleomagnetic studies on numerous Permian lava flows in North America show that during the Permian Period (see the geologic time scale in chapter 8) the north magnetic pole was apparently located at a point inside eastern Asia. This can be inferred because the iron-containing minerals in these lava flows, like compass needles locked in position, point toward Asia (figure 20.11). Because magnetic lines of force dip more steeply

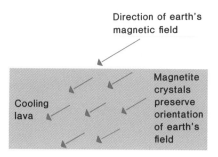

Figure 20.10 Some rocks preserve a record of the earth's magnetic field.

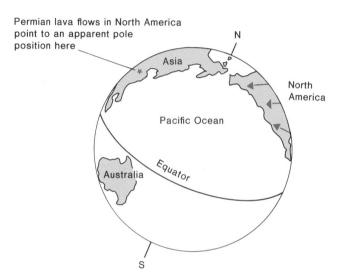

Figure 20.11 Paleomagnetic studies of Permian lava flows on North America indicate an apparent position for the north magnetic pole in eastern Asia.

as the north magnetic pole is approached, the inclination (dip) of the magnetized crystals in the lava flows can be used to determine the distance from a flow to the pole (figure 20.12). Since the magnetic minerals in Permian lava flows all over North America point to approximately the same spot in Asia, this spot can be interpreted as the position of the north magnetic pole during Permian time.

Further paleomagnetic studies in North America indicate that the magnetic minerals in Silurian lava flows point to a different spot (in the western Pacific Ocean), while from Cretaceous lava flows yet another point can be plotted. Lava flows of all ages in North America can be studied, and from these data the path of *apparent* movement of the north magnetic pole through time can be traced (figure 20.13). Paleomagnetic evidence thus verifies the idea of polar wandering that Wegener had suggested using paleoclimatic evidence.

Like Wegener's paleoclimatic evidence, the paleomagnetic evidence from a *single* continent can be interpreted in two ways: either the continent stood still and the

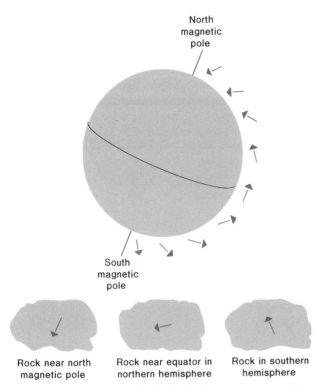

Figure 20.12 Magnetic dip (inclination) increases toward the north magnetic pole.

Rock near north magnetic pole | Rock near equator in northern hemisphere | Rock in southern hemisphere

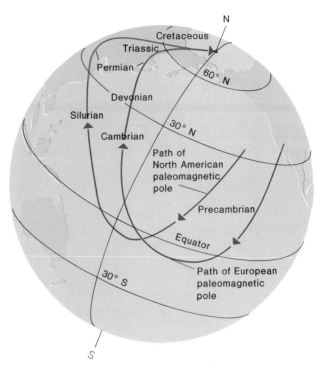

Figure 20.13 Polar wandering of the north magnetic pole as determined from measurements of rocks from North America and Europe.
From A. Cox and R. R. Doell, 1960, *Geological Society of America Bulletin.*

magnetic pole moved or the pole stood still and the continent moved. At first glance, paleomagnetic evidence does not seem to be a significant advance over paleoclimatic evidence. But when paleomagnetic evidence from *different* continents was taken into account, an important discovery was made.

Although the Permian lava flows of North America indicate a north magnetic pole position in Asia, data taken from Permian lava flows of *Europe* suggest a different location for the pole in Permian time (it is also in Asia, but closer to Japan). Does this mean there were two north magnetic poles during the Permian Period? An analysis of lava flows from all continents shows that each continent has its own series of north magnetic pole positions. Unless there were different north magnetic poles for each continent (which is highly unlikely), the best explanation for these data is that the pole stood still and the continents moved, splitting apart and rotating as they diverged.

The paths of north magnetic pole movement for the continents of North America and Europe are shown in figure 20.13. The paths are of similar shape, but the path for European poles is to the east of the North American path. If we mentally push North America back toward Europe, closing the Atlantic Ocean, and then consider the

paths of polar wandering, we find that the path for North America lies exactly on the path for Europe. This strongly suggests that there was one north magnetic pole and that the continents were joined together. The impression that there were two north magnetic poles comes because, in the movement of North America to the west, the rocks changed position, and their magnetic minerals now indicate different locations for the poles.

Additional Evidence for Continental Drift

Much evidence has been obtained in support of continental drift since the time of Wegener. Wegener's concept of polar wandering was given new life by paleomagnetic evidence. As interest revived in continental drift, new work was done on paleoclimates and fossil correlations between continents. For example, fossils of nearly identical freshwater animals, which could not have migrated across a saline ocean, have been found in rocks of the same age in the continents of the southern hemisphere. For these freshwater forms to have lived and evolved as they did suggests strongly that the southern continents were once connected.

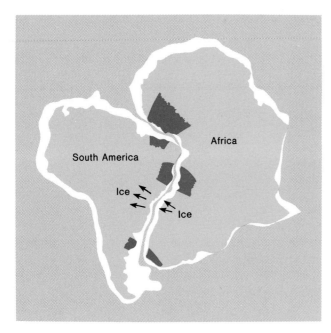

Figure 20.14 Continental fit and rock matches between South America and Africa. White areas around continents are continental shelves (part of continents). Shaded areas within continents are broad belts of rock that correlate in type and age from one continent to another. Arrows show direction of glacier movement as determined from striations.

In addition, the precision of the fit between continents has been greatly improved by using the middle of the continental slope as the edge of a continent rather than the present shoreline (figure 20.14). With the aid of computers, the best possible fit between continents was worked out.

The most convincing evidence for continental drift comes from a careful study of rock matches between continents. As continents are fitted together like pieces of a jigsaw puzzle, it is important that the "picture" match from piece to piece. Detailed rock matches between continents now separated by an ocean can indicate that the continents were once joined. Wegener made some general matches and correlations in the southern hemisphere in rocks of late Paleozoic and early Mesozoic age. Recent work has greatly refined rock matches between continents.

The matches between South America and Africa are particularly striking. Some distinctive rock contacts extend out to sea along the shore of Africa. If the two continents are fitted together, the identical contacts are found in precisely the right position on the shore of South America (figure 20.14). Radioactive ages of rocks also match between these continents.

Glacial striations show that during the late Paleozoic Era continental glaciers moved from Africa toward the present Atlantic Ocean while similar glaciers seemingly moved *from* the Atlantic Ocean *onto* South America (figure 20.14). Continental glaciers, however, cannot move from sea onto land. If the two continents had been joined together, the ice that moved off Africa could have been the ice that moved onto South America. This hypothesis has now been confirmed; from their lithology, many of the boulders in South American tillites have been traced to a source which is now in Africa.

Some of the best matches have been made between rocks in Brazil and rocks in the African country of Gabon. These rocks are similar in type, structure, sequence, fossils, ages, and degree of metamorphism. Such detailed matches are convincing evidence that continental drift did, in fact, take place.

History of Continental Positions

Rock matches show when continents were together, and polar wandering and magnetic anomaly evidence indicate the rate and direction of continental motion. By means of data drawn mostly from these sources, positions of the continents during the past have been determined. Figure 20.15 shows the gradual migration of continents from the supercontinent Pangaea 200 million years ago to their present-day positions.

Pangaea initially separated into two parts. *Laurasia* was the northern supercontinent, containing what is now North America and Eurasia (excluding India). *Gondwanaland* was the southern supercontinent, composed of all the present-day southern-hemisphere continents and India (which has drifted north).

Much older plate positions have been determined than those shown in figure 20.15. Plates apparently moved throughout the Paleozoic Era, and even as early as the Precambrian. Plate motion in the Paleozoic and Precambrian is more difficult to determine because of the lack of marine magnetic anomalies older than 200 million years.

Plates and Plate Motion

As described earlier, a **plate** is a large, mobile slab of rock that is part of the earth's surface (figure 20.1). The surface of a plate may be made up entirely of sea floor (as is the Nazca plate), or it may be made up of both continental and oceanic rock (as is the North American plate). Some of the smaller plates may be entirely continental, but all the large plates contain some sea floor.

Plate tectonics has added some new terms, based on rock behavior, to the zones of the earth's interior, as we have discussed in chapters 1 and 17. The plates are part of a rigid outer shell of the earth called the **lithosphere.** The thickness of the lithosphere is approximately 100 kilometers, so it includes the rocks of the earth's crust and

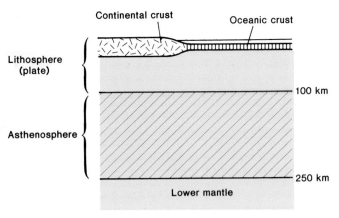

Figure 20.16 Lithosphere and asthenosphere.

uppermost mantle (figure 20.16). Below the rigid lithosphere is the **asthenosphere,** a zone approximately 150 kilometers thick that behaves plastically because of increased temperature and pressure. The plastic asthenosphere acts like a lubricating layer under the lithosphere, allowing the plates to move. The asthenosphere, made up of upper mantle rock, is the seismic low-velocity zone described in chapter 17. Below the asthenosphere is the more rigid lower mantle.

The idea that plates move is widely accepted by geologists, although the reasons for this movement are not fully known. Plates move away from the mid-oceanic ridge crest or other spreading centers. Some plates move toward oceanic trenches. If the plate is made up mostly of sea floor (as are the Nazca and Pacific plates), the plate can be subducted down into the mantle, forming an oceanic trench and its associated features. If the leading edge of the plate is made up of continental rock (as is the South American plate), subduction of that plate will not occur. Continental rock, being less dense (specific gravity 2.7) than oceanic rock (specific gravity 3.0), is too light to be subducted.

A plate is a rigid slab of rock that moves as a unit. As a result, the interior of a plate is relatively inactive tectonically. Plate interiors generally lack earthquakes, volcanoes, young mountain ranges, and other signs of geologic activity. According to plate tectonic theory, these features are caused by plate interactions at plate boundaries.

Earthquakes, volcanoes, and young mountain ranges are distributed in narrow belts separated by broad regions of inactivity, as you have seen in previous chapters. This distribution has puzzled geologists for a long time, and many hypotheses have been advanced to explain it. The plate tectonic concept is the latest attempt at explanation. Plates are actually identified and located by outlining the broad inactive regions on a map. Plate boundaries are

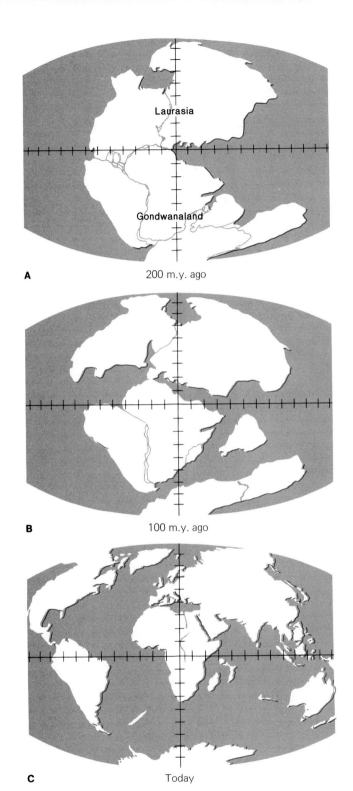

A 200 m.y. ago

B 100 m.y. ago

C Today

Figure 20.15 Pangaea breakup and continental drift.
(A) 200 million years ago. (B) 100 million years ago.
(C) Today.
From R. S. Dietz and J. C. Holden, *Journal of Geophysical Research,* vol. 75, pp. 4,939–56, 1970, copyrighted by American Geophysical Union.

defined and located by mapping narrow bands of geologic activity, such as belts of earthquakes (chapter 16) and belts of volcanoes (chapter 3).

Plate tectonics has become a unifying theory of geology because it can explain so many diverse features of the earth. Earthquake distribution, the origin of mountain ranges, the origin of sea-floor topography, the distribution and composition of volcanoes, and many other features can all be related to plate tectonics. It is a convenient framework that unifies geologic thought, indicating associations of features that were once studied separately and relating them to a single cause: plate interactions at plate boundaries.

Plate boundaries are of three general types, depending upon whether plates move away from each other, move toward each other, or move past each other. A **diverging plate boundary** is a boundary between plates that are moving apart. A **converging plate boundary** lies between plates that are moving toward each other. A **transform plate boundary** is one at which two plates move horizontally past each other.

Diverging Plate Boundaries

Diverging plate boundaries vary in character, depending upon whether the divergence begins in the middle of the ocean or in the middle of a continent.

Oceanic Divergence

The boundary between the Nazca and Pacific plates in the eastern Pacific Ocean (figure 20.1) is an example of a diverging plate boundary in the middle of an ocean.

A diverging boundary on the sea floor is marked by the crest of the mid-oceanic ridge (figure 20.17). The crest of the ridge is characterized by a narrow band of shallow-focus earthquakes. First-motion studies of these quakes (chapter 16) can be interpreted to show dip-slip fault motion along normal faults parallel to the ridge crest. If this interpretation is correct, such motion could be caused by horizontal tension perpendicular to the ridge crest.

Although first-motion studies can be interpreted in more than one way, confirmation of horizontal tension comes from other sources. The ridge crest in many regions is marked by a rift valley, which is almost certainly the result of the oceanic crust being torn apart here. Tensional cracks within the rift valley, and parallel to it, were observed by the geologists diving in small submarines during the FAMOUS expedition.

The rift valley is also marked by basaltic volcanism, which forms pillow lavas on the rift valley floor. This volcanism appears to be the result of the melting (either totally or partially) of the mantle beneath the ridge crest. The melting may be due to release of pressure on hot

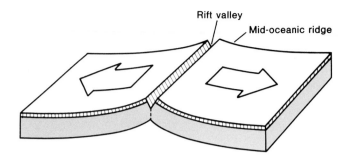

Figure 20.17 A diverging boundary between two oceanic plates.

mantle rock, either by the upward movement of mantle rock in a convection system or by the opening of the rift valley itself. Basaltic magma apparently flows upward in tensional cracks, creating dikes in the cracks and pillowed lavas on the sea floor where the lava emerges. These pillows and dikes were discussed in chapter 19 in connection with the structure of oceanic crust and the origin of magnetic anomalies.

The net effect of the basalt eruptions is the creation of new sea floor within the rift valley. This new sea floor is added to the trailing edges of the diverging plates and can increase the size of a plate if its leading edge is not being subducted.

The rift valley's existence may depend upon a delicate balance between the rate of plate motion (sea-floor spreading) and the rate of lava eruption. In the Atlantic and Indian Oceans the rift valley is clearly evident, but it is absent in most of the Pacific Ocean, where spreading is faster. The Pacific ridge may lack a rift valley because rapid eruptions of basalt fill in the tensional rift or because the rapidly spreading Pacific crust is too hot and plastic to be torn brittly apart.

The existence of the mid-oceanic ridge as a topographically high feature appears to be caused by mantle convection. The mantle rock is abnormally hot beneath the ridge crest, leading to a measurably high heat flow here. If there is localized heating deep within (or below) the mantle, then hot mantle rock may be rising due to its lower density and may actually be pushing the ridge up.

Some geologists, however, believe that upward convection is a result of plate divergence rather than of heating from below. If two adjacent blocks of floating wood are pushed apart, water will rise up between them to fill the gap (figure 20.18). If hot mantle rock rises between diverging plates in this way, then the elevation of the mid-oceanic ridge may be due to thermal expansion rather than pushing from below. Hot rock expands and takes up more space than cold rock. The ridge may be high in the center because it is hot and may become lower on the flanks as it progressively cools and contracts. Careful measurements of temperature and heat flow versus elevation

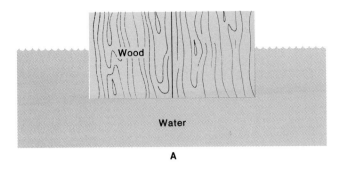

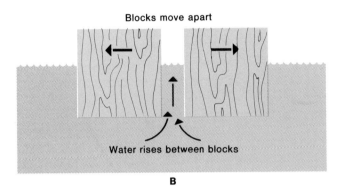

Figure 20.18 Water rises upward to fill the gap when (A) two floating blocks are (B) moved apart. The water moves as a result of the motion of the blocks.

of the ridge seem to support this view. Additional support comes from the near absence of gravity anomalies over the ridge. The ridge crest generally shows a very slight positive gravity anomaly or no anomaly at all. A much stronger positive anomaly would be expected if the ridge were being pushed up (chapter 17).

Continental Divergence

When a supercontinent such as Pangaea breaks up, a diverging boundary can be found in the middle of a continent. A diverging boundary on a continent is initially somewhat different from a diverging boundary at sea.

In the early stages of continental breakup the continent is elevated, just as the mid-oceanic ridge is at an oceanic boundary. This elevation stretches the crust, making it thinner above the uplift (figure 20.19A). Tensional forces produce shallow-focus earthquakes along normal faults, and a rift valley forms along a central graben (a down-dropped fault block).

The rift valley is marked by high heat flow and basaltic volcanism. Magma rises along the fractures to erupt within the rift valley, perhaps first as isolated cinder cones and later as more extensive plateau basalts. The source of the basaltic magma is probably the underlying mantle, just as it is in mid-oceanic ridge eruptions. An example

of a boundary that shows most of these characteristics is the African Rift Valleys in eastern Africa (figure 20.20), which apparently are grabens marking the site of the future breakup of Africa.

As divergence continues, the continental crust on the upper part of the plate clearly separates, and sea water may flood into the linear basin between the diverging pieces of the original continent (figure 20.19B). A complex pattern of step faults and basins filled with continental sediments develops on the edges of the continents, perhaps along curved fault planes that allow the fault blocks to rotate. The uplifted edges of the continents are rapidly eroded, filling the fault basins with continental sediment, such as sands and gravels. The edges of diverging continents, therefore, are thin for two reasons—"necking" caused by the original stretching, and erosion of the uplifted edges after the faulting begins.

In between the two new continents continued basaltic volcanism begins to build true oceanic crust, and the center of the narrow ocean is marked by a rift valley with its typical high heat flow and shallow earthquakes. The Red Sea is considered to be an example of a diverging margin at this stage (figure 20.21).

The new ocean is narrow, and the tilt of the adjacent land is away from the new sea, so rivers flow away from the sea (figure 20.19B). For these reasons the sea water that has flooded into the rift may evaporate, leaving behind a thick layer of rock salt overlying the continental sediments. The likelihood of salt precipitation increases if the continent is in one of the desert belts (chapter 13) or if one or both ends of the new ocean should become temporarily blocked, perhaps by volcanism. Not all diverging boundaries contain rock salt, however.

The plates continue to diverge, widening the sea, and eventually tearing the layer of rock salt (if it formed) in two. The ocean soon becomes so wide that complete evaporation is impossible, and a full-fledged mid-oceanic ridge develops (figure 20.19C). The trailing edges of the continents have been lowered both by erosion and continual subsidence due to cooling. Subsidence continues until the continents' edges are under water, forming continental shelves and continental slopes.

As the ocean widens even further, the flanks of the ridge subside to the point that broad stretches of relatively flat ocean basin floor develop on either side of the ridge. Continued subsidence of the edges of continents allows a thick sedimentary sequence to build up on the continental shelves. The deep continental rise forms on the ocean floor as sediment is carried down the continental slopes by turbidity currents and other mechanisms (figure 20.19D). The Atlantic Ocean is currently at this stage of divergence.

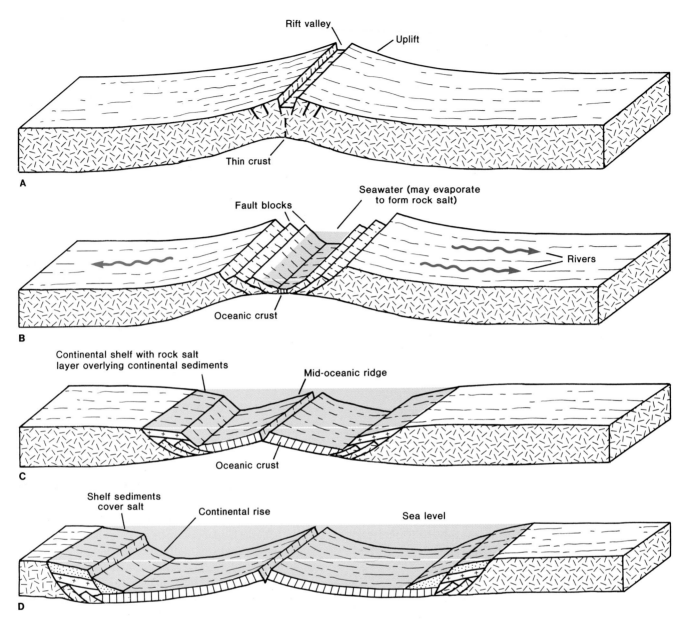

Rift valley

Uplift

Thin crust

A

Fault blocks

Seawater (may evaporate to form rock salt)

Rivers

Oceanic crust

B

Continental shelf with rock salt layer overlying continental sediments

Mid-oceanic ridge

Oceanic crust

C

Shelf sediments cover salt

Continental rise

Sea level

D

Figure 20.19   A diverging plate boundary forming in the middle of a continent will eventually create a new ocean.

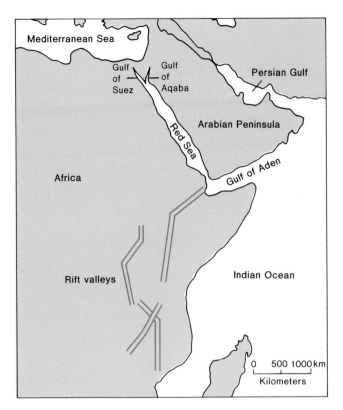

Figure 20.20   The East African Rift Valleys

Figure 20.21   Space photograph of sea water-filled rifts caused by continental divergence at the north end of the Red Sea (dark area at far right). View northeast across Gulf of Suez (dark area in foreground) and Gulf of Aqaba. Compare with figure 20.20. Note Dead Sea (small, dark area) in line with Gulf of Aqaba. Mediterranean Sea at upper left.
NASA

The shelves and slopes of diverging continents

The edges of diverging continents go through a complex history of normal faulting, basalt eruptions, continental sedimentation, subsidence due to cooling, and shallow marine sedimentation on continental shelves. Some edges include a thick bed of rock salt on top of the continental sediments and below the marine sediments (figure 20.22A). Marine sediments may be so abundant that they form thick layers draped over the continental shelf and down the continental slope, building the continent seaward. Slopes like this are particularly susceptible to giant submarine landslides that cause the sediment layers to slide down into deeper water (figure 20.22B). Coral and algal reefs may become established on shelf edges in warm tropical water, and build slowly upward as the shelf subsides. Such reefs become shelf-edge barriers, creating giant basins on the shelves that become filled with sediment derived from the reefs and from the continents (figure 20.22C). All three types of margins shown in figure 20.22 occur along the Atlantic and Gulf of Mexico coastlines of North America.

Converging Plate Boundaries

At converging plate boundaries two plates move toward each other. The character of the boundary depends partly on the type of plates that converge. A plate capped by oceanic crust can move toward another plate capped by oceanic crust, in which case one plate dives (subducts) under the other. If an oceanic plate converges with a plate capped by a continent, the dense oceanic plate subducts under the continental plate. If the two approaching plates are both carrying continents, the continents collide and crumple, but neither is subducted.

Ocean-Ocean Convergence

Where two plates capped by sea floor converge, one plate subducts under the other (the Pacific plate sliding under Japan is an example). The subducting plate bends downward, forming the outer wall of an oceanic trench, which usually forms a broad curve convex to the subducting plate (figure 20.23).

This convexity is probably a geometric requirement of sliding one part of a sphere under another part. Figure 20.24 illustrates how this convex curve might form. A rectangular "plate" is drawn on a Ping-Pong ball, with an arrow to show the direction of plate motion. A circular dent is then created by pushing on the ball. This represents subduction of the leading edge of the plate. Notice how part of the edge of the dent crosses the "plate" in a curved path. This edge represents the trench, which is convex toward the trailing edge of the plate that is still on the ball's "surface."

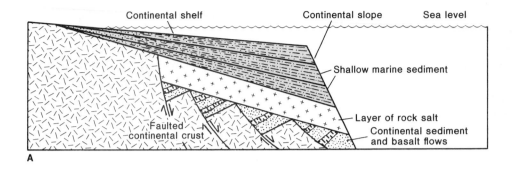

Continental shelf　　Continental slope　　Sea level

Shallow marine sediment

Faulted continental crust

Layer of rock salt

Continental sediment and basalt flows

A

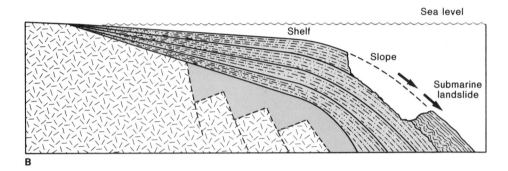

Sea level

Shelf

Slope

Submarine landslide

B

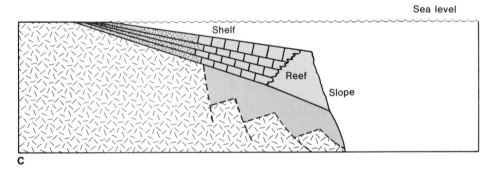

Sea level

Shelf

Reef

Slope

C

Figure 20.22 Three types of continental margins formed by continental breakup and divergence. The deep structure of the margin is the same in each case.

As one plate subducts under another, a Benioff zone of shallow-, intermediate-, and deep-focus earthquakes occurs within the upper portion of the downgoing lithosphere (figure 16.30). The various reasons for these earthquakes were discussed in chapter 16. The existence of deep-focus quakes to depths of 700 kilometers tells us that brittle plates continue to that depth. The pattern of quakes with depth shows that plates can change the angle of subduction with depth, becoming gentler or steeper, and that some plates crumple and break up as they descend (chapter 16).

The descending plate somehow generates andesitic magma along the subduction zone for one of the reasons discussed in chapter 3 and 4. Partial melting of the basaltic oceanic crust is one possibility. Just the lower-temperature, more silica-rich minerals of basalt may melt to form andesite (perhaps after magmatic differentiation), leaving behind a heavier, more mafic residue of unmelted minerals that increase the density of the downgoing slab.

Some water is carried down the subduction zone. Water is chemically combined with some minerals in oceanic crust, and it fills crustal fractures and sediment pores. The deep ocean floor is not smooth. It consists of hills and depressions caused by faulting and landsliding

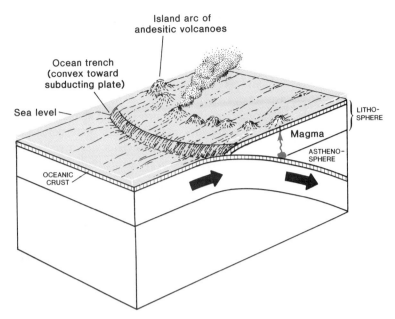

Figure 20.23 A converging plate boundary where one oceanic plate is subducted beneath another, forming an oceanic trench and an island arc. The size of the volcanoes is greatly exaggerated.

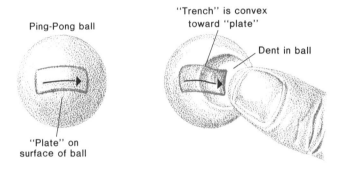

Figure 20.24 A dented Ping-Pong ball can show why trenches are curved.

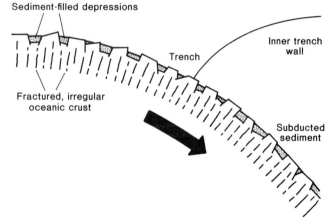

Figure 20.25 Subduction of marine sediment in sea floor depressions. Some sediment may be scraped off (not shown here) and added to the inner trench wall (figures 20.28 and 20.29).

during formation of the crust at the ridge crest. As the crust moves toward trenches, the depressions fill with sediment. Although most marine sediment may be scraped off the descending plate during subduction (and added to the upper plate, as you will see below), the sediment in the depressions would be protected and should be subducted (figure 20.25).

As this water is carried down the subduction zone, it may be released by the rise in temperature and pressure with depth. The released water would rise into the overlying plate and could trigger melting (perhaps partial melting) of hot rock by lowering its melting point, as described in chapter 4. Sediment may also melt, adding to any magma formed by other processes. Even if the original magma is not andesitic, part of it could differentiate into andesite.

However the andesitic magma is formed, it works its way upward to erupt as an **island arc,** a curved line of volcanoes that form a string of islands parallel to an oceanic trench (figure 20.23). The generation of andesitic magma apparently occurs where the top of the descending lithosphere comes in contact with the overlying asthenosphere, as shown in figure 20.26. If the subduction angle is steep, this location is close to the trench, so the horizontal distance between the arc and the trench is short

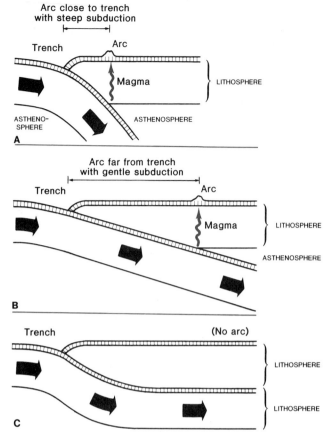

Figure 20.26 Andesitic magma is generated where the top of subducting lithosphere contacts the overlying asthenosphere, so subduction angle determines arc-trench spacing.

(figure 20.26*A*). If the subduction angle is gentle, the arc-trench distance is greater (figure 20.26*B*). In some locations the subduction angle is so gentle that one plate merely slides along under another. Since the top of the subducting plate never contacts asthenosphere, such very shallow subduction zones lack volcanism (figure 20.26*C*).

The plate being subducted is characterized by low heat flow, suggesting that oceanic plates cool continuously as they travel from the crest of the mid-oceanic ridge to oceanic trenches. It is conceivable that this cooling continually increases plate density until the lithosphere becomes heavy enough to sink back into the mantle. A downgoing plate may be sinking under its own weight in an attempt to come into isostatic equilibrium.

Trenches, however, are marked by very strong negative gravity anomalies—the strongest negative anomalies in the world. The anomalies imply that the sinking at trenches is not just an isostatic adjustment. Something must be pulling the plate down at this point. What that

something is is the subject of lively debate among geologists. If partial melting at depth increases the density of the lower part of the downgoing plate, then the trench may be pulled down by the leading edge of the plate far below. Pressure-collapse of minerals could also increase the density of descending lithosphere. If mantle convection drives plate motion, then a down-turning convection current of cool mantle rock may drag the plate down and form the trench. One thing seems clear: negative gravity anomalies show that trenches are being pulled down.

The inner trench wall The inner wall of a trench, toward the arc, has a very complex structure. Close to the trench is a *subduction complex* (or *mélange*) of highly contorted, thrust-faulted marine sediment. The continued motion of the subducting plate tends to drag the lower part of this complex downward in wedge-shaped slices (figure 20.27). This underthrusting of new slices added to the bottom of the stack pushes the subduction complex upward, forming a basin called a *forearc basin* between the complex and the volcanic arc. (The region on the trench side of an arc is the forearc; the region on the other side of the arc is the backarc.)

Because the thrust slices are wedge shaped, their movement down the subduction zone tends to steepen the angle of thrust faults near the top of the subduction complex. An individual fault becomes steeper upward because wedges of sediment are being forced underneath it. Underthrusting also steepens the front of the entire subduction complex (the inner trench wall) by continually removing material from the base of the slope.

Oversteepening of the inner trench wall causes landslides down the front of the subduction complex. Sediments in the landslides may mix with sea water and form turbidity currents which flow down into the trench, forming horizontal sediment layers on the trench floor (figure 20.28). Sediments apparently remain in trenches only for a short while; they become reincorporated into the subduction complex in the next underthrust slice.

The subduction complex thus tends to feed on itself, recycling its sediments as they are carried into the trench and reintroduced to the bottom of the complex by underthrusting. If no new sediment were added to the complex, it would remain the same size, but there are two potential sources of sediment to the subduction complex.

One source is *pelagic sediment* (chapter 19) carried on top of the subducting plate. If the thrust faults cut through this sediment, wedges of new pelagic sediment will be added to the subduction complex (figure 20.29*A*). Some geologists doubt that much pelagic sediment becomes incorporated into subduction complexes. Deep-sea drilling of inner trench walls and the study of subduction

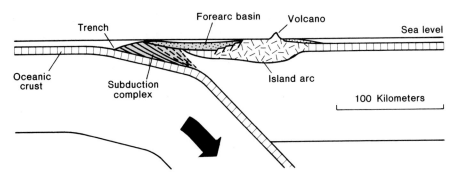

Figure 20.27 The inner wall of an oceanic trench (toward the arc) consists of a subduction complex and a forearc basin. Modified from W. R. Dickinson, 1977, in *Island Arcs, Deep Sea Trenches and Back-Arc Basins* (pp. 33–40), copyrighted by American Geophysical Union.

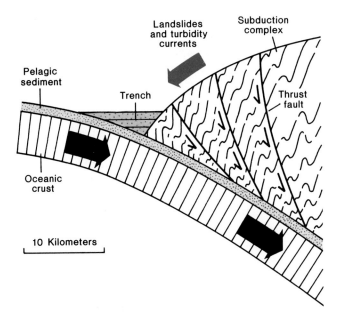

Figure 20.28 Underthrusting steepens the front of the subduction complex, causing landslides and turbidity currents that form horizontal layers of sediment on the trench floor. Low-angle thrust faults steepen as wedges of sediment are underthrust (angles of thrust faults are artificially steepened by vertical exaggeration in the figure).

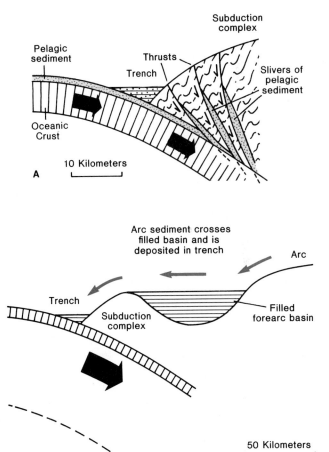

Figure 20.29 Two sources of new sediment to a subduction complex. (*A*) Slivers of pelagic sediment within thrust slices. (*B*) Volcanic sediment carried over filled forearc basin. (Note different scales.)

complexes exposed on land show little such sediment within the complexes. Note that figure 20.28 shows thrusting on top of pelagic sediment rather than in it. In this case, most of the pelagic sediment should be subducted.

The other source of new sediment is the *volcanic arc*. In order for the arc to contribute sediment to the subduction complex, the forearc basin between the arc and the complex must be completely filled with sediment. Before it is filled it acts as a sediment trap, ponding any volcanically derived sediment carried off the arc. Once the basin

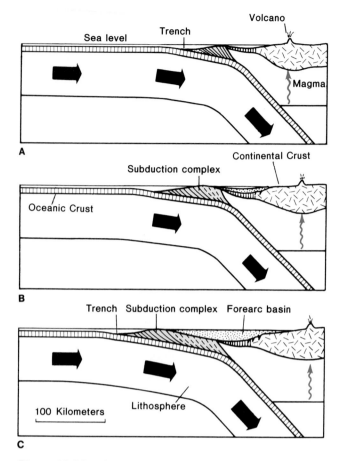

Figure 20.30 Growth of subduction complex seaward moves trench away from arc. Solid lines within subduction complex are active thrusts; dashed lines are inactive thrusts. Modified from W. R. Dickinson, 1977, in *Island Arcs, Deep Sea Trenches and Back-Arc Basins* (pp. 33–40), copyrighted by American Geophysical Union.

has filled, arc sediment can pass across it and down the subduction complex into the trench, to be incorporated into the bottom of the complex (figure 20.29*B*). Either source of new sediment will allow the complex to increase in size, building outward away from the arc and moving the trench floor away from the arc as well (figure 20.30).

Ocean-Continent Convergence

When a plate capped by oceanic crust is subducted under a continental plate, a subduction complex and forearc basin will form the inner wall of the trench, and the edge of the continent becomes deformed into a young mountain range. The andesitic magma that rises from the subduction zone forms a "magmatic arc" within the continental crust rather than an island arc at sea (figure 20.31). The subduction of the Nazca plate under South America is an example of this type of boundary.

The term *magmatic arc* is not as widely used and accepted by geologists as *island arc,* but it is a broad, useful term that includes both island arcs at sea and belts of igneous activity on continents. The visible part of an island arc is a line of volcanic islands, but within the thickened crust of the arc are undoubtedly large plutons. A magmatic arc on a continent may appear as a line of andesitic volcanoes, such as the volcanoes of the Cascades in the Pacific Northwest, or, if it is older and deeply eroded, as a group of plutons that form a batholith. Although geologists usually speak of "granitic" batholiths, the composition of the individual plutons that make up a batholith ranges from diorite (the plutonic equivalent of andesite) to granite. How granite originates is one of the longest-lasting, most hotly debated problems in geology, but it is worth noting that at least some parts of a batholith are diorite and could represent the source magmas of vanished andesitic volcanoes. So island arcs at sea and magmatic arcs on continents have some real similarities (although the differences can by no means be glossed over and lightly dismissed).

The hot magma rising upward from the subduction zone thickens the continental crust and probably makes it somewhat weaker and more mobile than cold crust. It is within this hot mobile zone that regional metamorphism takes place, as described in chapter 7. Crustal thickening causes uplift, so a young mountain range forms here as the thickened crust rises isostatically (chapter 17).

Another reason for the growth of the mountain range is the stacking up of thrust sheets on the continental (backarc) side of the magmatic arc (figure 20.31). As the cold continental crust of the continental interior moves toward the trench (because the plates are converging), it thrusts a short distance under the thick mobile core of the mountain range, resulting in a series of thrust slices that move over one another, thickening the crust here and causing uplift.

Note that there are two regions of thrusting associated with a young mountain range on the edge of a continent. On the ocean side of the arc (the forearc) the subduction complex near the trench involves very extensive underthrusting from subduction. Thousands of kilometers of ocean floor may have disappeared down the subduction zone. This leads to very intense deformation by folding, faulting, and shearing in the subduction complex. On the landward side of the arc (the backarc) the thrust belt results from the cold continental interior underthrusting the thick mobile core of the arc. The underthrusting both thickens the crust and shortens it horizontally. The amount of shortening in the backarc region is much less than the movement along the subduction zone—perhaps only 100 to 200 kilometers—so the backarc thrust sheets are not so deformed as the subduction complex.

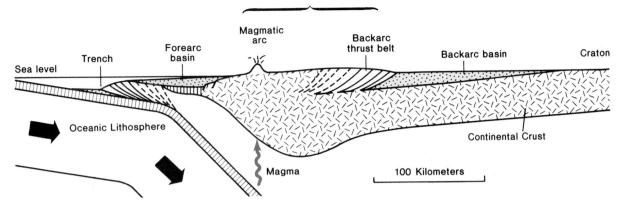

Figure 20.31 Subduction of an oceanic plate beneath a continent, forming a magmatic arc and a young mountain range on the edge of a continent. Craton underthrusts the arc slightly, producing backarc thrust belt and backarc basin.
Modified from W. R. Dickinson, 1977, in *Island Arcs, Deep Sea Trenches and Back-Arc Basins* (pp. 33–40), copyrighted by American Geophysical Union.

Inland of the backarc thrust zone a *backarc basin* forms. As the rigid, cold craton of the continental interior moves a short distance under the magmatic arc, the weight of the backarc thrust sheets depresses the craton isostatically. This backarc basin receives sediment from the arc and also from the surrounding craton. The sediment may be marine or continental, or may alternate between the two, depending upon the amount of subsidence of the craton. This backarc basin extends the effect of subduction far inland. Subduction of sea floor in California in the Mesozoic Era is thought to have resulted in backarc sedimentation as far east as the central Great Plains.

The continental shelf and slope at a converging boundary   On a continent with an active trench offshore, the continental slope is the highly deformed subduction complex, consisting of intricately folded, faulted, and sheared marine sediments. Studies of subduction complexes exposed on land show that ophiolite sequences (chapter 19) occur along with the marine sediments. This indicates that slivers of oceanic crust and upper mantle somehow become incorporated within the subduction complex, but the exact mechanism is unclear.

The continental shelf may be the top of a filled forearc basin (figure 20.32*A*). The rate of sedimentation determines whether a forearc basin will be filled. If sedimentation is slow, the basin will remain unfilled, forming a topographic low between the arc and the subduction complex (figure 20.32*B*). If sedimentation is rapid, the basin may fill until its surface lies above water (figure 20.32*C*).

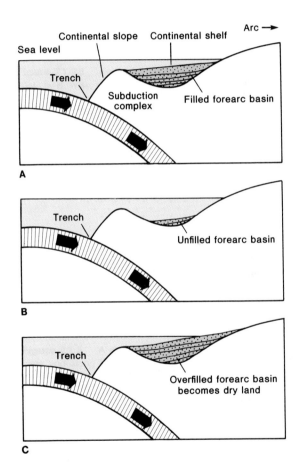

Figure 20.32 Three types of continental margins formed by the subduction of an oceanic plate under a continent.

The basin becomes part of the dry land, and the continental shelf in such cases may be very narrow and consist of the top of the subduction complex.

The Pacific coast of South America is the best example of a boundary where an oceanic plate converges with a continental plate. The Peru-Chile Trench marks

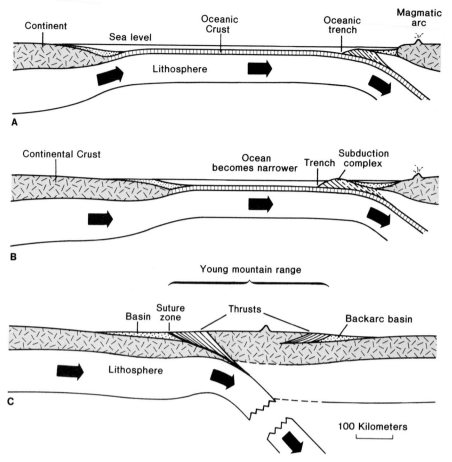

Figure 20.33 Continent-continent collision forms a young mountain range in the interior of a new, larger continent. Modified from W. R. Dickinson, 1977, in *Island Arcs, Deep Sea Trenches and Back-Arc Basins* (pp. 33–40), copyrighted by American Geophysical Union.

the site of subduction, and the Andes Mountains (which contain batholiths and andesitic volcanoes) represent the magmatic arc. The modern continental shelf and continental slope do not quite correspond to the model in figure 20.31) perhaps because subduction has removed some of the modern deposits. An older subduction complex and forearc basin are exposed on land between the arc and the Pacific coastline.

Continent-Continent Convergence

Two continents may approach each other and collide. They must be separated by an ocean floor that is being subducted under one continent and that lacks a spreading center to create new oceanic crust (figure 20.33). The edge of one continent will initially have a magmatic arc and all the other features of ocean-continent convergence.

As the sea floor is subducted, the ocean becomes narrower and narrower until the continents eventually collide.

Oceanic lithosphere is heavy and can sink into the mantle, but continental lithosphere is less dense and cannot sink. One continent may slide a short distance under another, but it will not go down a subduction zone. After collision the heavy oceanic lithosphere breaks off the continental lithosphere and continues to sink, leaving the continent behind (figure 20.33*C*).

The two continents are welded together along a dipping *suture zone* which marks the old site of subduction. Thrust belts and subsiding basins occur on both sides of the original magmatic arc, which has now become inactive. The presence of the original arc thickens the crust in the region of impact. The crust is thickened further by the shallow underthrusting of one continent beneath the other and also by the stacking of thrust sheets in the two thrust belts. The result is a mountain range in the interior of a continent (a new large continent formed by the collision of the two smaller continents). The entire region of impact is marked by a broad belt of shallow-focus earthquakes along the numerous faults, as described in chapter

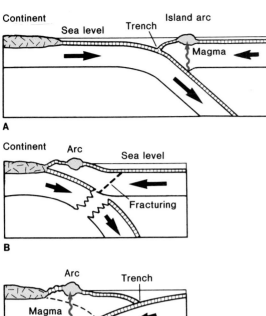

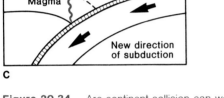

Figure 20.34 Arc-continent collision can weld an island arc onto a continent. Subduction direction changes after impact.

16. A few deeper quakes may occur within the sinking oceanic lithosphere beneath the mountain range.

The Himalaya Mountains in central Asia are thought to have formed in this way, as India collided with the rest of Asia. Paleomagnetic studies show that India was once in the southern hemisphere and drifted north to its present position. Impact with Asia occurred after an intervening ocean was destroyed by subduction.

Arc-Continent Collision

Another type of collisional boundary occurs when an island arc collides with a continent (figure 20.34). If an intervening ocean is destroyed by subduction (the subduction also causes the arc), then the arc will approach the continent. When collision occurs, the arc, like a continent, is too buoyant to be subducted. Continued convergence of the two plates may cause the remaining sea floor to break away from the arc and create a new site of subduction and a new trench seaward of the arc (figure 20.34C). Note that the direction of the new subduction is opposite to the direction of the original subduction, but it still may supply the arc with magma. The arc has now, however, become welded onto the continent, increasing the size of the continent.

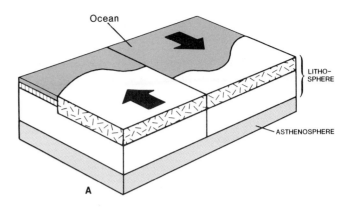

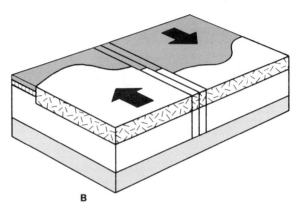

Figure 20.35 Transform boundaries (A) along a single fault; (B) along several parallel faults.

This type of collision has apparently occurred in northern New Guinea (north of Australia), and a similar collision may have added an island arc to the Sierra Nevada complex in California during Mesozoic time, when a subduction zone may have existed in what now is central California. Some geologists feel that much of westernmost North America along the Pacific shore has been built up by a series of arcs colliding with the craton (particularly north of central California).

Transform Boundaries

One plate can slide horizontally past another along a single fault or a group of parallel faults (figure 20.35). These faults are *transform faults,* which we discussed in chapter 19 in connection with fracture zones. There are actually several types of transform faults. Figure 20.36 shows how a transform boundary can connect two spreading centers (as fracture zones do), or a spreading center and a trench, or two trenches. There are other possibilities as well. Each of the three examples has strike-slip motion along the transform fault, and in each case the motion is in the same direction, as shown by the arrows.

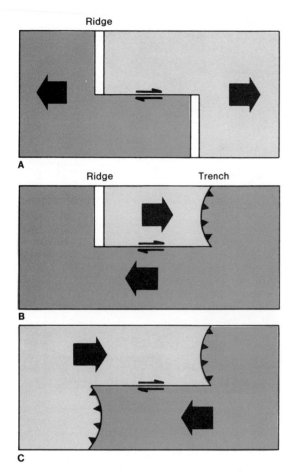

Figure 20.36 Transform boundaries (A) between two ridges; (B) between a ridge and a trench; and (C) between two trenches. Triangles on trenches point down subduction zones.

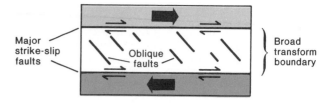

Figure 20.37 Two parallel strike-slip faults can cause a system of oblique faults to develop, leading to a broad, complex transform boundary.

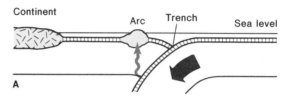

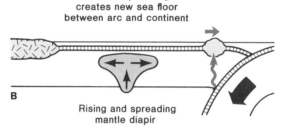

Figure 20.38 Backarc spreading. (A) Initial position of island arc, separated from a continent by a small sea. (B) Backarc spreading moves arc away from continent.

Transform boundaries are marked by shallow-focus earthquakes, either in a narrow zone if one fault makes up the boundary, or in a broad zone if many faults are parallel to one another (figure 16.28). First-motion studies of these quakes indicate strike-slip movement parallel to the faults.

If a transform boundary is very broad and the parallel faults are widely spaced, then a complex pattern of oblique faults may develop between the major faults as shown in figure 20.37. The smaller oblique faults are not parallel to the plate boundary, and the movement on these faults is dip-slip or oblique rather than strike-slip. Such a broad, complex pattern of faults can make it difficult to determine where the plate boundary actually is.

Although the boundary between the Pacific plate and the North American plate is usually drawn at the San Andreas fault in California, some geologists think that the boundary may extend through much of the western United States in a pattern similar to that shown in figure 20.37. If this is so, the smaller oblique faults represent the Basin and Range faults between the San Andreas fault in California and a fault system in Montana that is parallel to the San Andreas.

Backarc Spreading

Recent work in the western Pacific Ocean has shown that if an island arc forms a short distance away from a continent (figure 20.38A), it may eventually move farther away from the continent by a process called **backarc spreading** (figure 20.38B). If the arc moves, of course, the trench must move as well.

Backarc spreading requires the creation of new sea floor in the backarc region, but the process seems to be somewhat different from the creation of sea floor in the rift valley of the mid-oceanic ridge. No ridge or rift valley (or clear-cut parallel magnetic anomalies) develop in the backarc region, but the sea floor is young here and the heat flow is high. The widening of the backarc region is usually attributed to the rising and lateral spreading of a large blob of hot mantle rock called a *mantle diapir*.

Think for a moment about some of the implications of the model shown in figure 20.38*B*, which may represent the situation under Japan (separated from Asia by the young Sea of Japan). Cold, basaltic sea floor is being subducted at the trench. A short distance down the subduction zone we have to generate hot andesitic magma, and we have already discussed the uncertainty of how this might be done. Now, however, we add a new problem: generating a hot mantle diapir farther down the subduction zone. The difficulties in creating two *hot* places (the arc and the diapir) from the subduction of a *cold* plate have led to a lively discussion among geologists, as you might well imagine. The model in figure 20.38*B* may be wrong, of course, and may be discarded or modified in the future. That is how science works. The only way to tell whether the model is correct is to gather more data about backarc spreading. That is why regions such as the Sea of Japan are being so intensively studied today.

Backarc spreading may also occur within a continent, behind a magmatic arc at the continental edge (figure 20.39). The spreading should thin the continental crust and create a region of high heat flow and tensional faulting. Volcanic eruptions and earthquakes should accompany the spreading.

Because the Basin and Range province in Nevada has these characteristics, some geologists feel that its structure is due to backarc spreading. There is no subduction going on under Nevada today, so the onset of backarc spreading may be related to the cessation of subduction. While subduction continues, the edge of the continent is under compression caused by the convergence of the two plates. This compression causes the thrust faults and crustal thickening we have described above. When subduction stops, the compression stops, and a rising and spreading mantle diapir may change the regional stress to tension, causing normal faults and crustal thinning.

Note that we now have two totally different plate-tectonic interpretations of Basin and Range faulting (there are others as well). Some geologists believe the faults are due to shear along a transform boundary. Other geologists believe the faults are due to backarc spreading. Here again we have an excellent illustration of how science works. With more than one hypothesis on the origin of Basin and Range structure, geologists working there must live with uncertainty about how to interpret the region's geology. Only with further work can we discard incorrect hypotheses and retain the most likely one as the best possible interpretation.

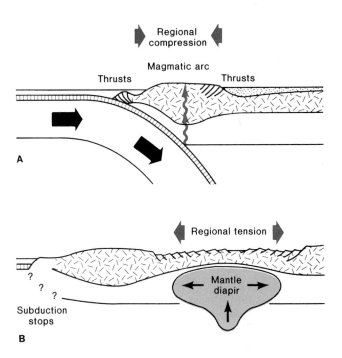

Figure 20.39 Backarc spreading within a continent. (*A*) Regional compression and thrusting caused by subduction. (*B*) Regional tension and normal faulting caused by rising mantle diapir and the cessation of subduction.

Plate Size

Plates can change in size. For example, new sea floor is being added on the trailing edge of the North American plate at the spreading center in the central Atlantic Ocean. Most of the North American plate is not being subducted along its leading edge because this edge is made up of lightweight continental rock. Thus the North American plate is growing as it moves slowly westward.

The Nazca plate probably is getting smaller. The spreading center is adding new rock along the trailing edge of the Nazca plate, but the leading edge is being subducted down the Peru-Chile Trench. If South America were stationary, the Nazca plate might remain the same size, because the rate of subduction and the rate of spreading are equal. But South America is slowly moving westward, pushing the Peru-Chile Trench in front of it. This means that the site of subduction of the Nazca plate is gradually coming closer to its spreading center to the west, and so the Nazca plate is getting smaller. The same thing is probably happening to the Pacific plate as the Eurasian plate moves eastward into the Pacific Ocean.

Note that the Atlantic Ocean is getting wider as the continents on either side of it move away from the spreading center while the Pacific Ocean is getting smaller as the continents move in from all sides.

The Attractiveness of Plate Tectonics

Most geologists accept the general concept of plate tectonics because it can explain in a general way the distribution and origin of many earth features. These features have been discussed throughout this book, and we summarize them here.

The distribution and composition of the world's *volcanoes* can be explained by plate tectonics. *Basaltic* volcanoes form at diverging plate margins when hot mantle rock rises at a spreading center. *Andesitic* volcanoes, particularly those in the circum-Pacific belt, result from subduction of an oceanic plate beneath either a continental plate or another oceanic plate. Although most of the world's volcanoes occur at plate margins, some do not (Hawaii being an example). We will discuss some of these isolated volcanoes later in the chapter when we describe mantle plumes.

Earthquake distribution and first motion (chapter 16) can largely be explained by plate tectonics. Shallow-focus earthquakes along normal faults are caused by the tension associated with diverging plate boundaries. Shallow-focus earthquakes occur on strike-slip faults and the transform faults of fracture zones when plates slide past one another. Broad zones of shallow-focus earthquakes are located where two continents collide. Dipping Benioff zones of shallow-, intermediate-, and deep-focus quakes are found along the giant reverse faults formed when an oceanic plate is subducted beneath another plate. Most of the world's earthquakes (like most volcanoes) occur along plate boundaries, although a few take place within plates and are difficult to explain in terms of plate tectonics.

Young mountain ranges—with their associated igneous intrusions, metamorphism, and folding and faulting caused by horizontal compression—are pushed up at converging plate boundaries. Subduction mountains are found at edges of continents where sea floor is sliding underneath the continents. Continental-collision mountains are formed in continental interiors when two small continental plates collide to form a larger continent. Old mountain ranges mark the position of old, inactive plate boundaries.

The major features of the sea floor can also be explained by plate tectonics. The *mid-oceanic ridge* with its *rift valley* forms where plates diverge, perhaps as a result of convection. *Oceanic trenches* are formed where oceanic plates are subducted down into the mantle.

Other hypotheses can explain some of these features, but not all of them. The compression that helps cause mountain ranges, for example, has been explained as a result of a contracting earth. The tension that causes rift valleys, on the other hand, has been explained as a result

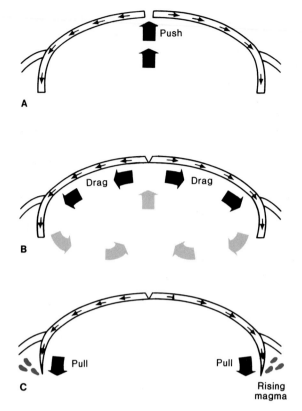

Figure 20.40 Three possible driving mechanisms for plate tectonics. (*A*) Intrusion pushes plates apart. (*B*) Convection drags plates horizontally. (*C*) Denser leading edges pull plates downward.

of an *expanding* earth. The two hypotheses are incompatible with each other and do not give a unifying view of the earth. Plate tectonics explains many more features than any other hypothesis or theory, and it provides a unifying framework for the study of the earth. That is why so many geologists support the concept.

What Causes Plate Motions?

No one is certain what drives plates, and much current research is directed toward finding the mechanism. Several different mechanisms have been proposed (figure 20.40).

Mantle Convection

One of the first suggestions was *mantle convection*. This mechanism was originally pictured as involving broad convection cells and hot mantle rock rising under the entire ridge crest. The driving mechanism of convection could be either magma intrusions on the ridge crest *pushing* the plates, or currents moving away from the ridge crest *carrying* the plates. Since tensional cracks have been found on the ridge crest, the acceptance of the pushing mechanism has declined among geologists.

Tensional cracks suggest *pulling,* so some geologists feel that *subduction* is the driving mechanism. As a plate descends into the mantle, the lighter weight components of the rock might melt and "distill" off the plate. The remaining heavy residue on the leading edge of the plate would sink more rapidly through the mantle, pulling the rest of the plate behind it.

Large negative gravity anomalies at trenches support the idea that trenches are being pulled downward. The fact that some subducting plates are in tension (chapter 16) also supports pulling, as does the fact that subducting plates can pull apart (the continued subduction of the oceanic part of a plate after continental collision is an example). Some subducting plates are in compression, however, and other plates subduct at such gentle angles that they move essentially horizontally. It is hard to imagine that these plates are being pulled (at least not downward).

Either pulling or carrying of plates would produce tensional cracks in the rift valley region of the ridge crest. Magma would tend to rise up and fill these cracks. Rising magma and mantle convection would, in this case, be a *result* of plate motion rather than its cause.

The *depth of mantle convection* (if it exists) is uncertain (figure 20.41). Hess suggested deep mantle convection in the original sea-floor spreading proposal, perhaps extending throughout the entire 2,900-kilometer thickness of the mantle. Recent workers have suggested shallow convection as a possibility. A moving plate would represent the top of a convection current, and return flow would occur in the asthenosphere beneath the moving plate, perhaps as a result of plate motion. Such shallow convection seems more compatible with a layered mantle (chapter 17) than does deep convection.

Plumes and Hot Spots

A modification of the convection process has been suggested by W. Jason Morgan, a geologist at Princeton University. Morgan believes that convection occurs in the form of **mantle plumes,** narrow columns of hot mantle rock that rise and spread radially outward (figure 20.42). This type of circulation has been observed in the atmosphere and in bodies of water; it is the basic cause of isolated, towering thunderhead clouds.

According to Morgan, upward convection of hot mantle rock is confined to the narrow plumes (figure 20.42) rather than occurring in long belts as in earlier models of convection. The downward sinking of cooled mantle rock takes place slowly throughout the rest of the mantle.

Morgan's hypothetical mantle plumes form "hot spots" of active volcanism at the earth's surface. Note in figure 20.43 that many plumes are located in regions of

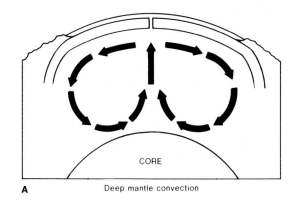

A   Deep mantle convection

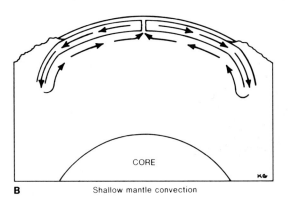

B   Shallow mantle convection

Figure 20.41 (*A*) Deep mantle convection. (*B*) Shallow mantle convection.

active volcanism at diverging plate boundaries. The plumes under Iceland are an example. These plumes and a few others along the ridge crest in the Atlantic Ocean may be driving the American plates westward by the radial flow of mantle material below the lithosphere. In this hypothesis the volcanic activity and high heat flow in Iceland are caused by the plumes, as is Iceland's elevation above sea level.

In Morgan's view, plate motion is caused by a few plumes, not a broad, rolling convection current along the entire ridge. These hypothetical plumes extend like vertical pipes deep into the mantle, perhaps to its very bottom. The radial flow of mantle material outward from the top of a plume tends to break up the lithosphere and move the plates.

A mantle plume rising beneath a continent, for example, should bulge the land upward, causing volcanic activity within the bulge. As the bulge forms, the stretched

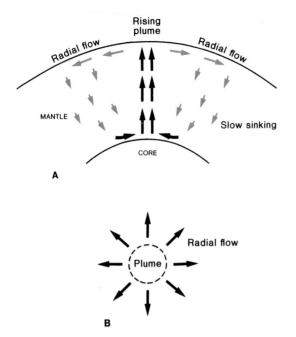

Figure 20.42 A mantle plume (*A*) in side view (cross section); (*B*) top view (map).

crust typically fractures in a three-pronged pattern (figure 20.44). Continued radial flow outward from the rising plume eventually separates the crust along two of the three fractures but leaves the third fracture inactive. In this model of continental breakup, the two active fractures become continental edges as new sea floor forms between the diverging continents. The third fracture is an **aulacogen** (or *failed arm*), an inactive rift that becomes filled with sediment.

An example of this type of fracturing may exist in the vicinity of the Red Sea (figure 20.45). The Red Sea and the Gulf of Aden are active diverging boundaries along which the Arabian Peninsula is being separated from northeastern Africa. The third, inactive, rift or aulacogen is the northernmost African Rift Valley, lying at an angle of about 120° to each of the narrow seaways. Note from figure 20.43 that a small group of mantle plumes rather than a single one occurs at the junction of the three rifts. This may complicate the pattern somewhat.

A location where a mantle plume might now be rising beneath a continent is Yellowstone National Park in the Wyoming-Montana-Idaho region. The area's volcanism,

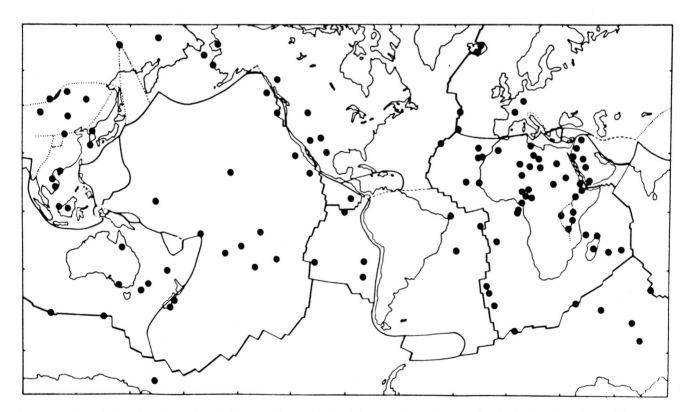

Figure 20.43 Distribution of hypothesized mantle plumes, identified by volcanic activity and structural uplift within the past few million years. The hot spots near the poles are not shown.
Compiled by W. S. F. Kidd and K. Burke, SUNY at Albany.

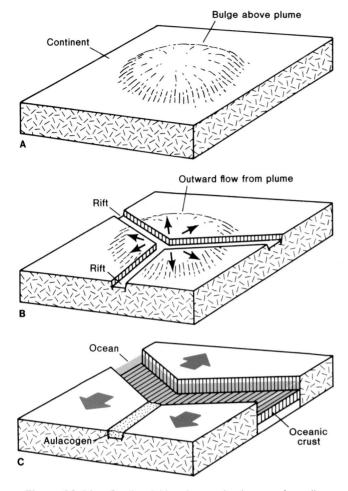

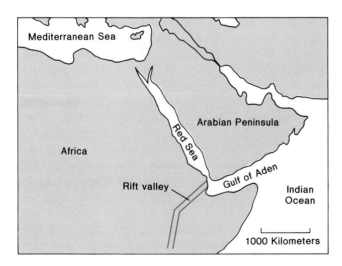

Figure 20.44 Continental breakup and aulacogen formation caused by a mantle plume. (A) A bulge forms over a mantle plume rising beneath a continent. (B) Three radial rifts develop due to outward radial flow from the top of the mantle plume. (C) Continent separates into two pieces along two of the three rifts, with new ocean floor forming between the diverging continents. The third rift becomes an aulacogen, an inactive "failed arm" filled with continental sediment.

high elevation, high heat flow, and hot spring and geyser activity all may be due to this plume. Radial flow of mantle rock beneath the western United States may be tearing the continent apart and causing the earthquakes in the region, including the 1959 earthquake near Madison Canyon, Montana. Eventually an ocean may form here as North America is split apart by the plume.

Some plumes rise beneath the center of oceanic plates. The plume under Hawaii rises in the center of the Pacific plate. Rather than breaking up the plate, the plume acts as an eruptive center, creating an aseismic ridge (chapter 19) by causing a long chain of volcanoes to form on the moving plate. Figure 19.19 shows some other aseismic ridges apparently caused by mantle plumes. If plumes do cause aseismic ridges, the age of the volcanoes making up such a ridge should increase away from the plume. The relation seems to hold in the Hawaiian chain and some other ridges, but deep-sea drilling has shown it definitely does not occur in all aseismic ridges. This evidence has led to alternate hypotheses for the origin of aseismic ridges. It may pose difficulties for the plume hypothesis.

A Cautionary Note

Geologists, like other people, are susceptible to fads. Although most geologists believe plate tectonics to be an exciting theory and accept it as a working model of the earth, the theory may or may not be conclusive. Most geologists today believe that plate tectonics activities are probably going on. But even if a belief is widespread, it may not be true.

Twenty years ago continental drift rated only a footnote in most introductory textbooks. Now there are many believers in continental motion, and some textbooks use it as a framework for the entire field of physical geology. Today the idea that continents are fixed in position rates only a footnote as an outmoded concept, although continental stability provided the framework for many past textbooks.

Objections have been raised to the concept of plate tectonics. The most important is that the geology of many continental regions does not fit into the theory of plate tectonics, in some cases not even slightly.

The geology of the North Cascade Mountains in the state of Washington, for example, is extraordinarily complex and does not fit readily into our models of mountain building by either subduction or continental collision. In addition, the Rocky Mountains in Wyoming and Colorado are difficult to explain by plate tectonics. The Rockies

Figure 20.45 An example of radial rifts and aulacogen origin. The Red Sea and the Gulf of Aden are the active rifts, as the Arabian Peninsula drifts away from Africa. The inactive aulacogen is the rift valley shown.

Plate Tectonics and Sea Level

Geologists have long known that at certain times in the geologic past the sea covered vast areas of the continents that are now dry land. Much of the interior of the United States, for example, is underlain by marine limestones deposited during parts of the Paleozoic Era. Were the continents lower at these times or was sea level higher?

As you have seen, the subsidence of backarc basins can depress the craton and allow vast regions of the continental interior to be flooded with sea water. Some marine deposits on the craton, however, are so extensive that they probably were caused by a rise in sea level.

Although several mechanisms such as glaciation can change sea level, the development of plate tectonics has led to a new hypothesis that may explain some of the ancient sea-level fluctuations.

During an episode of rapid plate motion, an active spreading center will be marked by a mid-oceanic ridge caused by the thermal expansion of rock on the rising limb of a convection current.

When plate motion stops, convection also stops, and the rock at an old spreading center cools off and contracts. This means that the mid-oceanic ridge subsides and eventually becomes level sea floor. That is, when plates move, a ridge is present; and when plates stop, the ridge is absent.

When a ridge is present, it displaces sea water, raising sea level and causing the sea to flood land areas. When the ridge is absent, the water returns to the ocean basin and the continents are dry once again.

The plates need not stop completely. A rapid spreading rate would cause a large ridge and a sea-level rise, and a slower spreading rate would cause a smaller ridge and a lower sea level. At the present time there is good evidence that some sea-level fluctuations can be correlated to changes in the spreading rate of the sea floor. Not all changes in sea level can be explained by this mechanism however. Glaciation and other factors clearly affect sea level too.

here are young, formed recently by faulting of the old rocks of the craton. Plate tectonics does not easily explain such a process, nor does it explain why the mountain building here is younger than the mountain building farther west, as in the Sierra Nevada of California. Some geologists have proposed that steep subduction under the Sierra Nevada suddenly changed to shallow subduction under Nevada and Utah, becoming steep again under the Rockies to cause their uplift. Supporters of plate tectonics may point to such a model as an indication that even the puzzling Rockies can be explained by plate motion. Opponents of plate tectonics may consider such models preposterous and feel that the only thing they indicate is that plate tectonic supporters have taken leave of their senses. The alternative hypotheses offered by opponents of plate tectonics, in turn, are often considered irritating by supporters of plate tectonics and are given very little serious attention.

It is wise to remember that at the time of Wegener most geologists felt that the idea of drifting continents was preposterous. Wegener's critics included most North American geologists, some of whom considered bitter sarcasm to be proper scientific discussion. The consensus of geologists in Wegener's day was that continental drift was dead wrong. The consensus today is that drift is correct and the early *geologists* were dead wrong. Science should not depend upon majority vote. Arguments of a dissenting minority, such as opponents of plate tectonics today, should be carefully studied and rationally and scientifically answered, if possible. This is the very heart of science, the careful consideration of *all* possible explanations of natural phenomena. In the rush to reinterpret the earth according to plate tectonic theory, however, it is clear that many geologists would rather be out front leading the parade than following along after it to clean up any messes it might create.

The evidence for plate tectonics is very convincing. The theory has been rightly called a revolution in earth science, comparable to the development of the theory of evolution in the biological sciences. It is an exciting time to be a geologist. Our whole concept of earth dynamics has changed in the last twenty years.

But part of education is learning how to form an opinion for yourself. No teacher should require you to "believe in" plate tectonics. You should know the data that led to the original hypotheses. You should understand the thought processes involved in the development of plate tectonics. You should be able to describe how plate tectonics can explain earth features.

But decide for yourself whether the evidence for plate tectonics is convincing. Is plate tectonics a hypothesis, a theory, or a "fact"? Examine the evidence. Weigh the data. Remain skeptical.

Summary

Plate tectonics is the idea that the earth's surface is divided into several large plates that change position and size. Intense geologic activity occurs at plate boundaries.

Plate tectonics combines the concepts of *sea-floor spreading* and *continental drift*.

Alfred Wegener proposed continental drift in the early 1900s. His evidence included coastline fit, similar fossils and rocks in now-separated continents, and paleoclimatic evidence for *polar wandering*. Wegener proposed that all continents were once joined together in the supercontinent *Pangaea*.

Wegener's ideas were not widely accepted until the 1950s, when work in paleomagnetism revived interest in polar wandering.

Evidence for continental drift includes careful fits of continental edges and detailed rock matches between now-separated continents. Positions of continents have been mapped for the past 200 million years.

Plates are composed of blocks of *lithosphere* riding on a plastic *asthenosphere*. Plates move away from spreading centers, which add new sea floor to the trailing edges of the plates.

Diverging plate boundaries are marked by rift valleys, shallow-focus earthquakes, high heat flow, and basaltic volcanism.

Converging plate boundaries can cause *subduction* or *continental collision*. Subducting plate boundaries are marked by trenches, low heat flow, Benioff zones, andesitic volcanism, and young mountain ranges or island arcs. Continental-collision boundaries have shallow-focus earthquakes and form young mountain ranges in continental interiors. An island arc can collide with a continent.

Transform boundaries between plates sliding past one another are marked by strike-slip faults and shallow-focus earthquakes.

Backarc spreading can move an island arc away from a continent or thin and break up continental crust if it occurs beneath a continent.

The distribution and origin of most volcanoes, earthquakes, young mountain ranges, and major sea-floor features can be explained by plate tectonics.

Suggested driving mechanisms for plate motion include shallow or deep *mantle convection*, which pushes or carries plates; and *subduction*, which may pull plates.

A suggested variation of convection is *mantle plumes*, narrow columns of rising, hot mantle rock. Plumes may drive plates and create aseismic ridges.

Aulacogens are inactive rifts on continents broken up by mantle plumes.

Terms to Remember

asthenosphere
aulacogen
backarc spreading
converging plate boundary
diverging plate boundary
island arc
lithosphere
mantle plume
plate
plate tectonics
polar wandering
transform plate boundary

Questions for Review

1. What was Wegener's evidence for continental drift?
2. What is polar wandering? What is the paleoclimatic evidence for polar wandering? What is the magnetic evidence for polar wandering? Does polar wandering require the poles to move?
3. What is the evidence that South America and Africa were once joined?
4. In a series of sketches show how the South Atlantic Ocean might have formed by the movement of South America and Africa.
5. What is Pangaea?
6. What is a "plate" in the concept of plate tectonics?
7. Define *lithosphere* and *asthenosphere*.
8. What is a transform fault?
9. Discuss possible driving mechanisms for plate tectonics.
10. Describe the various types of plate boundaries and the geologic features associated with them.
11. What is a mantle plume? What is the geologic significance of mantle plumes?

Question for Thought

1. Most earthquakes occur at plate boundaries. How can earthquakes occur in the interior of a plate?

Supplementary Readings

Cox, A., ed. 1973. *Plate tectonics and geomagnetic reversals*. San Francisco: W. H. Freeman.

Glen, W. 1975. *Continental drift and plate tectonics*. Columbus: Charles E. Merrill.

Hallam, A. 1973. *A revolution in the earth sciences: From continental drift to plate tectonics*. London: Oxford University Press.

Meyerhoff, A. A., and H. A. Meyerhoff. 1972. The new global tectonics: Major inconsistencies. *American Association of Petroleum Geologists Bulletin* 56:269–36.

Press, F., and R. Siever. 1974. *Planet earth—Readings from Scientific American*. San Francisco: W. H. Freeman.

Sullivan, W. 1974. *Continents in motion*. New York: McGraw-Hill.

Takeuchi, H., S. Uyeda, and H. Kanamori. 1970. *Debate about the earth*. San Francisco: Freeman, Cooper.

Tarling, D., and M. Tarling. 1971. *Continental drift*. New York: Doubleday.

Uyeda, S. 1978. *The new view of the earth—Moving continents and moving oceans*. San Francisco: W. H. Freeman.

Wilson, J. T., ed. 1976. *Continents adrift and continents aground*. San Francisco: W. H. Freeman.

Wyllie, P. J. 1976. *The way the earth works*. New York: John Wiley and Sons.

York, D. 1975. *Planet earth*. New York: McGraw-Hill.

21
Geologic Resources

Purpose

Throughout this book, we have mentioned human utilization of earth materials, most of which are nonrenewable. Our concern in this chapter is to survey briefly some important geologic resources of economic value.

We first look at energy resources to see which ones have a potential to help replace our disappearing supplies of petroleum. Then we discuss metals and their relation to igneous rocks and plate tectonics and conclude with nonmetallic resources such as sand and gravel.

Nearly every man-made object depends on some geologic resources for its manufacture. An automobile contains substantial amounts of iron, chromium, manganese, nickel, tin, copper, lead, and aluminum in its body and engine, and quartz sand is used for its window glass. It consumes petroleum in several forms—as fuel and lubricants, as synthetic rubber for tires, and as plastic for electrical parts, upholstery, and steering wheels. Dozens of other resources go into automobiles, from tungsten in light bulb filaments to sulfur in battery acid.

People are beginning to realize how heavily dependent on geologic resources they are. Some have tried to limit their consumption of resources, or at least the rate at which their consumption *increases*. But it is impossible to stop consumption of geologic resources. Think about some of the objects near you as you are reading this chapter. Your shirt may be partly polyester, which is made from petroleum, as are the plastic buttons. If you're wearing jeans, they may be made of fabric that is 100 percent cotton, but many jeans are made of shrinkproof fabrics that blend cotton with petroleum-based synthetic fibers. The brass zipper is made of copper and zinc. Some brands of jeans have pocket rivets made of copper. Leather tags on the back of some jeans used either aluminum or chromium during tanning. The fabric dye almost certainly came from petroleum. A pencil uses many geologic resources (figure 21.1) and a transistor radio many more.

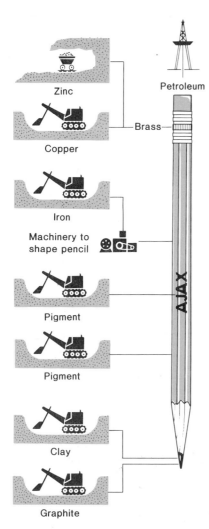

Figure 21.1 Mineral resources necessary to make a wooden pencil.

Phonograph records are made of vinyl, a petroleum derivative. Eyeglasses are made of quartz sand and petroleum. Dental fillings are made of mercury, silver, and other metals.

Types of Resources

Geologic resources are valuable materials of geologic origin that can be extracted from the earth. There are three main categories of geologic resources:

1. Energy resources—petroleum, natural gas, coal, uranium, and a few others, such as geothermal resources.
2. Metals—iron, copper, aluminum, lead, zinc, gold, silver, and many more.

3. Nonmetallic resources—sand and gravel, limestone (for cement), sulfur, gems, gypsum, fertilizers, and many more. Ground water (chapter 11) should also be regarded as an important geologic resource.

Geologic resources are sometimes called *mineral resources,* but the term, though widely used, is not accurate. Many geologic resources are not true minerals—for instance, most energy resources and many nonmetallic resources.

A very important point about geologic resources is that they are **nonrenewable resources.** They form so slowly that, at the present rapid rates of consumption, they can easily become exhausted. Some earth resources, such as food or timber, can be produced as fast as they are consumed. These are *renewable resources.* But petroleum, iron, lead, uranium, sulfur, sand and gravel, and all other geologic resources are being used at rates far greater than the rates at which new deposits form. This means that eventually these resources are going to run out or be priced so high as a result of scarcity that their use will drop to insignificant levels. Recycling, new discoveries, and substitutes can help prolong the life of some resources, but it is likely that within your lifetime some of the resources in common use today will be scarce or essentially used up. This need not mean that civilization will come to a standstill, but it does mean that technology must find inexpensive substitutes for these resources. Otherwise, skyrocketing costs will cause a drop in nearly everyone's standard of living.

Energy Resources and Use

The United States consumes huge amounts of energy. U.S. energy use in 1972 was double that in 1950. Beginning in 1973, with the steep price rises for petroleum and the temporary oil embargo imposed by the Arab countries, this rapid rate of increase began to slow. As oil prices soar, the need for fuel-efficient buildings and transportation becomes more and more apparent. In 1980 the United States used slightly less energy than it did in 1979, and the amount of oil imported dropped sharply (although the amount the U.S. had to pay for it rose sharply).

All the energy used in the United States during 1980 came from these sources:

Petroleum	46%
Natural gas	26%
Coal	20%
Hydroelectric	4%
Nuclear	4%

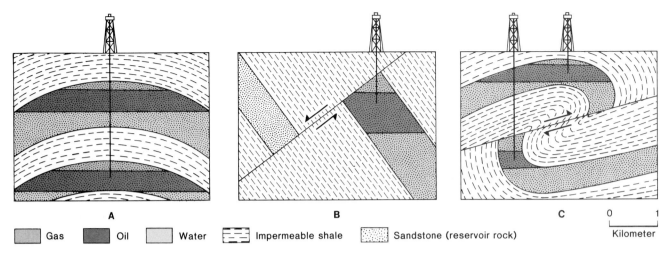

| | Gas | | Oil | | Water | | Impermeable shale | | Sandstone (reservoir rock) |

Kilometer
0   1

Figure 21.2   Structural traps for oil and gas. (*A*) Anticline.
(*B*) Normal fault. (*C*) Thrust fault. (Oil wells not drawn to scale.)

Note that petroleum and natural gas account for nearly three-quarters of the nation's energy supply.

Petroleum and Natural Gas

Petroleum (or **crude oil**) is a liquid mixture of naturally occurring hydrocarbons (compounds containing hydrogen and carbon), which can be distilled to yield a great variety of products.

Natural gas is a *gaseous* mixture of naturally occurring hydrocarbons. Its origin and occurrence closely parallel that of petroleum. Many wells that recover petroleum also recover natural gas, although either may exist alone.

The Origin of Oil and Gas

Petroleum and natural gas seem to originate from organic matter in marine sediment. Microscopic organisms, such as diatoms and single-celled algae, settle to the sea floor and accumulate in marine mud. The most likely environments where this happens are the continental shelves and the continental rise. Partial decomposition of the organic matter may occur, using up the dissolved oxygen in the sediment. As soon as the oxygen is gone, decay stops and the remaining organic matter is preserved.

Continued sedimentation buries the organic matter and subjects it to higher temperatures and pressures, which cause physical and chemical changes in the organic compounds. In this way liquid and gaseous hydrocarbons are formed. As muddy sediments compact, the gas and small droplets of petroleum may be squeezed out of the mud and may move into more porous and permeable sandy layers nearby. Over long periods of time large accumulations of gas and oil can collect in the sandy layers. Both oil and gas are less dense than water, so they generally tend to rise upward through water-saturated rock and sediment.

The Occurrence of Oil and Gas

Economically important concentrations of petroleum are found underground where three specific conditions occur together: (1) a **source rock** (such as shale) containing organic matter that is converted to petroleum by burial and other post-depositional changes; (2) a **reservoir rock** (usually sandstone or limestone) that is sufficiently porous and permeable to store and transmit the petroleum; and (3) an **oil trap,** a set of conditions to hold petroleum in a reservoir rock and prevent its escape by migration.

Natural gas requires the same conditions for accumulation. Gas can exist at greater depth than oil, however, and variations in source rock, depth of burial, and thermal history of the organic matter probably control whether gas, oil, or both accumulate in a region.

Figure 21.2 depicts several types of *structural traps* for oil and gas (some of these were also described in chapter 15). *Anticlines* are the most common oil traps (figure 21.2*A*). Where oil and water occur together in folded permeable beds, the oil droplets, being less dense than water, rise within the permeable rock toward the top of the fold. There the oil may be trapped by impermeable shale overlying the reservoir rock. Since natural gas is less dense than oil, the gas collects in a pocket, under fairly high pressure, on top of the oil.

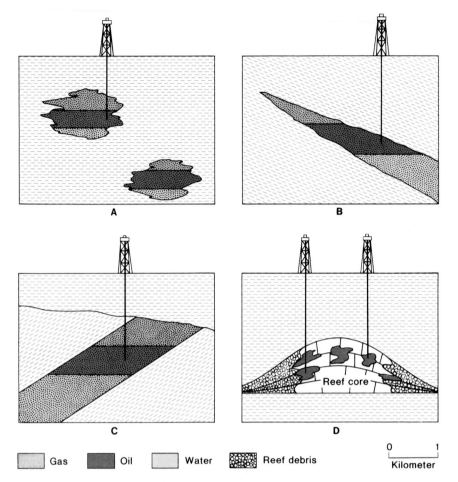

| Gas | Oil | Water | Reef debris |

0   1
Kilometer

Figure 21.3 Stratigraphic traps for oil and gas.
(*A*) Sandstone lenses in shale. (*B*) "Pinch-out" of sandstone in dipping shale. (*C*) Unconformity. (*D*) Reef.

Faults may create oil traps when permeable reservoir rocks break and slide next to impermeable rocks (figure 21.2*B*). Thrust faults are often associated with folds (figure 21.2*C*) because both are caused by compression. The backarc thrust belts (chapter 20) of both the Cordilleran and Appalachian mountain belts are currently being intensively explored for oil and gas.

A *stratigraphic trap* is a result of natural sedimentation rather than folding or faulting. It may be a lens of sandstone within a larger bed of shale (figure 21.3*A*), such as the "shoestring sandstones" described in chapter 6.

Another such trap is the narrow edge of a blanket sandstone where it pinches out within a shale sequence (figure 21.3*B*). Oil can collect under *unconformities* if shale seals off a reservoir rock (fig. 21.3*C*). Limestone *reefs* can form a variety of traps. The core of a reef is usually full of large openings formed by the irregular growth of coral and algae. Oil can collect both in a reef core and in the dipping beds of wave-broken debris on the reef flanks (figure 21.3*D*).

Salt domes create a variety of traps described in box 21.1.

Box 21.1
Salt Domes

Salt domes are vertical columns of rock salt that have risen upward through denser rock. They form from the thick layers of rock salt that mark some diverging continental margins. Subsidence of these continental margins carries the rock salt to great depth and allows it to be covered with a wedge of sedimentary rock (figures 20.19 and 20.22) perhaps 5–10 kilometers thick. The sedimentary rock on top of the salt layer is denser than the salt, and under the great pressure caused by the weight of the overlying rock, the salt begins to deform plastically and flow upward. Large columns of salt rise from the top of the salt bed and then break off (figure 21.4), perhaps assuming a streamlined teardrop shape one or more kilometers in diameter. As the salt continues to rise, it deforms the surrounding sedimentary rock, forming folds and faults that create oil traps, some of which may be under an overhanging mushroom-shaped top that is characteristic of some salt domes (figure 21.5).

When the salt rises into the zone of active ground-water circulation near the surface, it dissolves. Therefore, many salt domes never reach the surface. If the rock salt contains gypsum, it may develop a *cap rock* on its upper surface as the halite dissolves, but the less soluble gypsum does not. Gypsum, a calcium sulfate, contains sulfur that may form native elemental sulfur when it contacts bacteria and petroleum. Salt dome cap rocks, therefore, often contain thick beds of bright yellow sulfur.

Salt domes, then, supply a variety of valuable resources. Oil and gas are found around and above the domes. The salt itself is mined underground. Cap-rock sulfur can be mined by drilling into it and dissolving it with hot water. In the United States there is a broad belt of salt domes along the Texas and Louisiana coasts. The belt extends offshore, onto the continental shelf and beyond, forming a major source of oil, gas, salt, and sulfur.

How do we find salt domes that do not make it to the earth's surface? Some salt domes deform the surface. Some of the low, round islands in the

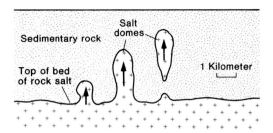

Figure 21.4 Salt domes rise from a thick layer of buried rock salt and move upward through overlying sedimentary rock.

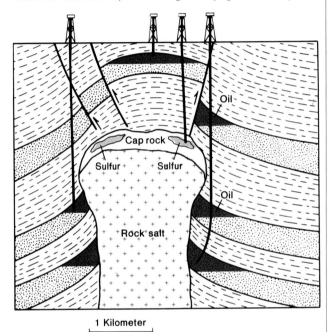

1 Kilometer

Figure 21.5 A salt dome. Oil and gas are trapped in folds and along faults above the dome and within upturned sandstones along the flanks of the dome. Insoluble cap rock may contain recoverable sulfur.

coastal swamps of Louisiana were pushed up by salt domes. If solution of the salt by ground water is very rapid, the overlying rock may subside, so some salt domes are marked by surface depressions. Most salt domes are found by geophysical surveys, however.

The density of rock salt is 2.2 grams per cubic centimeter, a value that does not change even if the rock salt is compressed. Sedimentary rocks within the Gulf Coast belt of domes have densities of 2.0 gm/cm^3 at the surface, increasing to values of 2.5 or greater at depth due to compaction. The salt dome rises because it is out

Box 21.1 *Continued*

of isostatic equilibrium with the heavier rock around it.

The density contrast between the salt and the surrounding rocks produces a negative gravity anomaly over the dome (figure 21.6). Gravity surveys are fast and fairly inexpensive, so this is how most salt domes are found. Seismic reflection can indicate the curved surface of the dome itself (figure 21.6) or of the deformed rock layers above the dome. Seismic refraction can also locate a dome, for seismic waves speed up in salt. The arrival of waves at a recording station before they are expected indicates that a high-speed material, such as salt, exists below the surface.

Drilling, of course, is the final proof that a salt dome is there, and drilling is needed to extract the resources. Because drilling is so expensive, however, several types of geophysical surveys are usually run first. If the surveys indicate that a dome is probably there, then drilling is usually a good gamble (many domes have no oil, gas, or sulfur).

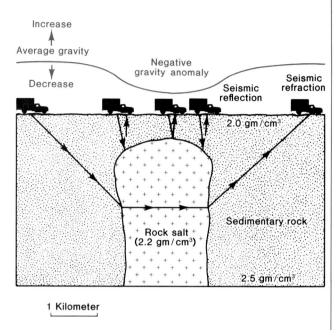

Figure 21.6 A salt dome can be detected by a gravity survey, by seismic reflection, and by seismic refraction.

The combination of circumstances that creates **oil pools,** or underground accumulations of oil, is not common. **Oil fields** are regions underlain by one or more oil pools. Figure 21.7 shows the location of most of the major North American oil fields. The two largest oil fields within the United States are in eastern Texas and on Alaska's North Slope. Most of the world's remaining oil lies in giant fields in the Soviet Union, the Middle East (especially in Saudi Arabia), and Mexico.

Recovering the Oil

When an oil pool or field has been discovered, wells are drilled into the ground. Permanent derricks used to be built to handle the long sections of drilling pipe. Now portable drilling rigs are set up to drill and are then dismantled and moved. When the well reaches a pool, the pressure from natural gas may cause oil to rise quickly up the well. Although this rise of oil is almost always carefully controlled today, spouts of oil, or *gushers,* were common in the past. Gas pressure gradually dies out, and oil is then pumped from the wells. Water or steam may be pumped down adjacent wells to help push the oil out. At a refinery the crude oil from underground is separated into natural gas, gasoline, kerosene, lubricating oil, fuel oil, grease, asphalt, and paraffin. *Petrochemicals* are manufactured from the components of the petroleum compounds. Petrochemicals include dyes, fertilizers, medicines,

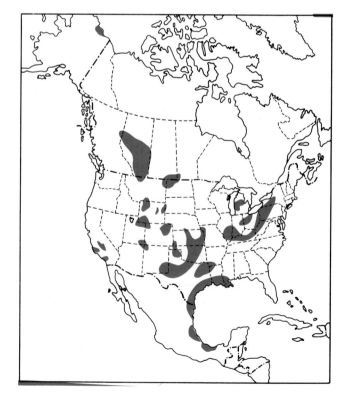

Figure 21.7 Major oil fields in North America.
From U.S. Geological Survey and other sources.

Figure 21.8 Drilling rig on Alaska's North Slope.

synthetic rubber, explosives, perfumes, paints, saccharin, solvents, synthetic fibers, and plastics used for such varied products as swimming pool liners, tube tents, phonograph records, floor tile, and garbage bags.

As oil becomes increasingly difficult to find, the search for it is extended into more hostile environments. The development of the oil field on the North Slope of Alaska near the shore of the Arctic Ocean (figure 21.8) and the construction of the Alaska pipeline are examples of the great expense and difficulty involved in new oil discoveries. Offshore platforms extend the search for oil to the ocean's continental shelves and even beyond. Approximately one-fifth of the world's oil comes from offshore regions, even though offshore drilling is six to seven times as expensive as drilling on land.

Environmental effects   Getting petroleum out of the ground and to the consumer can create environmental problems anywhere along the line. Pipelines carrying oil to a tanker ship, refinery, or market can leak because of a malfunction or a break caused by faulting, mass-wasting processes, acts of war, or sabotage, thereby causing an *oil spill.* Tanker spillage from loading operations, collisions, or groundings (such as the *Argo Merchant* on the Nantucket shoals off Massachusetts in the winter of 1976–77) can create oil slicks at sea. Offshore platforms may also lose oil (such as the Mexican platform that lost 3 million barrels into the Gulf of Mexico in 1979 and 1980). Oil slicks can drift ashore, fouling the beaches. *Subsidence* of the ground can occur as oil is removed. The Wilmington field near Long Beach, California, has subsided about 9 meters in 50 years; dikes have had to be built to prevent seawater from flooding the area. *Air pollution* can be caused by the refining and burning of petroleum and its products. Advancing technology and strict laws are helping control some of these adverse environmental effects.

How Much Oil Do We Have Left?

Resources and reserves   Two different terms are used to describe the amounts of geologic resources that have not yet been extracted from the earth. These terms apply not only to petroleum but to any geologic material. **Resources** is a broad term used for the total amount of a geologic material in all deposits, discovered and undiscovered. It includes both the deposits that can be economically extracted under present conditions and those that may be extracted economically in the future. It is very difficult to estimate resources because educated guesses must be made about the existence and sizes of deposits yet undiscovered as well as about what type of deposit might someday be economical to extract. **Reserves** are a small part of resources. They are the *discovered* deposits that can be extracted economically and legally under present conditions. That is, they are the short-term supply of a geologic material.

Once *resources* have been carefully estimated, the amount should not change from year to year, for an estimate of resources is basically an estimate of the total future supply. Estimates of *reserves,* however, change all the time. The extraction and use of a substance lowers reserves. New discoveries add to reserves, for part of the definition of reserves is that we have to know the deposit is there.

A deposit also has to be profitable to extract, and many factors determine whether a profit can be made or not. The cost of extraction, including workers' salaries and the energy and fuel used to run equipment, are important. New inventions that make extraction cheaper can increase reserves. The final price a company can receive for its product is also important. When prices are kept artificially low by the government, as was the case recently for natural gas and oil, reserves are naturally low because few deposits can be extracted profitably at that price. When prices rise, more deposits become economical, and reserves increase, even without new discoveries. Reducing the amount of taxes that extraction companies pay can also increase reserves.

Changes in laws can affect reserves. Large areas of government-owned land are off limits to mining and drilling, so any geologic materials under these areas are not legally extractable and cannot be included in reserves. Opening more land to extraction can therefore increase reserves.

The world situation   At the present time the world's oil *reserves* are estimated to be 500 to 600 billion barrels (a barrel contains 42 gallons). *Resources,* of course, are greater than reserves. One estimate is 2,000 billion barrels.

As the world's present consumption of petroleum is about 20 billion barrels per year, known reserves will yield only a 25- or 30-year supply. New discoveries and recovery techniques, as well as price rises, will add to reserves in the future. How much they will add is difficult to say.

Some petroleum cannot be recovered. The oil may be in a pool too small to warrant the expense of drilling. A pool may be too far from market or lie under regions in which drilling is forbidden, such as national parks or other public lands. During extraction of oil, only about 40 percent of the total pool can be brought to the surface. The rest remains underground because it is far too difficult and expensive to extract with present techniques and prices.

The outlook in the United States   U.S. consumption of oil is between 6 and 6.5 billion barrels per year (with 6 per cent of the world population, the U.S. uses about 33 per cent of the world's oil production each year). Estimates of United States *reserves* are currently less than 30 billion barrels (although rapid price rises make reserve estimates quickly outdated). The United States imports about 40 per cent of the oil it uses, so domestic production is about 3.5 billion barrels per year. At current production rates, therefore, we have less than 10 years' supply. If the production rate goes up, the lifetime of the reserves goes down.

Since the reserve estimate changes each year, an estimate of *resources* is more important for planning purposes. Such estimates have fluctuated wildly in the past 20 years. Recent government and industry estimates of resources are between 50 and 120 billion barrels (in *addition* to reserves). This means that, at our current production rate, we have 25 to 40 years' supply of oil left, counting both reserves and resources. The United States is truly running out of oil and will need alternate fuels in the future.

Estimates of *natural gas* have been similarly gloomy, largely because estimators assumed that gas discoveries are linked to oil discoveries. In the past, gas has been found in a fixed ratio to oil, so some estimators assume that because we are running out of oil, we are also running out of gas.

The United States uses about 20 trillion cubic feet (TCF) of natural gas per year. Reserve estimates are about 400 TCF, with resources perhaps 600 TCF. By these estimates, natural gas will be gone in the United States in 20 to 50 years.

The recent partial decontrol of natural gas prices, however, has led to renewed interest in gas and revised estimates of resources. The new estimates are based on unconventional gas sources, not linked to petroleum. There may be 300 to 500 TCF of gas within coal beds, for example (the gas is a hazard to coal miners because it is toxic and tends to explode). Tightly compacted sandstones ("tight sands") in the western United States may hold 200 to 800 TCF. Devonian shales rich in organic matter in the eastern United States may hold 500 to 600 TCF. Gas can exist at greater depth than oil, so it is likely that deep drilling (beyond 5 kilometers) in sedimentary basins can produce substantial amounts of gas. Gas is also dissolved in hot salty water within highly fractured rock along the Gulf Coast ("geopressured zones") that may contain as much as 3,000 TCF of gas. Truly staggering amounts of gas may be tied up as gas hydrates, a peculiar solid that forms from natural gas and water in two unusual environments: (1) on the deep sea floor and (2) under permafrost. Russian estimates of more than 1,000,000 TCF of gas in hydrate form (worldwide) have received some support in this country. All these estimates are for resources, not for recoverable reserves, which would be far lower. Some geologists discount all the resource estimates as wildly optimistic and misleading. All these unconventional gas sources are getting serious attention today, however, and although some difficult extraction problems remain unsolved, there is at least cautious optimism that the United States may not be as short of gas as we used to think.

Heavy Crude and Tar Sands

Heavy crude is dense, viscous petroleum. It may flow into a well, but its rate of flow is too slow to be economical. As a result, heavy crude is left out of reserve and resource estimates of less viscous "light oil," or regular petroleum. Heavy crude can be made to flow faster by injecting steam or solvents down wells, and if it can be recovered, it can be refined into gasoline and many other products just as light petroleum is.

Tar sands are asphalt-cemented sand or sandstone deposits. The asphalt is solid, so tar sands are often mined rather than drilled into, although the heavy-crude techniques for reducing viscosity often work on tar sands as well.

The origin of heavy crude and tar sands is uncertain. They may form from regular petroleum if the lighter components are lost by evaporation or other processes. Tar sands and asphalt seeps at the earth's surface (such as the Rancho La Brea Tar Pits in Los Angeles) probably formed from evaporating oil. But some heavy crudes and tar sands are found as much as 4,000 meters underground. Most of them have much higher concentrations of sulfur and metals, such as nickel and vanadium, than does regular petroleum. These facts suggest that heavy crude and tar sands may have a somewhat different origin than light petroleum.

The best-known tar sand deposit is the Athabasca Tar Sand in northern Alberta, Canada (figure 21.9). The deposit, currently being strip-mined, contains 1,000 billion barrels of oil, of which 300 billion barrels may be recoverable. The United States has more than 100 billion barrels of heavy crude and tar, including about 30 billion in the form of Tertiary tar sands in Utah. Half of it may be ultimately recoverable. This means that heavy crude and tar sands may supply as much oil in the future as our light petroleum reserves, and the U.S. may be able to import both from Canada and Venezuela (which has more tar sand than Canada.)

Oil Shale

Oil shale is a black or brown shale with a high content of solid organic matter from which oil may be extracted by distillation. The best known oil shale in the United States is the Green River Formation, which covers more than 40,000 square kilometers in Colorado, Wyoming, and Utah with deposits up to 650 meters thick (figures 21.9 and 21.10). The oil shale, which includes numerous fossils of fish skeletons, formed from mud deposited on the bottom of large, shallow Eocene lakes. The organic matter came from algae and other organisms that lived in the lakes.

The Green River Formation includes more than 400 billion barrels of oil in rich beds that yield over 25 gallons of oil per ton of rock. Another 1,400 billion barrels of oil occur in lower-grade beds yielding 10 to 25 gallons per ton. An estimated 300 to 600 billion barrels may be recoverable.

Relatively low-grade oil shales in Montana contain another 180 billion barrels of recoverable oil in shale that should be economical to mine because of its high content of vanadium, nickel, and zinc. Oil shale, therefore, can supply potentially vast amounts of oil in the future as our liquid petroleum runs out.

Several large distillation plants are under construction for extraction of shale oil. Small pilot plants have been operating on and off for decades, but the low price

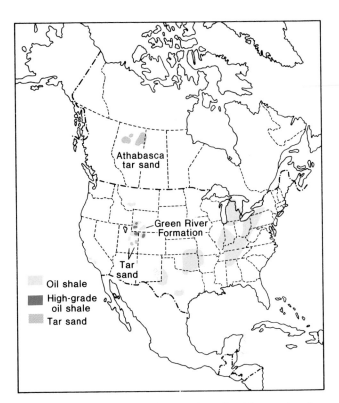

Figure 21.9 Distribution of major deposits of tar sand and oil shale in the United States and Canada. From U.S. Geological Survey and other sources.

for liquid petroleum in the past made shale oil uneconomical. The recent price increases for oil and the increasing support of the federal government have apparently made large-scale production of shale oil feasible.

The mining of oil shale has some environmental effects. There is a space problem, for during distillation the shale expands. Spent shale will probably be piled in valleys and compacted, but land reclamation will be troublesome. Water requirements are high, both for distillation and for reclamation, and water supply is always a problem in the arid West. New processing techniques that extract the oil in place without bringing the shale to the surface may eventually help solve some of the problems and lower the water requirements. It is possible to burn fractured oil shale in large underground excavations. The resulting heat separates most of the oil from the rock, and it can be collected in liquid form. Another proposal involves heating the shale with radio waves or microwaves to separate the liquid oil from the rock.

Figure 21.10 Cliffs of oil shale near Grand Valley, Colorado
Photo by D. E. Winchester, U.S. Geological Survey.

Coal

After petroleum and natural gas, coal is the third most used energy resource. It provided 90 percent of the energy used in the United States in 1900 but provides only 20 percent today. Coal use may increase in the future as petroleum becomes scarcer and more expensive.

More than 70 percent of the present use of coal in the United States is for generating electricity. Coal is also used to make *coke,* which is used in steel making. In the future, coal may be used instead of petroleum in the manufacture of some chemicals. *Coal gas* and *coal oil* made from coal also may replace petroleum in some other uses. These products are reasonable approximations of natural gas and petroleum and can be used for some of the same purposes, although they are still very expensive to produce. Coal can also be powdered and mixed with water to form a *slurry,* which can be transported through pipelines and burned as a liquid fuel.

Origin of Coal,

Coal is a sedimentary rock that forms from the compaction of plant material that has not completely decayed. Rapid plant growth and deposition in water with a low oxygen content are needed, so shallow swamps or bogs in a temperate or tropical climate are likely environments of deposition. The plant fossils in coal beds include leaves, stems, tree trunks, and stumps with roots often extending into the underlying shales, so it seems apparent that most coal formed right at the place where the plants grew.

Partial decay of the abundant plant material uses up any oxygen in the swamp water, so the decay stops and the remaining organic matter is preserved. Burial by sediment compresses the plant material, gradually driving out any water or other volatile compounds. The coal changes from brown to black as the amount of carbon in it increases.

Table 21.1 shows the common varieties (ranks) of coal. *Peat,* a mat of unconsolidated plant material, is not coal but probably represents the initial stage of coal development. When dry, it can be burned as a fuel (peat fires used to dry malted barley give Scotch whisky its smoky flavor). With compaction, peat can become *lignite* (*brown coal*), which may still contain visible pieces of wood. Lignite is soft and often crumbles as it dries in air. It may be subject to spontaneous combustion as it oxidizes in air, and this limits its use as a fuel somewhat. *Subbituminous coal* and *bituminous coal* (*soft coal*) are black and often banded with layers of different plant material. They are dusty to handle, ignite readily, and burn with a smoky flame. *Anthracite* (*hard coal*) is actually a metamorphic rock, generally formed only under the regional compression associated with folding. It is hard to ignite but is dustfree and smokeless.

Table 21.1

Varieties (Ranks) of Coal

	Color	Water Content (%)	Other Volatiles (%)	Fixed Carbon[2] (%)	Approximate Heat Value (BTUs of heat per pound of dry coal)
Peat[1]	Brown	75	10	15	varies
Lignite	Brown to brownish-black	45	25	30	7000
Subbituminous coal	Black	25	35	40	10,000
Bituminous coal (soft coal)	Black	5 to 15	20 to 30	50 to 75	12,000 to 15,000
Anthracite (hard coal)	Black	5	5	90	14,000

1. Peat is not a coal.

2. "Fixed carbon" means solid combustible material left after water, volatiles, and ash (noncombustible solids) are removed.

Figure 21.11 Bed of coal 2.5 meters thick in Dawson County, Montana.
Photo by M. R. Campbell, U.S. Geological Survey.

Figure 21.12 Underground coal mine near Axial, Colorado.
Photo by E. F. Patterson, U.S. Geological Survey.

Figure 21.13 Strip-mining of bed of coal 8.5 meters thick, Rosebud County, Montana.
Photo by C. E. Dobbin, U.S. Geological Survey.

Occurrence of Coal

Coal, a sedimentary rock, occurs in beds (figure 21.11) that range in thickness from less than one meter up to 50 meters. If the beds are deeply buried, underground mines are dug to extract the coal (figure 21.12). If the coal beds are close to the land surface, the coal is mined in a **strip mine,** in which the overburden is removed to expose coal at the surface (figure 21.13). When a strip of coal has been uncovered and removed, the resulting trench is filled in with the overburden from the adjoining strip.

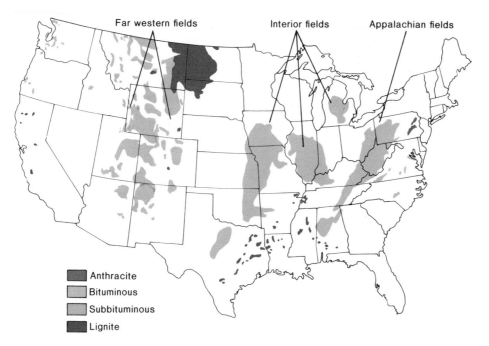

Far western fields   Interior fields   Appalachian fields

- **Anthracite**
- **Bituminous**
- **Subbituminous**
- **Lignite**

Figure 21.14 Coal fields of the United States. Alaska also has coal.
U.S. Geological Survey.

Figure 21.14 shows the coal fields of the "lower 48" states. We will discuss three major regions, the Appalachian fields, the interior fields, and the far western fields.

The major coal-producing fields in the United States are the *Appalachian fields,* which stretch from Pennsylvania to Alabama and contain extensive beds of bituminous coal. The coals are mostly of Pennsylvanian age, with Mississippian and Permian rocks containing some coal as well. The coal beds, which thin westward, were included in the late Paleozoic folding and faulting of the Appalachian orogeny, so they are strongly deformed in the eastern part of the belt. Steeply dipping coal beds here are mostly mined underground. The folds are gentler to the west, where the coals can be extracted by both underground and strip mining. Northeastern Pennsylvania has some anthracite that resulted from intense folding.

There are 25 to 50 coal beds over most of this region, each bed generally 2 meters or less in thickness, although some are locally thicker. The coal lies within repeated sequences of sandstone, shale, and limestone, which indicates alternating continental and marine conditions.

This implies a low-lying environment near the sea, such as lagoons, large deltas, and swampy coastal plains similar to those that exist in present-day Florida, Georgia, and South Carolina.

The *interior fields* extend from Michigan through Illinois to Texas and are extensions of the Appalachian rocks westward onto the continental interior. In Michigan and Illinois the rocks are preserved in large basins; the fields from Iowa to Texas are mostly horizontal. The coals are usually strip-mined where they are near the surface, particularly around the basin's edge in Illinois, Indiana, and Kentucky near major industrial centers.

The *far western fields* extend from New Mexico northward through the Rocky Mountains to Montana and the Great Plains of North Dakota (and also into Canada). The coal beds are thicker and younger than eastern coals. They are generally of Cretaceous age (some are Tertiary) and range up to 50 meters in thickness. The coals occur in large basins and are generally of low rank, being either lignite or subbituminous coal, although some good-quality bituminous coals occur in Colorado and Utah. Many thick beds are very close to the surface and are strip-mined, although underground mining is common in some states. Western coals are attractive fuels, presently in very high demand, because they typically have less sulfur than eastern coals (sulfur compounds can pollute the air when coal burns).

Environmental Effects

Both the extraction and the use of coal create environmental problems. The presence of a mine usually lowers the local water table as ground water is pumped out of the mine. The drainage out of the mines tends to be highly acid, polluting surface streams and water supplies. In the past, strip mines have been refilled as barren, unsightly piles, but new techniques of re-contouring the land and restoring removed overburden and topsoil help reclaim mined-out areas for other uses. When coal is burned, ash and sulfur gases can pollute air, but most of the harmful components can be removed with the existing technology. Solving environmental problems associated with coal, of course, raises the cost of extraction and the resulting price to the consumer.

Reserves and Resources

Coal production in the United States is 0.8 billion tons per year (the U.S. uses 0.7 billion tons and exports the rest). More than half the production is from surface strip mines. Although Kentucky, West Virginia, and Pennsylvania still produce almost half the coal, the rapid development of the huge beds of low-sulfur western coal may soon cause the Northern Rockies states to surpass the Appalachian states.

Recoverable *reserves* in the United States are nearly 800 billion tons (about one-quarter of this is North Dakota lignite). As you can see, there are centuries of coal left at the present rate of production.

Coal *resources* within 1,000 meters of the surface are 1,600 billion tons. A similar amount is estimated to lie deeper, so the total U.S. resources are an impressive 3,200 billion tons (much of which, of course, is not presently usable). Even as we step up extraction for the export market, it seems obvious that our coal supplies will last a very long time.

Uranium

The metal *uranium,* which powers nuclear reactors, occurs as *pitchblende,* a black uranium oxide found in hydrothermal veins, or, much more commonly in the United States, as yellow *carnotite,* a complex hydrated oxide found as incrustations in sedimentary rocks. Ground water easily transports oxidized uranium, which is highly soluble. Organic matter reduces uranium, making it relatively insoluble, so uranium precipitates in association with organic matter.

Most of the easily recoverable uranium in the United States is found in sandstone in New Mexico and Wyoming, some of it in and near petrified wood. In the 1950s uranium boom, western prospectors looked for petrified logs and checked them with Geiger counters. Some individual logs contained tens of thousands of dollars worth of uranium. Most of the uranium is in sandstone channels that contain plant fragments.

Organic phosphorite deposits of marine origin in Idaho and Florida also contain uranium. The uranium is not very concentrated, but the deposits are so large that overall they contain a substantial amount of uranium. The black Devonian shales of the eastern United States also contain uranium. These shales are really low-grade oil shales (figure 21.9), and they contain large amounts of natural gas, as you have seen. Uranium may be recovered from phosphorites or shales as a by-product of another mining operation.

Uranium is used in nuclear reactors to produce electricity and in nuclear weapons and some naval craft. At present, nuclear reactors produce about 4 percent of the energy needs of the United States. This figure may or may not rise appreciably in the future, depending on public acceptance of nuclear power. Nuclear plants produce long-lived waste products that remain dangerous for centuries, and the 1979 Three Mile Island reactor accident in Pennsylvania caused many people to reassess the desirability of nuclear power.

Recoverable reserves of 300 thousand tons of uranium oxide in western sandstones seem adequate to power the 72 operational reactors and 85 others under construction (in 1980) well past the turn of the century. About 1 million tons of uranium oxide exist in the richest phosphorite deposits in Idaho and Florida, and another 5 million tons in lower-grade phosphorites. Black shales should contain another 7 million tons. Uranium is not presently being recovered from either phosphorite or black shale, but some extraction by solution might be possible in the future if the use of nuclear power expands.

Alternative Sources of Energy

Several other sources may contribute enough energy in the future to help reduce the expected demand for petroleum, natural gas, coal, and uranium. *Hydroelectric power* contributes about 4 percent of U.S. energy needs. Electricity is generated by turbines turned by water falling from dammed reservoirs. The potential for increased hydroelectric power does not seem great because most suitable rivers in the United States have already been dammed. Public pressure is growing to preserve most of the remaining undammed rivers in their wild state, despite the danger of floods. *Geothermal power* (chapter 11) may contribute substantially to our power needs, particularly if successful techniques are developed for tapping the heat of areas not

marked by surface hot springs. *Solar power* and *wind power* may contribute to our needs in the future, particularly if improved methods of storing the energy are devised. At the present time a great effort is being made to improve the technology for the collection of solar energy. More exotic forms of energy generation include harnessing *tidal power, wave power, ocean current power,* and the energy represented by *vertical temperature differences in the sea. Nuclear fusion* reactors may be in operation before the end of the century. Burning of *hydrogen from the dissociation of water* also may be developed. However, major technological problems are slowing the adoption of these last two methods.

Metals and Ores

The search for metals depends on finding rocks that contain metal-bearing minerals from which the metals can be extracted without too much difficulty and expense. What a mining geologist looks for are **ores,** which are naturally occurring materials that can be profitably mined. (Ores usually, but not always, contain metal.) Whether or not a mineral (or rock) is considered an ore depends on its chemical composition, the percentage of extractable metal, and the market value of the metal. The mineral hematite (Fe_2O_3), for example, is a good *iron ore* because it contains 70 percent Fe by weight. Limonite ($Fe_2O_3.nH_2O$) contains less Fe than hematite and hence is not as extensively mined. Even a mineral containing a high percentage of metal is not described as an *ore* if the metal is too difficult to extract or the site is too far from a market; profit is part of the definition of ore. As the prices of metals and the energy used to extract them fluctuate, so do the potential profits from minerals. Some of the common ore minerals are listed in table 21.2.

Table 21.2
Common Ore Minerals

Metal	Ore Mineral	Composition
Aluminum	Bauxite (a mineral mixture)	$Al_2O_3 \cdot nH_2O$
Chromium	Chromite	$FeCr_2O_4$
Copper	Chalcocite	Cu_2S
	Chalcopyrite	$CuFeS_2$
Gold	Native gold	Au
Iron	Hematite	Fe_2O_3
	Magnetite	Fe_3O_4
Lead	Galena	PbS
Manganese	Pyrolusite	MnO_2
Mercury	Cinnabar	HgS
Nickel	Pentlandite	(Fe, Ni)S
Silver	Native silver	Ag
	Argentite	Ag_2S
Tin	Cassiterite	SnO_2
Uranium	Pitchblende	U_3O_8
	Carnotite	$K(UO_2)_2(VO_4)_2 \cdot 3H_2O$
Zinc	Sphalerite	ZnS

Table 21.3
Some Ways Ore Deposits Form

Type of Ore Deposit	Some Metals Found in This Type of Ore Deposit
Crystal settling within cooling magma	Chromium, platinum, iron
Hydrothermal deposits (contact metamorphism, hydrothermal veins, disseminated deposits, hot-spring deposits)	Copper, lead, zinc, gold, silver, iron, molybdenum, tungsten, tin, mercury, cobalt
Pegmatites	Lithium, rare metals
Chemical precipitation in layers	Iron, manganese, copper
Placer deposits	Gold, tin, platinum, titanium
Concentration by weathering and ground water	Aluminum, nickel, copper, silver, uranium, iron, manganese, lead, tin, mercury

Origin of Metallic Ore Deposits

Table 21.3 summarizes most of the ways ore deposits form. Several of the processes have been discussed in earlier chapters.

Ores Associated with Igneous Rocks

Crystal settling occurs as early-forming minerals crystallize and settle to the bottom of a cooling body of magma (figure 21.15). This process was described under differentiation in chapter 4. The metal chromium comes from chromite ore bodies near the base of sills and other intrusions. In South Africa a huge sill 8 kilometers thick and 500 kilometers long, called the Bushveldt Complex, contains up to 25 layers of chromite near its base, some of them up to 2 meters thick. Above the chromite are similar layers enriched in platinum. Most of the world's chromium and platinum come from this single intrusion. In Montana, another huge Precambrian sill called the Stillwater Complex contains similar but lower grade deposits of these two metals.

Hydrothermal fluids are the most important source of ore deposits. The hot water and other fluids might be part of the magma itself, injected into the surrounding country rock during the last stages of magma crystallization (figure 21.16*A*). Atoms of metals such as copper and gold, which do not fit into the growing crystals of feldspar and other minerals in the cooling pluton, would be concentrated residually in the remaining water-rich magma. Eventually a hot solution, rich in metals and silica (quartz is the lowest-temperature mineral on Bowen's reaction series), could move into the country rock to create ore deposits.

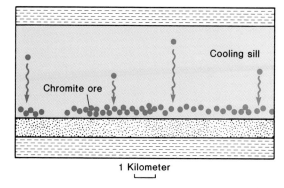

Figure 21.15 Early-forming minerals such as chromite may settle through magma to collect in layers near the bottom of a cooling sill.

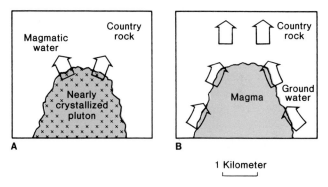

Figure 21.16 Two possible origins of hydrothermal fluids. (*A*) Residually concentrated magmatic water moves into country rock when magma is nearly all crystallized. (*B*) Ground water becomes heated by magma (or cooling solid pluton), and a convective circulation is set up.

Some hydrothermal fluids may be regular ground water, circulating in a convection pattern caused by the heat of the pluton. As water becomes heated by the pluton, it rises above it, drawing in new water from the sides to take its place. The new water then becomes heated and rises, and a continual circulation of water past the cooling pluton is set up (fig. 21.16*B*). The hot water moving near and through the pluton could leach metals from the pluton and carry them upward to be deposited elsewhere as ore. However the hydrothermal solutions form, they tend to create four general types of hydrothermal ore deposits: (1) contact metamorphic deposits, (2) hydrothermal veins, (3) disseminated deposits, and (4) hot-spring deposits.

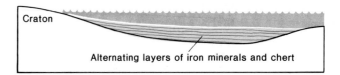

Figure 21.18 Banded iron ores of Precambrian age probably accumulated in shallow basins.

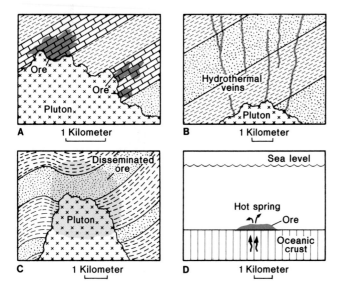

Figure 21.17 Hydrothermal ore deposits. (A) Contact metamorphism in which ore replaces limestone. (B) Ore emplaced in hydrothermal veins. (C) Disseminated ore within and above a pluton. (D) Ore precipitated around submarine hot spring (size of ore deposit exaggerated).

Contact metamorphism (chapter 7) can create ores of copper, lead, zinc, silver, and other metals in country rock. The country rock may be completely or partially removed and replaced by ore (figure 21.17*A*). This is particularly true of limestone beds, which react readily with hydro-thermal solutions. The ore bodies can be quite large and very rich. Most hydrothermal ores are metallic sulfides, often mixed with milky quartz. The origin of the sulfur is widely debated.

Hydrothermal veins are narrow ore bodies formed along joints and faults (figure 21.17*B*). They can extend great distances from their apparent plutonic sources. Some extend so far that it is questionable if they are even associated with plutons. The fluids can precipitate ore (and quartz) within cavities along the fractures and may also replace the wall rock of the fractures with ore. Hydrothermal veins form most of the world's great deposits of lead, zinc, silver, gold, tungsten, tin, mercury, and, to some extent, copper.

Hot solutions can also form *disseminated deposits* in which metallic sulfide ore minerals are distributed in very low concentration through large volumes of rock, both above and within a pluton (figure 21.17*C*). Most of the world's copper comes from disseminated deposits (also called *porphyry copper deposits* because the associated pluton is usually porphyritic). Along with the copper are deposited many other metals, such as lead, zinc, molybdenum, silver, and gold (and iron, though not in commercial quantities).

Where hot solutions rise to the earth's surface, *hot springs* form. Hot springs on land may contain large amounts of dissolved metals. Some California hot springs contain so much mercury that the water is unfit to drink. More impressive are hot springs on the sea floor (figure 21.17*D*), which can precipitate large mounds of metallic sulfides, sometimes in commercial quantities. We will look at submarine hot springs later in the chapter in connection with plate tectonics.

Pegmatites (box 4.1) are another type of ore deposit associated with igneous rocks. They may contain important concentrations of minerals containing lithium, beryllium, and other rare metals, as well as gemstones such as emeralds and sapphires.

Ores Formed by Surface Processes

Chemical precipitation in layers is the most common origin for ores of iron and manganese. A few copper ores form in this way too. Banded iron ores, usually composed of alternating layers of iron minerals and chert, formed as sedimentary rocks in many parts of the world during the Precambrian, apparently in shallow, water-filled basins (figure 21.18). Later folding, faulting, metamorphism, and solution have destroyed many of the original features of the ore, so the origin of the ore is difficult to interpret. The water may have been fresh or marine, and the iron may have come from volcanic activity or deep weathering of the surrounding continents. The alternating bands may have been created by some rhythmic variation in volcanic activity, river runoff, basin water circulation, growth of organisms, or some other factor. Since banded iron ores are all Precambrian, their origin might be connected to an ancient atmosphere or ocean that differed chemically from today's.

Placer deposits are found where running water or waves have concentrated heavy sediment grains in a river bar or on a beach (figure 21.19). Grains concentrated in this manner include gold nuggets and dust, native platinum, diamonds and other gemstones, and worn pebbles or sand grains composed of the heavy oxides of titanium and tin.

Concentration by weathering can occur in several ways. The concentration of diamonds by weathering is illustrated in figure 21.20. Diamonds are brought to the

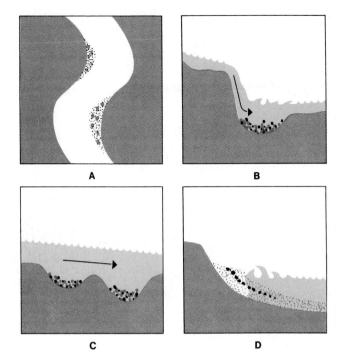

Figure 21.19 Types of placer deposits. (*A*) Stream bar. (*B*) Below waterfall. (*C*) Depressions on stream bed. (*D*) Beach.

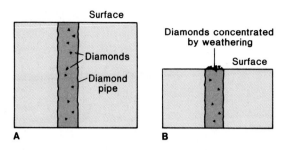

Figure 21.20 Residual concentration by weathering. (*A*) Cross-section view of diamonds widely scattered within diamond pipe. (*B*) Diamonds concentrated on surface by removal of rock by weathering and erosion.

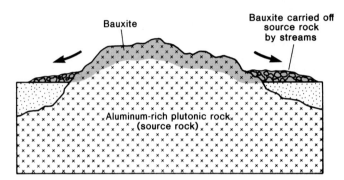

Figure 21.21 Bauxite forms by intense tropical weathering of a source rock.

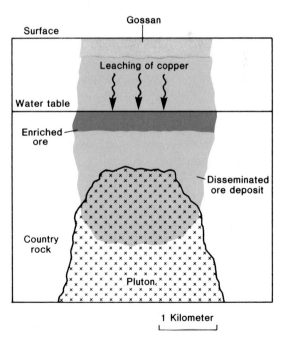

Figure 21.22 Supergene enrichment. Ground water leaches copper from upper part of disseminated deposit and precipitates it below the water table, forming rich ore.

surface of the earth in *diamond pipes,* columns of brecciated ultramafic rock that has risen from the upper mantle. Diamonds are widely scattered in diamond pipes when they form. At the earth's surface the ultramafic rock in the pipe can be weathered and eroded away. The diamonds, being more resistant to weathering, are left behind, concentrated in rich deposits on top of the pipes. Rivers may redistribute the diamonds into placer deposits, as in South Africa.

Bauxite, the primary ore of aluminum, forms by lateritic weathering in tropical climates (chapter 5), particularly on aluminum-rich rocks (figure 21.21). Under tropical conditions of high rainfall and high temperature, most weathering products are soluble—even silica. The least soluble product is aluminum oxide, which remains on top of the weathering rocks, forming bauxite in a soil very rich in aluminum. Like the diamonds, the aluminum has been concentrated residually by the removal of everything else. The aluminum ores may be redistributed slightly by running water (figure 21.21). Nickel ores can also form in laterites.

Another type of concentration by weathering is the *supergene enrichment* of disseminated ore deposits. The major ore mineral in a disseminated copper deposit is chalcopyrite, a copper-iron sulfide containing about 35 percent copper. Near the earth's surface, downward-moving ground water can leach copper and sulfur from the ore, leaving the iron behind (figure 21.22). Below the water table the dissolved copper can react with chalco-pyrite in the lower part of the disseminated deposit, form-ing a richer ore mineral such as chalcocite, which is about 80 percent copper:

$$3\,Cu^{++} \quad + \quad CuFeS_2 \quad \rightarrow \quad 2\,Cu_2S \; + \; Fe$$

Copper dissolved   Chalcopyrite   Chalcocite   Iron in
in ground water   solution

In this way copper is removed from the top of the deposit and added to the lower part. The ore below the water table may be several times richer than in the rest of the deposit (silver can move with the copper). The iron left behind at the earth's surface forms a rusty cap called a *gossan,* which is a visible clue to the ore below.

Mining

Mining can be carried out on the earth's surface or un-derground (figure 21.23). Two forms of surface mine are *strip mines,* used for mining some beds of coal, and **open-pit mines,** in which ore is exposed in a large excavation. Some geologists use *strip mine* and *open-pit mine* inter-changeably. However, strip mines generally expose coal or another resource in a long band, while open-pit mines are roughly circular and are excavated to extract metallic ores, usually from disseminated deposits. **Placer mines** are surface mines in which valuable sediment grains are ex-tracted from stream bar or beach deposits.

Environmental Effects

Some of the environmental problems associated with min-ing can be partially resolved if care is taken. *Waste rock,* for example, in the past was routinely left in unsightly heaps and dumps (figure 21.24). The excavations for strip mines and placer mines can be filled in with waste rock, leveled or graded, and then covered over with topsoil to restore the land to usable condition. In some cases crops can be grown on reclaimed land within two or three years after mining operations are completed. Open pits, being larger, are rarely filled in, for the filling cannot be done gradually while mining is in progress. Underground mines are sometimes back-filled with waste rock to prevent land *subsidence* after ore is removed. Figure 21.25 shows ex-tensive subsidence caused by mine collapse. This happens when an underground mine is not back-filled or the job is not done properly.

One of the more difficult problems to deal with is *acid drainage* from mines caused by ground water running or being pumped out of a mine. Sulfide ore minerals are most often the source of the trouble (table 21.2). Ground water dissolves some of the sulfide, which oxidizes in air to form sulfuric acid. Some mines conduct expensive programs of holding and neutralizing drainage water to prevent pol-lution of surface streams and harm to forests and wildlife.

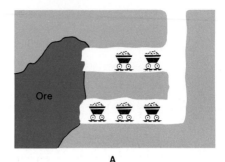

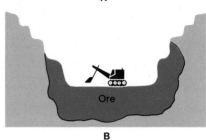

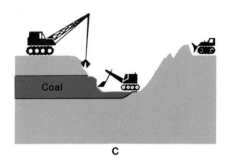

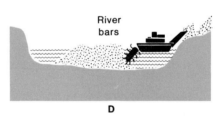

Figure 21.23 Types of mines. (*A*) Underground. (*B*) Open pit. (*C*) Strip. (*D*) Placer.

The worst problem is with long-abandoned mines that are still draining acid waters. Many of these may never be neutralized.

Some Important Metals

Iron

The basis for any modern, industrialized economy is *iron,* which is used to make steel. Iron and steel are used in a huge variety of products, from cast-iron frying pans to locomotives. World use of iron ore is about one billion tons per year. World reserves are about 250 billion tons (and resources are over 750 billion tons), so the supply of iron ore seems assured for a long time.

Figure 21.24 Waste rock piles in 1903 at Cripple Creek mining district, Colorado.
Photo by F. L. Ransome, U.S. Geological Survey.

Figure 21.25 Subsidence caused by caving of underground mine in Arizona.
Photo by F. L. Ransome, U.S. Geological Survey.

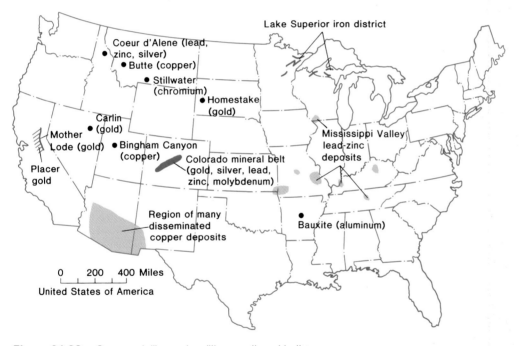

Figure 21.26 Some metallic ore localities mentioned in the text.

The major iron ore minerals are hematite and magnetite. Most of the iron in the United States comes from Minnesota and Michigan in the region around Lake Superior (figure 21.26). The ores are banded iron ores of Precambrian age, typical of most iron ores in the world. Mining is done mostly by open-pit methods.

Copper

Less abundant is *copper,* another important metal for industry. More than half the copper used in the United States goes into electrical wire and equipment, and one-third into the manufacture of brass, a copper-zinc alloy. Annual world consumption of copper is about 8 million tons. World resources may total more than 700 million tons, but less than half these resources may be reserves. In 40 to 50 years copper may be very scarce.

Most copper ores are sulfides. Chalcopyrite is the most important copper ore mineral. Some vein deposits of copper exist (as at Butte, Montana), but most major deposits are disseminated through large volumes of rock;

so most copper mines are open pits. Arizona, Utah, and a few other western states are the major producers in the United States (figure 21.26). The concentration of copper averages about 0.5 percent in most currently worked deposits; that is, 1 kg of copper is recovered for every 200 kg of rock processed. (The largest open-pit mine in the world, at Bingham Canyon, Utah, is described in chapter 7.)

Aluminum

Widely used in the United States, *aluminum* is consumed in the manufacture of beer and soft drink cans, airplanes, electrical cable, and many other products. The use of aluminum is increasing rapidly.

The ore of aluminum is bauxite, which forms under tropical weathering conditions. The United States has very little bauxite, so it imports 90 percent of its aluminum ore from tropical countries. The largest mine in the United States is in Arkansas (figure 21.26). Open-pit mining is the usual technique for extracting bauxite.

World reserves of bauxite are probably 12 to 15 billion tons, with resources even greater. Annual world production is about 75 *million* tons, so there is an ample supply of aluminum for the foreseeable future.

Lead

The most important use of *lead* (53 percent) is in batteries. World production of lead from ore is about 4 million tons per year. Substantial amounts are also recycled, largely from automobile batteries. World reserves are about 140 million tons, so only a 35-year supply now exists at the present rate of consumption.

The most important ore of lead is galena. Major deposits occur in Missouri, Idaho, Utah, and Colorado (figure 21.26). The Missouri deposits are mostly found in limestone beds; their precise origin is a matter of some controversy. The ore is mined both underground and from open pits. Deposits in Idaho occur mostly as veins and are usually mined underground.

Zinc

Widely used in industry, *zinc* is necessary for galvanizing and the manufacture of brass and other alloys. Annual world consumption is about 6 million tons. Recoverable reserves of about 240 million tons would yield a 40-year supply at present use rates. Large resources may add to reserves.

The major zinc ore is sphalerite. As sphalerite usually is found closely associated with galena, most lead mines also extract zinc. Zinc occurs without lead in some areas, however.

Silver

Coins, tableware, jewelry, photographic film, and many other products are made of *silver*. World use of newly mined silver is about 0.3 billion ounces per year, and large quantities are recycled. Total world resources are probably 2 to 5 billion ounces, and not all these resources are reserves. A severe shortage of silver could occur in 10 years.

Silver, found as a native metal and in sulfide ores, is a common by-product of lead and copper mining. The lead-zinc mines of Idaho (the Coeur d'Alene district) are the largest silver producers in the United States (figure 21.26).

Gold

This rare and valuable metal is used in coins, jewelry, decoration, dentistry, electronics, and the space program. Gold bars are stored to back national currency, although this use and its use in coins are rapidly disappearing. Whereas other metal reserves are measured in tons, world production of *gold* is about 45 million *ounces* per year, and the world reserves are estimated at 350 to 1,000 million ounces. At the present rate of consumption, gold could be used up in 10 to 20 years. New reserves are badly needed.

Gold is most often found as a native element in the form of nuggets and grains. In some parts of the world these are concentrated in placer deposits (California's Gold Rush of 1849 was triggered by discoveries of placer gold). Gold nuggets, flakes, and dust can be separated from the other sediments by (1) *panning;* (2) *sluice-boxes* (figure 21.27), which catch the heavy gold on the bottom of a box as gravel is washed through it; (3) *hydraulic mining* (figure 21.28), which washes gold-bearing gravel from a hillside into a sluice-box; or (4) floating *dredges* (figure 21.29), which separate gold from gravel aboard a large barge, piling the spent gravel behind. When gold is found in hydrothermal veins associated with milky quartz, as it is in parts of Colorado and in California's Mother Lode (figure 21.26), it is mined underground. Gold disseminated in limestone is mined in an open-pit mine near

Figure 21.27 Sluice box used to separate gold from gravel, Alaska.
Photo by H. L. Foster, U.S. Geological Survey.

Figure 21.28 Hydraulic mining, Lemhi County, Idaho, 1899.
Photo by B. Willis, U.S. Geological Survey.

Figure 21.29 A gold dredge near Nome, Alaska.
Photos by H. M. Eakin, U.S. Geological Survey.

Carlin, Nevada. The largest gold mine in the United States is the Homestake Mine in South Dakota, where finely disseminated gold is extracted from folded metamorphic rock.

Other Metals

Many other metals are vital to our economy. *Chromium, nickel, cobalt, manganese, molybdenum, tungsten* and *vanadium* are all important in the steel industry, particularly in the manufacture of specialty products such as stainless steel. Most of these metals have other uses as well. *Tin* is used in solder and for plating steel in "tin cans." *Mercury* is used in thermometers, silent electrical switches, medical compounds, and batteries. *Magnesium* is used in aircraft and flashbulbs. *Titanium,* as strong as steel but weighing half as much, is used in aircraft. *Platinum* is used in catalytic converters to clean automobile exhaust.

Metal Ores and Plate Tectonics

Diverging plate boundaries are often marked by lines of hot springs that carry and precipitate metals. Geologists in small submarines have observed hot springs in several localities along the rift valley of the mid-oceanic ridge. The hot springs, caused by the high heat flow and basaltic magma in the rift valley, range in temperature from about 20°C up to an estimated 350°C.

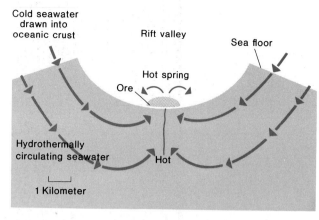

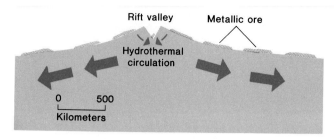

Figure 21.30 Hydrothermal circulation of seawater at ridge crest creates hot springs and metallic ores in rift valley. Cold seawater is drawn into fractured crust on ridge flanks. (Size of ore deposit exaggerated.)

Figure 21.31 Sea-floor spreading carries metallic ores away from rift valley. (Size of ore deposits exaggerated.)

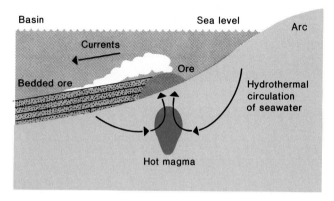

Figure 21.32 On island arcs metallic ores can form over hot springs and be redistributed into layers by currents in shallow basins.

As the hot water rises in the rift valley, cold water is drawn in from the sides to take its place. This creates a circulation pattern in which cold sea water is actually drawn *downward* through cracks in the basaltic crust of the ridge flanks and then moves horizontally toward the rift valley, where it reemerges on the sea floor after being heated (figure 21.30). As the sea water moves through the crust it dissolves metals and sulfur from the crustal rocks and magma. When the hot, metal-rich solutions contact cold sea water, metal sulfides are precipitated in a mound around the hot spring. This process has been filmed in the Pacific, where some springs spew clouds of fine-grained ore minerals that look like black smoke.

The metals in rift-valley hot springs are predominantly iron, copper, and zinc, with smaller amounts of manganese, gold, and silver. Although the mounds are nearly solid metal sulfide, they are small and widely scattered on the sea floor, so commercial mining of them may not be practical. Occasionally the ores may be concentrated in richer deposits. On the floor of the Red Sea metallic sediments worth billions of dollars have precipitated in basins filled with hot spring solutions. Although the solutions are hot (up to 60°C), they are very dense due to their high salt content (they are seven times saltier than sea water). The Red Sea brines are so dense that they collect in seafloor depressions instead of mixing with the overlying sea water.

Hot metallic solutions are also found along some diverging continental boundaries. Near the Salton Sea in southern California, which lies along the extension of the mid-oceanic ridge inland, hot water very similar to the Red Sea brines has been discovered underground. The hot water is currently being used to run a geothermal power plant. The high salt and metal content is corrosive to equipment, but metals such as copper and silver may one day be recovered as valuable by-products.

Sea-floor spreading carries the metallic ores away from the ridge crest (figure 21.31). Slivers of *ophiolite* on land may contain these rich ore deposits in relatively intact form. A notable example of such ores occurs on the island of Cyprus in the Mediterranean Sea. Banded chromite ores may also be contained in the serpentinized ultramafic rock at the bottom of ophiolites.

Volcanism at *island arcs* can also produce hot-spring deposits on the flanks of the andesitic volcanoes. Pods of very rich ore collect above local bodies of magma, and the ore is sometimes distributed as sedimentary layers in shallow basins (figure 21.32). The circulation pattern and the ore-forming processes are quite similar to those of spreading centers, but the island arc ores usually contain more lead. Rich *massive sulfide deposits* overlying fractured volcanic rock in the Precambrian shield area of Canada may have formed in this way on ancient island arcs.

Subduction of the sea floor beneath a continent produces broad belts of metallic ore deposits on the edge of the continent. Figure 21.33 shows how the distribution of some metals in the western United States might be related to depth along a subduction zone (the figure shows only one of several competing theories relating ore deposits to plate tectonics). The pattern of ore belts has probably been disturbed by changing subduction angles, strike-slip faulting, and backarc spreading. (Each of these processes may also have added new metals to the pattern shown).

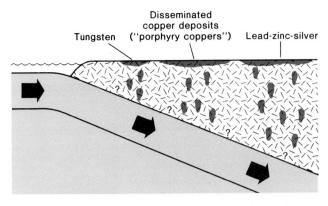

Figure 21.33 Possible relation of ore belts in the western United States to depth along the subduction zone. Different metallic ores (and different igneous rocks) are generated at different depths along a subducted plate.

Similar patterns of ore belts occur in other subduction mountain ranges, notably the Andes.

The origin of the continental ores above a subduction zone is not clear. The hot-spring deposits from the ridge crest are subducted with oceanic crust and could become remobilized to rise into the continent above. The ores may also "distill" off other parts of the descending oceanic crust or upper mantle. The metals may also be derived from the continental crust itself or the asthenosphere below it. The metals may be concentrated somehow by the heat of a rising blob of magma or the hydrothermal circulation associated with it.

It is tempting to think that *mantle plumes* may cause ore concentration when they rise beneath continents, for plumes provide a magma source and hydrothermal circulation. The "Mississippi-Valley-type" lead-zinc deposits of the continental interior are very puzzling features. Over broad areas metal ore has been emplaced in limestone and dolomite, both by cavity filling and replacement, and there is no obvious connection between the ores and any igneous rocks, which may be absent in the ore regions. One of many hypotheses of the origin of these ores is the movement of the continent over a mantle plume. There are at least two arguments against this hypothesis, however. One is that mantle plumes erupt large quantities of volcanic rock, and there are no volcanics associated with the Mississippi Valley ores. The other is that where probable plumes exist today, as beneath Yellowstone, there are very few ore deposits.

Nonmetallic Resources

With the exception of the gemstones such as diamonds and rubies, nonmetallic resources do not have the glamour of many metals or energy resources. Nonmetallic resources are generally inexpensive and are needed in large

Figure 21.34 Sand and gravel pit.
Photo by California Division of Mines and Geology.

quantities (again, except for gemstones). The large demand and low unit price means that these resources are best taken from local sources. Transportation over long distances would add significantly to the cost.

Construction Materials

Sand and *gravel* are both needed for the manufacture of concrete for building and highway construction. Sand is also used in mortar, which holds bricks and cement blocks together. The demand for sand and gravel in the United States has more than doubled in the last 25 years. Sand dunes, river channel and bar deposits, glacial outwash, and beach deposits are common sources for sand and gravel. Cinder cones are mined for "gravel" in some areas. Sand and gravel are ordinarily mined in open pits (figure 21.34).

Stone refers to rock used in blocks to construct buildings or crushed to form roadbed. Most stone in buildings is limestone or granite, and most crushed stone is limestone. Huge quantities of stone are used each year in the United States. Stone is removed from open pits called *quarries* (figure 21.35).

Limestone has many uses other than building stone or crushed roadbed. Cement, used in concrete and mortar, is made from limestone. Pulverized limestone is in demand as a fertilizer and soil conditioner and is the principal ingredient of numerous chemical products.

Figure 21.35 Limestone quarry in Illinois.

Figure 21.36 Loading potassium minerals in an underground mine, Eddy County, New Mexico. Photo by H. I. Smith, U.S. Geological Survey.

Fertilizers and Evaporites

Fertilizers (phosphate, nitrate, and potassium compounds) are extremely important to agriculture today, so much so that they are one of the few nonmetallic resources transported across the sea. *Phosphate* is produced from rock phosphate, a deposit composed of certain remains of marine organisms. Major phosphate deposits in the United States are in Idaho, Wyoming, and Florida. *Nitrate* can form directly as an evaporite deposit, but today is usually made from atmospheric nitrogen. *Potassium* compounds are often found as evaporites. Figure 21.36 shows an underground mine for potassium compounds.

Rock salt is coarsely crystalline halite formed as an evaporite. Salt beds are mined underground in New York, Ohio, and Michigan; underground salt domes are mined in Texas and Louisiana. (Some salt is also extracted from sea water by evaporation.) Rock salt is used in many ways—road de-icing in winter, food preservation, table salt, and the manufacture of hydrochloric acid and sodium compounds for baking soda, soap, and other products. Rock salt is heavily used by industry.

Gypsum forms as an evaporite. Beds of gypsum are mined in many states, notably California, Michigan, Iowa, and Texas. Gypsum, the essential ingredient of plaster and wallboard, is used mainly by the construction industry, although there are other uses.

Sulfur occurs in bright-yellow deposits of elemental sulfur. Most of its commercial production comes from the cap rock of salt domes (see box 21.1). Sulfur is widely used in agriculture as a fungicide and fertilizer and by industry to manufacture sulfuric acid, matches, and many other products.

Other Nonmetallics

Gemstones (called *gems* when cut and polished) include precious stones such as diamonds, rubies, emeralds, and sapphires and semiprecious stones such as beryl, garnet, jade, spinel, topaz, turquoise, and zircon. Gems are used for jewelry, phonograph needles, and bearings and abrasives (most are above 7 on Mohs' scale of hardness.) Diamond drills and diamond saws are used to drill and cut rock. Watches often have hard gems at bearing points of friction ("17-jewel watches"). Gemstones are often found in pegmatites or in close association with other igneous intrusives. Some are recovered from placer deposits.

Asbestos is a fibrous variety of serpentine. The fibers can be separated and woven into fireproof fabric used for firefighters' clothes and theater curtains. Other uses are in the manufacturing of insulators, shingles, and brake linings. The United States produces little asbestos, mostly from belts of serpentinized ultramafic rocks in the Appalachians and the Pacific Coast states. Large amounts are mined in Canada, chiefly in Quebec. *Talc,* used in talcum powder and other products, is often found associated with asbestos (see box 18.1).

Other nonmetallic resources are important. *Mica* is used in insulators. *Barite* ($BaSO_4$), because of its high specific gravity, is used to make heavy drilling mud to prevent oil gushers. *Borates* are boron-containing evaporites used in fiberglass, cleaning compounds, and ceramics. *Fluorite* (CaF_2) is used in toothpaste, Teflon finishes, and steel-smelting. *Clays* are used in ceramics and as filters and absorbents. *Diatomite* is used in swimming pool filters. *Glass sand,* which is over 95 percent quartz, is the main component of glass. *Graphite* is used in foundries, lubricants, steel-making, batteries, and pencil "lead."

Substitutes, Recycling and Conservation

Substitutes for many geologic resources now exist, and others will be found. Aluminum is replacing the more expensive copper in many electrical uses, particularly in transmission lines. Glass fibers also are replacing copper for telephone lines. Aluminum and tin-coated steel are essentially interchangeable for beverage containers. Cotton and wool use could increase, replacing polyester and other petroleum-based synthetic fibers in clothes.

Suitable substitutes, however, seem unlikely for some resources. Nothing yet developed can take the place of steel in bridges, mercury in thermometers, or silver in photography. Cobalt is vital for strong, permanent magnets. Although substitutes may help prolong the life of the supplies of some resources, they are not available for many others.

Recycling helps augment the supply of some resources. No resource, however, receives even half its supply from recycling. Increased volunteer recycling on the part of the public and waste reclaiming of urban trash could increase these percentages. New ore will always be needed, however, because some uses of products prevent the material from being recyclable. A steel can that rusts away beside a road can never be recycled. The iron oxides are scattered in low percentage in the soil and can never be recovered. Many resources, such as petroleum and coal, are consumed during use and cannot be recycled.

Conservation of scarce resources is extremely important. The United States use of petroleum declined from 1979 to 1981 as a result of conservation efforts such as the 55 mile-per-hour speed limit, more fuel-efficient automobiles, the upgrading of insulation in buildings, and the elimination of unneeded heating and lighting. In the difficult times ahead as the United States changes from a petroleum-based economy to one based on other fuels, the need for conserving fuel will be repeatedly stressed. Conservation of metals, particularly those imported in large quantities, will become increasingly important. Smaller automobiles and more durable appliances can help conserve metals.

Some Future Trends

Increased ocean mining and offshore petroleum drilling will continue in the near future. Mining of *manganese nodules* from the deep-sea floor (chapter 19) could provide the United States with substantial amounts of copper and nickel, together with far more manganese than United States industry can consume. Copper content of many nodules is 1 to 2 percent, higher than most deposits on land. *Metallic brines and deposits* of the Red Sea type may be a source of several metals in the future.

Several tools are of great help in mineral exploration on land. Highly sophisticated *geochemical tests* of soils and soil gases point to ore bodies underground. *Geophysical techniques* continue to be refined for resource exploration. LANDSAT satellites photograph the earth's surface in many different wavelengths of energy, and careful analysis of satellite imagery is proving to be of great help in prospecting. Economic returns from the LANDSAT program will far outweigh its costs.

As the relation of plate tectonics to the distribution of resources such as metals and petroleum becomes clearer, the selection of areas for exploration for these materials should become better defined.

Summary

Geologic resources include energy resources, metals, and nonmetallic resources. All are nonrenewable.

Petroleum and natural gas supply almost 75 percent of the energy used by the United States.

The occurrence of *petroleum* and *natural gas* is limited to regions having these three conditions together: *source rocks, reservoir rocks,* and *oil traps,* such as anticlines, faults, stratigraphic traps, and salt domes.

Reserves are known deposits that can be legally and economically recovered now—the short-term supply. *Resources* include reserves as well as other known and undiscovered deposits that may be extracted in the future.

At the present rate of consumption, the United States oil supply will last about 25 years.

Natural gas, *heavy crude, tar sand,* and *oil shale* may all help replace liquid petroleum in the future. Most of these resources are in the western states.

The United States has huge *coal* reserves, enough for centuries of use at the present rate. Coal, now used mostly for generation of electricity, will probably be used more widely in the future as oil runs out. The United States now exports coal. Increased production will come largely from near-surface, low-sulfur western coals.

The United States has ample *uranium* for its reactor program, mostly in sandstones in western states.

Metals are often associated with igneous rocks, particularly their hydrothermal fluids which can form *contact metamorphic deposits, hydrothermal veins, disseminated deposits,* and submarine *hot-spring deposits.* Iron occurs in sedimentary layers and aluminum ores form from weathering.

Ores are mined *underground* and also at the earth's surface in *strip mines, open-pit mines,* and *placer mines.*

Metals are vital to an industrial economy, particularly *iron* for steel production and *copper* for electrical equipment.

The world has large reserves of iron and aluminum, moderate reserves of copper, lead, and zinc, and scanty reserves of gold and silver.

Metal ores form from hot springs at diverging plate boundaries, on the flanks of island arcs, and in belts in continents above subduction zones. The association of ores with mantle plumes has been suggested.

Nonmetallic resources such as *sand and gravel* and *limestone* for crushed rock and cement are used in huge quantities. *Fertilizers, rock salt, gypsum, sulfur,* and *clays* are also widely used.

Substitutes, recycling, and conservation can help cut consumption of some resources but will not eliminate the need for finding new deposits.

Deep-sea mining and increasingly sophisticated exploration techniques will help supply some of our future resource needs.

Terms to Remember

geologic resources	ore
heavy crude	petroleum (crude oil)
natural gas	placer mine
nonrenewable resources	reserves
oil field	reservoir rock
oil pool	resources
oil shale	source rock
oil trap	strip mine
open-pit mine	tar sands

Questions for Review

1. Name the three major classes of geologic resources. Give four examples of each class.
2. Discuss the United States' supplies and potential use of natural gas, heavy crude, tar sand, oil shale, and uranium.
3. List in decreasing order of use the energy resources used in the United States. Discuss possible future trends in this ranking of importance.
4. What geologic conditions are necessary for the accumulation of petroleum and natural gas?
5. Differentiate between *reserves* and *resources.* Can reserves be increased? Can resources be increased?
6. Compare petroleum reserves with coal reserves. What might this indicate for the future use of each?
7. Describe several ways that ore deposits are formed. Which are the most important?
8. Describe four ways in which resources are mined.
9. Discuss environmental effects of petroleum extraction and of coal mining.
10. Discuss common uses for iron, copper, lead, zinc, and aluminum.
11. Which of the metals discussed in the chapter are in short supply? Which have large reserves?
12. Describe the potential of substitutes, conservation, recycling, and deep-sea mining for meeting increased future needs of geologic resources.

Question for Thought

1. Many underdeveloped countries would like to have the standard of living enjoyed by the United States, which uses 15 to 40 percent of the world production of many resources. As these countries become industrialized, what happens to the world demand for geologic resources? Where will these needed resources come from?

Supplementary Readings

Bonatti, E. 1978. The origin of metal deposits in the oceanic lithosphere. *Scientific American,* February 1978, pp. 54–61.

Committee on Geological Sciences, National Research Council—National Academy of Sciences, 1972. *The earth and human affairs.* San Francisco: Canfield Press.

Committee on Resources and Man, National Academy of Sciences—National Research Council, 1969. *Resources and man.* San Francisco: W. H. Freeman.

Jensen, M. L., and A. M. Bateman. 1979. *Economic mineral deposits.* 3d ed. New York: John Wiley & Sons.

Levorsen, A. I. 1967. *Geology of petroleum.* 2d ed. San Francisco: W. H. Freeman.

Mero, J. L. 1965. *The mineral resources of the sea.* New York: American Elsevier.

Park, C. F., Jr. 1968. *Affluence in jeopardy: Minerals and the political economy.* San Francisco: Freeman, Cooper.

Park, C. F., Jr. 1975. *Earthbound: Minerals, energy, and man's future.* San Francisco: Freeman, Cooper.

Park, C. F., Jr., and R. A. MacDiarmid. 1975. *Ore deposits.* 3d ed. San Francisco: W. H. Freeman.

Riley C. M. 1959. *Our mineral resources.* Huntington, N.Y.: Robert E. Krieger.

Scientific American, September 1971 (vol. 224, no. 3). Issue on energy and power.

Skinner, B. J. 1976. *Earth resources.* 2d ed. Englewood Cliffs, N.J.: Prentice-Hall.

U.S. Bureau of Mines. *Minerals yearbook* (published annually). Washington, D.C.: U.S. Government Printing Office.

22
Astrogeology

Purpose

In 1969, astronaut Neil Armstrong set foot on the moon in the most dramatic moment of the Space Age. His first small step truly did represent a giant step forward for science. The mission returned to Earth with the first samples of rock collected away from our planet. From this and later Apollo missions to the moon, from the unmanned landings on Mars and Venus, and from fly-bys of other planets we gained a wealth of information that will take decades to analyze fully. A brand new science, astrogeology, emerged from the space program. Astrogeology combines the disciplines of geology and astronomy, depending heavily on the truly remarkable technology of the Space Age.

We have only begun our exploration of the solar system. Nevertheless, the explosion of knowledge about extraterrestrial bodies makes it impossible to provide a thorough review of astrogeology. Our purpose here is only to provide a short summary of what we know about the solar system from the perspective of a geologist. We do not attempt to show how present theories have evolved through the steps of the scientific method; nor can we speculate on how long today's theories will remain valid as new information is obtained from space probes.

In studying geology, one of the most difficult concepts to understand and accept is that of long periods of *time*. An equally difficult concept—that of great *distance*—appears when we look beyond Earth.

Earth is one of nine large bodies and many millions of smaller bodies that revolve around the Sun, a star that is 150 million kilometers away. The Sun and all these objects that revolve about it are referred to as the **solar system**. The solar system is part of a vast lens-shaped collection of billions of stars, dust, and gas, 1,000 billion billion kilometers across, called the Milky Way galaxy. The Milky Way galaxy is, in turn, a member of a group of galaxies called the Local Group, and this group of galaxies is part of a group of groups of galaxies.

It is perhaps not surprising that geologists should wonder how Earth compares to some of these other bodies in the universe, and many geologists are beginning to study those objects that are nearest to Earth and so easiest to study, including the planets, satellites, and meteorites.

The Sun

The Sun, with a diameter of over a million kilometers and a mass 330,000 times that of the earth, is, nevertheless, an ordinary, everyday star of average size. It is, however, of more than average significance to us because it is the nearest star; the one about which Earth revolves and the source of virtually all our energy.

As other stars do, the Sun radiates heat, light, and a steady stream of particles (mostly protons and electrons) into space. The heat and light are produced by the fusion of hydrogen nuclei in the Sun's interior, where the temperature is several million degrees centigrade and the density is almost imcomprehensibly high.

The Sun is composed entirely of gas (technically, *plasma*, which consists of atomic nuclei stripped of their electrons), 98 percent of which is hydrogen and helium. The gas is in layers, not sharply delineated but grading into one another.

The Sun's Structure

The **photosphere** is the deepest layer of the Sun that is visible to us. Beneath the photosphere the gases are thick enough to be opaque; above the photosphere they are transparent. The photosphere is about 400 kilometers thick and has a temperature of about 6,000 degrees C. Photographs of the photosphere show columns of gas rising and descending, giving the photosphere a mottled appearance resembling rice grains.

Sunspots are dark areas, about 1,500 to 150,000 kilometers across, in the photosphere (fig. 22.1). They appear dark because they are cooler than the rest of the photosphere, about 5,000 degrees C. Sunspots have a central darker region called the *umbra* and a surrounding brighter ring called the *penumbra*. The average lifetime of a sunspot is about three months, but at least one sunspot lasted 1.5 years. By measuring the length of time it takes for sunspots to travel around the Sun, the Sun's rotation period can be measured. It can also be seen that the Sun, unlike Earth, rotates at different rates at different latitudes. The number of sunspots varies over a period of about 11 years, from a time when none may be visible to a peak period and then back to the minimum.

Sunspots have magnetic fields several thousand times as strong as Earth's magnetic field. They usually occur in east-west oriented pairs or in groups dominated by two large spots. The two spots in a sunspot pair have opposite

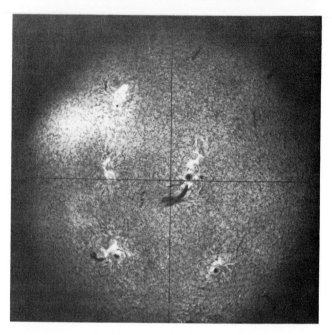

Figure 22.1 Sunspots on the Sun's surface. Photograph was taken by an astronaut through a telescope in Skylab. NASA.

magnetic polarities. All pairs in the Sun's northern hemisphere have the same magnetic polarity orientation; all those in the southern hemisphere have the opposite orientation. At the end of each 11-year sunspot cycle, the two hemispheres reverse magnetic polarity. Why this occurs is not known.

Solar flares are very bright spots in the Sun's photosphere, due to sudden outbursts of large amounts of energy. They usually occur near a sunspot group and last several minutes to several hours. Flares often disrupt radio communications on Earth and produce notable aurora ("northern lights" or "southern lights") by disturbing the Earth's ionosphere. The cause of solar flares is not known.

The reddish layer about 8,000 kilometers thick that extends outward from the photosphere is known as the **chromosphere.** Small, jet-like columns of rising gas similar to those in the photosphere occur in the chromosphere, as do clouds of hydrogen and other elements called *prominences*. Brighter portions of the chromosphere are also seen. The element helium was discovered in the chromosphere before it was discovered on Earth.

The outermost layer of the Sun, the **corona,** is of extremely low density and very high temperature (with a maximum of about 3.5 million degrees C). The corona is visible only during a total eclipse of the Sun. The shape of the corona changes to correspond with the sunspot cycle, being uniformly round when sunspots are numerous and uneven at other times.

Table 22.1

Information about the Planets

	Mercury	Venus	Earth	Mars	Jupiter	Saturn	Uranus	Neptune	Pluto
Distance from Sun (in millions of kilometers)	58	108	150	228	778	1427	2870	4497	5900
Period of revolution	88 d	225 d	365¼ d	687 d	11.9 y	29.5 y	84 y	164.8 y	248.4 y
Period of rotation	58.6 d	243.1 d	23 h 56 m	24 h 37 m	9 h 55 m	10 h (?) 40 m	13– 24 h (?)	18 h	6.4 d
Mean diameter (kilometers)	4,670	12,200	12,730	6,760	140,000	115,000	47,300	45,100	2,400 to 2,900
Mass (In multiples of Earth's mass)	.05	.81	1	.11	318.0	95.2	14.6	17.2	.002 (?)
Presence of magnetic field	yes	no	yes	no	yes				
Number of satellites		1	2	16	15	5	2	1	
Presence of Rings	no	no	no	no	yes	yes	yes		
Composition									
Core	Ni-Fe	Ni-Fe	Ni-Fe	iron suflide (?)	silicates, Ni-Fe (?)			Silicates, Ni-Fe (?)	(?)
Mantle	silicates	silicates	silicates	silicates	hydrogen			hydrogen compounds	(?)
Atmosphere	none	CO	N	CO	hydrogen compounds			hydrogen, helium	(?)

The Planets

The largest objects orbiting around the Sun are called the "major planets" or sometimes just the **planets.** There are nine of these, mostly named after Roman and Greek deities: Mercury, Venus, Earth, Mars, Jupiter, Saturn, Uranus, Neptune, and Pluto (table 22.1).

The major planets can be divided into two groups—those like Earth and those like Jupiter. Those in the first group (Mercury, Venus, Earth, Mars, and probably Pluto) are known as the *terrestrial* planets. They are small, rotate slowly, and have high densities, thin atmospheres (if any), and few or no satellites. Planets in the second group are called *Jovian* planets. They are large, rotate rapidly, and have thick atmospheres, low densities, and many satellites.

The Asteroids

The "minor planets" or **asteroids** are smaller objects found mostly in the space between the orbits of Mars and Jupiter. Occasional asteroids have very elliptical orbits and some pass near the Earth. The asteroid that comes closest to Earth is Hermes, which comes as close as a million kilometers.

The largest asteroid and first to be discovered is Ceres. Only about a dozen are more than 150 kilometers in diameter, but there are probably 100,000 large enough to be seen with the largest telescopes. Large asteroids are usually spherical, but smaller asteroids are irregular in shape and many may be broken fragments of larger bodies. Some asteroids may be differentiated, with iron-rich cores and silicate mantles.

Asteroids have been named for heroines from Wagnerian operas, wives, husbands, friends, flowers, cities, colleges, pets, and even favorite desserts.

Comets

Comets are small objects, with nuclei no more than 1 or 2 kilometers in diameter, composed of dry ice (frozen carbon dioxide), frozen methane, frozen ammonia, and water ice, with small solid particles and dust imbedded in the ices. It was probably a small comet that landed in Siberia in 1908, rattling windows 450 kilometers away, knocking down trees 30 kilometers away, and causing much speculation about the event. It is believed that most comets orbit on the fringes of the solar system and only come within the central part of the solar system when their orbits are disturbed by the gravitational pulls of passing stars. Some comets orbit the Sun in highly elliptical orbits; at their nearest approach to the Sun they sometimes come close enough that some of their ices evaporate and, along with the released dust particles, are swept out into a long tail. Some of these tails are more than 150 million kilometers long. Comets' tails are mostly empty space. In 1910, the Earth passed through the tail of Halley's Comet, and it could not even be detected.

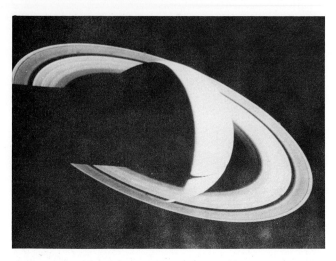

Figure 22.2 Saturn and its rings.
NASA.

Satellites and Rings

Secondary bodies that orbit many of the major planets are called **satellites** or "moons." Four of the satellites in the solar system are probably larger than the planet Mercury, and 11 others are larger than the asteroid Ceres.

At least 3 of the major planets, Saturn, Jupiter and Uranus, have billions of small solid particles, composed of or covered with ice and a few centimeters to a meter in diameter, orbiting about them in systems of **rings** (fig. 22.2). The rings are no more than a few kilometers thick but extend great distances outward from the planets.

Meteors and Meteorites

Small solid particles of ice, stone, and/or metal orbiting the Sun are called *meteoroids*. When these particles encounter the Earth and pass through the Earth's atmosphere they are heated to incandescence by friction and partially or totally vaporized. We sometimes call them "shooting stars" or "falling stars," but the correct term is **meteor.** About a million meteors that can be seen without a telescope enter the Earth's atmosphere each hour. Most of these glowing particles are about the size of a pinhead.

Occasionally larger objects (such as asteroids, fragments of asteroids, and comets) collide with the Earth. About 150 of these objects per year are able to pass all the way through the atmosphere without being consumed and thus strike the Earth's surface. These objects are called *meteorites*. The largest fragment of a meteorite found (in South Africa) weighs 50 tons but much larger meteorites have hit the Earth's surface in the past.

Effects of Impact

Many very large meteorites have produced large craters when they have collided with Earth's surface. One well-known meteorite crater is Meteor Crater in Arizona, which is a little more than a kilometer in diameter. Many much larger craters are known in Canada, Germany, Australia, and other places. Craters produced by meteorite impact have several identifying characteristics. For example, some rare minerals are produced by the metamorphism of quartz and some other minerals as a result of the brief, very high, pressures that occur on impact. The impact often produces shock damage in minerals at the impact site, melts some minerals that then harden into glass, and produces a type of breccia. Beds of rock near the rims of impact craters sometimes appear to have been overturned in all directions away from the crater.

Classification

Meteorites, like igneous rocks, are usually classified on the basis of their textures and compositions. The three basic types are stones, stony-irons, and irons.

Stones are by far the most abundant type of meteorite, but because they are very similar in appearance to ordinary Earth rocks, they are not often collected unless they are actually seen to fall. Irons, on the other hand, are often found long after they fall and so appear more often than stones in museum collections.

Iron meteorites are principally iron-nickel alloy, with small amounts of other minerals.

Stony-iron meteorites are made up of silicate minerals and nickel-iron alloy in approximately equal amounts.

Stony meteorites are made up mostly of plagioclase and iron-magnesium silicates such as olivine and pyroxene; but they may be as much as 20 percent iron-nickel alloy. About 90 percent of stony meteorites contain round silicate grains called **chondrules** and are referred to as *chondrites.* The remaining 10 percent are called *achondrites.*

Chondrules, composed largely of olivine and pyroxene, can vary in appearance from distinct spheres in a very fine-grained groundmass of silicates and iron-nickel alloy to indistinct bodies with fuzzy outlines imbedded in a coarse-grained groundmass. Chondrites having coarse-grained textures and indistinct chondrules are thought to have been reheated and partially recrystallized after forming. The terrestrial rock most similar in composition to chondrites is probably the ultramafic rock peridotite; but peridotite does not have either a chondritic texture or the nickel-iron content of stony meteorites.

One kind of chondrite is composed mostly of serpentine or pyroxene and contains up to 5 percent organic materials, including carbon, hydrocarbon compounds, and amino acids. These meteorites are called **carbonaceous chondrites.** All available evidence indicates that the "organic" compounds were in fact produced by inorganic processes. Carbonaceous chondrites are of particular interest to scientists because they are believed to have the same composition as the original material from which the solar system was formed.

Achondrites are generally similar to terrestrial rocks in composition and texture. In composition they are probably most similar to basalts. Some have textures like ordinary igneous rocks, and others are breccias with fragments of different compositions and textures.

Many meteorites have coarse-grained textures, and such textures are formed only by slow cooling inside a large body. Coarse-grained textures and the fact that the iron-nickel alloys in iron meteorites, stony meteorites, and stony-iron meteorites are very similar in composition suggest that some meteorites represent fragments of larger bodies that were partially melted and differentiated to form an iron-rich core and a silicate-rich outer zone. Meteorites have been dated using radiometric methods and all meteorites seem to be about the same age, about 4.5 billion years old.

The Moon

Earth's satellite is unusually large relative to Earth itself, and for this reason, Earth and the Moon are sometimes referred to as a double planet. Even the most casual inspection, though, shows striking differences between the two.

Surface Features

Approximately one-third of the Moon's surface consists of nearly circular, dark-colored, smooth, relatively flat lava plains. The remaining two-thirds is rugged terrain with thousands of overlapping craters. The lava plains, found mostly on the near side of the Moon, are called **maria** (singular, *mare;* literally, "seas"), and the rugged regions are called **highlands.**

These two kinds of terrain represent two significant periods in the Moon's history—an earlier period when intense meteorite bombardment formed craters, and a later period when large lava flows flooded parts of the Moon's surface, filling in low places including some earlier formed craters, especially the very largest ones. Since the initial period of extensive crater formation, occasional meteorites have continued to strike the Moon's surface, producing other craters.

Bright streaks radiate from the most recent craters, giving them the name **rayed craters** (fig. 22.3). The streaks are apparently composed of dust particles and other debris ejected from the crater at impact. Continued

Figure 22.3 The moon. Note rayed craters and dark maria. NASA.

bombardment by small meteorites will eventually erase the streaks, just as it has erased the streaks from the older craters.

Craters are certainly the most common landform on the Moon. There may be as many as 400,000 craters larger than a kilometer in diameter. Most craters are circular, surrounded by a blanket of material that was ejected from the crater. A rim higher than the lunar surface encircles a central depressed area. Craters more than about 20 kilometers in diameter often have terraced rim walls and central peaks. The terracing is due to slumping of the crater walls inward, and the formation of central peaks may be the result of the rebounding of surface rock layers—although it is not known whether the rebound occurs immediately after the impact or is spread over a long period of time, perhaps with some associated volcanic activity.

Craters range in size from those visible only with a microscope to giant craters over one thousand kilometers in diameter, such as Oceanus Procellarum, Mare Imbrium, and Mare Australe. These largest craters are usually called **multi-ringed basins** because they are surrounded by a series of concentric rings with intervening lowlands (fig. 22.4). Many of the large multi-ringed basins are partially or completely filled by extensive maria lava flows. In some instances, as in Oceanus Procellarum, the central depressions have been completely filled and the lava has covered the surrounding rings and lowlands as well, completely hiding the ring structure.

Surface features other than craters and lava flows are rare on the Moon. The only three that commonly occur are rilles, wrinkle ridges, and volcanoes.

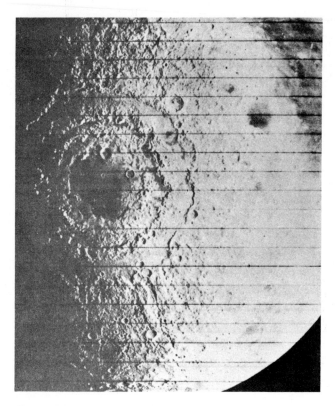

Figure 22.4   Mare Orientale.
NASA.

Figure 22.5   Astronaut on the lunar surface. Photographed in a mountainous region during the Apollo 17 flight, 1972. NASA.

Rilles are elongate trenches or crack-like valleys, found mainly in the smoother portions of the lunar maria. They range in length from a few kilometers to hundreds of kilometers and are often quite deep. Some rilles are straight and are believed to be similar to block-faulted valleys (called *graben*) on Earth, produced perhaps by local subsidence. Others are arc-shaped or crooked and may be collapsed lava tubes, channels eroded by ash flows, fractures along which gas has escaped, strings of overlapping small craters, or even ditches made by boulders sliding or rolling downhill.

Wrinkle ridges are wrinkles on maria surfaces, frequently found near the maria edges. Some are hundreds of kilometers long and several kilometers wide. The ridges may be compressional features produced as the lava cooled and subsided or may be the surface expression of underlying intrusions.

There are a few shield **volcanoes** on the Moon, notably a group of small volcanoes named the Marius Hills. These volcanoes are probably not active at the present time.

Lunar Minerals

Over 100 minerals, many especially rich in iron and titanium compounds, have been found in lunar rocks. The four most common minerals on the Moon are pyroxenes such as augite, Ca-rich plagioclase, Mg-rich olivine, and ilmenite, an iron titanium oxide. Several common Earth minerals are not found on the Moon. These include the amphiboles, the micas, the clay minerals, hematite and limonite. Minerals such as these are hydrated and/or formed by weathering processes and would not be expected on the Moon, with its lack of an atmosphere and the absence of water. Also found on the Moon have been a few new minerals such as pyroxferrite (a mineral that is related to pyroxene but is richer in iron) and armalcolite (an iron magnesium titanium oxide whose name is derived from the first letters in the names of the astronauts of the first manned landing mission).

Lunar Rocks

Three different kinds of material are known to exist on the surface of the Moon. These are crystalline rocks with igneous textures; loose, unconsolidated material known as **regolith**; and breccias (fig. 22.5).

Crystalline rocks   Most of the crystalline rocks appear to be simple igneous rocks that have crystallized and solidified from magma at or near the surface of the Moon. A few of the crystalline rocks are apparently made of material that melted during impacts and then recrystallized as it cooled.

The rock type most common in the maria seems to be very similar to basalt. Mare basalts are composed primarily of calcium-rich plagioclase feldspar, pyroxene, and ilmenite. Many of the rocks, especially the finer-grained ones, also contain olivine as a major or minor component. The rocks have a wide range of textures, including porphyritic, but most have rather even textures with crystals of about the same size. Vesicles are common.

Lunar basalts appear to have greater quantities of elements that do not evaporate easily, such as titanium, chromium, and zirconium, than Earth basalts do, and smaller amounts of easily evaporated elements such as potassium and sodium. In addition, lunar basalts contain no water. These chemical differences probably indicate that the lunar materials were heated to temperatures higher than the highest temperature reached by Earth materials. The easily vaporized material was driven off, leaving behind a higher percentage of materials able to withstand high temperatures.

Crystalline rocks from the lunar highlands are of two principal types: (1) a basalt often called **KREEP** because it is enriched in *potassium* (K), the *rare earth elements* (REE) and *phosphorus* (P); and (2) **anorthosite,** a rock composed almost entirely of calcium-rich plagioclase feldspar.

Lunar maria basalts range in age from about 3.9 to 3.3 billion years, indicating that most lava flows occurred during that span. Anorthosite rocks and KREEP basalts have been dated at more than 4 billion years old, confirming an earlier age for the highlands than for the maria.

Current theories about the origin of the three principal crystalline lunar rock types suggest that a surface layer of anorthosite was produced during the initial differentiation of the Moon into crust, mantle, and core; that the KREEP was formed by partial melting of the lower part of the anorthosite crust and subsequent eruption of material onto the surface; and that the maria basalt was formed by partial melting of the upper mantle and subsequent eruption.

Regolith   The loose, unconsolidated material of the lunar regolith is made up of rock fragments, mineral grains, and glassy particles. It has apparently been produced by the continual bombardment of the lunar surface by meteorites, a process that breaks rocks into smaller and smaller fragments and sometimes melts them to produce glass. The regolith varies in composition from place to place because it forms from different rock in different places. In general, the older the surface (i.e., the longer it has been exposed to meteorite bombardment), the thicker the regolith and more finely crushed its grains.

Breccia   Lunar breccias are of two principal types: regolith lithified by the shock of meteorite impact; and material welded together as it accumulated in a hot mass after being thrown out during the formation of an impact crater. All the particle types found in the regolith occur in the breccias, along with some meteorite fragments. Some of the rock fragments in the breccias are themselves breccias, indicating more than one cycle of breakage and reconsolidation.

Ages for lunar regolith and breccias generally are greater than those obtained for the crystalline rocks; they cluster around 4.6 billion years. This may represent the most common age of the rocks from which the regolith and breccias were derived and, therefore, the age of the Moon's formation.

Some lunar rocks are slightly magnetic. The Moon does not have a magnetic field at the present time, but the magnetism in these lunar rocks may be "left over" from a time when the Moon did possess a magnetic field.

The Moon's Interior
Very little is known about the Moon's interior. Some information has been obtained by studying changes in the velocities of seismic waves as they travel through the Moon's interior during a moonquake. There are very few moonquakes, however, and they are very small. Most moonquakes are produced by tidal stresses caused by Earth's gravitational pull; a few may be produced by meteorite impact or landsliding.

The crust of the Moon consists of a thin layer (about 1.5 kilometers thick) of highly shattered rocks overlying, first, a layer of basalt (about 25 kilometers thick), and below that, a layer of anorthosite (about 40 kilometers thick). Below the lunar crust is the lunar mantle (fig. 22.6). The composition of the lunar mantle is not known, but it is probably composed of rocks more mafic than those in the crust, perhaps rocks rich in olivine and pyroxene. The mantle is about 1,000 kilometers thick. The Moon's core is small and may be composed of a nickel-iron alloy. It may be partially molten because shear waves (S waves) do not appear to pass through it.

Mercury
Mercury's surface is remarkably similar to that of the Moon. There are densely cratered highlands, with craters ranging in size from barely visible to large, multi-ringed basins up to 1,300 kilometers in diameter, as well as extensive areas covered by lava flows, corresponding to the lunar maria.

Some of Mercury's craters are highly eroded older features, while others were formed recently enough that they are still surrounded by extensive systems of rays (fig. 22.7). Because Mercury is larger than the Moon and therefore has a larger gravitational pull, material thrown out of craters on Mercury falls closer to the crater rim

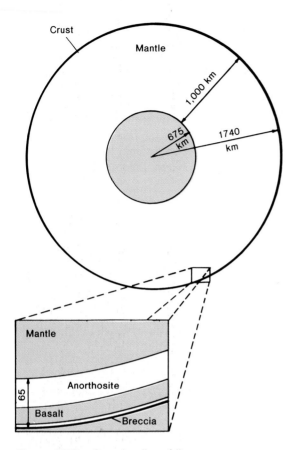

Figure 22.6   Cross section of the moon.

Figure 22.7   Surface of Mercury. Note craters, some of which are rayed.
NASA.

Figure 22.8   Fresh impact crater on Mercury. The diameter of the crater is 120 kilometers.
NASA.

(fig. 22.8). The result is that recent cratering on Mercury has not obliterated older surfaces nearly as much as recent cratering on the Moon has covered over traces of older lunar surfaces.

Mercury's craters are shallower than those on the Moon. This is probably due to more landsliding of the crater rims because of the greater gravitational pull.

Mercury's maria, like those on the Moon, were formed during a widespread outpouring of lava that followed the formation of the highly cratered highlands. These lava flows filled the multi-ringed basins, covered the floors of many smaller craters, and spread to form a thin and discontinuous layer over larger areas outside the basins. Wrinkle ridges are very common in the maria on Mercury.

Also common on Mercury, though rare on the Moon, are cliffs apparently caused by faulting. It has been suggested that this faulting may have occurred as a result of the shrinking of Mercury's core as it cooled.

Opposite Caloris, the largest of Mercury's multi-ringed basins, is an area of what is called "peculiar" terrain. This jumbled, chaotic, hilly area is probably composed of material shattered by the convergence of shock waves from the impact that produced the basin. The only other place in the solar system where similar terrain exists is on the Moon, opposite Maria Imbrium and Orientale.

The surface of Mercury is covered with a fine-grained regolith of rock fragments and dust. Rocks on Mercury are probably somewhat less rich in iron than lunar rocks and considerably less rich in titanium than lunar maria rocks.

The density of Mercury is unusually high, probably indicating the presence of a large nickel-iron core, extending outward from the center for as much as three-quarters of the planet's radius. Unlike the Moon, Mercury has a weak magnetic field, about 1 percent as strong as that of the Earth. This may indicate that Mercury's core is partially molten.

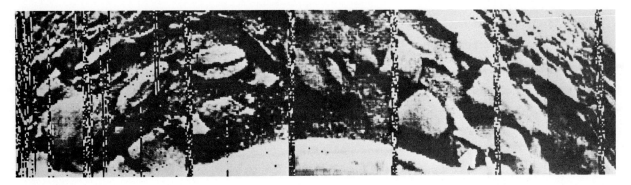

Figure 22.9   Venus surface with rocks.
Sovfoto.

Venus

The surface of the planet Venus is concealed from view by thick layers of clouds. The atmosphere of Venus is 100 times as dense as Earth's and is composed mainly of carbon dioxide, with significant amounts of such corrosive compounds as sulfuric acid. The amount of water vapor is very low. Almost continuous lightning has been observed by spacecraft. Surface winds are low in velocity but can have a great erosive effect because of the thick, hot, highly corrosive Venusian atmosphere.

Because the atmosphere acts like a greenhouse, letting in radiation from the Sun but allowing little heat to escape, the surface temperature of Venus is above the melting point of such metals as lead and zinc.

Much of the Venusian surface has been mapped by radar. Plateaus 1,000 km across and 6 km high have been identified, including one with long parallel ridges rising another 6 km higher. Large volcanoes, some in chains, have been found and molten lava lakes may exist. Shallow impact craters, some at least 250 km in diameter, many with central peaks, are known to exist and at least one great canyon, apparently fault controlled and perhaps similar to a terrestrial rift valley, has been identified.

Soviet spacecraft that landed on the surface of Venus photographed angular to rounded rocks abundantly scattered about the landing sites (fig. 22.9). These rocks are slab-like, and some appear to be layered. They are chemically similar in composition to terrestrial igneous rocks such as granite and basalt.

Mars

The planet Mars (fig. 22.10) has long intrigued people on Earth, and many guesses have been made about the nature of its surface features and internal processes. What we now know about Mars is far more interesting than what we previously imagined.

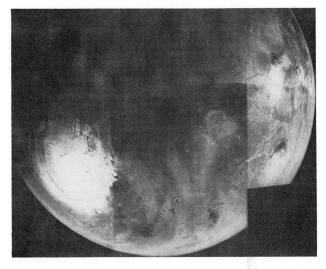

Figure 22.10   Mars with polar cap and several large volcanoes.
NASA.

Surface Features

Martian craters   Large areas of Mars, especially in its southern hemisphere, are covered with thousands of craters. These craters are up to 2,000 kilometers in diameter and as much as 3 kilometers deep. Most of the craters were formed by meteorite impact during the first billion years after the formation of Mars; a few are from more recent meteorite impacts and some are volcanic in origin.

Martian craters are shallower and smoother than those on the Moon. This is the result of more landsliding of material from the crater rims (because of the greater gravitational pull on Mars) and of erosion of the crater rims and filling of the crater depressions by sediments deposited by agents such as wind. There are few rayed craters, perhaps because the Martian winds blow fine ray material away or deposit fine material from elsewhere on top of the ray material, or maybe because the thickness of the Martian atmosphere prevents ray material from moving through it.

Figure 22.11 The rampart crater Arandas on Mars. Material around it appears to have flowed along the surface. NASA.

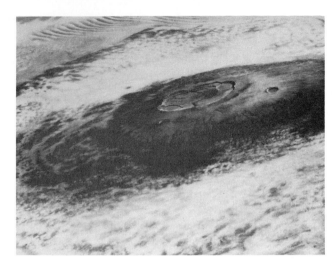

Figure 22.12 Olympus Mons, partially covered by clouds. NASA.

Many Martian craters are surrounded by material that appears to have flowed from the point of impact (fig. 22.11). It has been suggested that a surface layer of Mars may contain large quantities of water ice, like permafrost on Earth, which could have melted as a result of an impact and, along with rock fragments, sloshed outward from the impact area.

Mars has several multi-ringed basins that, except for being more eroded, are very similar to such basins on the Moon. The largest basin, Hellas, is about 2,000 kilometers in diameter.

Volcanic features Nearly half the planet may be covered with volcanic material. There are areas of extensive lava flows similar to the lunar maria and a number of volcanoes, some with associated lava flows.

Most of the northern half of Mars seems to have been flooded by a series of thin lava flows that occurred during an early period of extensive volcanism. These lava flows partially or completely filled the multi-ringed basins and covered over large numbers of earlier formed craters. Wrinkle ridges are common.

The largest Martian volcano, Olympus Mons, is three times the height of Mount Everest and wider than the state of California (fig. 22.12). Its caldera is more than 65 kilometers across. Olympus Mons and at least 18 other large Martian volcanoes are shield volcanoes, probably composed of basalt.

There are a number of smaller Martian volcanoes with steeper slopes than the shield volcanoes. These steeper slopes imply that the lava that formed these volcanoes was more viscous than that of the shield volcanoes.

Martian volcanoes occur widely spread over the planet, but the largest shield volcanoes appear to be concentrated in one area, within an uplifted region known as the Tharsis Ridge.

Martian volcanoes vary widely in age. This can be determined by comparing crater densities on their surfaces and by noting differences in the amount of erosion they have undergone. The youngest volcanoes are Olympus Mons and the other shield volcanoes of the Tharsis Ridge area.

Canyons Uplifting of large, elevated areas such as the Tharsis Ridge has caused stretching of the Martian surface and the formation of numerous huge cracks or fractures called **canyons.** These canyons may have been further modified by such processes as landsliding, erosion by running water or wind, or subsidence due to the melting of underground ice or the removal of magma to produce shield volcanoes. The largest of the Martian canyons is Valles Marineris (fig. 22.13). It is about four times as deep and eight times as wide as Grand Canyon in Arizona, and almost as long as the United States is wide.

Channels There is no liquid water on the surface of Mars today. With the present surface temperatures, atmospheric pressures, and water content in the Martian atmosphere, any liquid water would immediately evaporate. There are some indications, however, that conditions may have been different in the past and that liquid water may have existed on Mars, at least temporarily. Certain features on Mars, called **channels,** resemble very closely

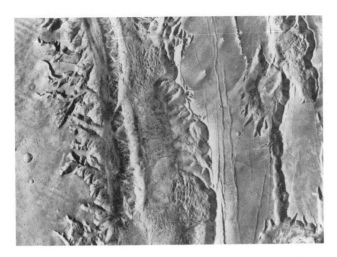

Figure 22.13 A portion of Valles Marineris. The far wall of the main canyon shows several large landslides.

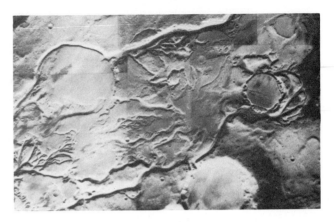

Figure 22.14 Sinuous Martian channels. NASA.

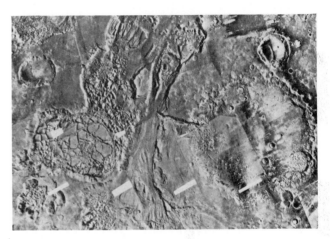

Figure 22.15 Chaotic and fretted terrain with associated channels on Mars. NASA.

certain types of stream channels on Earth. They have tributary systems and meanders and are sometimes braided. The channels trend downslope and tend to get wider toward their mouths. These Martian channels are restricted to certain areas and appear to have been formed by intermittent episodes of erosion.

Martian channels of one type are similar in appearance to channels in the Channeled Scablands of Washington state. The terrestrial channels were formed by extensive flooding during the Pleistocene glacial ages when a naturally formed ice dam broke and released the waters from a large lake. Several flooding events may have been responsible for the Martian channels, but the source of the water is not known. It may have been produced by the melting of ground ice, which may in turn have been caused by climatic changes or nearby volcanic activity.

A second kind of Martian channel occurs on the sides of some volcanoes, and some impact craters. Here the channels form systems of dendritic canyons and gullies (fig. 22.14).

Chaotic and fretted terrain　Patches of jumbled and broken angular slabs and blocks called **chaotic terrain** occur in some places on Mars (fig. 22.15). Some channels originate in these areas, and it is believed that this terrain may be caused by melting of ground ice and consequent collapse of the ground. Subsidence due to withdrawal of magma has also been suggested as the cause of chaotic terrain.

Melting of ground ice may also be responsible for producing another kind of terrain. **Fretted terrains** are flat lowlands with some scattered high plateaus. The plateaus are bounded by high cliffs and scarps, some more than a

kilometer high and 800 kilometers long. Ground ice exposed in the cliffs may melt, causing the cliff tops to be undermined and to landslide, converting plateau regions into lowlands.

The Martian Atmosphere and Wind Activity
The planet Mars has an atmosphere, but its density is only about 1/200th that of Earth's atmosphere. The atmosphere of Mars is composed mostly of carbon dioxide (95 percent) but contains small amounts of nitrogen and a trace of some other gases, including argon, water vapor, and carbon monoxide. Dust in the atmosphere scatters sunlight, making the Martian sky pink. Although the amount of water vapor in the Martian atmosphere is very small, clouds are formed, as are local thin layers of frost.

Because Mars has an atmosphere, winds blow, eroding material, transporting it to other locations, and depositing it. Because the atmosphere is not very dense, high

Figure 22.16 Martian landscape showing rocks and dunes. Boulder at left is 3 meters long. Viking lander antenna obscures middle of photo, taken in 1976.
NASA.

winds are necessary to transport sand and dust. Wind velocities exceeding 200 kilometers per hour have been observed and, because some photographs show large portions of Olympus Mons obscured by dust storms, it is known that the wind carries some particles more than 15 kilometers high. The lower gravitational field of Mars permits the wind to carry particles four times as high as a wind of the same velocity would on Earth.

Some linear grooves and streamlined ridges on Mars have been attributed to wind erosion, as has a cliff more than a kilometer high at the base of Olympus Mons. Several crater rims show evidence of having been worn down or abraded. On the other hand, the preservation of many small craters suggests that wind erosion has been very slow.

Localized dust storms are quite common on Mars. In addition, once each Martian year, a great dust storm covers a large portion of the planet. It may be started by heating of dust particles in the Martian atmosphere. This large dust storm is responsible for seasonal changes in light and dark markings on the Martian surface. As the storm dies down, it deposits a light-colored blanket of particles over the Martian surface. As local winds remove the light particles from some areas, they appear darker.

Dark- and light-colored streaks are common on the Martian surface, particularly downwind from craters. Sand dunes also have been observed on Mars (fig. 22.16). They are particularly common on the floors of some craters, where they form vast dune fields.

Polar Regions

The polar regions of Mars are covered with ice caps (fig. 22.10), which are only a few meters thick and are composed mostly of frozen carbon dioxide (dry ice). During the summer on each hemisphere, the ice caps shrink markedly as the carbon dioxide vaporizes; however, a small cap remains. This small residual cap (400 kilometers in diameter) is probably composed of water ice.

Two distinctive types of terrain can be observed in the Martian polar regions. **Laminated terrain** is the name given to areas where series of alternating light and dark layers can be seen. The layers are essentially horizontal, and each is about 15 to 35 meters thick. As many as 50 layers have been counted in one location. The layers are thought to represent alternating beds of high dust content (loess deposits?) and high ice content, and their alternation may be due to some kind of climatic change. That the layers are stratified outwash from glaciers has also been suggested. Near the margins of the polar caps are large troughs and ridges that could be glacial valleys and moraines.

Underlying the laminated terrain is another terrain, which is characterized by small pits. The pits of this **etch-pitted terrain** may be due to wind erosion and, if so, they would be deflation basins (blowouts). They may also be glacial kettles.

Martian Rocks

Photographs show that the surface of Mars is covered by a fine-grained, orangish-pink dust. Limonite and clay minerals are known to be present. Several different kinds of rocks have been observed; they vary greatly in size, texture, and color, and include breccia and basalt.

The Martian Interior

Marsquakes occur and, along with studies of the gravitational field, have provided some information about the Martian interior. The Martian crust varies in thickness but is generally between 15 and 80 kilometers thick, being thickest under uplifted areas such as the Tharsis Ridge. The crust contains large amounts of water ice and other substances that evaporate at relatively low temperatures. The low density of Mars suggests that any Martian core must be small. Mars lacks a magnetic field, but 5 to 10 percent of the material at the surface is magnetic.

Life on Mars?

There has long been speculation about the possibility of life on Mars. Three experiments designed to detect life have been performed (four times apiece) on the Martian surface by the Viking missions.

Experiment 1 was designed to see whether organisms exist that produce the gases generally produced during life processes—hydrogen, nitrogen, oxygen, methane, carbon dioxide. A soil sample was placed in an evacuated chamber, heated, and saturated with nutrients. Measurements were made to detect emitted gases. Oxygen and carbon dioxide were produced, but hydrogen and methane were not.

Experiment 2 was designed to see whether organisms exist that can manufacture food. A soil sample was placed in an atmosphere of carbon dioxide and carbon monoxide. Some of the carbon was carbon-14, a radioactive tracer. Any organism present should have absorbed the gases and used them in its life processes. After a period of time, the atmosphere was removed, and the remaining soil sample was heated to vaporize any organic compounds that were present. The vaporized organic compounds were to be detected through the radioactive carbon-14 that would have been incorporated into organic matter. Significant amounts of radioactive gases were found.

Experiment 3 was designed to see whether organisms exist that can consume nutrients and produce carbon dioxide. Nutrients containing carbon-14 were added to a soil sample that was then heated. Measurements were made to detect radioactive carbon dioxide gas, which would be given off by any organisms present. Radioactive carbon dioxide gas was found.

Despite the apparent success of these life-detection tests, it is generally believed that life does *not* exist on Mars. This is primarily because no organic compounds have been found in the Martian soil, and it is difficult to imagine life that leaves no remains. The test results are probably due to unusual chemical reactions rather than to biological activity.

Mars's Moons

Mars has two moons, Phobos and Deimos. The moons are small (both less than 25 kilometers in diameter), potato-shaped, and densely cratered (fig. 22.17). Much of the surface of Phobos is scarred by deep grooves that may be the result of impacts or of cracking because of tidal forces. Fragmented material probably covers most of the moons' surfaces. It is possible that Phobos and Deimos are asteroids that were pulled into orbit about Mars.

Figure 22.17 Phobos, one of Mars's moons. NASA.

The Jovian Planets

The Jovian planets are essentially large bodies with very thick atmospheres and, at most, very small solid cores. The atmospheres of the Jovian planets are composed mostly of hydrogen, helium, and methane, with small amounts of ammonia and other gases. Photographs of the planets show parallel alternating dark- and light-colored bands in their atmospheres (fig. 22.18). These bands are probably similar to wind belts on the Earth. On the Jovian planets, the light-colored bands represent areas of rising gas where clouds of ammonia crystals form, and the dark-colored bands represent areas of descending gas where we can see layers deeper within the planets' atmospheres. Large atmospheric storms are common and often long-lived. The storms appear as various colored spots, such as the famous Great Red Spot on Jupiter (fig. 22.18). This spot, almost 40,000 kilometers across, has been observed for over 300 years.

The liquid layers of the Jovian planets are probably mostly hydrogen. The outer portion probably is composed of liquid hydrogen in its molecular form (two atoms of hydrogen per molecule), while the inner portion is probably composed of individual atoms of hydrogen. In the atomic form, hydrogen is a metal, and the fluid would be a conductor of electricity. (This form of hydrogen has not been observed on Earth because it exists only at extremely high pressures.)

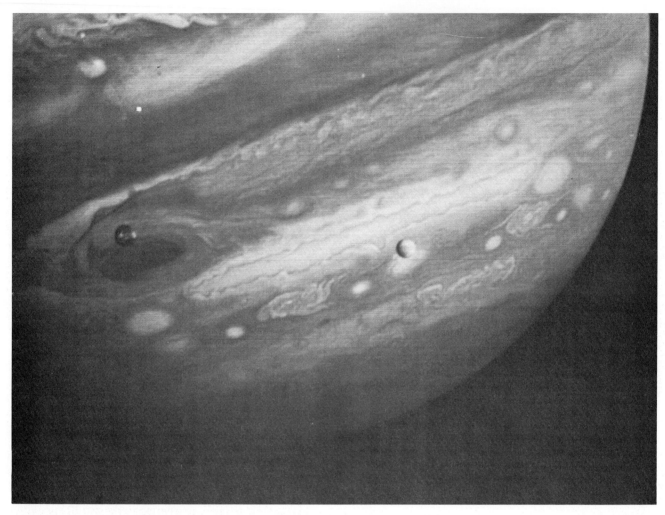

Figure 22.18 Jupiter, showing cloud bands and the Great Red Spot.
JPL

Jupiter has a strong and complex magnetic field and emits radio waves. The magnetic field may be due to convection currents in the liquid metallic hydrogen layer.

If the Jovian planets have cores, they are likely to be composed mainly of iron alloys and silicate compounds.

The Satellites of Jupiter and Saturn

Geologists are particularly interested in the larger satellites of the Jovian planets because they are similar in size to the terrestrial planets and because they have solid surfaces. Several of these satellites (Jupiter's Io, Europa, Ganymede, and Callisto, and Saturn's Titan) have been studied extensively by spacecraft (fig. 22.19).

Jupiter's Io is the only object in the solar system besides the Earth that is known to have currently active volcanoes. Ten have been observed by spacecraft and at least 7 of those have erupted for more than 4 months.

Material very rich in sulfur compounds is thrown at least 500 kilometers into space at speeds of up to 3,200 kilometers per hour. This material often forms umbrella-shaped clouds as it spreads out and falls back to the surface. Lakes of molten sulfur and huge multi-colored (black, yellow, red, orange, and brown) lava flows of sulfur or a sulfur-silicate mixture are common. More than 100 calderas larger than 25 kilometers across have been observed, including one which vents sulfur gases. Clouds of sulfur and sulfur dioxide often form and precipitate reddish sulfur dioxide "snow." The energy source for Io's volcanoes may be the gravitational pulls of Jupiter and two of its other larger satellites, causing Io to heat up much as a piece of wire will do if it is flexed continuously. Below Io's solid crust a layer of molten sulfur may exist and beneath that layer is a core of silicate rocks.

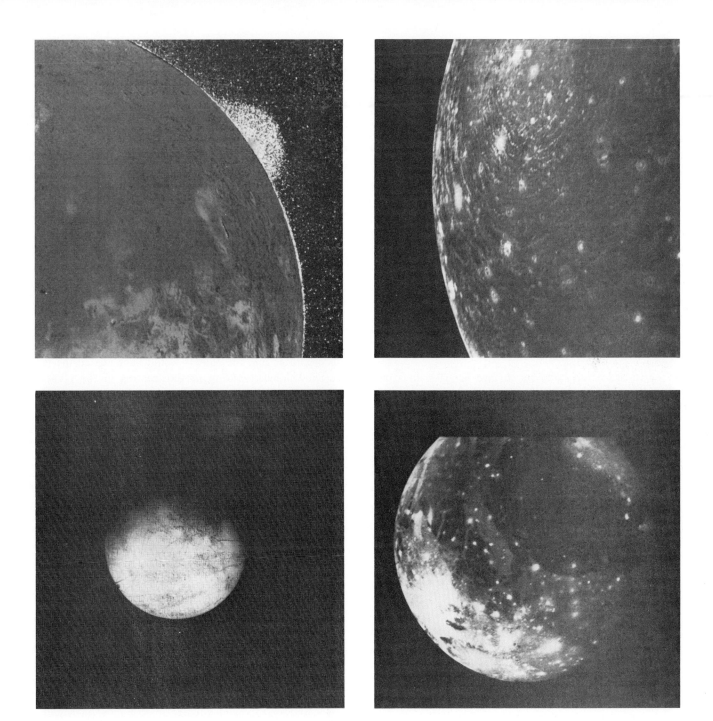

Figure 22.19 Four of Jupiter's moons: Io, showing an eruption (*top left*), Callisto (*top right*), Europa (*bottom left*), and Ganymede (*bottom right*).
NASA

Ganymede, Europa, and Callisto are all believed to have rocky cores covered by shells of ice and possibly liquid water. Ganymede and Callisto may be at least half water ice. These three satellites have vastly different surface markings however.

Callisto is one of the most cratered objects in the solar system. One giant impact produced a basin with concentric ridges that look like frozen ripples and extend more than 3,000 kilometers.

Ganymede has heavily cratered polygon-shaped darker regions separated by lighter zones made up of closely spaced parallel ridges and troughs. In some zones at least 20 ridges and troughs can be counted, each several kilometers wide and hundreds of kilometers long. This "grooved" terrain may have been caused by liquid water rising to the surface along cracks and then freezing.

Europa is crisscrossed by thousands of dark intersecting stripes, tens of kilometers wide and thousands of kilometers long. The dark stripes may have originated as cracks that were then filled by some kind of material from below.

Saturn's Titan hides its surface beneath an atmosphere composed mainly of nitrogen but appears to have a polar ice cap and may be covered with an ocean of liquid nitrogen.

Saturn's remaining satellites are covered with water ice and some are composed mostly of water ice. Rhea, Dione, Mimas, and Tethys are heavily cratered. Mimas has one crater one-third the diameter of the satellite, with long, narrow grooves. Tethys has a 750-km-long valley, perhaps caused by cracking as the ice of which the satellite is composed formed and expanded. Dione and Rhea exhibit bright wispy areas, perhaps where large fractures have allowed water to escape and form frost. Rhea also has linear grooves and troughs. Encelades apparently lacks large craters.

The Origin of the Solar System

The solar system began with the condensation of a large volume of interstellar gas and dust called a **nebula.** Much of the material in the nebula collected in the center to form the Sun, but some of it remained farther out. Small groupings of particles formed randomly, and because of the combined gravitational pull of the particles in the group, they attracted other particles. The groupings continued to increase in size until, on the average, they were probably several kilometers in diameter.

These larger bodies sometimes joined together by collision and sometimes became fragmented. The largest bodies tended to increase in size by capturing smaller ones, and the smaller bodies tended to be fragmented and/or captured. The bodies that grew larger became the planets and satellites; those that were fragmented became interstellar dust, asteroids, and the like; and those that were captured were incorporated into the planets and satellites.

Variations in composition among the planets can be partially explained by differences in their sizes. Larger planets were able to attract and hold larger amounts of lighter gases, such as hydrogen and helium. Another important factor in determining planetary composition was the location within the nebula where the planet formed. Those bodies nearest the center (Mercury, Venus, Earth, the Moon, and Mars) would have experienced higher temperatures and so retained smaller percentages of materials that are easily vaporized. The outer planets and their satellites were formed at a great enough distance from the Sun that large quantities of gases and ices could collect around their rocky cores.

A Short History of the Terrestrial Planets

Energy from the decay of radioactive elements that were incorporated into the planets would have heated the terrestrial planets, causing partial melting of the planets' interiors. Heavier materials such as iron-nickel alloys would sink to the planets' centers, while lighter materials such as silicate magmas would rise to form crusts.

Mercury, nearest the Sun, has the largest core relative to planet size, followed by Venus, and then the Earth. All these cores are apparently iron-nickel alloys. Mars's core may be mostly iron sulfide. Apparently core sizes and their compositions are related to distance from the Sun. The crusts of all the terrestrial planets are made up almost entirely of silicates. On Earth, the original crust was mostly basalt, with some granitic rocks. The areas of granitic rocks would have formed the first continents. Convection in the mantle would probably have begun at the time of crustal differentiation and would have set in motion plate tectonic processes. On Venus, which is about the same size as the Earth, the presence of surface rocks such as granite and basalt and possible folded mountain belts (the parallel ridges that have been observed) and chains of volcanoes suggest that differentiation and plate motions may have occurred in a similar way. Mars, Mercury, and the Moon, all smaller objects, show no evidence of granitic rocks. The absence of folded mountain chains and the presence of large numbers of undeformed craters on Mars indicate that plate tectonic activity has not occurred on Mars, although some suggestions have been made that Mars is in the initial stages of developing a system of convection. It has been noted that the very large size of volcanoes such as Olympus Mons could be explained by assuming a stationary lithosphere over a mantle plume. Mercury and the Moon show no evidence of plate tectonic processes having occurred. Perhaps crustal composition and the extent to which plate tectonic processes occur is related to planetary size.

Space "debris" would continue to be swept up by the planets throughout their early histories, producing heavily cratered surfaces and multi-ringed basins. The Moon and Mercury are still heavily cratered. The Earth, too, was subjected to an early period of intensive bombardment. But the Earth is a restless planet, and erosion and tectonic activity have erased most of those early-formed craters. Venus and Mars retain more of their early scars than the Earth does, because of less erosion and tectonic activity.

Heating up of planetary interiors would produce great quantities of magma that would rise to the surface along fractures produced by meteorite impact or by some tectonic process. Vast areas of the Moon, Mercury, and Mars are covered with volcanic rocks, most formed early in the history of the solar system. Similar early extrusive activity must have occurred on Venus and on the Earth. Volcanic activity on a much smaller scale still occurs on the Earth and may still be occurring on Venus and on Mars. However, this later volcanic activity is related to tectonic processes.

Gases would escape from planetary interiors as a result of volcanic activity, later condensing to form atmospheres, oceans, ice shells, and polar caps. Lighter elements would quickly have escaped from objects as small as the Moon and Mercury, but could have been partially retained by the Earth, Venus, and Mars. The distances of these planets from the Sun might determine whether these light elements exist mostly as atmospheres (as on Venus), as atmospheres, oceans, underground water, and ice caps (as on Earth), or mostly as icecaps and underground ice (as on Mars). On planets with appropriate conditions and temperature ranges life may have formed, as it did on the Earth. The presence of life on the Earth has certainly extensively modified the Earth's atmosphere (by producing oxygen, for example).

The presence of atmospheres, oceans, underground ice, et cetera would have determined the extent to which weathering and erosion have modified a planet's surface. Because of extensive erosion on Earth (and because of tectonic activity) it is necessary to examine other planets to understand the earliest history of the Earth.

Summary

Our solar system, formed from the condensation of a large cloud of gas and dust, is composed of a star called the Sun, and all those objects that revolve about it. These include Earth and the other major planets, their moons, the minor planets (asteroids), comets, and meteoroids.

The Sun's layers are the *interior,* the *photosphere,* the *chromosphere,* and the *corona.* In the very hot and dense interior, nuclear fusion produces the Sun's heat and light. The most obvious features of the photosphere are sunspots and solar flares; prominences are easily observed in the chromosphere.

The major planets are Mercury, Venus, Earth, Mars, Jupiter, Saturn, Uranus, Neptune, and Pluto.

Mercury's surface looks very similar to that of Earth's Moon, with craters and lava flows; but unlike the Moon, Mercury is very dense and has a magnetic field. Venus's surface is obscured by its very thick atmosphere, but radar has detected plateaus, mountains and craters, and rocks have been photographed on the Venusian surface.

Mars also has craters and lava flows and, in addition, some large shield volcanoes. Extensive erosion has occurred on the Martian surface, probably including erosion by running water. Liquid water does not exist at present on the Martian surface, but there is water in the Martian polar caps and perhaps in extensive permafrost deposits. Some Martian landforms may be the result of erosion or deposition by Martian winds. Despite some interesting experimental results, life does not appear to exist on Mars.

Jupiter, Saturn, Uranus, and Neptune—the *Jovian planets*—have extremely thick atmospheres composed of gases such as hydrogen, helium, and methane. We know very little about their interiors. The satellites of the Jovian planets are of more interest to geologists than the Jovian planets themselves.

The Moon is Earth's satellite and the only other object to which people have traveled. The principal surface features of the Moon are craters, highlands, and lava flows (*maria*). The Moon's surface is essentially made up of loose material (*regolith*) overlying layers of rock. The loose material is produced by the bombardment of meteoroids, the process that is also responsible for most of the lunar craters. Rocks found on the Moon include crystalline igneous rocks, mostly volcanic in origin, and breccias, formed by meteoroid impact.

Meteoroids sometimes strike Earth also, surviving the trip through Earth's atmosphere and landing on the surface. They may be either metallic in composition (iron), or composed of silicate minerals, or a mixture of metals and silicate minerals. Most of the stony meteorites (*chondrites*) contain *chondrules,* and a few contain carbon compounds.

Terms to Remember

anorthosite
asteroids
canyon (Martian)
carbonaceous chondrite
channel (Martian)
chaotic terrain
chondrules
chromosphere
comets
corona
etch-pitted terrain
fretted terrain
highlands
iron meteorite
KREEP
laminated terrain
maria
meteor

meteorite
meteoroid
multi-ringed basins
nebula
photosphere
planet
rayed crater
regolith
rilles
rings
satellite
solar flares
solar system
stony-iron meteorite
stony meteorite
sunspots
wrinkle ridge

Questions for Review

1. From what process is the Sun's energy obtained?
2. Name the layers in the Sun and give a short description of each layer.
3. What are sunspots? How would the number of sunspots and their magnetic polarities change over a period of 22 years?
4. What are solar flares? How do they affect Earth?
5. List the major planets, in order of increasing distance from the Sun.
6. What are the characteristics of the terrestrial planets? Of the Jovian planets?
7. What are comets composed of? How large are they? What changes do comets undergo as they orbit the Sun?
8. Explain the differences between *meteoroid, meteor,* and *meteorite.*
9. What is some of the evidence that can be used to identify an impact crater?
10. What are the three principal types of meteorites? Which of these types includes chondrites?
11. How are craters different on Mercury and on the Moon?
12. How were the lunar highlands produced?
13. How are lunar breccias formed?
14. What igneous rocks occur on the Moon?
15. Is there life on Mars? What evidence is there to support your answer?
16. What is the origin of the dark and light bands in Jupiter's atmosphere? What causes spots like the Great Red Spot?

Questions for Thought

1. Describe a day on Mars.
2. If the Moon once had a magnetic field, why doesn't it have one now?
3. Why doesn't Earth have as many craters as the Moon?
4. Why is Earth so different from the other planets? Why is it so different from the Moon?

Supplementary Readings

Arvidson, R. E.; Binder, A. B.; and Jones, K. L. 1978. The surface of Mars. *Scientific American,* March 1978.

Bergamini, D. 1969. *The universe.* New York: Time-Life Books.

French, B. M. 1977. *The Moon book.* New York: Penguin Books.

Hartmann, W. K. 1977. Cratering in the solar system. *Scientific American,* January 1977.

Horowitz, N. H. 1977. The search for life on Mars. *Scientific American,* November 1977.

Scientific American, 1975. New frontiers in astronomy. San Francisco: W. H. Freeman.

Scientific American, 1975. The solar system. San Francisco: W. H. Freeman.

Wood, J. A. 1968. *Meteorites and the origin of planets.* New York: McGraw-Hill.

Appendix A
Identification of Minerals

Each mineral is identified by a unique set of physical or chemical properties. To determine some of these properties requires specialized equipment and techniques. Most common minerals, however, can be distinguished from one another by tests involving simple observations. Cleavage is an especially useful property. If cleavage is present, you should determine the number of cleavage directions, estimate the angles between cleavage directions, and note the quality of each direction of cleavage. Other easily performed tests and observations include hardness (abbreviated H), luster, color, and determination of crystal form (if present). A simple chemical test can be made using dilute hydrochloric acid to see if the mineral effervesces.

The identification tables included here may be used to identify the most common minerals (the rock-forming minerals) and some of the most common ore minerals. For identifying less common minerals, refer to one of the books on mineralogy listed at the end of chapter 2. Mineral identification takes practice, and you will probably want to verify your mineral identifications with a geology instructor.

Because the common rock-forming minerals are the ones you are most likely to encounter, we have included a simple key for identifying them. The key is based on first determining cleavage (or the absence of cleavage) and then checking other properties that should lead to identification of the mineral. You should verify your identification by seeing whether other properties of your sample correspond to those listed for the mineral in table A.1.

Ore minerals are usually distinctive enough so that a key is unnecessary. To identify an ore mineral, read through table A.2 and determine which set of properties best fits the unknown mineral.

Key for Identifying Common Rock-Forming Minerals

If you have a grain or crystal of a mineral that is large enough to show cleavage (if it is present), proceed as follows:

I. Cleavage present (If cleavage is not present, proceed to II.)
  A. Determine the number of directions of cleavage present in an individual grain or crystal:
    1. One direction
      a. Perfect cleavage in flexible sheets: *mica.*
        Clear or white—*muscovite mica*
        black or dark brown—*biotite mica*
    2. Two directions
      a. Cleavage at or near 90°:
        good: *feldspar*
          If striations are visible on cleavage surface—*plagioclase*
          If pink or salmon-colored—*orthoclase*
          If white or light gray without striations, it could be either *orthoclase* or *plagioclase*
        fair:
          Dark green to black—*pyroxene* (augite)
      b. Cleavage at other than 90°:
        excellent cleavage: *amphibole* (hornblende)
    3. Three directions
      a. All three at 90° to one another (cubic cleavage):
        perfect: *halite*
      b. All three at other than 90°:
        perfect:
          If effervesces in dilute acid—*calcite*
          If effervesces in dilute acid only after being pulverized—*dolomite*
II. No cleavage present
  A. Harder than glass:
    1. Vitreous luster:
      a. Olive green or brown—*olivine*
      b. Reddish brown or in equidimensional crystals with twelve or more faces—*garnet*
      c. Usually light-colored—*quartz*
    2. Metallic luster:
      a. Bright yellow—*pyrite*
    3. Greasy or waxy luster, mottled green and black—*serpentine*
  B. Softer than glass, in masses of material too fine to distinguish individual grains:
    1. Earthy luster—*clay group* (for instance, *kaolinite*)

Table A.1
Diagnostic Properties of the Common Rock-Forming Minerals

Name (mineral groups shown in capitals)	Chemical Composition	Chemical Group	Diagnostic Properties	Other Properties
AMPHIBOLE (A mineral group in which *hornblende* is the most common member.)	$XSi_8O_{22}(OH)_2$ (*X* is a combination of Ca, Na, Fe, Mg, Al)	Chain silicate	2 good cleavage directions at 60° (120°) to each other.	H=5–6 (barely scratches glass). Hornblende is dark green to black; tends to form in needle-like or elongate crystals; vitreous luster.
Augite (see Pyroxene)				
Biotite (see Mica)				
Calcite	$CaCO_3$	Carbonate	3 excellent cleavage directions, *not* at right angles (they define a rhombohedron). H=3. Effervesces vigorously in weak acid.	Usually white, gray or colorless; vitreous luster. Clear crystals show double refraction.
CLAY MINERALS (*kaolinite* is a common example of this large mineral group.)	Compositions include $XSi_4O_{10}(OH)_8$ (*X* is Al, Mg, Fe, Ca, Na, K)	Sheet silicate	Generally microscopic crystals. Masses of clay minerals are softer than fingernail. Earthy luster. Smell clay-like when damp.	Seen as a chemical weathering product of feldspars and most other silicate minerals. A constituent of most soils.
Dolomite	$CaMg(CO_3)_2$	Carbonate	Identical to calcite (rhombohedral cleavage, H = 3) except effervesces in weak acid only when pulverized.	Usually white, gray or colorless. Vitreous luster.
FELDSPAR (Most common group of minerals.) The group includes:	Framework	Network silicates	H = 6 (scratch glass) 2 good cleavage directions at about 90° to each other.	Vitreous luster but surface may be weathered to clay giving an earthy luster. Perfect crystal shaped like an elongated box.
Orthoclase (potassium feldspar)	$KAlSi_3O_8$		White, pink, or salmon-colored.	Never has striations on cleavage surfaces.
Plagioclase (sodium and calcium feldspar)	mixture of: $CaAl_2Si_2O_8$ and $NaAlSi_3O_8$		White, light to dark gray, rarely other colors. *May* have striations on cleavage surfaces.	Calcium-rich varieties generally a darker gray and may show an iridescent play of colors.
GARNET	$XSiO_4$ (*X* is a combination of Ca, Mg, Fe, Al, Mn)	Isolated silicate	No cleavage. Usually reddish brown. Tends to occur in perfect equidimensional crystals, usually 12 sided. H=7.	Rarely yellow, green or black. Usually found in metamorphic rocks. Vitreous luster.
Gypsum	$CaSO_4 \cdot 2H_2O$	Sulfate	H=2. 1 good and 2 perfect cleavage directions. Vitreous or silky luster.	Clear, white, or pastel colors. Flexible cleavage fragments.

Table A.1
(continued)

Name (mineral groups shown in capitals)	Chemical Composition	Chemical Group	Diagnostic Properties	Other Properties
Halite	NaCl	Halide	3 excellent cleavage directions at 90° to each other (cubic). H=2½. Salty taste. Soluble in water.	Usually clear or white.
Hematite (*see* Ore mineral table)				
Hornblende (*see* Amphibole)				
Kaolinite (*see* Clay)				
MICA The group includes:	$K(X)(AlSi_3O_{10})(OH)_2$	Sheet silicate	1 perfect cleavage direction (splits easily into flexible sheets)	H=2–3. Vitreous luster.
Biotite	(X is Mg, Fe, and Al)		Black or dark brown.	
Muscovite	(X is Al)		White or transparent.	
Olivine	X_2SiO_4 (X is Fe, Mg)	Isolated silicate	No cleavage. Generally olive green or brown. H=6–7 (scratches glass). Vitreous luster.	Usually as small grains in mafic or ultramafic igneous rocks.
Orthoclase (*see* Feldspar)				
Plagioclase (*see* Feldspar)				
Pyrite ("fools gold")	FeS_2	Sulfide	H=6 (scratches glass). Bright yellow, metallic luster. Black streak.	Commonly occurs as perfect crystals: cubes or crystals with five-sided faces. Weathers to brown.
PYROXENE (a mineral group; *Augite* is most common member)	$XSiO_3$ (X is Fe, Mg, Al, Ca)	Chain silicate	2 fair cleavage directions at 90° to each other.	H=6. Augite is dark green to black. Vitreous luster; usually stubby crystals.
Quartz	SiO_2	Network silicate	H = 7. No cleavage. Vitreous luster. Does not weather to clay.	Almost any color, but commonly white or clear. Good crystals have six-sided "column" with complex "pyramid" on top.
Serpentine	$Mg_6Si_4O_{10}(OH)_8$	Sheet silicate	Hardness variable, but softer than glass. Mottled green and black. Greasy luster. Fractures along smooth curved surfaces.	Sometimes fibrous (asbestos).

Table A.2

Diagnostic Properties of the Most Common Ore Minerals

Name	Chemical Composition	Diagnostic Properties	Other Properties
Azurite	$CuCO_3(OH)$	Azure blue; effervesces in weak acid.	$H = 3-4$.
Bauxite	$Al_2O_3 \cdot nH_2O$	Earthy luster. A variety of clay. Generally pea-sized spheres included in a fine-grained mass.	
Bornite	Cu_3FeS_4	Metallic luster, tarnishes to iridescent purple color.	Gray streak; $H = 3$ (softer than glass).
Chalcopyrite	$CuFeS_2$	Metallic luster, brass-yellow. Softer than glass.	Black streak.
Cinnabar	HgS	Scarlet red, bright red streak.	Softer than glass. Generally an earthy luster.
Galena	PbS	Metallic luster, gray; 3 directions of cleavage at 90° (cubic). High specific gravity.	Softer than glass; gray streak.
Gold	Au	Metallic luster, yellow. $H = 3$ (softer than glass, can be pounded into thin sheets, easily deformed).	Yellow streak; high specific gravity.
Halite	$NaCl$	Salty taste; 3 cleavage directions at 90° (cubic).	Clear or white; easily soluble in water.
Hematite	Fe_2O_3	Red-brown streak.	Either in earthy reddish masses or in metallic, silver-colored flakes or crystals.
Limonite	$Fe_2O_3 \cdot nH_2O$	Earthy luster; yellow-brown streak.	Color yellow to brown; softer than glass.
Magnetite	Fe_3O_4	Metallic luster, black; magnetic.	Harder than glass; black streak.
Malachite	$Cu_2(CO_3)(OH)_2$	Bright-green color and streak.	Softer than glass; effervesces in weak acid.
Sphalerite	ZnS	Color brown to yellow; 6 directions of cleavage.	Luster-like resin; yellow or cream-colored streak; softer than glass.
Talc	$Mg_3Si_4O_{10}(OH)_2$	White, gray or green; softer than fingernail ($H = 1$).	Greasy feel.

Appendix B
Identification of Rocks

Igneous Rocks

Igneous rocks are classified on the basis of texture and composition. For some rocks, texture alone suffices for naming the rock. For most igneous rocks, composition as well as texture must be taken into account. Ideally, the mineral content of the rock should be used to determine composition; but for fine-grained igneous rocks, accurate identification of minerals may require a polarizing microscope or other special equipment. In the absence of such equipment, we rely on the color of fine-grained rocks and assume the color is indicative of the minerals present.

To identify a common igneous rock, use either table B.1 or follow the key given below.

Key for Identifying Common Igneous Rocks

I. What is the texture of the rock?
   A. Is it glassy (a very vitreous luster)? If so, it is *obsidian,* regardless of its chemical composition. Obsidian exhibits a pronounced conchoidal fracture.
   B. Is it frothy-appearing? If so, it is *pumice,* regardless of its chemical composition. Pumice should be light in weight and feel abrasive (it probably will float on water).
   C. Does it have angular fragments of rock embedded in a volcanic-derived matrix? If so, it is a *volcanic breccia.* If the precise nature of the rock fragments and matrix can be identified, modifiers may be used; for instance, the rock may be an *andesite* breccia or a *rhyolite* breccia.
   D. Is the rock composed of interlocking, very coarse-grained minerals? (The minerals should be more than 1 centimeter across.) If so, the rock is a *pegmatite.* Most pegmatites are mineralogically equivalent to granite, with feldspars and quartz being the predominant minerals.
   E. Is the rock entirely coarse-grained? (That is, does it have an interlocking crystalline texture in which nearly all grains are more than 1 mm across?) If so, go to part II of this key.
   F. Is the rock *entirely* fine-grained? (Grains less than 1 mm across or too fine to distinguish with the naked eye?) If so, go to part III of this key.
   G. Is the matrix fine-grained with some coarse-grained minerals visible in the rock? If so, go to part III and add the adjective *porphyritic* to the name of the rock.

II. Igneous rocks composed of interlocking coarse-grained minerals.
   A. Is quartz present? If so, the rock is a *granite*. Confirmation: Granite should be composed predominantly of feldspar—generally white, light gray or pink (indicating high amounts of potassium or sodium in the feldspar). Rarely are there more than 20 percent ferromagnesian minerals in a granite.
   B. Are quartz and feldspar absent? If so, the rock should be composed entirely of ferromagnesian minerals and is *ultramafic*. Confirmation: Identify the minerals as being olivine, or pyroxene (or less commonly, amphibole or biotite).
   C. Does the rock have less than 50 percent feldspar and no quartz? If so, the rock should be a *gabbro*. Confirmation: Most of the rock should be ferromagnesian minerals. Plagioclase may be medium or dark gray. There would be no pink feldspars.
   D. Is the rock composed of 30 to 60 percent feldspar (and no quartz)? If so, the rock is a *diorite*. Confirmation: Feldspar (plagioclase) is usually white to medium gray, but never pink.

III. Igneous rocks that are fine-grained.
   A. Can quartz be identified in the rock? If so, the rock is a *rhyolite*.
   B. If the rock is too fine-grained to determine whether quartz is present, but is white, light gray, pink or pale green, the rock is most likely a *rhyolite*.
   C. Is the rock composed predominantly of ferromagnesian minerals? If so, the rock is *basalt*.

D. If the rock is too fine-grained to identify ferromagnesian minerals, but is black or dark gray, the rock is probably a *basalt*.

    1. Does the rock have rounded holes in it? If so, it is a *vesicular basalt* or *scoria*.

E. Is the rock composed of roughly equal amounts of white or gray feldspar and ferromagnesian minerals (but no quartz)? If so, the rock is an *andesite*.

Confirmation: Most andesite is porphyritic, with numerous identifiable crystals of white or light-gray feldspar and lesser amounts of hornblende crystals within the darker fine-grained matrix. Andesite is usually medium to dark gray or green.

Sedimentary Rocks

Clastic Sedimentary Rocks

Sedimentary breccia is coarse-grained, composed largely of rubble (angular rock fragments with sharp edges and corners) cemented together. The rock fragments are often large enough to identify. They may vary widely in composition, depending on the original source rock. Breccia often has considerable matrix between the larger rock fragments. The matrix may be sand, silt, or clay, or any combination of these finer grains. The composition of the matrix, often difficult to determine in hand specimens, may be the same as or different from the large rock fragments.

Conglomerate is coarse-grained, composed largely of gravel (rounded pebbles, cobbles, or boulders, or a mixture of these sizes) cemented together. As in breccia, the rock fragments are usually large enough to identify, can be of variable composition, and are surrounded by finer matrix of similar or different composition than the gravel.

Sandstone is medium-grained, composed largely of sand grains cemented together. Sand grains may be angular or rounded, and be uniform or variable in composition. Most sandstones contain a substantial number of quartz grains because of quartz's resistance to chemical weathering. Sand grains may also be composed of feldspar, ferromagnesian minerals, micas, calcite, many other minerals, or sand-sized rock fragments. Sandstones range from well sorted, containing only sand grains and cement, to poorly sorted, containing sand grains in a matrix of silt and clay, perhaps with scattered coarse grains as well. A poorly cemented sandstone is weak—sand grains will rub off as you brush your fingers over it. A well-cemented sandstone is strong—sand grains are removed with difficulty. Cement may be calcite, silica, or iron oxide. Sandstone has a gritty feel. It varies in color. Many are white,

tan, or buff, particularly sandstones with a high percentage of quartz. Other types of sand grains and matrix can impart different colors such as brown or gray. Weathering can change the outer color of a sandstone drastically; iron oxide stains many sandstones red, brown, or yellow-brown. Special types of sandstone are *quartzose sandstone, arkose,* and *graywacke.*

Quartzose sandstone contains 90 percent or more quartz grains. A quartzose sandstone is generally very well sorted, containing very little or no matrix.

Arkose is a coarse-grained, feldspar-rich sandstone. Grains are commonly angular. Some grains may be larger than sand size; arkose commonly grades into breccia. Sorting is moderate to poor, with up to 15 percent matrix that includes clay, mica, and rock fragments. Although quartz dominates, feldspar makes up 25 percent or more of the rock. Because the grains are angular, coarse, and mostly quartz and feldspar, arkose resembles granite, particularly in its gray or pink color. Arkose has a clastic texture, however, while granite is crystalline.

Graywacke is a dark, hard, tough sandstone, generally coarse-grained and poorly sorted. Grains are angular and are composed of quartz, feldspar, and rock fragments. Although there are many conflicting definitions of graywacke, most authors agree on two distinguishing characteristics—a noticeable amount of rock fragments (perhaps 20 percent or more, and often from metamorphic rocks) and an abundance of matrix (perhaps 15 percent or more, and composed largely of clay minerals and mica). Graywackes are usually dark green, dark gray, or occasionally black.

Siltstone is a relatively fine-grained clastic rock composed mostly of silt grains. It is generally composed of quartz and clay minerals, although silt grains are too small to be identified with the unaided eye. Siltstone lacks both the gritty feel of sandstone and the splitting characteristics of shale. It has a slightly coarser grain than mudstone—siltstone is mostly silt, with minor clay.

Shale is fine-grained, with a distinctive splitting ability called *fissility*. The rock often has very fine layers (laminae) that are generally visible due to subtle color changes. Shale splits parallel to those layers, breaking into small, thin chips a few centimeters long. Shale contains a high percentage of clay-sized particles; it may also contain some silt. It is soft, but will not disintegrate when wet. It feels smooth, and is often gray, tan, green, black, brown, or even red or blue.

Mudstone is very much like shale, but lacks shale's fissility. It therefore occurs in blocky pieces, rather than thin chips. It has more clay than siltstone.

Table B.1

Identification of Igneous Rocks

Coarse-Grained	Granite	Diorite	Gabbro	Ultramafic Rocks
Fine-Grained	Rhyolite	Andesite	Basalt	—
Mineral Content	Quartz, feldspars (white, light gray or pink) Minor ferromagnesian minerals.	Feldspars (white or gray) and about 30–60 percent ferromagnesian minerals. No quartz.	Predominance of ferromagnesian minerals. Rest of rock is plagioclase feldspar (medium to dark gray).	Entirely ferromagnesian minerals (usually olivine and pyroxene).
Color of Rock (Most Commonly)	Light-colored	Medium-gray or medium-green	Dark gray to black	Very dark green to black

ROCKS NAMED SOLELY ON THE BASIS OF TEXTURE:
Obsidian—volcanic glass
Pumice—frothy volcanic glass
Volcanic breccia—coarsely fragmental volcanic rock
Tuff—volcanic rock composed of fine fragments (a microscope is usually necessary to distinguish tuff from the fine-grained rocks described above).
Pegmatite—very coarse-grained rock generally having the same mineral content as granite.

The following adjectives may be applied to igneous rocks to give a more complete description:
Porphyritic—some of the grains are very much larger than the majority of the grains.
Vesicular—a rock containing holes created by gas trapped in the cooling lava.

Chemical and Organic Sedimentary Rocks

Rock salt is composed of coarsely-crystalline halite. It is often white, but can be gray or stained with iron oxide. It is easily identified by the salty taste of the halite crystals. It may show color bands from impurities.

Gypsum is both a rock name and a mineral name. The rock called gypsum is a crystalline rock composed of an aggregation of fine- to coarse-grained crystals of the mineral gypsum. The mineral gypsum is very soft, with a hardness of 2 on Mohs' scale, so your fingernail can scratch individual gypsum crystals. Be sure that you are scratching *single crystals*—many rocks may powder under a scratch, but the powder is formed by dislodging individual grains that are weakly stuck together, not by scratching crystals. Gypsum is often white, buff, colorless, or pink from iron-staining. It can also be gray or brown.

Limestone is formed mostly of calcite. It has such a variety of origins that it has many appearances. Its texture may be clastic or crystalline, coarse grained or fine grained. Limestone is usually gray, but it may be white, black, or occasionally almost any color. It often contains visible fossils of marine organisms (such as shells and coral skeletons); many limestones have no fossils, however, and other sedimentary rocks such as shale and sandstone may also be fossiliferous. The best test for limestone is the chemical test for calcite: the rock will effervesce (fizz) when a drop of dilute hydrochloric acid is placed on it.

Dolomite, like gypsum, is a name for both a rock and a mineral. Dolomite looks like limestone, generally because it often forms by chemical replacement of limestone.

Table B.2

Clastic Sedimentary Rocks

	Original Sediment	
Rock name	Dominant particle type	Dominant composition
Sedimentary breccia	Angular rubble	Rock fragments
Conglomerate	Rounded gravel	Rock fragments
Sandstone	Sand	
Quartzose sandstone	Well-sorted sand	Quartz
Arkose	Sand and fine rubble	Quartz, 25 percent or more feldspar
Graywacke	Sand, matrix of silt and clay	Quartz, feldspar, rock fragments, matrix
Siltstone	Silt	Quartz, clay minerals
Shale, mudstone	Clay and silt	Clay minerals, quartz

An acid test distinguishes between dolomite and limestone: a drop of cold, dilute hydrochloric acid causes limestone (calcite) to effervesce strongly. The same acid on dolomite (rocks or mineral) will generally cause no effervescence, but if the dolomite is ground to powder, it will effervesce weakly in acid.

Chalk is a variety of fine-grained limestone, usually white or light-colored. It forms by the cementation of the shell-like hard parts of microscopic marine organisms. These fossils are too small to see with the unaided eye, but they form the familiar powdered streak when natural or commercial chalk is used to write on a blackboard. Chalk often leaves a fine white powder on your fingers. It effervesces strongly in acid, since the fossils are composed of calcite.

Coquina is a porous, coarse-grained, clastic limestone formed almost entirely of visible shells and shell fragments. Its appearance (and strong effervescence in acid from the calcite in the shells) should identify it.

Chert is a hard, compact, very fine-grained rock formed almost entirely of silica. It is often light-colored, but may be darkened by impurities. Common colors are white, tan, gray, green, red, black, or brown. Chert often breaks along conchoidal fractures. Pieces of chert can scratch glass. Chert can occur in layers like other sedimentary rocks, or as irregular lumpy nodules within other rocks, particularly limestones. *Flint* is a dark gray or black variety of chert, often found as nodules within limestone.

Diatomite is a porous, soft, lightweight rock formed by the cementation of shells of microscopic organisms called *diatoms*. Diatom remains are composed of *opal*, which is hydrated silica. Diatomite is usually light in color, often tan or white. It resembles chalk but does not effervesce in acid. Some geologists prefer the term *diatomaceous earth* for a soft, porous deposit of diatoms, either unconsolidated or weakly cemented; they reserve the term *diatomite* for well-consolidated diatomaceous earth that has become dense and chert-like.

Coal is a rock formed from the consolidation of accumulated plant material. It burns readily. There are several varieties of coal, depending on the type of original plant material and the degree of compaction. Most varieties are black (some are dark brown) and some varieties will leave a black powder on the fingers. Coal may be dull or shiny.

Metamorphic Rocks

The characteristics of a metamorphic rock are largely governed by (1) the composition of the parent rock and (2) the particular combination of temperature, confining pressure, and directed pressure. These factors cause different textures in rocks formed under different sets of conditions. For this reason, texture is usually the main basis for naming a metamorphic rock. Determining the composition (that is, mineral content) is necessary for naming some rocks (e.g., *quartzite*), but for others, the minerals present are used as adjectives to describe the rock completely (e.g., *biotite* schist).

Metamorphic rocks are identified by determining first whether the rock has a *foliated* or *nonfoliated* texture.

Nonfoliated Rocks

If the rock is *nonfoliated,* then it is identified on the basis of its mineral content:

Does the rock consist of mostly quartz? If so, the rock is a *quartzite.* A quartzite has a mosaic texture of interlocking grains of quartz and will easily scratch glass.

Is the rock comprised of interlocking coarse grains of calcite or dolomite? If so, it is *marble.* (The individual grains should exhibit rhombohedral cleavage; the rock is softer than glass.)

Is the rock a dense, dark mass of grains mostly too fine to identify with the naked eye? If so, it probably is a *hornfels.* A hornfels may have a few larger crystals of uncommon minerals enclosed in the fine-grained mass.

Foliated Rocks

If the rock is *foliated,* determine the type of foliation and then, if possible, identify the minerals present.

Is the rock very fine-grained and does it split into sheet-like slabs? If so, it is *slate.* Most slate is composed of extremely fine-grained clay minerals, and the rock has an earthy luster.

If the rock has developed a silky sheen, but otherwise appears similar to slate, it is a *phyllite.*

Is the rock composed mostly of visible grains of platy or needle-like minerals that are approximately parallel to one another? If so, the rock is a *schist.* If the rock is composed mainly of mica, it is a *mica schist.* If it also contains garnet, it is called a *garnet mica schist.* If hornblende is the predominant mineral the rock is a *hornblende schist.* If talc prevails, it is a *talc schist* (sometimes called soapstone). A schistose rock composed of serpentine is called a *serpentinite.*

If dark and light minerals are found in separate lenses or layers, the rock is a *gneiss.* The light layers are composed of feldspars and perhaps quartz, whereas the darker layers commonly are formed of biotite, amphibole, or pyroxene. A gneiss may have an appearance similar to granite or diorite, but can be distinguished from these igneous rocks by the foliation.

Table B.3
Chemical and Organic Sedimentary Rocks

Rock Name	Composition	Origin
Rock salt	NaCl (halite)	Inorganic precipitation by evaporation of water (usually sea water).
Gypsum	$CaSO_4 \cdot 2H_2O$	Inorganic precipitation by evaporation of water (usually sea water).
Limestone	$CaCO_3$ (calcite)	Organic or inorganic precipitation from water (may be reworked by waves before lithification).
Dolomite	$CaMg(CO_3)_2$	Replacement of Ca by Mg in limestone; inorganic precipitation from water.
Chalk	$CaCO_3$ (Calcite)	Accumulation of "shells" of microscopic marine organisms.
Coquina	$CaCO_3$ (calcite)	Accumulation of shells of marine organisms.
Chert	SiO_2 (silica)	Inorganic precipitation from water; replacement of other rocks by silica; accumulation of "shells" of microscopic marine organisms.
Diatomite	$SiO_2 \cdot nH_2O$ (opaline silica)	Accumulation of "shells" of microscopic marine or freshwater organisms.
Coal	Plant material	Accumulation, compression, and partial distillation of plant material.

Table B.4
Summary of Common Metamorphic Rocks and Their Characteristics

Nonfoliated Rocks:

Rock Name	Identifying Characteristics
Quartzite	Rock composed of interlocking small granules of quartz. Has a sugary appearance and vitreous luster; scratches glass.
Marble	Coarse interlocking grains of calcite (or, less commonly, dolomite). Calcite (or dolomite) has rhombohedral cleavage, hardness intermediate between glass and fingernail. Calcite effervesces in weak acid.
Hornfels	A fine-grained, dark rock that generally will scratch glass. May have a few coarser minerals present.

Foliated Rocks:

Rock Name	Identifying Characteristics
Slate	A fine-grained rock having an earthy luster. Splits easily into thin, flat sheets.
Phyllite	Fine-grained rock with a silky luster. Generally splits along wavy surfaces.
Schist	Composed of visible platy or elongated minerals which show parallel alignment. A wide variety of minerals may be found in various types of schist (e.g., garnet mica schist; hornblende schist, etc.).
Gneiss	Light and dark minerals are found in separate, parallel layers or lenses. Commonly, the dark layers include biotite and hornblende; the light-colored layers are composed of feldspars and quartz. The layers may be folded or appear contorted.

Appendix C
The Elements Most Significant to Geology

Atomic Number	Name	Symbol	Atomic Weight	Some Usual Charges of Ions
1	Hydrogen	H	1.0	+1
2	Helium	He	4.0	0 inert
3	Lithium	Li	6.9	+1
4	Beryllium	Be	9.0	+2
5	Boron	B	10.8	+3
6	Carbon	C	12.0	+4
7	Nitrogen	N	14.0	+5
8	Oxygen	O	16.0	−2
9	Fluorine	F	19.0	−1
10	Neon	Ne	20.2	0 inert
11	Sodium	Na	23.0	+1
12	Magnesium	Mg	24.3	+2
13	Aluminum	Al	27.0	+3
14	Silicon	Si	28.1	+4
15	Phosphorus	P	31.0	+5
16	Sulfur	S	32.1	−2
17	Chlorine	Cl	35.5	−1
18	Argon	Ar	39.9	0 inert
19	Potassium	K	39.1	+1
20	Calcium	Ca	40.1	+2
22	Titanium	Ti	47.9	+4
23	Vanadium	V	50.9	
24	Chromium	Cr	52.0	
25	Manganese	Mn	54.9	
26	Iron	Fe	55.8	+2, +3
27	Cobalt	Co	58.9	

Atomic Number	Name	Symbol	Atomic Weight	Some Usual Charges of Ions
28	Nickel	Ni	58.7	
29	Copper	Cu	63.5	
30	Zinc	Zn	65.4	
33	Arsenic	As	74.9	
35	Bromine	Br	79.9	
37	Rubidium	Rb	85.5	
38	Strontium	Sr	87.3	
40	Zirconium	Zr	91.2	
42	Molybdenum	Mo	95.9	
47	Silver	Ag	107.9	
48	Cadmium	Cd	112.4	
50	Tin	Sn	118.7	
51	Antimony	Sb	121.8	
52	Tellurium	Te	127.6	
55	Cesium	Cs	132.9	
56	Barium	Ba	137.4	
74	Tungsten	W	183.9	
78	Platinum	Pt	195.2	
80	Gold	Au	200.6	
82	Lead	Pb	207.2	
83	Bismuth	Bi	209.0	
88	Radium	Ra	226.1	
90	Thorium	Th	232.1	
92	Uranium	U	238.1	
94	Plutonium	Pu	239.0	

Appendix D
Selected Conversion Factors

Length and distance	inch (in)	2.54	centimeters (cm)	0.4	inch (in)
	foot (ft)	0.3048	meter (m)	3.28	feet (ft)
	inch (in)	0.026	meter (m)	39.4	inches (in)
	mile, statute (mi)	1.61	Meter kilometers (km)	0.62	mile (mi)
Area	square inch (in)	6.45	square centimeters (cm)	0.16	square inch (in)
	square foot (ft)	0.093	square meter (m)	10.8	square feet (ft)
	square mile (mi)	2.59	square kilometers (km)	0.39	square mile (mi)
	acre	0.4	hectare	2.47	acres
Volume	cubic inch (in)	16.4	cubic centimeters (cm)	0.06	cubic inch (in)
	cubic yard (yd)	0.76	cubic meter (m)	1.3	cubic yards (yd)
	cubic foot (ft)	0.0283	cubic meter (m)	35.3	cubic feet (ft)
	quart (qt)	0.95	liter	1.06	quarts (qt)
Weight	ounce (oz)	28.3	grams (g)	0.04	ounce (oz)
	pound (lb)	0.45	kilogram (kg)	2.2	pounds (lb)
	ton, short (2,000 lb)	907	kilograms (kg)	0.001	ton, short
	ton, short	0.91	ton, metric	1.1	tons, short
Temp.	degrees Fahrenheit (°F)	$-32° \times 5/9$	degrees Celsius (°C) (centigrade)	$\times 1.8 + 32°$	degrees Fahrenheit (°F)

Appendix E
Rock Symbols

Shown below are the rock symbols used in the text. In general, these symbols are used by all geologists, although they sometimes are modified slightly.

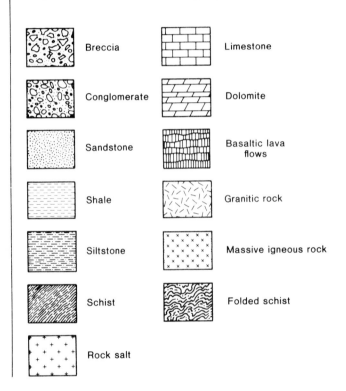

Breccia

Conglomerate

Sandstone

Shale

Siltstone

Schist

Rock salt

Limestone

Dolomite

Basaltic lava flows

Granitic rock

Massive igneous rock

Folded schist

Glossary

aa
A lava flow that solidifies with a spiny, rubbly surface.

abrasion
The grinding away of rock by friction and impact during transportation.

absolute age
Age given in years or some other unit of time.

abyssal fan
Great fan-shaped deposits of sediment on the deep-sea floor at the base of many submarine canyons.

abyssal plain
Very flat regions of the deep-sea floor, usually at the base of the continental rise.

accretion stage
Stage in the evolution of major mountain belts characterized by accumulation of great thicknesses (several kilometers) of sedimentary or volcanic rocks.

advancing glacier
Glacier with a positive budget, so that accumulation results in the lower edges being pushed outward and downward.

aftershock
Small earthquake that follows a main shock.

A horizon
The top layer of soil, characterized by the downward movement of water; also called zone of leaching.

alkali soil
Soil containing such a great quantity of sodium salts precipitated by evaporating ground water that it is generally unfit for plant growth.

alluvial fan
Large fan-shaped pile of sediment that usually forms where a stream's velocity decreases as it emerges from a narrow canyon onto a flat plain at the foot of a mountain range.

alpine glaciation
Glaciation of a mountainous area.

amphibole
Mineral group in which all members are double-chain silicates.

andesite
Fine-grained igneous rock of intermediate composition; composed of about equal amounts of ferromagnesian minerals and plagioclase feldspar.

angle of dip
A vertical angle measured downward from the horizontal plane to an inclined plane.

angular
Sharp-edged; lacking rounded edges or corners.

angular unconformity
An unconformity in which younger strata overlie an erosion surface on tilted or folded layered rock.

anorthosite
A crystalline rock composed almost entirely of calcium-rich plagioclase feldspar.

anticline
An arched fold in which the rock layers dip away from the axis of the fold.

aquifer
A body of saturated rock or sediment through which water can move readily.

arch (sea arch)
Bridge of rock left above an opening eroded in a headland by waves.

arête
A sharp ridge that separates adjacent glacially carved valleys.

arid region
An area with less than 25 cm of rain per year.

artesian aquifer
An aquifer confined above, and sometimes below, by less permeable rocks.

artesian well
A well in which water rises above the aquifer.

artificial recharge
Ground-water recharge increased by engineering techniques.

aseismic ridge
Submarine ridge with which no earthquakes are associated.

ash (volcanic)
Fine pyroclasts (less than 4 mm).

assimilation
The process in which very hot magma melts country rock and assimilates the newly molten material.

asteroid
Small bodies of the solar system, found mostly in the area between the orbits of Mars and Jupiter.

asthenosphere
A region of the earth's outer shell beneath the lithosphere. The asthenosphere is of indeterminate thickness and behaves plastically.

Atlantic-type continental margin
A margin that includes a continental shelf, continental slope, and continental rise that generally extends down to an abyssal plain at a depth of about 5 kilometers.

atom
Smallest possible particle of an element that retains the properties of that element.

atomic mass number
The total number of neutrons and protons in an atom.

atomic weight
The sum of the weight of the subatomic particles in an average atom of an element, given in atomic mass units.

augite
Mineral of the pyroxene group found in mafic igneous rocks.

aulacogen
An inactive, sediment-filled rift that forms above a rising mantle plume. The aulacogen becomes inactive (a "failed arm") as two other rifts widen to form an ocean.

axial plane
A plane containing all of the axes of a fold.

backarc spreading
A type of sea-floor spreading that occurs between an island arc and a continent, moving the island arc away from the continent. It may also occur inland of a magmatic arc on the edge of a continent, thinning and fracturing the continental crust.

backshore
Upper part of the beach, landward of the high-water line.

bajada
A broad, gently sloping, depositional surface formed at the base of a mountain range in a dry region by the coalescing of individual alluvial fans.

bar
A ridge of sediment, usually sand or gravel, that has been deposited in the middle or along the banks of a stream by a decrease in stream velocity.

barchan
A crescent-shaped dune with the horns of the crescent pointing downwind.

barrier island
Ridge of sand paralleling the shoreline and extending above sea level.

basal sliding
Movement in which the entire glacier slides along as a single body on its base over the underlying rock.

basalt
A fine-grained mafic igneous rock made of ferromagnesian minerals and calcium-rich plagioclase feldspar.

base level
A theoretical limit for stream erosion of the earth's surface.

batholith
A large discordant pluton with an outcropping area greater than 100 square kilometers.

bauxite
The principal ore of aluminum; $Al_2O_3 \cdot nH_2O$.

baymouth bar
A ridge of sediment that cuts a bay off from the ocean.

beach
Strip of sediment, usually sand but sometimes pebbles, boulders, or mud, that extends from the low-water line inland to a cliff or zone of permanent vegetation.

beach face
The section of the beach exposed to wave action.

bedding
An arrangement of layers or beds of rock.

bedding plane
A nearly flat surface separating two beds of sedimentary rock.

bed load
Heavy or large sediment particles in a stream that travel near or on the stream bed.

Benioff zone
Distinct earthquake zone that begins at an oceanic trench and slopes landward and downward into the earth at an angle of about 30° to 60°.

bergschrund
The crevasse that develops where a glacier is pulling away from a cirque wall.

berm
Platform of wave-deposited sediment that is flat or slopes slightly landward.

B horizon
A soil layer characterized by the accumulation of material leached downward from the A horizon above; also called zone of accumulation.

biotite
Iron-magnesium-bearing mica.

block
Large angular pyroclast.

blowout
A depression on the land surface caused by wind erosion.

body wave
Seismic wave that travels through the earth's interior.

bomb
Large spindle- or lens-shaped pyroclast.

bonding
Attachment of an atom to one or more adjacent atoms.

bottomset bed
A delta deposit formed from the finest silt and clay, which are carried far out to sea by river flow, or by sediments sliding downhill on the sea floor.

boulder
A sediment particle with a diameter greater than 256 mm.

Bowen's reaction series
The sequence in which minerals crystallize from a cooling basaltic magma.

braided stream
A stream that flows in a network of many interconnected rivulets around numerous bars.

breaker
A wave that has become so steep that the crest of the wave topples forward, moving faster than the main body of the wave.

breakwater
An offshore structure built to absorb the force of large breaking waves and provide quiet water near shore.

butte
A narrow pinnacle of resistant rock with a flat top and very steep sides.

calcareous
Containing calcium carbonate.

calcite
Mineral with the formula $CaCO_3$.

Caldera
A volcanic depression much larger than the original crater.

canyon (*Mars*)
A crack or fracture on the Martian surface, caused by uplifting of large elevated areas.

capillary fringe
A thin zone near the water table in which capillary action causes water to rise above the zone of saturation.

carbonaceous chondrite
Stony meteorite containing chondrules and composed mostly of serpentine and large quantities of organic materials.

cave (cavern)
Naturally formed underground chamber.

cement
The solid material that precipitates in the pore space of sediments, binding the grains together to form solid rock.

cementation
The chemical precipitation of material in the spaces between sediment grains, binding the grains together into a hard rock.

Cenozoic Era
The most recent of the eras; followed the Mesozoic Era.

chain silicate
Silicate structure in which two of each tetrahedron's oxygen ions are shared with adjacent tetrahedrons, resulting in a chain of tetrahedrons.

channel (*Mars*)
Feature on the surface of the planet Mars which resembles very closely certain types of stream channels on the earth.

chaotic terrain (*Mars*)
Patch of jumbled and broken angular slabs and blocks on the surface of Mars.

chemical sedimentary rock
A rock composed of material precipitated directly from solution.

chemical weathering
The decomposition of rock resulting from exposure to water and atmospheric gases.

chert
A hard, compact, fine-grained sedimentary rock formed almost entirely of silica.

chondrule
Round silicate grain within some stony meteorites.

C horizon
A soil layer composed of incompletely weathered parent material.

chromosphere
Reddish-colored layer of the sun that extends outward from the photosphere.

cinder (volcanic)
Pyroclast between 4 and 32 millimeters in diameter.

cinder cone
A volcano constructed of loose rock fragments ejected from a central vent.

circum-Pacific belt
Major belt around the edge of the Pacific Ocean on which most composite volcanoes are located and where many earthquakes occur.

cirque
A steep-sided, amphitheater-like hollow carved into a mountain at the head of a glacial valley.

clastic (detrital) sedimentary rock
A sedimentary rock composed of fragments of pre-existing rock.

clastic texture
An arrangement of rock fragments bound into a rigid network by cement.

clay
Sediment composed of particles with diameter less than .004 mm (4 microns).

clay mineral
A hydrous aluminum-silicate that occurs as a platy grain of microscopic size with a sheet silicate structure.

clay mineral group
Collective term for several clay minerals.

cleavage
The ability of a mineral to break along preferred planes.

coal
A sedimentary rock formed from the consolidation of plant material. It is rich in carbon, usually black, and burns readily.

coarse-grained rock
Rock in which most of the grains are larger than one millimeter (igneous) or two millimeters (sedimentary).

coast
The land near the sea, including the beach and a strip of land inland from the beach.

coastal straightening
The gradual straightening of an irregular shoreline by wave erosion of headlands and wave deposition in bays.

cobble
A sediment particle with a diameter of 64 to 256 mm.

column
A dripstone feature formed when a stalactite growing downward and a stalagmite growing upward meet and join.

columnar structure
Volcanic rock in parallel, usually vertical columns, mostly six-sided; also called columnar jointing.

comet
Small objects in space, no more than a few kilometers in diameter, composed of frozen methane, frozen ammonia, and water ice, with small solid particles and dust imbedded in the ices.

compaction
A loss in overall volume and pore space of a rock as the particles are packed closer together by the weight of overlying material.

composite volcano (stratovolcano)
A volcano constructed of alternating layers of pyroclastics and rock solidified from lava flows.

compressive directed pressure
Directed pressure that tends to compress some portions of a body more than other portions.

compressive force
A force that tends to shorten a body.

conchoidal fracture
Curved fracture surfaces.

concordant
Parallel to layering or earlier developed planar structures.

concretion
Hard, rounded mass that develops when a considerable amount of cementing material precipitates locally in a rock, often around an organic nucleus.

cone of depression
A depression of the water table formed around a well when water is pumped out; it is shaped like an inverted cone.

confining pressure
Pressure applied equally on all surfaces of a body; also called static pressure.

conglomerate
A coarse-grained sedimentary rock formed by the cementation of rounded gravel.

consolidation
Any process that forms firm, coherent rock from sediment or from liquid.

contact
Boundary surface between two different rock types or ages of rocks.

contact metamorphism
Metamorphism under conditions in which high temperature is the dominant factor.

continental crust
The thick, granitic crust under continents.

continental drift
A concept suggesting that continents move over the earth's surface.

continental glaciation
The covering of a large region of a continent by a sheet of glacial ice.

continental rise
A wedge of sediment that extends from the lower part of the continental slope to the deep-sea floor.

continental shelf
A submarine platform at the edge of a continent, inclined very gently seaward generally at an angle of less than 1°.

continental slope
A relatively steep slope extending from a depth of 100 to 200 meters at the edge of the continental shelf down to oceanic depths.

contour current
A bottom current that flows parallel to the slopes of the continental margin (along the contour rather than down the slope).

contour line
A line on a topographic map connecting points of equal elevation.

convection (convection cell)
A very slow circulation of a substance driven by differences in temperature and density within that substance.

converging plate boundary
Boundary between two plates that are moving toward one another.

core
The central zone of the earth.

corona
Outermost layer of the sun.

correlation
Determination of age relationships between rock units or geologic events in separate areas.

country rock
Any rock that was older than and intruded by an igneous body.

covalent bonding
Bonding due to the sharing of electrons by adjacent atoms.

crater (of a volcano)
A basin-like depression over a vent at the summit of a volcanic cone.

craton
Portion of a continent that has been structurally stable for a prolonged period of time.

creep
Very slow, continuous downslope movement of soil or debris.

crevasse
Open fissure in a glacier.

cross-bedding
An arrangement of relatively thin layers of rock inclined at an angle to the more nearly horizontal bedding planes of the larger rock unit.

cross-cutting relationships, principle or law of
A disrupted pattern is older than the cause of disruption.

cross section, geological
A representation of a portion of the earth in a vertical plane.

crust
The outer layer of rock, forming a thin skin over the earth's surface.

crustal rebound
The rise of the earth's crust after the removal of glacial ice.

crystal
A homogeneous solid with an orderly internal atomic arrangement.

crystal form
Arrangement of various faces on a crystal in a definite geometric relationship to one another.

crystal lattice
Orderly, three-dimensional arrangement of atoms within a crystal.

crystalline
Describing a substance in which the atoms are arranged in a regular, repeating, orderly pattern.

crystalline texture
An arrangement of interlocking crystals.

crystallization
Crystal development and growth.

crystal settling
The process whereby the minerals that crystallize at a high temperature in a cooling magma move downward in the magma chamber due to being denser than the magma.

daughter product
The isotope produced by radioactive decay.

debris
Any unconsolidated material at the earth's surface.

debris avalanche
Very rapid and turbulent downslope movement of debris.

debris fall
A free-falling mass of debris.

debris slide
Rapid movement of debris as a coherent mass.

deflation
The removal of clay, silt, and sand particles from the land surface by wind.

delta
A body of sediment deposited at the mouth of a river when the river velocity decreases as it flows into a standing body of water.

dendritic pattern
Drainage pattern of a river and its tributaries that resembles branches of a tree or veins in a leaf.

deposition
The settling or coming to rest of transported material.

depth of focus
Distance between the focus and the epicenter of an earthquake.

desert
A region with low precipitation (usually defined as less than 25 cm per year).

desert pavement
A thin layer of closely packed gravel that protects the underlying sediment from further deflation; also called pebble armor.

differential weathering
Varying rates of weathering that result when some rocks in an area are more resistant to weathering than others.

differentiation
Separation of different ingredients from an originally homogeneous mixture.

dike
A tabular, discordant intrusive structure.

diorite
Coarse-grained igneous rock of intermediate composition. Composed of approximately equal amounts of plagioclase feldspar and ferromagnesian minerals.

dip
The angle and direction at which a plane is inclined from horizontal.

dip-slip fault
A fault in which movement is parallel to the dip of the fault surface.

directed pressure
Pressure applied unequally on the surfaces of a body; also called dynamic pressure.

direction of dip
The compass direction in which the angle of dip is measured.

disconformity
A surface that represents missing rock strata but is parallel to beds above and below that surface.

discordant
Not parallel to any layering or parallel planes.

dissolved load
The portion of the total sediment load in a stream that is carried in solution.

distributary
Small shifting river channel that carries water away from the main river channel and distributes it over a delta's surface.

diverging boundary
Boundary separating two plates moving away from each other; a spreading center.

dolomite
A sedimentary rock composed mostly of the mineral dolomite.

dolomitic marble
Marble in which dolomite, rather than calcite, is the prevalent mineral.

dome
A structure in which beds dip away from a central point.

double refraction
The splitting of light into two components when it passes through certain crystalline substances.

downcutting
A valley-deepening process caused by erosion of a stream bed.

drainage basin
Total area drained by a stream and its tributaries.

drainage divide
Line dividing one drainage basin from another.

drainage pattern
The arrangement in map view of a river and its tributaries.

drawdown
The lowering of the water table near a pumped well.

dripstone
Deposits of calcite (and, rarely, other minerals) built up by dripping water in caves.

drumlin
A long, streamlined hill made of till.

dust (volcanic)
Finest sized pyroclasts.

dynamic pressure
See directed pressure.

earthflow
Slow-to-rapid mass wasting in which debris moves downslope as a very viscous fluid.

earthquake
A trembling or shaking of the ground caused by the sudden release of energy stored in the rocks beneath the surface.

earthy luster
A luster giving a substance the appearance of unglazed pottery.

elastic rebound
The sudden release of progressively stored strain in rocks, resulting in movement along a fault.

elastic strain
Strain in which a deformed body recovers its original shape after the stress is released.

electron
A single, negative electric charge that contributes virtually no mass to an atom.

element
A substance that cannot be broken down to other substances by ordinary chemical methods. Each atom of an element possesses the same number of protons.

emergent coast
A coast in which land formerly under water has recently been placed above sea level, either by uplift of the land or by a drop in sea level.

end moraine
A ridge of till piled up along the front edge of a glacier.

environment of deposition
The location in which deposition occurs, usually marked by characteristic physical, chemical, or biological conditions.

epicenter
The point on the earth's surface directly above the focus of an earthquake.

epoch
Each period of the standard geologic time scale is divided into epochs (e.g., Pleistocene Epoch of the Quaternary Period).

equilibrium
Material is in equilibrium if it is adjusted to the physical and chemical conditions of its environment so that it does not change or alter with time.

Era
Major subdivision of the standard geologic time scale (e.g., Mesozoic Era).

erosion
The physical removal of rock by an agent such as running water, glacial ice, or wind.

erratic
An ice-transported boulder that has not been derived from bedrock near its present site.

esker
A long, sinuous ridge of sediment deposited by glacial melt water.

estuary
Drowned river mouth.

etch-pitted terrain (*Mars*)
A terrain on the surface of Mars characterized by small pits.

eugeosyncline
See volcanic portion of a geosyncline.

evaporites
Rocks that form from crystals precipitating during evaporation of water.

exfoliation
The stripping of concentric rock slabs from the outer surface of a rock mass.

exfoliation dome
A large, rounded landform developed in a massive rock, such as granite, by the process of exfoliation.

extrusive rock
Any igneous rock that forms at the earth's surface, whether it solidifies directly from a lava flow or is pyroclastic.

faceted rock
A rock fragment with one or more flat surfaces caused by erosive action.

fall
In mass wasting, when material free-falls or bounces down a cliff.

fault
A fracture in bedrock along which movement has taken place.

fault-block mountain range
A range created by uplift along normal or vertical faults.

faunal succession, principle or law of
Fossil species succeed one another in a definite and recognizable order; in general, fossils in progressively older rock show increasingly greater differences from species living at present.

feldspar
Group of most common minerals of the earth's crust. All feldspars contain silicon, aluminum, and oxygen and may contain potassium, calcium, and sodium.

felsic rocks
Silica-rich igneous rocks with a relatively high content of potassium and sodium.

ferromagnesian minerals
Iron-magnesium-bearing minerals, such as augite, hornblende, olivine, and biotite.

fine-grained rock
A rock in which most of the mineral grains are less than one millimeter across.

fiord
A coastal inlet that is a glacially carved valley, the base of which is submerged.

firn
A compacted mass of granular snow, transitional between snow and glacier ice.

firn limit
An irregular line marking the highest level to which the winter snow cover on a glacier is lost during a melt season.

flank eruption
An eruption in which lava erupts out of a vent on the side of a volcano.

flash flood
Flood of very high discharge and short duration; sudden and local in extent.

flood plain
A broad strip of land built up by sedimentation on either side of a stream channel.

flowage
In mass wasting, downslope motion in which the descending mass moves as a viscous fluid.

flowstone
Calcite precipitated by flowing water on cave walls and floors.

focus
The point within the earth from which seismic waves originate in an earthquake.

fold
Bend in layered bedrock.

fold axis
Hingeline of a fold.

foliation
Parallel alignment of textural and structural features of a rock.

footwall
The underlying surface of an inclined fault plane.

foreset bed
A sediment layer in the main part of a delta, deposited at an angle to the horizontal.

foreshore
The zone that is regularly covered and uncovered by the rise and fall of tides.

formation
A body of rock of considerable thickness that has a recognizable unity or similarity making it distinguishable from adjacent rock units. Usually composed of one bed or several beds of sedimentary rock, although the term is applied to units of metamorphic and igneous rock also. A convenient unit for mapping, describing, or interpreting the geology of a region.

fossil
Traces of plants or animals preserved in rock.

fracture
The way a substance breaks where not controlled by cleavage.

fracture zone
Major line of weakness in the earth's crust that crosses the mid-oceanic ridge at approximately right angles.

fracturing
Cracking or rupturing of a body under stress.

framework silicate
Crystal structure in which all four oxygen ions of a silica tetrahedron are shared by adjacent ions.

fretted terrain (*Mars*)
Flat lowland with some scattered high plateaus on the surface of Mars.

frost action
Mechanical weathering of rock by freezing water.

frost heaving
The lifting of rock or soil by the expansion of freezing water.

frost wedging
A type of frost action in which the expansion of freezing water pries a rock apart.

gabbro
A mafic, coarse-grained igneous rock composed predominantly of ferromagnesian minerals and calcium-rich plagioclase feldspar.

gaining stream
A stream that receives water from the zone of saturation.

geode
Partly hollow, globe-like body found in limestone or other cavernous rock.

geologic map
A map representing the geology of a given area.

geologic resources
Valuable materials of geologic origin that can be extracted from the earth.

geology
The scientific study of the earth.

geophysics
The application of physical laws and principles to a study of the earth.

geosyncline
A very long (thousands of kilometers) and relatively narrow (a few hundred kilometers) basin that acts as a collecting area for marine sedimentary and volcanic rocks.

geothermal energy
Energy produced by harnessing naturally occurring steam and hot water.

geothermal gradient
Rate of temperature increase associated with increasing depth beneath the surface of the earth (normally about 25°C/km).

geyser
A type of hot spring that periodically erupts hot water and steam.

geyserite
A deposit of silica that forms around many geysers and hot springs.

glacier
A large long-lasting mass of ice, formed on land by the compaction and recrystallization of snow, which moves because of its own weight.

glassy (or vitreous) luster
A luster that gives a substance a glazed, porcelain-like appearance.

glowing avalanche
Very hot flow of pyroclastics.

gneiss
A metamorphic rock comprised of light and dark layers or lenses.

gneissic
The texture of a metamorphic rock in which minerals are separated into light and dark layers or lenses.

graded bedding
An arrangement of particle sizes within a single bed, with coarse grains at the bottom of the bed and progressively finer grains toward the top of the bed.

graded stream
A stream that exhibits a delicate balance between its transporting capacity and the sediment load available to it.

granite
A felsic, coarse-grained, intrusive igneous rock composed mostly of potassium with sodium-rich feldspars and quartz.

granitization
The process by which granite is created from other rock without a melt being involved.

gravel
Rounded particles coarser than sand.

gravity
The force of attraction that two bodies exert on one another that is proportional to the product of their masses and inversely proportional to the square of the distance from the centers of the two bodies.

gravity meter
An instrument that measures the gravitational attraction between the earth and a mass within the instrument.

groin
Short wall built perpendicular to shore to trap moving sand and widen a beach.

ground moraine
A blanket of till deposited by a glacier or released as glacier ice melted.

ground water
The water that lies beneath the ground surface, filling the cracks, crevices, and pore space of rocks.

guyot
Flat-topped seamounts.

half-life
The time it takes for a given amount of a radioactive isotope to be reduced by one-half.

hanging valley
A smaller valley that terminates abruptly high above a main valley.

hanging wall
The overlying surface of an inclined fault plane.

hardness
The relative ease or difficulty with which a smooth surface of a mineral can be scratched; commonly measured by Mohs' scale.

headland
Point of land along a coast.

headward erosion
The lengthening of a valley in an uphill direction above its original source by gullying, mass wasting, and sheet erosion.

heat flow
Gradual loss of heat (per unit of surface area) from the earth's interior out into space.

heavy crude
Dense, viscous petroleum that flows slowly or not at all.

hematite
A type of iron oxide that has a brick-red color when powdered; Fe_2O_3.

horn
A sharp peak attributed to cirques cut back into a mountain on several sides.

hornblende
Common amphibole frequently found in igneous and metamorphic rocks.

hornfels
A fine-grained, unfoliated metamorphic rock.

hot spring
Spring with a water temperature warmer than human body temperature.

hydraulic action
The ability of water to pick up and move rock and sediment.

hydrologic cycle
The movement of water and water vapor from the sea to the atmosphere, to the land, and back to the sea and atmosphere again.

hydrothermal metamorphism
Alteration of a rock by hot water passing through it.

hydrothermal rock
Rock deposited by precipitation of ions from solution in hot water.

hypothesis
A tentative theory.

iceberg
Block of glacier-derived ice floating in water.

ice cap
A glacier covering a relatively small area of land, but not restricted to a valley.

ice fall
A chaotic jumble of crevasses that split glacier ice into pinnacles and blocks.

ice sheet
A glacier covering a large area (more than 50,000 square kilometers) of land.

igneous rocks
Rocks formed or apparently formed from solidification of magma.

incised meander
A meander that retains its sinuous curves as it cuts vertically downward below the level at which it originally formed.

inclusion
A fragment of rock that is distinct from the body of igneous rock in which it is enclosed.

index fossil
A fossil from a very short-lived species known to have existed during a specific period of geologic time.

intensity
A measure of an earthquake's size by its effect on people and buildings.

intermediate rocks
Rocks with a chemical content between felsic and mafic compositions.

intrusive rock
Rock that appears to have crystallized from magma emplaced in surrounding rock.

intrusive structure (intrusion)
A body of intrusive rock classified on the basis of size, shape, and relationship to surrounding rocks.

ion
An electrically charged atom or group of atoms.

ionic bonding
Bonding due to the attraction between positively charged ions and negatively charged ions.

iron meteorite
A meteorite composed principally of iron-nickel alloy.

island arc
A curved line of islands.

isoclinal fold
A fold in which the limbs are parallel to one another.

isolated silicate structure
Silicate minerals that are structured so that none of the oxygen atoms are shared by silica tetrahedrons.

isostasy
The balance or equilibrium between adjacent blocks of crust resting on a plastic mantle.

isostatic adjustment
Concept of vertical movement of sections of the earth's crust to achieve balance or equilibrium.

isotherm
Line connecting equal temperature.

isotopes
Atoms (of the same element) that have different numbers of neutrons but the same number of protons.

jetty
Rock wall protruding above sea level, designed to protect the entrance of a harbor from sediment deposition and storm waves; usually built in pairs.

joint
A fracture or crack in bedrock along which essentially no displacement has occurred.

joint set
Joints oriented in one direction approximately parallel to one another.

karst topography
An area having many sinkholes and a cave system beneath the land surface and usually lacking a surface stream.

kettle
A depression caused by the melting of a stagnant block of ice that was surrounded by sediment.

KREEP (*Moon*)
A lunar basalt enriched in potassium (K), the rare earth elements (REE) and phosphorus (P).

laccolith
A concordant intrusive structure, similar to a sill, with the central portion thicker and domed upward.

laminar flow
Slow, smooth flow, with each drop of water traveling a smooth path parallel to its neighboring drops.

laminated terrain (*Mars*)
Area where series of alternating light and dark layers can be seen on the surface of Mars.

landsliding
The general term for slowly to very rapidly descending rock or debris.

lateral erosion
Erosion and undercutting of stream banks caused by a stream swinging from side to side across its valley floor.

lateral moraine
A low ridge-like pile of till along the side of a glacier.

laterite
Highly leached soil that forms in regions of tropical climate with high temperatures and very abundant rainfall.

lava
Magma on the earth's surface.

left-lateral fault
A strike-slip fault in which the block seen across the fault appears displaced to the left.

limb
Portion of a fold shared by an anticline and a syncline.

limestone
A sedimentary rock composed mostly of calcite.

limonite
A type of iron oxide that is yellowish-brown when powdered; $Fe_2O_3 \cdot nH_2O$.

lithification
The consolidation of sediment into sedimentary rock.

lithosphere
The rigid outer shell of the earth, approximately 100 kilometers thick.

loess
A fine-grained deposit of wind-blown dust, composed of angular unweathered grains of quartz, feldspar, and other minerals—unconsolidated, but usually held together by calcareous cement.

longitudinal dune (seif)
Large, symmetrical ridge of sand parallel to the wind direction.

longitudinal profile
A line showing a stream's slope, drawn along the length of the stream as if it were viewed from the side.

longshore current
A moving mass of water that develops parallel to a shoreline.

longshore drift
Movement of sediment parallel to shore when waves strike a shoreline at an angle.

losing stream
Stream that loses water to the zone of saturation.

low-velocity zone
Mantle zone at a depth of about 100 kilometers where seismic waves travel more slowly than in shallower layers of rock.

luster
The quality and intensity of light reflected from the surface of a mineral.

L wave
Seismic surface wave.

mafic rocks
Silica-poor igneous rocks having a relatively high content of magnesium, iron, and calcium.

magma
Molten rock, usually mostly silica. The liquid may contain dissolved gasses as well as some solid minerals.

magmatic arc
A line of batholiths or volcanoes. Generally, the line, as seen from above, is curved.

magnetic anomaly
A deviation from the average strength of the earth's magnetic field.

magnetic field
Region of magnetic force that surrounds the earth.

magnetic pole
An area where the strength of the magnetic field is greatest and where the magnetic lines of force appear to leave or enter the earth.

magnetic reversal
A change in the polarity of the earth's magnetic field.

magnetometer
An instrument that measures the strength of the earth's magnetic field.

magnitude
A measure of the energy released during an earthquake.

major mountain belt
A long chain (thousands of kilometers) of mountain ranges.

mantle
A thick shell of rock that separates the earth's crust above from the core below.

mantle plume
Narrow column of hot mantle rock that rises and spreads radially outward.

marble
A coarse-grained rock composed of interlocking calcite crystals.

maria (*Moon*)
Lava plains on Moon's surface (singular, *mare*).

marine terrace
A broad, gently-sloping platform that may be exposed at low tide.

mass wasting (or mass movement)
Movement, caused by gravity, in which bedrock, rock debris, or soil moves downslope.

matrix
Fine-grained material found in the space between larger grains.

meander
Pronounced sinuous curve along a stream's course.

meander cutoff
A new, shorter channel across the narrow neck of a meander.

meander scar
An abandoned meander filled with sediment and vegetation.

mechanical weathering
The physical disintegration of rock into smaller pieces.

medial moraine
A single long ridge of till on a glacier formed by adjacent lateral moraines joining and being carried downglacier.

Mediterranean-Himalayan belt (Mediterranean belt)
A major concentration of earthquakes and composite volcanoes that runs through the Mediterranean Sea, crosses the Mideast and the Himalayas, and passes through the East Indies.

mesa
A broad, flat-topped hill bounded by cliffs and capped with a resistant rock layer.

mesosphere
The rigid lower part of the earth's mantle.

Mesozoic Era
The era that followed the Paleozoic Era and preceded the Cenozoic Era.

metallic luster
Luster giving a substance the appearance of being made of metal.

metamorphic facies
Pressure and temperature stability fields for metamorphic rocks as determined by mineral assemblages.

metamorphic rock
A rock produced by metamorphism.

metamorphism
The transformation of pre-existing rock into texturally or mineralogically distinct new rock as a result of high temperature, high pressure, or both, but without the rock melting in the process.

metasomatism
Metamorphism coupled with the introduction of ions from an external source.

meteor
Fragment that passes through the earth's atmosphere, heated to incandescence by friction; sometimes called "shooting" or "falling" stars.

meteorite
Meteor that strikes the earth's surface.

meteoroid
Small solid particles of stone and/or metal orbiting the sun.

mica
Group of minerals with a sheet silicate structure.

mid-oceanic ridge
A giant mountain range that lies under the ocean and extends around the world.

migmatite
Mixed igneous and metamorphic rock.

mineral
A naturally occurring, inorganic, crystalline solid that has a definite chemical composition and possesses characteristic physical properties.

mineraloid
A substance that is not crystalline but otherwise would be considered a mineral.

miogeosyncline
See nonvolcanic portion of a geosyncline.

model
In science, a model is an image— graphic, mathematical, or verbal—that is consistent with the known data.

modified Mercalli scale
Scale expressing intensities of earthquakes (judged on amount of damage done) in Roman numerals ranging from I to XII.

Mohorovičič discontinuity
The boundary separating the crust from the mantle beneath it (also called *Moho*).

Mohs' hardness scale
Ten minerals designated as standards of hardness.

moraine
A body of till either being carried on a glacier or left behind after a glacier has receded.

mountain range
A group of closely spaced mountains or parallel ridges.

mud
Term loosely used for silt and clay, usually wet.

mudcracks
Polygonal cracks formed in very fine-grained sediment as it dries.

mudflow
A flowing mixture of debris and water, usually moving down a channel.

multi-ringed basin (*Moon*)
Large lunar crater surrounded by a series of concentric rings with intervening lowlands.

muscovite
Transparent or white mica that lacks iron and magnesium.

natural gas
A gaseous mixture of naturally occurring hydrocarbons.

natural levee
Low ridges of flood-deposited sediment formed on either side of a stream channel, which thin away from the channel.

nebula
A large volume of interstellar gas and dust.

negative gravity anomaly
Less than normal gravitational attraction.

negative magnetic anomaly
Less than average strength of the earth's magnetic field.

neutron
A subatomic particle that contributes mass to an atom and is electrically neutral.

nonconformity
An unconformity in which an erosion surface on plutonic or metamorphic rock has been covered by younger sedimentary or volcanic rock.

nonmetallic luster
Luster that gives a substance the appearance of being made of something other than metal (e.g., glassy).

nonrenewable resources
Resources that are forming at such extremely slow rates that they are likely to become exhausted at the present rates of consumption.

nonvolcanic portion of a geosyncline
The part of a geosyncline formed of a thick sequence of limestone, sandstone, and shale with little or no volcanic rock; called *miogeosyncline*.

normal fault
A fault in which the hanging-wall block moved down relative to the footwall block.

nuée ardente
Cloud of red-hot ash and dust caused by very explosive volcanic activity (French for *glowing cloud*).

oblique-slip fault
A fault having both strike-slip and dip-slip components.

obsidian
Volcanic glass.

oceanic crust
The thin, basaltic crust under oceans.

oceanic trench
A narrow, deep trough parallel to the edge of a continent or an island arc.

oil
See petroleum.

oil field
An area underlain by one or more oil pools.

oil pool
Underground accumulations of oil.

oil shale
Shale with a high content of organic matter from which oil may be extracted by distillation.

oil trap
A set of conditions that hold petroleum in a reservoir rock and prevent its escape by migration.

olivine
A ferromagnesian mineral with the formula $(Fe, Mg)_2 SiO_4$.

open fold
A fold with gently dipping limbs.

open-pit mine
Mines in which ore is exposed at the surface in a large excavation.

ore
Naturally occurring materials that can be profitably mined.

ore mineral
A mineral having commercial value.

organic sedimentary rock
Rocks composed mostly of the remains of plants and animals.

original horizontality, principle or law of
Most water-laid sediment is deposited in horizontal or near-horizontal layers that are essentially parallel to the earth's surface.

orogeny
An episode of intense deformation of the rocks in a region, generally accompanied by metamorphism and plutonic activity.

orthoclase feldspar
A feldspar with the formula $KAISi_3O_8$.

outwash
Material deposited by debris-laden meltwater from a glacier.

overturned fold
A fold in which both limbs dip in the same direction.

oxbow lake
A crescent-shaped lake occupying the abandoned channel of a stream meander that is isolated from the present channel by a meander cutoff and sedimentation.

Pacific-type continental margin
A margin consisting of a continental shelf, a continental slope, and an oceanic trench.

pahoehoe
A lava flow characterized by a ropy or billowy surface.

paired terraces
Stream terraces (*see* definition) that occur at the same elevation on each side of a river.

paleomagnetism
A study of ancient magnetic fields.

Paleozoic Era
The era that followed the Precambrian and began with the appearance of complex life, as indicated by fossils.

parabolic dune
A deeply curved dune in a region of abundant sand. The horns point upwind and are apt to be anchored by vegetation.

parent rock
Original rock before being metamorphosed.

partial melting
Melting of the components of a rock having the lowest melting temperatures.

peat
A brown, lightweight, unconsolidated or semi-consolidated deposit of plant remains.

pebble
A sediment particle with a diameter of 2 to 64 mm.

pedalfer
A soil characterized by the downward movement of water through it, downward leaching, and abundant humus. Found in humid climates.

pediment
A gently sloping erosional surface cut into the solid rock of a mountain range in a dry region; usually covered with a thin veneer of gravel.

pedocal
A soil characterized by little leaching, scant humus, the upward movement of water through it, and the precipitation of salts. Found in dry climates.

pegmatite
Extremely coarse-grained igneous rock.

pelagic sediment
Sediment made up of fine-grained clay and the skeletons of microscopic organisms that settle slowly down through the ocean water.

peneplain
A nearly flat erosional surface presumably produced as mass wasting, sheet erosion, and stream erosion reduce a region almost to base level.

penumbra (*Sun*)
Bright surrounding ring on a sunspot.

per capita use
Individual use.

perched water table
A water table separated from the main water table beneath it by a zone that is not saturated.

Period
Each era of the standard geologic time scale is subdivided into periods (e.g., the Cretaceous Period).

permafrost
Ground that remains permanently frozen over a period of many years.

permeability
The capacity of a rock to transmit a fluid such as water or petroleum.

petrified wood
A material that forms as the organic matter of buried wood is replaced by inorganic silica carried in by ground water.

petroleum (crude oil)
A liquid mixture of naturally occurring hydrocarbons.

phenocrysts
Large crystals in porphyritic igneous rock.

photosphere
Deepest layer of the sun that is visible to us.

phyllite
A metamorphic rock in which clay minerals have recrystallized into microscopic micas, giving the rock a silky sheen.

physical continuity
Being able to physically follow a rock unit between two places.

physical geology
A large division of geology concerned with earth materials, changes of the surface and interior of the earth, and the forces that cause those changes.

pillow structure
Rocks, generally basalt, formed in pillow-shaped masses closely fitting together; caused by underwater lava flows.

placer mine
Surface mines in which valuable mineral grains are extracted from stream bar or beach deposits.

plagioclase feldspar
A feldspar containing sodium and/or calcium in addition to aluminum, silicon and oxygen.

planet
Largest of the objects in the solar system orbiting around the sun.

plastic
Capable of being molded and bent under stress.

plastic flow of ice
Movement within a glacier in which the ice is not fractured.

plastic strain
Strain in which a body is molded or bent under stress and does not return to its original shape after the stress is released.

plate
A large, mobile slab of rock making up part of the earth's surface.

plateau
Broad, flat-topped areas elevated above the surrounding land and bounded, at least in part, by cliffs.

plateau basalts
Layers of basalt flows that have built up to great thicknesses.

plate tectonics
A theory that the earth's surface is divided into a few large, thick plates that are slowly moving and changing in size. Intense geologic activity occurs at the plate boundaries.

playa
A very flat, dry lake bed of hard, mud-cracked clay.

playa lake
A shallow temporary lake (following a rainstorm) on a flat valley floor in a dry region.

Pleistocene
An epoch of the Quaternary Period characterized by several glacial ages.

plunging fold
A fold in which the axis is not horizontal.

pluton
An igneous body that crystallized deep underground.

plutonic rock
Igneous rock formed at great depth.

pluvial lake
A lake formed during an earlier time of abundant rainfall.

point bar
A stream *bar* (*see* definition) deposited on the inside of a curve in the stream, where the water velocity is low.

polar wandering
An apparent movement of the earth's poles.

pore space
The total amount of space taken up by openings between sediment grains.

porosity
The percentage of a rock's volume that is taken up by openings.

porphyritic rock
An igneous rock in which large crystals are enclosed in a matrix (or ground mass) of much finer-grained minerals or obsidian.

positive gravity anomaly
Greater than normal gravitational attraction.

positive magnetic anomaly
Greater than average strength of the earth's magnetic field.

pothole
Depression eroded into the hard rock of a stream bed by the abrasive action of the stream's sediment load.

Precambrian
The vast amount of time that preceded the Paleozoic Era.

Precambrian shield
A complex of old Precambrian metamorphic and plutonic rocks exposed over a large area.

principle of uniformitarianism
See uniformitarianism.

progressive metamorphism
Metamorphism in which progressively greater pressure and temperature act on a rock type with increasing depth in the earth's crust.

prominence (*Sun*)
Clouds of hydrogen and other elements in the sun's chromosphere.

proton
A subatomic particle that contributes mass and a single positive electrical charge to an atom.

pumice
A frothy volcanic glass.

P wave
A compressional wave (seismic wave) in which rock vibrates parallel to the direction of wave propagation.

P-wave shadow zone
The region on the earth's surface, 103° to 142° away from an earthquake epicenter, in which P waves from the earthquake are absent.

pyroclast
Fragment of rock formed by volcanic explosion.

pyroxene
Mineral group, all members of which are single-chain silicates.

quartz
Mineral with the formula SiO_2.

quartzite
A rock composed of sand-sized grains of quartz that have been welded together during metamorphism.

quartzose sandstone
A sandstone with 90 percent or more of its grains composed of quartz.

Quaternary
The youngest geologic period; includes the present time.

radial pattern
A drainage pattern in which streams diverge outward like spokes of a wheel.

radioactivity
The spontaneous nuclear disintegration of atoms of certain isotopes.

rain shadow
A region on the downwind side of mountains that has little or no rain because of the loss of moisture on the upwind side of the mountains.

rayed crater (*Moon*)
Crater with bright streaks radiating from it on the moon's surface.

receding glacier
A glacier with a negative budget, which causes the glacier to grow smaller as its edges melt back.

recessional moraine
An end moraine built during the retreat of a glacier.

recharge
The addition of new water to an aquifer or to the zone of saturation.

reclamation
Restoration of the land to usable condition after mining has ceased.

recrystallization
The development of new crystals in a rock, often of the same composition as the original grains.

rectangular pattern
A drainage pattern in which tributaries of a river change direction and join one another at right angles.

recumbent fold
A fold overturned to such an extent that the limbs are essentially horizontal.

regional metamorphism
Metamorphism involving relatively high temperature and pressure (directed and confining); also called dynamothermal metamorphism.

regolith
Loose, unconsolidated rock material resting on bedrock.

relative time
The sequence in which events took place (not measured in time units).

relief
The vertical distance between points on the earth's surface.

reserves
The discovered deposits of a geologic material that are economically feasible to recover under present circumstances.

reservoir rock
A rock that is sufficiently porous and permeable to store and transmit petroleum.

residual clay
Fine-grained particles left behind as insoluble residue when a limestone containing clay dissolves.

residual soil
Soil that develops directly from weathering of the rock below.

resources
The total amount of a geologic material in all its deposits, discovered and undiscovered (*see* reserves).

reverse fault
A fault in which the hanging-wall block moved up relative to the footwall block.

rhyolite
A fine-grained felsic igneous rock made up mostly of feldspar and quartz.

Richter scale
A numerical scale of earthquake magnitudes.

rift valley
A large crack, apparently of tensional origin, running down the crest of the mid-oceanic ridge.

right-lateral fault
A strike-slip fault in which the block seen across the fault appears displaced to the right.

rigid zone
Upper part of a glacier in which there is no plastic flow.

rille (*Moon*)
Elongate trenched or crack-like valley on the lunar surface.

rip-current
Narrow currents that flow straight out to sea in the surf zone, returning water seaward that has been pushed ashore by breaking waves.

ripple marks
Small ridges formed on sediment surfaces exposed to moving wind or water. The ridges form perpendicularly to the motion.

rock
Naturally formed, consolidated material composed of grains of one or more mineral. (There are a few exceptions to this definition.)

rock avalanche
A very rapidly moving, turbulent mass of broken-up bedrock.

rock-basin lake
A lake occupying a depression caused by glacial erosion of bedrock.

rock cycle
A theoretical concept relating tectonism, erosion, and various rock-forming processes to the common rock types.

rockfall
Rock falling freely or bouncing down a cliff.

rock flour
A powder of fine fragments of rock produced by glacial abrasion.

rockslide
Rapid sliding of a mass of bedrock along an inclined surface of weakness.

rounding
The grinding away of sharp edges and corners of rock fragments during transportation.

rubble
Angular fragments coarser than sand.

saltation
A mode of transport that carries sediment downcurrent in a series of short leaps or bounces.

sand
Sediment composed of particles with a diameter of .062 to 2 mm.

sand dunes
Mounds of loose sand grains heaped up by the wind.

sandstone
A medium-grained sedimentary rock formed by the cementation of sand grains.

satellite
Secondary body that orbits about a planet.

scale
The relationship between distance on a map and distance on the terrain being represented by that map.

schist
A metamorphic rock characterized by coarse-grained minerals oriented approximately parallel.

schistose
The texture of a rock in which visible platy or needle-shaped minerals have grown essentially parallel to each other under the influence of directed pressure.

scientific method
The means by which knowledge is gained through objective procedures.

scoria
A basalt that is highly vesicular.

sea cave
A cavity eroded by wave action at the base of a sea cliff.

sea cliff
Steep slope that retreats inland by mass wasting as wave erosion undercuts it.

sea-floor spreading
The concept that the ocean floor is moving away from the mid-oceanic ridge and across the deep ocean basin, to disappear beneath continents and island arcs.

seamount
Conical mountain rising 1,000 meters or more above the sea floor.

seawall
A wall constructed along the base of retreating cliffs to prevent wave erosion.

sediment
Loose, solid particles that can originate by (1) weathering and erosion of pre-existing rocks; (2) chemical precipitation from solution, usually in water; and (3) secretion by organisms.

sedimentary breccia
A coarse-grained sedimentary rock composed of lithified rubble.

sedimentary facies
Significantly different rock types occupying laterally distinct parts of the same layered rock unit.

sedimentary rock
Rock that has formed from (1) lithification of any type of sediment; (2) precipitation from solution; or (3) consolidation of the remains of plants or animals.

sedimentary structures
Features found within sedimentary rocks, usually formed during or shortly after deposition of the sediment and before lithification.

seismic reflection
The return of part of the energy of seismic waves to the earth's surface after the waves bounce off a rock boundary.

seismic refraction
The bending of seismic waves as they pass from one material to another.

seismic waves
Waves of energy produced by an earthquake.

seismogram
Paper record of earth vibration.

seismograph
A seismometer with a recording device that produces a permanent record of earth motion.

seismometer
An instrument designed to detect seismic waves or earth motion.

shale
A fine-grained sedimentary rock that has a pronounced splitting capability.

shearing
Movement in which parts of a body slide relative to one another and parallel to the forces being exerted.

shear stress
Stress due to forces that tend to cause movement or strain parallel to the direction of the forces.

sheet erosion
The removal of a thin layer of surface material, usually topsoil, by a flowing sheet of water.

sheet-jointing
The development of cracks parallel to the outer surface of an expanding rock.

sheet silicate
Crystal structure in which each silica tetrahedron shares three oxygen ions.

sheetwash
Water flowing down a slope in a layer.

shield volcano
Broad, gently sloping cone constructed of solidified lava flows.

sial
Rock rich in silicon and aluminum; characteristic of continental crust.

silica
A term used for oxygen plus silicon.

silicate
A substance that contains silica as part of its chemical formula.

silica tetrahedron
Four-sided pyramid-like object that visually represents the four oxygen atoms surrounding a silicon atom; the basic building block of silicate minerals.

sill
A tabular intrusive structure concordant with the country rock.

silt
Sediment composed of particles with a diameter of .004 to .062 mm (4 to 62 microns).

sima
Rock rich in silicon and magnesium; characteristic of oceanic crust.

sinkhole
A closed depression found on land surfaces underlain by limestone.

sinter
A deposit of silica that forms around some hot springs and geysers.

slate
A fine-grained rock that splits easily along flat, parallel planes.

slaty
Describing a rock that splits easily along nearly flat and parallel planes.

slaty cleavage
A rock that is slaty possesses slaty cleavage.

slide
In mass wasting, movement of a descending mass along a plane approximately parallel to the slope of the surface.

slip
In mass wasting, movement of a relatively coherent descending mass along one or more well-defined surfaces.

slip face
The steep downwind slope of a dune; formed from loose, cascading sand that generally keeps the slope at the angle of repose (about 34°).

slump
In mass wasting, movement along a curved surface in which the upper part moves vertically downward while the lower part moves outward.

soil
A layer of weathered, unconsolidated material on top of bedrock; often also defined as containing organic matter and being capable of supporting plant growth.

soil horizons
Layers of soil that are distinguishable by characteristic physical or chemical properties.

solar flare (*Sun*)
Very bright spot in the sun's photosphere.

solar system
The sun and all objects that revolve about it.

solifluction
Flow of water-saturated debris over impermeable material.

sorting
Process of selection and separation of sediment grains according to their grain size (or grain shape or specific gravity.)

source rock
A rock containing organic matter that is converted to petroleum by burial and other post-depositional changes.

spatter cone
A small, steep-sided cone built from lava spattering out of a vent.

specific gravity
The ratio of the mass of a substance to the mass of an equal volume of water, determined at a specified temperature.

spheroidally weathered boulder
Boulder that has been rounded by weathering from an initial blocky shape.

spit
A finger-like ridge of sediment attached to land but extending out into open water.

spreading center
The crest of the mid-oceanic ridge, where sea floor is moving away in opposite directions on either side.

spring
A place where water flows naturally out of rock onto the land surface.

stable
Describing a mineral that will not react with or convert to a new mineral or substance, given enough time.

stack
Erosional remnant of a headland left behind as a wave-eroded coast retreats inland.

stalactite
Icicle-like pendant of dripstone formed on cave ceilings.

stalagmite
Cone-shaped mass of dripstone formed on cave floors, generally directly below a stalactite.

standard geologic time scale
A worldwide relative scale of geologic time divisions.

static pressure
See confining pressure.

stock
A small discordant pluton with an outcropping area of less than 100 square kilometers.

stony-iron meteorite
A meteorite composed of silicate minerals and nickel-iron alloy in approximately equal amounts.

stony meteorite
A meteorite made up mostly of plagioclase and iron-magnesium silicates.

stoping
Upward movement of a body of magma by fracturing of overlying country rock. Magma engulfs the blocks of fractured country rock as it moves upward.

strain
Change in size (volume) or shape of a body (or rock unit) in response to stress.

stratovolcano
See composite volcano.

streak
Color of a pulverized substance; a useful property for mineral identification.

stream
A moving body of water, confined in a channel and running downhill under the influence of gravity.

stream channel
A long, narrow depression, shaped and more or less filled by a stream.

stream discharge
Volume of water that flows past a given point in a unit of time.

stream gradient
Downhill slope of a stream's bed or the water surface, if the stream is very large.

stream headwaters
The upper part of a stream near the source.

stream mouth
The place where the stream enters the sea, a large lake, or a larger stream.

stream terrace
Step-like landform found above a stream and its flood plain.

stream velocity
The speed at which water in a stream travels.

stress
A force acting on a body, or rock unit, that tends to change the size or shape of that body, or rock unit.

striations
(1) On minerals, extremely straight, parallel lines; (2) Glacial—straight scratches in rock caused by abrasion by a moving glacier.

strike
The compass direction of a line formed by the intersection of an inclined plane (such as a bedding plane) with a horizontal plane.

strike-slip fault
A fault in which movement is parallel to the strike of the fault surface.

strip mine
A mine in which the valuable material is exposed at the surface by removal of a strip of overburden.

structural basin
A structure in which the beds dip toward a central point.

structural geology
The branch of geology that is concerned with the internal structure of bedrock and the shapes, arrangement, and interrelationships of rock units.

subduction
The sliding of the sea floor beneath a continent or island arc.

subduction zone
Elongate region in which subduction takes place.

submarine canyon
V-shaped valleys that run across the continental shelf and down the continental slope.

submergent coast
A coast in which formerly dry land has been recently drowned, either by land subsidence or a rise in sea level.

sunspot
Calm areas in the sun's photosphere.

superposition, principle or law of
Within a sequence of undisturbed sedimentary rocks, the oldest layers are on the bottom, the youngest on the top.

surf
Breakers.

surface waves
Seismic waves that travel on the earth's surface.

suspended load
Sediment in a stream that is light enough in weight to remain lifted indefinitely above the bottom by water turbulence.

S **wave**
A seismic wave propagated by a shearing motion, which causes rock to vibrate perpendicular to the direction of wave propagation.

S-**wave shadow zone**
The region on the earth's surface (at any distance more than 103° from an earthquake epicenter) in which *S* waves from the earthquake are absent.

syncline
A fold in which the layered rock dips toward an axis.

talus
An accumulation of broken rock at the base of a cliff.

tar sand
Asphalt-cemented sand deposits.

tectonic forces
Forces generated from within the earth that result in uplift, movement or deformation of part of the earth's crust.

tensional force
A force that tends to elongate or pull apart a body.

tephra
Fragments of rock produced by volcanic explosion.

terminal moraine
An end moraine marking the farthest advance of a glacier.

terminus
The lower edge of a glacier.

terrigenous sediment
Land-derived sediment that has found its way to the sea floor.

theory
An explanation for observed phenomena that has a high possibility of being true.

theory of glacial ages
At times in the past, colder climates prevailed during which significantly more of the land surface of the earth was glaciated than at present.

thermal metamorphism
Metamorphism under conditions in which high temperature is the dominant factor; also called contact metamorphism.

thrust fault
A reverse fault in which the dip of the fault plane is at a low angle to horizontal.

till
Unsorted and unlayered rock debris carried by a glacier.

tillite
Lithified till.

time-transgressive rock unit
An apparently continuous rock layer in which different portions formed at different times.

tombolo
A bar of marine sediment connecting a former island or stack to the mainland.

topographic map
A map on which elevations are shown by means of contour lines.

topset bed
In a delta, a nearly horizontal sediment bed of varying grain size formed by distributaries shifting across the delta surface.

traction
Movement by rolling, sliding, or dragging of sediment fragments along a stream bottom.

transform boundary
Boundary between two plates that are sliding past one another.

transform fault
The portion of a fracture zone between two offset segments of mid-oceanic ridge crest.

transportation
The movement of eroded particles by agents such as rivers, waves, glaciers, or wind.

transported soil
Soil not formed from the local rock but from parent material brought in from some other region and deposited, usually by running water, wind, or glacial ice.

transverse dune
A relatively straight, elongate dune oriented perpendicular to the wind.

travel-time curve
A plot of seismic-wave arrival times against distance.

travertine
A porous deposit of calcite that often forms around hot springs.

trellis pattern
A drainage pattern consisting of parallel main streams with short tributaries meeting them at right angles.

tributary stream
Small stream flowing into a large stream adding water to the large stream.

truncated spur
Triangular facet where the lower end of a ridge has been eroded by glacial ice.

tsunami
Huge ocean wave produced by displacement of the sea floor; also called seismic sea wave.

tuff
A rock formed from fine-grained pyroclastic particles (ash and dust).

turbidity current
A flowing mass of sediment-laden water that is heavier than clear water and therefore flows downslope along the bottom of the sea or a lake.

turbulent flow
Eddying, swirling flow in which water drops travel along erratically curved paths that cross the paths of neighboring drops.

ultramafic rock
Rock composed entirely or almost entirely of ferromagnesian minerals.

umbra (Sun)
Central darker region of sunspot.

unconformity
A surface that represents a break in the geologic record, with the rock unit immediately above it being considerably younger than the rock beneath.

unconsolidated
In referring to sediment grains, loose, separate, or unattached to one another.

uniformitarianism
Geological processes that are operating at present are the same processes that have operated in the geologic past; the present is the key to the past.

unloading
The removal of a great weight of rock.

unpaired terraces
Stream terraces (*see* definition) that do not have the same elevation on opposite sides of a river.

U-shaped valley
Characteristic cross-profile of a valley carved by glacial erosion.

valley glacier
A glacier confined to a valley. The ice flows from a higher to a lower elevation.

varve
Two thin layers of sediment, one dark and the other light in color, representing one year's deposition in a lake.

vent
The opening in the earth's surface through which a volcanic eruption takes place.

ventifact
Boulder, cobble, or pebble with flat surfaces caused by the abrasion of wind-blown sand.

vesicle
A cavity in volcanic rock caused by gas in a lava.

viscosity
Resistance to flow.

vitreous luster
See glassy luster.

volcanic breccia
Rock formed from large pieces of volcanic rock (cinders, blocks, bombs).

volcanic dome
Steep-sided, dome or spine-shaped mass of volcanic rock formed from viscous lava that solidifies in or immediately above a volcanic vent.

volcanic neck
An intrusive structure that apparently represents magma that solidified within the throat of a volcano.

volcanic portion of a geosyncline
A thick sequence of submarine lava flows and marine sedimentary rock, much of which has been derived from volcanic ash and from sediment eroded from volcanic rocks; called eugeosyncline.

volcano
A hill or mountain constructed by the extrusion of lava or rock fragments from a vent.

wastage
Glacial ice or snow that is lost by melting, evaporation, or breaking off into icebergs.

water table
The upper surface of the zone of saturation.

wave crest
The high point of a wave.

wave-cut platform
A horizontal bench of rock formed beneath the surf zone as a coast retreats because of wave erosion.

wave height
The vertical distance between the crest (the high point of a wave) and the trough (the low point).

wave length
Horizontal distance between two wave crests (or two troughs).

wave refraction
Change in direction of waves due to slowing as they enter shallow water.

wave trough
Low point of a wave.

weathering
The group of processes that change rock at or near the earth's surface.

welded tuff
A rock composed of pyroclasts welded together.

well
A hole, generally cylindrical and usually walled or lined with pipe, that is dug or drilled into the ground to penetrate an aquifer below the zone of saturation.

wind ripple
Small, low ridge of sand produced by the saltation of wind-blown sand.

wrinkle ridge (*Moon*)
Wrinkle on lunar maria surface.

zone of accumulation
(1) That portion of a glacier with a perennial snow cover; (2) *See* B horizon (a soil layer).

zone of aeration
Subsurface zone in which the rock openings are filled partly with water and partly with air; located above the zone of saturation.

zone of leaching
See A horizon (a soil layer).

zone of saturation
Subsurface zone in which all rock openings are filled with water.

zone of wastage
That portion of a glacier in which ice is lost or wasted.

Index